D1083617

MECHANICS
OF MATERIALS

MECHANICS
OF MATERIALS

By

E. P. POPOV

Professor of Civil Engineering
-University of California

PRENTICE-HALL OF INDIA (PRIVATE) LTD.

New Delhi, 1965

Rs. 15.00

MECHANICS OF MATERIALS by Popov

PRENTICE-HALL INTERNATIONAL, INC. Englewood Cliffs
PRENTICE-HALL OF INDIA (PRIVATE) LTD. New Delhi
PRENTICE-HALL INTERNATIONAL, INC. London
PRENTICE-HALL OF AUSTRALIA PTY. LTD. Sydney
PRENTICE-HALL OF CANADA LTD. Toronto
PRENTICE-HALL OF JAPAN, INC. Tokyo
PRENTICE-HALL DE MEXICO. S.A. Mexico City

Reprinted in India by special arrangement with Prentice-Hall, Inc., Englewood Cliffs, N.J., U.S.A. and Macdonald & Co. (Publishers) Ltd., London, U.K.

This book has been published with the assistance of the Joint Indian-American Standard Works Programme.

Printed by G. D. Makhija at the India Offset Press, Delhi, and published by Prentice-Hall of India (Private) Ltd., New Delhi.

1082-E

FOREWORD

Dr. Popov's book is a noteworthy example of an engineering text that blends the best aspects of the practical and the fundamental scientific points of view. This integration is effected logically and simply by building upon elementary mathematics, physics, and mechanics. At the same time, the examples are chosen so as to give the reader an understanding of the practical side of the subject, the limitations of the theories, and the application of the results.

The book provides a sound basis for more advanced professional and technical subjects, and will prepare the reader adequately for later work in the theories of elasticity and plasticity, and in structural or machine design.

The purpose of the Prentice-Hall Series in Civil Engineering and Engineering Mechanics is to meet the requirements of teachers who seek to train their students for a place at the forefront of engineering progress. *Mechanics of Materials* by Dr. Popov, the third in the series, and its predecessors, *Engineering Mechanics* by Higdon and Stiles and *Numerical Methods in Engineering* by Salvadori and Baron have set the standard for the titles that will follow.

N. M. NEWMARK

PREFACE

This book is designed for use in an undergraduate course in Strength or Mechanics of Materials. Fundamental principles of the subject are emphasized throughout. Applications are selected from the various fields of engineering.

It is assumed that the reader has completed a course in Statics. However, those topics which are particularly important in Mechanics of Materials are reviewed where introduced.

The various articles are arranged in a logical sequence that has proved very effective in the author's teaching experience. However, some instructors may wish to combine the study of Chapter 1 with Chapter 4, treating this part of the course as a review of Statics. Many may find it advantageous to proceed to the articles in Chapter 10 on the construction of shear and moment diagrams after the study of Chapter 4. For this purpose, Articles 10-5 through 10-8 and Article 11-14 are recommended. Other instructors may find it desirable to introduce combined stresses by assigning for simultaneous reading the early articles in Chapter 8 with those in Chapter 9.

The book contains material for a year's course. However, to assist instructors in selecting material for a one-semester course, articles of an advanced or specialized nature are preceded by an asterisk for possible omission. Moreover, with very few exceptions, each chapter is written to introduce *gradually* the more complex material. Thus, study of a particular topic may be terminated where desired.

More advanced topics are interspersed throughout the book wherever justified for logical development of the subject. This treatment has two desirable effects. First, the more inquisitive reader is presented with the elaborate treatment he prefers. Second, the book can serve as a reference work after it has served its purpose as a text.

Among the more advanced topics treated in detail are the generalized Hooke's law, stress concentrations, inelastic bending with reference to limit design, curved bars, shear center, Mohr's circle of strain, strain rosettes, a description of the photoelastic method of stress analysis, virtual work method for deflection of beams and trusses, and analysis of thick-walled cylinders. The double-integration and the moment-area methods for beam

vii

deflection are discussed thoroughly.   The method of moment distribution is not discussed, since it is seldom actually taught in a first course-in Mechanics of Materials.

Many illustrative examples are given to show not only how to set up a problem, but to explain the limitations of the solution.   A large number of problems for solution appear at the end of each chapter.   These are presented to parallel the text discussion, and are arranged in order of difficulty.   The statements of longer or more difficult problems are preceded with asterisks.   Wherever a common statement of the problem is applicable to several problem diagrams, the latter are enclosed in a frame.   Answers are given to most problems.   More than a third of all the problems were used in examinations.   In many instances the data given are selected so as to simplify numerical solution for the reader.   Some problems are academic, designed to emphasize the principles studied.   And to maintain student interest realistic problems are interspersed throughout the text. Many problem solutions require the use of free-body diagrams to bolster the student's knowledge of Statics and to make the course in Mechanics of Materials truly continuous with the one in Statics.

The development of this book was influenced by the author's teachers, colleagues, and students.   His point of view was molded by the works of Seely, Timoshenko, Laurson and Cox, Boyd, and others; and also by the inspiring teaching of Professor S. Timoshenko.

Many colleagues in the Structural Group in the Division of Civil Engineering at the University of California contributed to the growth of the book during the long trial stage of the mimeographed edition.   The author wishes to thank Professor C. T. Wiskocil for much friendly advice and encouragement; Professor H. D. Eberhart for stimulating discussions on the subject matter; Professor A. Scordelis for his assistance and the assembly of some of the problems for solution; Professor R. W. Clough for the photograph of a photoelastic experiment and several problems for solution; and other members of the staff who read portions of the manuscript and/or furnished some problems for solution as follows: Professor B. Bresler, J. W. Kelly, D. Pirtz, M. Polivka, C. M. Smith, G. E. Troxell, and Messrs. M. S. Aghbabian, C. Monismith, A. Olitt, and C. F. Scheffey.   Miss Vina Colgan prepared the drawings.

Professor N. M. Newmark of the University of Illinois read the entire manuscript and offered several excellent suggestions.

Finally, the author wishes to express his particular gratitude to Karl Stark Pister, a former student and staff member at the University of California, whose critical readings of the manuscript drafts were invaluable.

E. P. POPOV

Berkeley, Calif.

CONTENTS

LIST OF ABBREVIATIONS AND SYMBOLS*

Abbreviations

allow	allowable
av	average
cr	critical
ft	feet
Hp	horsepower
I	I-beam
in.	inches
k	kips
kip	kilo-pound (1,000 lb)
ksi	kips per square inch
lb	pounds (from Latin *libra* meaning weight)
max	maximum
min	minimum
NA	neutral axis
psi	pounds per square inch
rpm	revolutions per minute
ult	ultimate
WF	wide flange beam
yp	yield point

Greek Letter Symbols

α	(alpha)	linear coefficient of thermal expansion, general angle
γ	(gamma)	shearing strain, weight per unit volume
Δ	(delta)	total deformation or deflection, change of any designated function
ϵ	(epsilon)	normal strain
θ	(theta)	slope angle for elastic curve, angle of inclination of line on body
μ	(mu)	Poisson's ratio
ρ	(rho)	radius, radius of curvature
σ	(sigma)	tensile or compressive stress (i.e., normal stress)
τ	(tau)	shearing stress
φ, ϕ	(phi)	total angle of twist, general angle
ω	(omega)	angular velocity

* With very few exceptions, the abbreviations and letter symbols conform with those approved by the American Standards Association.

Roman Letter Symbols

A	area, area of cross section
A_{fghj}	partial area of beam cross sectional area
b	breadth, width
c	distance from neutral axis or from center of twist to extreme fibre
d	diameter, distance, depth
E	modulus of elasticity in tension or compression
F	force
G	modulus of elasticity in shear
g	acceleration of gravity
h	height, depth of beam
I	moment of inertia of cross sectional area
J	polar moment of inertia of cross sectional area
K	stress concentration factor
k	spring constant, constant
L	length
M	moment, bending moment
m	mass, moment caused by virtual unit load
N	number of revolutions per minute
n	number, ratio of moduli of elasticity
P	force, concentrated load
p	pressure intensity
Q	first or statical moment of area A_{fghj} around neutral axis
q	shear flow
R	reaction, radius
r	radius, radius of gyration
T	torque, temperature
t	thickness, width, tangential deviation
U	strain energy, work
u	internal force caused by virtual unit load, radial displacement
V	shearing force (often vertical), volume
W	total weight
w	weight or load per unit of length
y	distance from neutral axis, deflection of beam
Z	section modulus $(Z = I/c)$

Chapter One

STRESS—AXIAL LOADS

1-1. Introduction. In all engineering construction the component parts of a structure must be assigned definite physical sizes. Such parts must be properly proportioned to resist the actual or probable forces that may be imposed upon them. Thus, the walls of a pressure vessel must be of adequate strength to withstand the internal pressure; the floors of a building must be sufficiently strong for their intended purpose; the shaft of a machine must be of adequate size to carry the required torque; a wing of an airplane must safely withstand the aerodynamic loads which may come upon it in flight or landing. Likewise, the parts of a composite structure must be rigid enough so as not to deflect or "sag" excessively when in operation under the imposed loads. A floor of a building may be strong enough but may deflect excessively, which in some instances may cause misalignment of manufacturing equipment, or in other cases result in the cracking of a plaster ceiling attached underneath. The subject of Mechanics of Materials, or Strength of Materials as it has been traditionally called in the past, occupies itself with the methods which provide the means of determining the adequate sizes of the various load-carrying members for *strength* as well as for desired *deflection* characteristics. Alternately, the subject may be termed the Mechanics of Solid Deformable Bodies.

Mechanics of Materials is a fairly old subject. It is generally dated from the work of Galileo in the early part of the seventeenth century. Prior to his investigations into the behavior of solid bodies under loads, constructors followed precedent and used the "rule of thumb." Galileo was the first to attempt to explain the behavior of some of the members under load on a rational basis. He studied members in tension and compression, and notably beams used in the construction of hulls of ships for the Italian navy. Of course much progress has been made since that time, but in passing it must be noted that much is owed in the development of this subject to the French investigators, among whom a group of outstanding men such as Coulomb, Poisson, Navier, St. Venant, and Cauchy, who worked at the break of the nineteenth century, has left an indelible impression on this subject.

The subject of Mechanics of Materials cuts broadly across all branches

1

of the engineering profession with remarkably many applications. Its methods are needed by the civil engineer in the design of bridges and buildings; by the mining engineer and the architectural engineer, each of whom is interested in structures; by the mechanical and chemical engineers, who rely upon the methods of this subject for the design of machinery and pressure vessels; by metallurgists, who need the fundamental concepts of this subject in order to understand how further to improve existing materials; finally, by the electrical engineer, who needs the methods of this subject because of the importance of the mechanical engineering phases of many portions of electrical equipment. Mechanics of Materials has characteristic methods all its own. It is a definite discipline; thus it is one of the most fundamental subjects of an engineering curriculum, standing alongside other basic subjects such as fluid mechanics, thermodynamics, and a basic course in electricity.

The behavior of a member subjected to forces depends not only on the fundamental laws of Newtonian mechanics governing the equilibrium of the forces but also on the *physical characteristics* of the materials of which the member is fabricated. The necessary information regarding the latter comes from the laboratory where materials are subjected to the action of accurately known forces and the behavior of test specimens is observed with particular regard to such phenomena as the occurrence of breaks, deformations, etc. Determination of such phenomena is a vital part of the subject, but this branch of the subject is left to other books.* Here the end results of such investigations are of interest, and this course is concerned with the analytical or mathematical part of the subject in contradistinction to experimentation. For the above reasons, it is seen that Mechanics of Materials is a blended science of experiment and Newtonian postulates of analytical mechanics. From the latter is borrowed the branch of the science called *statics*, a subject with which the reader of this book is presumed to be familiar, and on which the subject of this book primarily depends.

This text will be limited to the simpler topics of the subject as it is an introductory one. However, in spite of the relative simplicity of the methods employed here, the resulting techniques are unusually useful as they do apply to a vast number of technically important problems.

This is essentially a problem course, hence the subject matter can be mastered only by solving numerous problems. This subject will not tax the memory of the student. The number of formulas necessary for the analysis and design of structural and machine members by the methods of Mechanics of Materials is remarkably small. However, throughout this study the student must develop an ability to *visualize* the problem at hand and the nature of the quantities being computed. **Complete, care-**

* Davis, H. E., Troxell, G. E., and Wiskocil, C. T., *Testing and Inspection of Engineering Materials.* New York: McGraw-Hill, 1941.

fully drawn diagrammatic sketches of problems to be solved will pay large dividends in a quicker and more complete mastery of the subject.

1-2. Method of Sections. One of the main problems of Mechanics of Materials is the investigation of the internal resistance of a body, that is, *the nature of forces set up within a body to balance the effect of the externally applied forces.* For this purpose, a uniform method of approach is employed. A complete diagrammatic sketch of the member to be investigated is prepared, on which *all* of the external forces acting on a body are shown at their respective points of application. Such a sketch is called a *free-body* diagram. All forces acting on a body, including the reactive forces caused by the supports and the weight* of the body itself, are considered external forces. Moreover, since a stable body at rest is in equilibrium, the forces acting on it satisfy the equations of static equilibrium. Thus, if the forces acting on a body such as shown in Fig. 1-1a satisfy the equations of static equilibrium and are all shown acting on it, the sketch represents a free-body diagram. Next, since a determination of the internal forces caused by the external ones is one of the principal concerns of this subject, an arbitrary section is passed through the body, completely separating it into two parts.

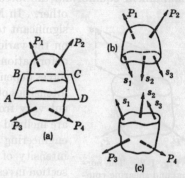

Fig. 1-1. Sectioning of a body.

The result of such a process may be seen in Fig. 1-1b and c where an arbitrary plane *ABCD* separates the original solid body of Fig. 1-1a into two *distinct* parts. This process will be referred to as the *method of sections.* Then, if the body as a whole is in equilibrium, *any part* of it must also be in equilibrium. For such parts of a body, however, some of the forces necessary to maintain equilibrium must act at the cut section. These considerations lead to the following fundamental conclusion: *the externally applied forces to one side of an arbitrary cut must be balanced by the internal forces developed at the cut,* or briefly, the external forces are balanced by the internal forces. Later it will be seen that the cutting planes will be oriented in a particular direction to fit special requirements. However, the above concept will be relied upon as a first step in solving *all* problems where internal forces are being investigated.

In discussing the method of sections, it is significant to note that some bodies, although not in static equilibrium, may be in dynamic equilibrium. These problems

---

* Strictly speaking, the weight of the body and dynamic forces due to accelerations, etc., are "body forces," and act throughout the body in a manner associated with the units of volume of the body. However, in most instances, these body forces can be considered as external loads.

can be reduced to problems of static equilibrium. First, the acceleration of the part in question is computed, then it is multiplied by the mass of the body, giving a force. The force so computed, if applied to the body in a direction opposite to the acceleration at its mass center, reduces the dynamic problem to one of statics. This is the so-called *d'Alembert principle*. With this point of view, all bodies can be thought of as being instantaneously in a state of static equilibrium. Hence for any body, whether in static or dynamic equilibrium, a free-body diagram can be prepared on which the necessary forces to maintain the body as a whole in equilibrium can be shown. From then on the problem is the same as discussed above.

1-3. Stress. In general, the internal forces necessary at a cut may be of varying magnitudes and directions, as is shown diagrammatically in Fig. 1-1b and c, hence they are vectorial in nature. These internal forces maintain in equilibrium the forces applied to one side of the cut or the

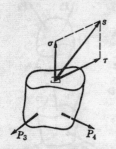

other. In Mechanics of Materials it is particularly significant to determine the *intensity* of these forces on the various portions of the cut, as resistance to deformation and the capacity of materials to resist forces depend on these intensities. In general, these intensities of force acting on infinitesimal areas of the cut vary from point to point, and, in general, they are inclined with respect to the plane of the cut. In engineering practice it is customary to resolve this intensity of force perpendicular and parallel to the section investigated. Such a resolution of the inten-sity of a force on an infinitesimal area is shown in Fig. 1-2. The intensity of the force *perpendicular* or

Fig. 1-2. The nor-mal and shearing com-ponents of stress.

normal to the section is called the **normal stress** at a point. In this book it will be designated by the Greek letter σ (sigma). As a particular stress in general holds true only at a point, it is defined mathematically as

$$\sigma = \lim_{\Delta A \to 0} \frac{\Delta F}{\Delta A}$$

where F is a force acting *normal* to the cut, while A is the corresponding area. It is customary to refer to the normal stresses that cause traction or tension on the surface of a cut as *tensile* stresses. On the other hand, those that are pushing against the cut are *compressive* stresses.

The other component of the intensity of force acts *parallel to the plane of the elementary area*, Fig. 1-2. This component of the intensity of force is called the **shearing stress**. It will be designated by the Greek letter τ (tau). Mathematically it is defined as

$$\tau = \lim_{\Delta A \to 0} \frac{\Delta V}{\Delta A}$$

where A as before represents area, and V is the component of the force parallel to the cut.

The student should form a clear mental picture of the stresses called normal and those called shearing. To repeat, normal stresses result from force components perpendicular to the plane of the cut, while shearing stresses result from components parallel to the plane of the cut.

It is seen from the above definitions of normal and shearing stresses that, since they represent the intensity of force on an area, stresses* are measured in units of force divided by units of area. Since a force is a vector and an area is a scalar, their ratio, stress, is a *vectorial* quantity.† In the English system, the usual units for stress are pounds per square inch, abbreviated in this text as *psi*. In many cases it will be found convenient to use as a unit of force the coined word *kip,* meaning *kilo*-pound or 1,000 lb. The stress in kips per square inch is abbreviated as *ksi*.

It should be noted that *stresses multiplied by the respective areas on which they act give forces, and it is the sum of these forces at an imaginary cut that keeps a body in equilibrium.*

If in addition to a plane such as *ABCD* in Fig. 1-1a another plane an infinitesimal distance away and parallel to the first were passed through the body, a thin element of the body would be isolated. Then, if an additional two pairs of planes were passed normal to the first pair, an elementary cube of infinitesimal dimensions would be isolated from the body. Such a cube is shown in Fig. 1-3. Here, for identification purposes, the process of resolution of stresses into components has been carried further than discussed above. At each surface the shearing stress τ has been resolved into two components parallel to a particular set of axes. The subscripts of the σ's designate the direction of the normal stress along a particular axis, while the stress itself acts on a plane perpendicular to the same axis. The first subscripts of the τ's associate the shearing stress with a plane which is perpendicular to a given axis, while the second designate the direction of the shearing stress.

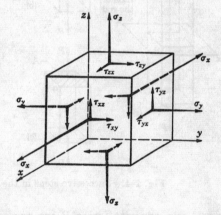

Fig. 1-3. The most general state of stress acting on an element.

An infinitesimal cube, as shown in Fig. 1-3, could be used as the basis for an exact formulation of the problem in Mechanics of Materials. However, the methods for the study of the behavior of such a cube (which involve the writing of an equation for its equilibrium and making certain that such a cube, after deformations caused in it by the action of forces, will be geometrically compatible with the adjoining infinitesimal cubes) are beyond the scope of this course. They are in the realm of the Mathematical Theory of Elasticity. The procedures used in this text do not resort to the generality implied in Fig. 1-3. The methods used here will be much simpler.

* In some books the term "unit stress" is used to indicate stress per unit of area. However, in this text the word "stress" is used for this concept. Also note that many books use s or f for σ, and s_s or f_s for τ.

† For further details see Art. 8-2.

1-4. Axial Load; Normal Stress. In many practical situations, if the direction of the imaginary plane cutting a member is judiciously selected, the stresses that act on the cut will be found both particularly significant and simple to determine. One such important case occurs in a straight *axially* loaded rod in tension, *provided a plane is passed perpendicular to the axis of the rod.* The tensile stress acting on such a cut is the *maximum* stress, as any other cut not perpendicular to the axis of the rod provides a larger surface for resisting the applied force. The maximum stress is the most significant one, as it tends to cause the failure of the material.*

To obtain an algebraic expression for this maximum stress, consider the case illustrated in Fig. 1-4a. If the rod is assumed weightless, two

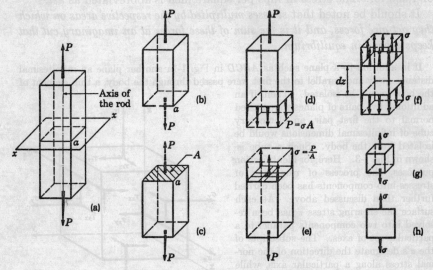

Fig. 1-4. Successive steps in the analysis of a body for stress.

equal and opposite forces P are necessary, one at each end to maintain equilibrium. Then, as stated in Art. 1-2, since the body as a whole is in equilibrium, any part of it is also in equilibrium. A part of the rod to either side of the cut x-x is in equilibrium. At the cut, where the cross-sectional area of the rod is A, a force equivalent to P as shown in Fig. 1-4b and c must be developed. Whereupon, from the definition of stress, the normal stress, or the stress which acts perpendicularly to the cut, is

$$\sigma = \frac{P}{A} \quad \text{or} \quad \frac{force}{area} \qquad \left[\frac{\text{lb}}{\text{in.}^2}\right] \quad (1\text{-}1)$$

* Some materials exhibit a far greater relative strength to normal stresses than to shearing stresses. For such materials failure takes place on an oblique plane. This will be discussed in Chapter 9.

This **normal** stress is *uniformly* distributed over the cross-sectional area A.* The nature of the quantity computed by Eq. 1-1 may be seen graphically in Fig. 1-4d and e. *In general, the force P is a resultant of a number of forces to one side of the cut or another.*

If an additional cut parallel to the plane x-x in Fig. 1-4a were made, the isolated section of the rod could be represented as in Fig. 1-4f, and upon further "cutting," an infinitesimal cube as in Fig. 1-4g results. The only kind of stresses that appear here are the normal stresses on the two surfaces of the cube. Such a *state of stress* on an element is referred to as **uniaxial stress**. In practice, isometric views of a cube as shown in Fig. 1-4g are seldom employed; the diagrams are simplified to look like those of Fig. 1-4h. Nevertheless, the student must never lose sight of the three-dimensional aspect of the problem at hand.

At a cut the system of tensile stresses computed by Eq. 1-1 provides an equilibrant to the externally applied force. When these normal stresses are multiplied by the corresponding infinitesimal areas and then summed over the whole area of a cut, the summation is equal to the applied force P. Thus the system of stresses is *statically equivalent* to the force P. Moreover, the resultant of this sum must act through the **centroid** of a section. Conversely, to have a uniform stress distribution in a rod, the applied axial force must act through the centroid of the cross-sectional area investigated. For example, in the machine part shown in Fig. 1-5a the stresses cannot be obtained from Eq. 1-1 alone. Here, at a cut such as A-A, a statically equivalent system of forces developed

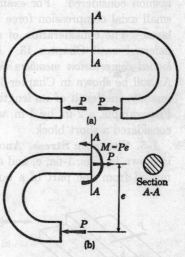

Fig. 1-5. A member with a non-uniform stress distribution at Section A-A.

within the material must consist not only of the force P but also of a couple or a bending moment M that must maintain the externally applied force in equilibrium. This causes nonuniform stress distribution in the member which will be treated in Chapter 7.

In accepting Eq. 1-1, it must be kept in mind that the material's behavior is *idealized*. Each and every particle of a body is assumed to contribute equally to the resistance of the force. A perfect homogeneity of the material is implied by such an

---

* Equation 1-1 strictly applies only if the cross-sectional area is constant along the rod. For a discussion of situations where an abrupt discontinuity in the cross-sectional area occurs, see Art. 2-11.

assumption. Real materials, such as metals, consist of a great many grains, while wood is fibrous. In real materials some particles will contribute more to the resistance of a force than others. Stresses as shown in Fig. 1-4d and e actually do not exist. The diagram of true stress distribution varies in each particular case and is a highly irregular, jagged affair. However, on the average, or statistically speaking, computations based on Eq. 1-1 are correct, and hence the computed stress represents a highly significant quantity.

Similar reasoning applies to compression members. The maximum normal or compressive stress may also be obtained by passing a section perpendicular to the axis of a member and applying Eq. 1-1. The stress so obtained will be of uniform intensity as long as the resultant of the applied forces coincides with the *centroid* of the area at the cut. However, one must exercise additional care when compression members are investigated. These may be so slender that they may not behave in the fashion considered. For example, an ordinary yardstick under a rather small axial compression force has a tendency to buckle sidewise and collapse. The consideration of such *instability* of compression members is deferred until Chapter 13. *Equation 1-1 is applicable only for axially loaded compression members that are rather chunky,* i.e., to short blocks. As will be shown in Chapter 13, a block whose *least* dimension is approximately one-tenth of its length may usually be considered a short block. For example, a 2 in. by 4 in. wooden piece may be 20 in. long and still be considered a short block.

1-5. Shearing Stress. Another situation frequently arising in practice is shown in Figs. 1-6a, c, and e. In all of these cases the forces are transmitted from one part of a body to the other by causing stresses in the

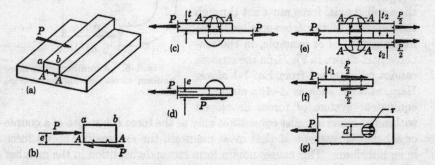

Fig. 1-6. Loading conditions causing shearing stresses.

plane parallel to the applied force. To obtain stresses in such instances, cutting planes as *A-A* are selected and free-body diagrams* as shown in Figs. 1-6b, d, and f are used. The forces are transmitted through the

---

* A small unbalance in moment equal to Pe exists in the first two cases shown in Fig. 1-6, but, being small, is commonly ignored.

respective areas which are cut.   Hence, *assuming* that the stresses which act *in the plane of these cuts are uniformly distributed*, a relation for stress is

$$\tau = \frac{P}{A} \quad \text{or} \quad \frac{force}{area} \qquad \left[\frac{\text{lb}}{\text{in.}^2}\right] \quad (1\text{-}2)$$

where τ by definition is the **shearing** stress, P is the total force acting across and parallel to the cut, often called *shear*, and A is the cross-sectional area of the cut member.   Like the normal stress, the shearing stress is usually measured in units of pounds per square inch.   However, physically it is an entirely different kind of stress and has a markedly different effect on materials.   For reasons to be discussed later, unlike normal stress, the shearing stress given by Eq. 1-2 is only *approximately* true.   For the cases shown, the shearing stresses actually are distributed in a non-uniform fashion across the area of the cut.   The quantity given by Eq. 1-2 represents an *average* shearing stress.

The shearing stress as computed by Eq. 1-2 is shown diagrammatically in Fig. 1-6g.   Note that for the case shown in Fig. 1-6e there are *two planes* of the rivet which resist the force.   Such a rivet is referred to as being in *double* shear.

1-6. Bearing Stress.   Besides the situations cited in the preceding two articles, cases often arise where one body is supported by another.   If the resultant of the applied forces coincides with the centroid of the contact area between the two bodies, the intensity of force or stress between the two bodies can be determined from Eq. 1-1.   The stress so computed is called a **bearing stress.** An illustration of this is shown in Fig. 1-7 where a short block bears on a concrete pier and the latter bears on the soil.   The bearing stresses are obtained by dividing the applied force P by the corresponding area of contact.   Here the bearing stress is a special case of a normal stress.

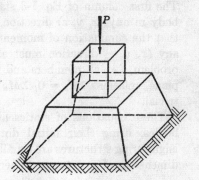

Fig. 1-7.   Bearing stresses occur between the block and pier.

Another instance of bearing stress occurs around rivets or bolts, Figs. 1-6c and e.   In such cases, as the force P is applied, a highly irregular pressure* develops *between* the bolt and the plates.   The *average nominal* intensity of this pressure is obtained by dividing the force transmitted by the *projected area of the bolt onto the plate.*   The bearing stress in Fig. 1-6c is $\sigma_b = P/(td)$, where t is the thickness of the plate, and d is the diameter of the rivet.   For the case shown in Fig. 1-6e the bearing stresses for the

---

* For more details see Chapter 14.

middle plate and the outer plates are $\sigma_1 = P/(t_1d)$ and $\sigma_2 = P/(2t_2d)$, respectively.

1-7. Problems in Normal, Bearing, and Shearing Stress. Once P and A are determined in a given problem, Eqs. 1-1 and 1-2 are easy to apply. These equations have a clear physical meaning. Moreover, it seems reasonably clear that the desired magnitudes of stresses are the *maximum stresses*, as they are the greatest imposition on the strength of a material. The greatest stresses occur at a cut or section of *minimum* cross-sectional area and the greatest axial force. Such sections are called *critical sections*. The critical section for the particular arrangement being analyzed may usually be found by inspection. However, to determine the force P that acts through a member is usually a more difficult task. In the majority of problems treated in this text the latter information is obtained from statics.

For the equilibrium of a body in space, the equations of statics require the fulfillment of the following conditions:

$$\left.\begin{array}{ll} \Sigma F_x = 0 & \Sigma M_x = 0 \\ \Sigma F_y = 0 & \Sigma M_y = 0 \\ \Sigma F_z = 0 & \Sigma M_z = 0 \end{array}\right\} \qquad (1\text{-}3)$$

The first column of Eq. 1-3 states that the sum of *all* forces acting on a body in any (x, y, z) direction must be zero. The second column notes that the summation of moments of *all* forces around *any* axis parallel to any (x, y, z) direction must also be zero for equilibrium. In a *planar* problem, *i.e.*, all members and forces lie in a single plane such as the x-y plane, relations $\Sigma F_z = 0$, $\Sigma M_x = 0$, and $\Sigma M_y = 0$, while still valid, are trivial.

These equations of statics are directly applicable to deformable solid bodies, using their initial dimensions. The deformations tolerated in engineering structures are usually negligible in comparison with the over-all dimensions of structures. Therefore, *for the purposes of obtaining the forces in members, the initial undeformed dimensions of members are used in computations.*

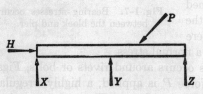

There are problems where equations of statics are not sufficient to determine the forces *in*, or those acting *on*, the member. For example, the reactions for a straight beam, shown in Fig. 1-8, supported

Fig. 1-8. A statically indeterminate beam.

vertically at three points, cannot be determined from statics alone. In this planar problem there are four unknown reaction components, while only three *independent* equations of statics are available. Such problems are termed *statically indeterminate*. The consideration of statically indeterminate problems is postponed until Chapter 12. *For the present, and in the succeeding ten chapters of this text, all structures and members considered will be statically determinate,* i.e., all of the external forces acting on such bodies can be determined by Eqs. 1-3. There is no dearth of statically determinate problems that are practically significant.

Equations 1-3 should already be familiar to the student. However, several examples where they are applied are given in following paragraphs, the professional techniques for their use being stressed. These examples will serve as an informal review of some of the principles of statics, and will show applications of Eqs. 1-1 and 1-2.

Example 1-1. Consider the beam *BE*, shown in Fig. 1-9a, used for hoisting machinery. It is anchored by two bolts at *B*, and at *C* it rests squarely on a parapet wall.

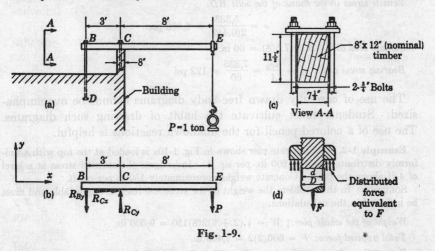

Fig. 1-9.

The essential details are given in the figure. If this arrangement is used to lift equipment of one ton (2,000 lb) weight, determine the stress in the bolts *BD* and the bearing stress at *C*. Assume that the weight of the beam is negligible in comparison with the loads handled.

SOLUTION: In Mechanics of Materials, to solve this, or any other problem, the actual situation is idealized, and a free-body diagram is made on which *all* known *and unknown* forces are indicated. This is shown in Fig. 1-9b. The vertical reactions at *B* and *C* are unknown. They are indicated respectively as R_{By} and R_{Cy}, where the first subscript identifies the location and the second the line of action of the unknown force. As the long bolts *BD* are not effective in resisting the horizontal force, only an unknown horizontal reaction at *C* is assumed and marked as R_{Cz}. The applied known force *P* is shown in its proper location. *After* a free-body diagram is prepared, the equations of statics are applied and solved for the unknown forces. The subscripts of *M* indicate the point around which the summation of moments is made.

$$\Sigma F_x = 0 \qquad R_{Cx} = 0$$
$$\Sigma M_B = 0 \circlearrowright +, \qquad +2{,}000(8 + 3) - R_{Cy}(3) = 0, \quad R_{Cy} = 7{,}333 \text{ lb} \uparrow$$
$$\Sigma M_C = 0 \circlearrowright +, \qquad +2{,}000(8) - R_{By}(3) = 0, \qquad R_{By} = 5{,}333 \text{ lb} \downarrow$$
$$Check: \ \Sigma F_y = 0 \uparrow +, \qquad -5{,}333 + 7{,}333 - 2{,}000 = 0$$

These steps complete and check the work of determining the forces. The various areas of the material that resist these forces are determined next and Eq. 1-1 is applied.

Cross-sectional area of one $\frac{3}{4}$ in. bolt: $A = \frac{1}{4}\pi \, (0.75)^2 = 0.442$ in.^{2}

This is *not* the minimum area of a bolt as threads, Fig. 1-9d, reduce its cross-sectional area. This reduction in area depends on the kind of threads used. In Table 9 of the Appendix the diameter at the root of threads (d in Fig. 1-9d) and the corresponding area for a few "American Standard" threads are given. More extensive tables may be found in handbooks.*

From Appendix, the cross-sectional area of one $\frac{3}{4}$ in. bolt at the root of the threads:

$$A_{\text{net}} = 0.302 \text{ in.}^2$$

Maximum normal tensile stress† in each of the two bolts BD:

$$\sigma_{\max} = \frac{R_{By}}{2A} = \frac{5,333}{2(0.302)} = 8,800 \text{ psi}$$

Tensile stress in the shank of the bolts BD:

$$\sigma = \frac{5,333}{2(0.442)} = 6,000 \text{ psi}$$

Contact area at C: $A = 7.5(8) = 60$ in.^{2}

Bearing stress at C: $\sigma_b = \dfrac{R_{Cy}}{A} = \dfrac{7,333}{60} = 122$ psi

The use of carefully drawn free-body diagrams cannot be overemphasized. Students must cultivate the habit of drawing such diagrams. The use of a colored pencil for the unknown reactions is helpful.

Example 1-2. The concrete pier shown in Fig. 1-10a is loaded at the top with a uniformly distributed load of 600 lb. per sq. ft. Investigate the state of stress at a level of 4 ft above the base. Concrete weighs approximately 150 lb per cu. ft.

SOLUTION: In this problem the weight of the structure itself is appreciable and must be included in the calculations.

Weight of the whole pier:‡ $W = \frac{1}{2} (2 + 6)2(8)150 = 9,600$ lb.

Total applied force: $P = 600(2)2 = 2,400$ lb.

From $\Sigma F_y = 0$, reaction at base: $R = W + P = 12,000$ lb.

These forces are shown in the diagrams schematically as concentrated forces acting through their respective *centroids*. Then, to determine the stress at the desired level, the body is cut into two separate parts. A free-body diagram for *either* part is sufficient to solve the problem. For comparison the problem is solved both ways.

Using upper part of the pier as a free body, Fig. 1-10b:
    Weight of the pier above the cut:

$$W_1 = \tfrac{1}{2} (2 + 4)2(4)150 = 3,600 \text{ lb.}$$

From $\Sigma F_y = 0$, force at the cut: $F_A = P + W_1 = 6,000$ lb. Hence, using Eq. 1-1, the normal stress at the level A-A is

$$\sigma_{A\text{-}A} = \frac{F_A}{A} = \frac{6,000}{2(4)} = 750 \text{ lb per sq ft,} \quad \text{or} \quad \frac{750}{144} = 5.2 \text{ psi}$$

This stress is *compressive* as F_A acts *on* the cut.

---

* For example, see Oberg, E., and Jones, F. D., *Machinery's Handbook*. New York: Industrial Press.

† See also discussion on stress concentrations, Art. 2-11.

‡ $\frac{1}{2} (2 + 6)$ is an average width of the pier.

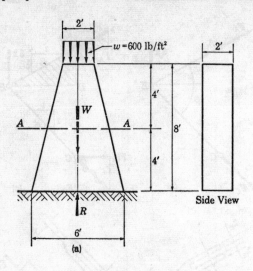

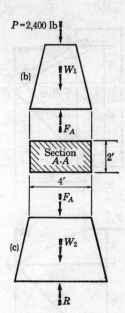

Fig. 1-10.

Using lower part of the pier as a free body, Fig. 1-10c:

Weight of the pier below the cut:

$$W_2 = \tfrac{1}{2}(4+6)2(4)150 = 6,000 \text{ lb.}$$

From $\Sigma F_y = 0$, force at the cut: $F_A = R - W_2 = 6,000$ lb.

The remainder of the problem is the same as before. The stress σ_{A-A} acts *down* on the cut. This conclusion can be reached from "action-reaction" considerations.

Note that the units employed must always be watched carefully for consistency. Also note that after the cut is made through a body, *all* of the forces to one side of this cut, *or* the other, must be considered. The pier considered here has a vertical axis of symmetry. This fact makes the application of Eq. 1-1 possible.*

Example 1-3. A bracket of negligible weight shown in Fig. 1-11a is loaded with a force P of 3 kips. For interconnection purposes the bar ends are clevised (forked) Pertinent dimensions are shown in the figure. Find the normal stresses in the members AB and BC and the bearing and shearing stresses for the pin C.

SOLUTION: First an idealized free-body diagram consisting of the two bars pinned at the ends is prepared, Fig. 1-11b. As there are no intermediate forces acting on the bars and the applied force acts through the joint at B, the forces in the bars are directed along the lines AB and BC, and the bars AB and BC are loaded *axially*. The magnitudes of the forces are unknown and are labeled F_A and F_C in the diagram.† These forces may be determined graphically by completing a triangle of forces F_A, F_B, and P. These forces may also be found analytically from two simultaneous equations $\Sigma F_y = 0$

---

* Strictly speaking, the solution obtained is not exact as the sides of the pier are sloping. If the included angle between these sides is large, this solution is altogether inadequate. For further details see Timoshenko, S. and Goodier, J. N., *Theory of Elasticity*, p. 96. New York: McGraw-Hill, 1951, Second Edition.

† In frameworks it is convenient to assume all unknown forces as tensile. A negative answer in the solution then indicates that the bar is in compression.

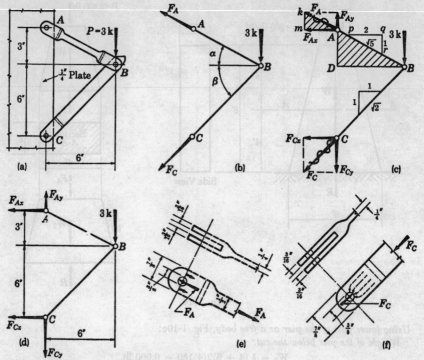

Note: ⅜″ diam. fitted bolts are inserted in all joints.

Fig. 1-11.

and $\Sigma F_z = 0$, written in terms of the unknowns F_A and F_C, a known force P, and two known angles α and β. Both of these procedures are legitimate. However, in this course it will usually be found advantageous to proceed in a different way. Instead of treating forces F_A and F_C directly, their components are used, and instead of $\Sigma F = 0$, $\Sigma M = 0$ becomes the main tool.

Any force may be resolved into components. For example, F_A may be resolved into F_{Ax} and F_{Ay} as shown in Fig. 1-11c. Conversely, if *any one* of the components of a *directed* force is known, the force itself may be determined. This follows from similarity of dimension and force triangles. In Fig. 1-11c the triangles Akm and ABD are similar triangles (both are shaded in the diagram). Hence if F_{Ax} is known, $F_A = \dfrac{AB}{DB} F_{Ax}$. Similarly, $F_{Ay} = \dfrac{AD}{DB} F_{Ax}$. However, note further that AB/DB or AD/DB are *ratios*, hence *relative* dimensions of members may be used. Such relative dimensions are shown by a little triangle on the member AB and again on BC. In the problem at hand

$$F_A = \frac{\sqrt{5}}{2} F_{Ax} \quad \text{and} \quad F_{Ay} = \tfrac{1}{2} F_{Ax}$$

Adopting the above procedure of resolving forces, the revised free-body diagram, Fig. 1-11d, is prepared. *Two* components of force are necessary at the pin joints. After the forces are determined by statics, Eq. 1-1 is applied several times, thinking in terms of a free body of an individual member.

$$\Sigma M_C = 0 \ \circlearrowleft +, \qquad +F_{Ax}(3+6) - 3(6) = 0, \qquad F_{Ax} = +2 \text{ kips}$$

$$F_{Ay} = \tfrac{1}{2} F_{Ax} = \tfrac{1}{2}(2) = 1 \text{ kip}, \quad F_A = 2(\sqrt{5}/2) = +2.23 \text{ kips}$$

$$\Sigma M_A = 0 \ \circlearrowright +, \qquad +3(6) + F_{Cz}(9) = 0, \qquad F_{Cz} = -2 \text{ kips (compression)}$$

$$F_{Cy} = F_{Cz} = -2 \text{ kips}, \qquad F_C = \sqrt{2}\,(-2) = -2.83 \text{ kips}$$

Check:
$$\Sigma F_x = 0, \qquad F_{Ax} + F_{Cx} = 2 - 2 = 0$$
$$\Sigma F_y = 0, \qquad F_{Ay} - F_{Cy} - P = 1 - (-2) - 3 = 0$$

Stress in main bar AB:

$$\sigma_{AB} = \frac{F_A}{A} = \frac{2.23}{(\tfrac{1}{4})(\tfrac{1}{2})} = 17.8 \text{ ksi} \qquad \text{(tension)}$$

Stress in clevis of bar AB, Fig. 1-11e:

$$(\sigma_{AB})_{\text{clevis}} = \frac{F_A}{A_{\text{net}}} = \frac{2.23}{2(\tfrac{3}{16})(\tfrac{7}{8} - \tfrac{3}{8})} = 11.9 \text{ ksi} \qquad \text{(tension)}$$

Stress in main bar BC:

$$\sigma_{BC} = \frac{F_C}{A} = \frac{2.83}{(\tfrac{7}{8})(\tfrac{1}{4})} = 12.9 \text{ ksi} \qquad \text{(compression)}$$

In the compression member the net section at the clevis need not be investigated; see Fig. 1-11f for the transfer of forces. The bearing stress at the pin is more critical.

Bearing between pin C and clevis:

$$\sigma_b = \frac{F_C}{A_{\text{bearing}}} = \frac{2.83}{(\tfrac{3}{8})(\tfrac{3}{16})2} = 20.1 \text{ ksi}$$

Bearing between the pin C and the main plate:

$$\sigma_b = \frac{F_C}{A} = \frac{2.83}{(\tfrac{3}{8})(\tfrac{1}{4})} = 30.1 \text{ ksi}$$

Double shear in the pin C:

$$\tau = \frac{F_C}{A} = \frac{2.83}{2\pi(\tfrac{3}{16})^2} = 12.9 \text{ ksi}$$

For a complete analysis of this bracket, other pins should be investigated. However, it may be seen by inspection that the other pins in this case are stressed the same amount as computed above, or less.

The advantages of the method used in the above example for finding forces in members should now be apparent. It can also be applied with success in a problem such as the one shown in Fig. 1-12. The force F_A transmitted by the curved member AB acts through points A and B, since the forces applied at A and B must be collinear. By resolving this force at A', the same procedure may conveniently be followed. A wavy line through F_A and F_C indicates that these

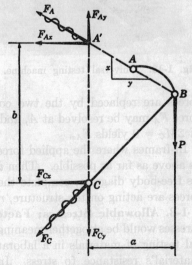

Fig. 1-12.

Fig. 1-13. Universal testing machine. (Courtesy Baldwin-Lima-Hamilton Corp.)

forces are replaced by the two components shown. Alternatively, the force F_A may be resolved at A, and since $F_{Ay} = (x/y)F_{Ax}$, the application of $\Sigma M_C = 0$ yields F_{Ax}.

In frames where the applied forces do not act through a joint, proceed as above as far as possible. Then *isolate an individual member*, and using its free-body diagram, complete the determination of forces. If inclined forces are acting on the structure, *resolve them into convenient components*.

1-8. Allowable Stresses; Factor of Safety. The determination of stresses would be altogether meaningless were it not for the fact that physical testing of materials in a laboratory provides information regarding a material's resistance to stress. In a laboratory, specimens of known material, manufacturing process, and heat treatment are carefully prepared to desired dimensions. Then these specimens are subjected to successively increasing known forces. In the most usual test, a round rod is subjected to tension and the specimen is loaded until it finally ruptures. The force necessary to cause rupture is called the *ultimate* load. By dividing this ultimate load by the *original* cross-sectional area of the specimen, the *ultimate strength* (stress) of a material is obtained. Figure 1-13 shows a testing machine used for this purpose. Figure 1-14 is a photograph of a

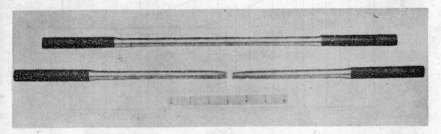

Fig. 1-14. A typical tension-test specimen of mild steel, (a) before fracture, (b) after fracture.

tension-test specimen. The tensile test is used most widely. However, compression, bending, torsion, and shearing tests are also employed. Table 1 of the Appendix gives ultimate strengths and other physical properties for a few materials.

For the design of members the stress level called the *allowable stress* is set considerably lower than the ultimate strength found in the so-called "static" test mentioned above. This is necessary for several reasons. The exact magnitudes of the forces that may act upon the designed structure are seldom accurately known. Materials are not entirely uniform. Some of the materials stretch unpermissible amounts prior to an actual break, so to hold down these deformations, stresses must be kept low.* Some materials seriously corrode. Some materials flow plastically under a sustained load, a phenomenon called *creep*. With a lapse of time this may cause large deformations that cannot be tolerated.

For applications where a force comes on and off the structure a number of times, the materials cannot withstand the ultimate stress of a static test. In such cases the "ultimate strength" depends on the number of times the force is applied as the material works at a particular stress level. Figure 1-15 shows the results of tests† on a number of the same kind of specimens at different stresses. Experimental points indicate the number of cycles required to break the specimen at a particular stress under the application of a fluctuating load. Such tests are called "fatigue tests"

---

* See Chapter 2 for more details.

† Zambrow, J. L., and Fontana, M. G., "Mechanical Properties, including Fatigue, of Aircraft Alloys at Very Low Temperatures," *Trans. ASM*, 1949, vol. 41, p. 498.

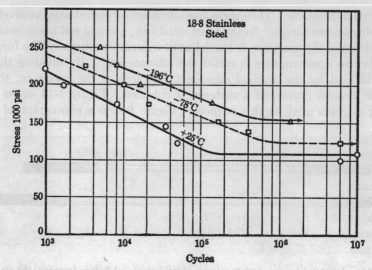

Fig. 1-15. Fatigue strength of 18–8 stainless steel at various temperatures (reciprocating-beam test).

and the corresponding curves are termed *S-N* (stress-number) diagrams. As may be seen from Fig. 1-15, at smaller stresses the material can withstand an ever-increasing number of cycles of load application. For some materials, notably steels, the *S-N* curve for low stresses becomes essentially horizontal. This means that at a low stress an infinitely large number of reversals of stress may take place before the material fractures. The limiting stress at which this occurs is called the *endurance limit* of the material. This limit, being dependent on stress, is measured in pounds per square inch.

Some care must be exercised in interpreting the *S-N* diagrams, particularly with regard to the range of the applied stress. In some tests complete reversal (tension to compression) of stress is made, in others the applied load is varied in a different manner, such as tension to no load and back to tension. The major part of fatigue testing is done on specimens in bending.

In some cases another item deserves attention. As materials are manufactured they are often rolled, peened, and hammered. In castings materials cool unevenly. These processes set up high internal stresses, which are called *residual stresses*. In all cases treated in this text the materials are assumed to be entirely free of such stresses.

The afore-mentioned facts, coupled with the impossibility of determining stresses accurately in complicated structures and machines, necessitate a substantial reduction of stress compared to the ultimate strength of a material in a static test. For example, ordinary steel will withstand an ultimate stress in tension of 60,000 psi and more.　However, it deforms rather suddenly and severely at the stress level of about 35,000 psi, and it is customary in the United States to use an allowable stress of around 20,000 psi for structural work.　This allowable stress is even further reduced to about 10,000 psi for parts that are subjected to alternating loads because of the fatigue characteristics of the material.　*Fatigue properties of materials are of utmost importance in mechanical equipment.　Many failures in machine parts can be traced to disregard of this important consideration.*　(Also see Art. 2-11.)

Large companies, as well as city, state, and federal authorities, prescribe or recommend * allowable stresses for different materials, depending on the application.　Often such stresses are called the allowable *fiber*† stresses.

Since according to Eq. 1-1 stress times area is equal to a force, the allowable and ultimate stresses may be converted into the allowable and ultimate forces or "loads" which a member may resist.　Also a significant ratio may be formed:

$$\frac{ultimate\ load\ for\ a\ member}{allowable\ load\ for\ a\ member}$$

This ratio is called a *factor of safety* and must always be greater than unity. Although not commonly used, perhaps a better term for this ratio is a *factor of ignorance.*

This factor is identical with the ratio of ultimate to allowable stress for tension members.　For more complexly stressed members, the former definition is implied, although the ratio of stresses is actually used.　As will become apparent from subsequent reading, the two are not necessarily synonymous.

In the aircraft industry the term factor of safety is replaced by another defined as

$$\frac{ultimate\ load}{design\ load} - 1$$

and known as the *margin of safety.*　In normal usage this also reverts to

$$\frac{ultimate\ stress}{maximum\ stress\ caused\ by\ the\ design\ load} - 1$$

1-9. Design of Axially Loaded Members and Pins.　The design of members for axial forces is rather simple.　From Eq. 1-1 the required area of a member is

---

* For example, see the American Institute of Steel Construction *Manual*, Building Construction Code of any large city, ANC-5 *Strength of Aircraft Elements* issued by the Army-Navy Civil Committee on Aircraft Design Criteria, etc.

† The adjective *fiber* in the above sense is used for two reasons.　Many original experiments were made on wood, which is fibrous in character.　Also, in several derivations that follow, the concept of a continuous filament or fiber in a member is a convenient device for visualizing its action.

$$A = \frac{P}{\sigma_{\text{allow}}} \qquad (1\text{-}1a)$$

In all statically determinate problems the axial force P is determined from statics and the intended use of the material sets the allowable stress. For tension members, the area A so computed is the required *net* cross-sectional area of a member. For short compression blocks, Eq. 1-1a is also applicable; however, *for slender members, do not attempt to use the above equation prior to study of the chapter on columns.*

The simplicity of Eq. 1-1a is unrelated to its importance. A large number of problems requiring its use occur in practice. The following problems illustrate some applications of Eq. 1-1a as well as provide additional review in statics.

Example 1-4. Reduce the weight of bar AB in Example 1-3 by using a better material such as chrome-vanadium steel. The ultimate strength of this steel is approximately 120,000 psi. Use a factor of safety of $2\frac{1}{2}$.

SOLUTION: $\sigma_{\text{allow}} = 120/2.5 = 48$ ksi.

From Example 1-3 *the force in the bar AB:* $F_A = +2.23$ kips.

Required area: $A_{\text{net}} = 2.23/48 = 0.0464$ sq in.

Adopt $\frac{3}{16}$ in. by $\frac{1}{4}$ in. bar. This provides an area of $(3/16)(1/4) = 0.0468$ in.², which is slightly in excess of the required area. Many other proportions of the bar are possible.

With the cross-sectional area selected, the actual or *working* stress is somewhat below the allowable stress: $\sigma_{\text{actual}} = 2.23/0.0468 = 47.6$ ksi. The actual factor of safety is $120/47.6 = 2.52$, and the actual margin of safety is 1.52.

In a complete redesign, clevis and pins should also be reviewed, and, if possible, decreased in dimensions.

Example 1-5. Select members FC and CB in the truss of Fig. 1-16a to carry an inclined force P of 150 kips. Set the allowable tensile stress at 20,000 psi.

SOLUTION: If all members of the truss were to be designed, forces in all members would have to be found. Professionally this is done by constructing a Maxwell-Cremona* diagram or analyzing the truss by the method of joints. However, if only a few members are to be designed or checked, the method of sections is quicker.

It is generally understood that a planar truss such as shown in the figure is *stable* in the direction perpendicular to the plane of the paper. Practically this is accomplished by introducing braces at right angles to the plane of the truss. In this example the design of compression members is avoided as this will be treated in the chapter on columns.

To determine the forces in the members to be designed, the reactions for the whole structure are computed first. This is done by complete disregard of the interior framing. *Only reaction and force components definitely located at their points of application are indicated on a free-body diagram of the whole structure,* Fig. 1-16b. After the reactions are determined, free-body diagrams of a part of the structure are used to determine the forces in the members considered, Figs. 1-16c and d.

Using free body in Fig. 1-16b:

$\Sigma F_x = 0$	$R_{Dx} - 120 = 0,$	$R_{Dx} = 120$ kips
$\Sigma M_E = 0 \ \circlearrowright +,$	$+R_{Dy}(120) - 90(20) - 120(60) = 0,$	$R_{Dy} = 75$ kips
$\Sigma M_D = 0 \ \circlearrowleft +,$	$+R_E(120) + 120(60) - 90(100) = 0,$	$R_E = 15$ kips

Check: $\Sigma F_y = 0,$ $\qquad +75 - 90 + 15 = 0$

* For example, see Sutherland, H., and Bowman, H. L., *Structural Theory.* New York: Wiley, 1950. Fourth Edition.

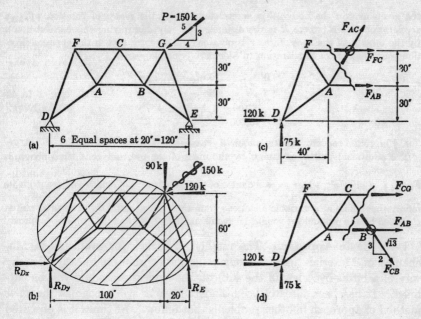

Fig. 1-16.

Using free body in Fig. 1-16c:

$$\Sigma M_A = 0 \circlearrowright +, \qquad +F_{FC}(30) + 75(40) - 120(30) = 0, \quad F_{FC} = +20 \text{ kips}$$

$$A_{FC} = \frac{F_{FC}}{\sigma_{\text{allow}}} = 1 \text{ in.}^2 \qquad (\text{use } \tfrac{1}{2} \text{ in. by 2 in. bar})$$

Using free body in Fig. 1-16d:

$$\Sigma F_y = 0, \qquad -(F_{CB})_y + 75 = 0, \qquad (F_{CB})_y = +75 \text{ kips}$$

$$F_{CB} = \sqrt{13}\,\frac{(F_{CB})_y}{3} = +90.2 \text{ kips}$$

$$A_{CB} = \frac{F_{CB}}{\sigma_{\text{allow}}} = \frac{90.2}{20} = 4.51 \text{ in.}^2 \qquad (\text{use 2 bars } 1\tfrac{1}{8} \text{ in. by 2 in.})$$

Example 1-6. Consider the idealized dynamic system shown in Fig. 1-17. The shaft AB rotates at a constant speed of 600 rpm. A light rod CD is attached to this shaft at point C and at the end of this rod a 10 lb weight is fastened. In describing a complete circle the weight at D spins on a "frictionless" plane. Select the size of the rod CD so that the stress in it will not exceed 10,000 psi. In calculations neglect the weight of the rod.

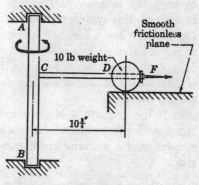

Fig. 1-17.

SOLUTION: The acceleration of gravity g is 32.2 ft per sec per sec or $32.2(12) = 386$ in. per sec per sec. The angular velocity ω is $600(2\pi)/60 = 20\pi$ radians per sec.* For

* 2π radians correspond to one complete revolution of the shaft; 60 in denominator converts revolutions per minute to revolutions per second.

the given motion the body W is accelerated toward the center of rotation with an acceleration of $\omega^2 R$, where R is the distance CD. By multiplying this acceleration a by the mass m of the body, force F is obtained. This force acts in the *opposite* direction from that of the acceleration (d'Alembert principle), see Fig. 1-17.

$$F = ma = \frac{W}{g} \omega^2 R = \frac{10}{386}(20\pi)^2(10.75) = 1,100 \text{ lb}$$

$$A_{net} = \frac{F}{\sigma_{allow}} = \frac{1,100}{10,000} = 0.11 \text{ in.}^2$$

A $\frac{3}{8}$ in. round rod provides the required cross-sectional area.

The additional pull at C caused by the mass of the rod, not considered above, is

$$F_1 = \int_0^R (m_1 \, dr)\omega^2 r,$$ where m_1 is the mass of the rod per inch of length and $(m_1 \, dr)$ is its infinitesimal mass at a variable distance r from the vertical rod AB. The total pull at C caused by the rod and the weight W at the end is $F + F_1$.

1-10. Basic Approach. The method of attack for problems in Mechanics of Materials follows along remarkably uniform lines. Now, by way of a bird's-eye view of the subject, the typical procedure will be outlined. It has been already used, and the reader will recognize the *same* method of approach in other problems that follow. At times it is obscured by intermediate steps, but in the final analysis it is always applied.

1. From a particular arrangement of parts, a single member is isolated. Such a member is indicated on a diagram with *all* the forces and reactions acting on it. *This is a free body of the whole member.*

2. The reactions are determined by the application of the equations of statics. In indeterminate problems, statics is supplemented by additional considerations.

3. At a point where the magnitude of the stress is wanted, a section *perpendicular* to the axis of the body is passed, and a portion of the body, to either one side of the section or the other, is *completely* removed.

4. At the section investigated, the system of internal forces necessary to keep the isolated part of the member in *equilibrium* is determined. In general, this system of forces consists of an axial force, a shear, a bending moment, and a torque.* These quantities are found by treating a *part* of the member as a free body.

5. With the system of forces at the section *properly resolved*, the formulas of Mechanics of Materials enable one to determine the stresses at the section considered.

6. If the magnitude of the maximum stress at a section is known, one can provide proper material for such a section; or, conversely, if the physical properties of a material are known, one can select a member of adequate size.

* A complete appreciation of these terms will result only after a study of Chapters 3 and 4.

7. In certain other problems, a further study of a member at a section enables one to predict the deformation of the structure as a whole and hence, if necessary, to design members that do not deflect or "sag" excessively.

Very few basic formulas are used in Mechanics of Materials. These will be learned by their repeated application. In the study of this text, memory will not be taxed. *However, visualization of the nature of the quantities being computed is essential.* Free-body diagrams help this immensely.

Problems for Solution

1-1. If an axial tensile force of 110 kips is applied to a member made of an 8 WF 31 section, what will the tensile stress be? What will the stress be if the member is a 12 ⌐⌐ 20.7 section? For designation and cross-sectional areas of these members see Tables 4 and 5 in the Appendix.

1-2 and 1-3. Short cast iron members have the cross-sectional dimensions shown in the figures. If they are subjected to axial compressive forces of 10 kips each, find the points of application for these forces to cause no bending, and determine the normal stresses.

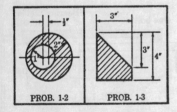

PROB. 1-2   PROB. 1-3

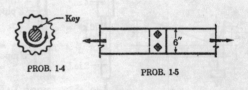

PROB. 1-4   PROB. 1-5

1-4. A gear transmitting a torque of 4,000 in.-lb to a $2\frac{3}{16}$ in. shaft is keyed to it as shown in the figure. The $\frac{1}{2}$ in. square key is 2 in. long. Determine the shearing stress in the key. *Ans.* 3,650 psi.

1-5. Two $\frac{3}{8}$ in. thick steel plates are fastened together as shown in the figure, by means of two $\frac{3}{4}$ in. bolts which fit tightly into the holes. If the joint transmits a tensile force of 10 kips, determine (a) the average normal stress in the plates at a section where no holes occur; (b) the average normal stress at the critical section; (c) the average shearing stress in the bolts; and (d) the average bearing stress between the bolts and the plates. *Ans.* (a) 4,430 psi; (b) 5,910 psi; (c) 11,320 psi; (d) 17,800 psi.

1-6. In Example 1-2, find the stress 2 ft above the base. Show the result on an infinitesimal element. *Ans.* −6.03 psi.

1-7. Determine the bearing stresses caused by the applied force at A, B, and C for the structure shown in the figure.

1-8. A lever mechanism used to lift panels of a portable army bridge is shown in the figure. Calculate the shearing stress in pin A caused by a load of 500 lb.

1-9. Calculate the shearing stress in pin A of the bulldozer if the total forces acting on the blade are as shown in the figure. Note that there is a $1\frac{1}{2}$ in. diameter pin on each side of the bulldozer. Each pin is in single shear.

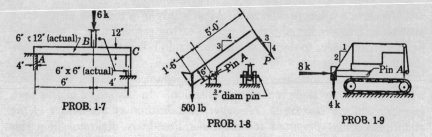

PROB. 1-7

500 lb

PROB. 1-8

PROB. 1-9

1-10. A steel bar 1 in. in diameter is loaded in double shear until failure; the ultimate load is found to be 100,000 lb. If the allowable stress is to be based on a factor of safety of 4, what must the diameter of a pin designed for an allowable load of 6,000 lb in single shear be?

1-11. A 6 in. by 6 in. (actual size) wooden post delivers a force of 12 kips to a concrete footing, as shown in Fig. 1-7. (a) Find the bearing stress of the wood on the concrete. (b) If the allowable pressure on the soil is one ton per sq ft, determine the required dimensions in plan view of a square footing. Neglect the weight of the footing. *Ans.* 333 psi, 29.5 in.

1-12. An arrangement of three rods is used to suspend a 10 kip weight as shown in the figure. The rods AB and BD are $\frac{3}{4}$ in. in diameter, the rod BC is $\frac{1}{2}$ in. in diameter. Find the stresses in the rods. *Ans.* $+21.4$ ksi, $+22.6$ ksi and 16.1 ksi.

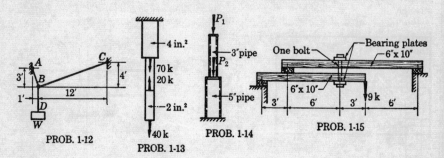

PROB. 1-12

PROB. 1-13

PROB. 1-14

PROB. 1-15

1-13. A rod of variable cross-section is subjected to three axial forces as shown in the figure. Find the maximum normal stress. *Ans.* 22.5 ksi.

1-14. A short column is made up of two standard steel pipes, one on top of the other as shown in the figure. If the allowable stress in compression is 15,000 psi, (a) what is the allowable axial load P_1 if the axial load $P_2 = 50$ kips; (b) what is the allowable load P_1 if the load $P_2 = 15$ kips? Neglect the weight of the pipes.

1-15. For the structure shown in the figure, calculate the size of the bolt and area of the bearing plates required if the allowable stresses are 18,000 psi in tension and 500 psi in bearing. Neglect the weight of the beams.

1-16. A 7,000 lb weight is supported by means of a pulley as shown in the figure. The pulley is supported by the frame ABC. Find the required cross-sectional areas for members AC and BC if the allowable stress in tension is 20,000 psi and in compression, determined by the method of Chapter 13, is 14,000 psi. *Ans.* 0.5 in.² and 0.8 in.²

1-17. A force of 100 kips is applied at joint B to a system of two pin-joined bars as shown in the figure. Determine the required cross-sectional area of the bar BC if the allowable stresses are 15 ksi in tension and 10 ksi in compression. *Ans.* 0.993 in.²

1-18. Find the stress in the mast of the derrick shown in the figure. All members are in the same vertical plane and are joined by pins. The mast is made from an 8 in. standard steel pipe weighing 28.55 lb/ft. Neglect the weight of the members. *Ans.* —446 psi.

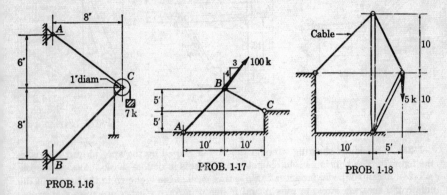

PROB. 1-16

PROB. 1-17

PROB. 1-18

1-19. Find the required cross-sectional areas for all tension members in Example 1-5. The allowable stress is 20 ksi.

1-20. A signboard 15 ft by 20 ft in area is supported by two frames as shown in the figure. All members are actually 2 in. by 4 in. in cross-section. Calculate the stress in each member due to a horizontal wind load of 20 lb per ft² on the sign. Assume all joints to be connected by pins and that one-quarter of the total wind force acts at B and at C. Neglect the possibility of buckling of the compression members. Neglect the weight of the structure.

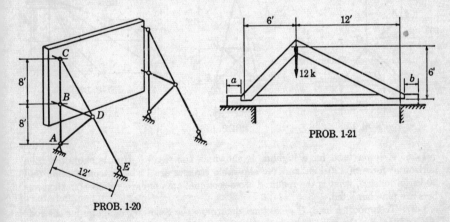

PROB. 1-20

PROB. 1-21

1-21. What distances, a and b, are required beyond the notches in the horizontal member of the truss shown? All members are nominally 8 in. by 8 in. in cross-section (see Table 10, Appendix for actual size). Assume the ultimate strength of wood in shear parallel to the grain to be 500 psi. Use a factor of safety of 5. (This detail is not recommended.) *Ans. a* = 10.7 in.

1-22. What is the required diameter of the pin B for the bell crank mechanism shown in the figure if an applied force of 12 kips at A is resisted by a force P at C? The allowable shearing stress is 15,000 psi. *Ans.* 0.60 in.

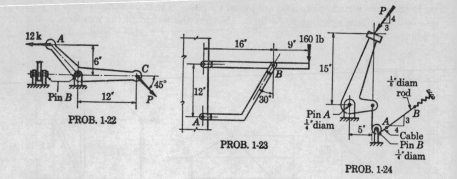

PROB. 1-22

PROB. 1-23

PROB. 1-24

1-23. What is the shearing stress in the bolt A caused by the applied load shown in the figure? The bolt is $\frac{1}{4}$ in. in diameter, and it acts in double shear. *Ans.* 4,250 psi.

1-24. A control pedal for actuating a spring mechanism is shown in the figure. Calculate the shearing stress in pins A and B due to a force P when it causes a stress of 10,000 psi in the rod AB. Both pins are in double shear.

1-25. A beam with a force of 100 kips at one end is supported by a strutted cable as shown in the figure. Find the horizontal and vertical components of the reactions at A, B, and D. If the allowable tensile stress is 20,000 psi and the allowable compressive stress is 10,000 psi, what is the required cross-sectional area of members AC, BC, and CE? (*Hint*: isolate the beam DF first.) *Ans.* $A_{AC} = A_{CE} = 10$ in.² and $A_{BC} = 5.66$ in.²

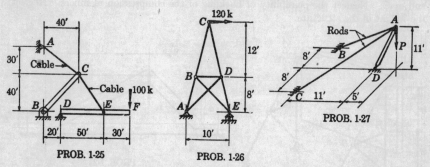

PROB. 1-25

PROB. 1-26

PROB. 1-27

1-26. A tower used for a highline is shown in the figure. If it is subjected to a horizontal force of 120 kips and the allowable stresses are 15 ksi in compression and 20 ksi in tension, what is the required cross-sectional area of each member? All members are pin-connected.

1-27. To support a load, $P = 20$ tons, determine the necessary diameter for the rods AB and AC for the tripod shown in the figure. Neglect the weight of the structure and assume that the joints are pin-connected. No allowance need be made for threads. The allowable tensile stress is 18 ksi.

1-28. A 10 lb weight moves in a horizontal circle at the end of a 5 ft wire with such an angular velocity that the wire makes an angle of 30° with the vertical. What is the proper diameter for the wire if the allowable tensile stress for high strength steel is 40 ksi?

Chapter Two

STRAIN—HOOKE'S LAW—
AXIAL LOAD PROBLEMS

2-1. Introduction. This chapter will be devoted to the further examination of some of the physical properties of the materials of construction. An investigation of the nature of the deformations that take place in a stressed body will be the primary objective. These deformations will be related to the magnitudes of the stresses which cause them. Lastly, some additional limitations that must be imposed on Eqs. 1-1 and 1-2 of the previous chapter are pointed out.

2-2. Strain. In Art. 1-8 it was stated that information regarding the physical properties of materials comes from the laboratory. In the particularly common tension test, not only the ultimate strength, but other properties are usually observed, especially those pertaining to the study of deformation as a function of the applied force. Thus, while a specimen is being subjected to an increasing force P, as shown in Fig. 2-1, a change in length between two points, as A and B, on the specimen is observed. Initially, two such points can be selected an arbitrary distance apart. Thus, depending on the test, either a 2 in. or an 8 in. distance is commonly used. This initial distance between the two points is called a *gage distance*. In an experiment it is the change in length of this distance that is noted. With the same load and a longer gage distance,

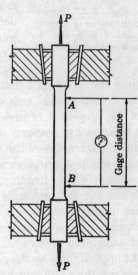

Fig. 2-1. Diagram of a tension specimen in a testing machine.

a larger deformation is observed, or vice versa. Therefore it is more fundamental to refer to the observed elongation *per unit of length of the gage*. If Δ is the total elongation in a given *original* gage length L, the elongation per unit of length, ϵ (epsilon), is

$$\epsilon = \frac{\Delta}{L} \tag{2-1}$$

27

This elongation per unit of length is termed **strain**.* It is a dimensionless quantity, but it is customary to refer to it as having the dimensions of inches per inch (feet per foot is just as acceptable). Sometimes strain is given in percent. The quantity ϵ is a **very small** one, except for a few materials such as rubber. If the strain is known, the total deformation of an axially loaded bar is ϵL. This relationship holds for any gage length until some local deformation takes place on an appreciable scale. The latter effect, exemplifying the behavior of a mild steel rod near a breaking point, is shown in Fig. 2-2. This phenomenon is referred to as "necking." Brittle materials do not exhibit it at usual temperatures, although they too contract transversely a little in a tension test, and expand in a compression test.

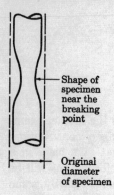

Shape of specimen near the breaking point

Original diameter of specimen

Fig. 2-2. Typical contraction of a specimen of mild steel in tension near the breaking point.

2-3. Stress-Strain Diagram. It is apparent from this discussion that for general purposes the deformations of a rod in tension or compression are most conveniently expressed in terms of strain. Similarly, stress rather than force is the more significant parameter in the study of materials, since the effect on a material of an applied force P depends primarily on the cross-sectional area of the member. As a consequence, in the study of the properties of materials, it is customary to plot diagrams on which a relationship between *stress* and *strain* for a particular test is reported. Such diagrams establish a relationship between stress and strain, and for most practical purposes are assumed to be independent of the size of specimen or its gage length. For these *stress-strain diagrams*, it is customary to use the ordinate scale for stress and the abscissa for strains. Stresses are usually computed on the basis of the *original* area of a specimen, although, as mentioned earlier, some transverse contraction or expansion of a material always takes place. If the stress is computed by dividing the applied force by the corresponding *actual* area of a specimen at the same instant, the so-called *true* stress is obtained. A plot of true stress vs. strain is called a *true* stress-strain diagram. Such diagrams are seldom used in practice.

Experimentally determined stress-strain diagrams differ considerably for different materials. Even for the same material they differ, depending on the temperature at which the test was conducted, the speed of the test, and several other variables.† However, speaking broadly, two types

---

* The term *unit* strain is sometimes used.

† For more details, see Davis, H. E., Troxell, G. E., and Wiskocil, C. T., *Testing and Inspection of Engineering Materials*, Chapters II and IV. New York: McGraw-Hill, 1941.

of diagrams may be recognized.   One type is shown in Fig. 2-3, which is
for mild steel, a *ductile* material widely used in construction.   The other
type is shown in Fig. 2-4.   Such
diverse materials as tool steel, concrete, copper, etc., have curves of
this variety, although the extreme
value of strain that these materials
can withstand *differs drastically.*
The "steepness" of these curves
varies considerably.   Numerically
speaking, each material has its own
curve.   The terminal point on a
stress-strain diagram represents
the complete failure (rupture) of
a specimen.

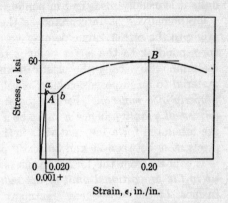

Fig. 2-3.   Stress-strain diagram for mild
steel.

2-4. Hooke's Law.   Fortunately, one feature of stress-strain
diagrams is applicable with suf-
ficient accuracy to nearly all materials.   It is a fact that for a *certain
distance* from the origin the experimental values of stress vs. strain lie
essentially on a straight line.   This holds
true almost without reservations for glass.
It is true for mild steel up to some point,
as *A* in Fig. 2-3.   It holds nearly true up
to very close to the failure point for many
high-grade alloy steels.   On the other
hand, the straight part of the curve hardly
exists in concrete, annealed copper, or
cast iron.   Nevertheless, up to some such
point as *A* (also in Fig. 2-4), *the relationship between stress and strain may be said
to be linear for all materials*   This sweep-
ing idealization and generalization applicable to all materials became known
as *Hooke's law.**   Symbolically this law
may be expressed by the equation

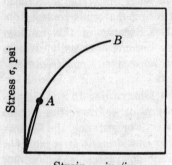

Fig. 2-4.   Stress-strain diagram
for a brittle material.

$$\sigma = E\epsilon \qquad \text{or} \qquad E = \frac{\sigma}{\epsilon} \tag{2-2}$$

which simply means that stress is directly proportional to strain where
the constant of proportionality is E.   This constant E is called the *elastic*

---

* Actually Robert Hooke, an English scientist, worked with springs and not with
rods.   In 1676 he announced an anagram "c e i i i n o s s s t t u v," which in Latin is
Ut Tensio sic Vis (the force varies as the stretch).

modulus, modulus of elasticity, or Young's modulus.* As ϵ is dimensionless, E has the units of stress in this relation. In the English system of units it is usually measured in pounds per square inch

Graphically E is interpreted as the slope of a straight line from the origin to the rather vague point A on a stress-strain diagram. The stress corresponding to the latter point is termed the *proportional limit* of the material. Physically the elastic modulus represents the stiffness of the material to an imposed load. *The value of the elastic modulus is a definite property of a material.* From experiments it is known that ϵ is *always a very small quantity*, hence E must be a large one. Its approximate values are tabulated for a few materials in Table 1 of the Appendix. For most steels, E is between 29 and 30 $\times$ 10^6 psi.

It follows from the foregoing discussion that **Hooke's law applies only up to the proportional limit of the material.** This is highly significant as in most of the subsequent treatment the derived formulas are based on this law. Clearly then, such formulas will be limited to the material's behavior in the lower range of stresses.

Some materials, notably single crystals, possess different elastic moduli in different directions with reference to their crystallographic planes. Such materials, having different physical properties in different directions, are termed nonisotropic. A consideration of such materials is *excluded* from this text. The vast majority of engineering materials consist of a large number of *randomly* oriented crystals Because of this random orientation of crystals, properties of materials become essentially alike in any direction.† *Throughout this text complete homogeneity and isotropy of materials is assumed.*

2-5. Further Remarks on Stress-Strain Diagrams. In addition to the proportional limit defined in Art. 2-4, several other interesting points may be observed on the stress-strain diagrams. For instance, the highest points (B in Figs. 2-3 and 2-4) correspond to the *ultimate* strength of a material. *Stress* associated with the remarkably long plateau ab in Fig. 2-3 is termed the *yield point* of a material. As will be brought out later, this remarkable property of mild steel, in common with other *ductile* materials, is significant in stress analysis. For the present, note that at an essentially constant stress, strains 15 to 20 times those that take place up to the proportional limit occur during yielding. At the yield point a large amount of deformation takes place at a constant stress. The yielding phenomenon is absent in most materials, particularly in those that behave in a brittle fashion.

A study of stress-strain diagrams shows that the yield point is so near

---

* Young's modulus is so called in honor of Thomas Young, an English scientist. His *Lectures on Natural Philosophy*, published in 1807, contain a definition of the modulus of elasticity.

† Rolling operations produce preferential orientation of crystalline grains in some materials.

the proportional limit that for most purposes the two may be taken as one. However, it is much easier to locate the former. For materials which do not possess a well-defined yield point, one is actually "invented" by the use of the so-called "offset method." This is illustrated in Fig. 2-5 where a line offset an *arbitrary* amount of 0.2% of strain is drawn parallel to the straight-line portion of the original stress-strain diagram.* Point C is then taken as the "yield point" of the material at 0.2% offset.

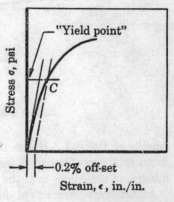

Finally, the technical definition of the *elasticity* of a material should be made. In such usage it means that a material is able to regain *completely* its original dimensions upon removal of the applied forces. At the beginning of loading, if a small force is applied to a body, the body deforms a certain small amount. If such a force is removed, the body returns to its initial size and shape. With increasing magnitude of force this continues to take place while the material behaves elastically. However, eventually a stress is reached which causes permanent deformation, or set, in the material. The corresponding stress level is called the *elastic limit* of the material. Practically speaking, the *elastic limit* corresponds closely to the proportional limit of the material.

Fig. 2-5. Off-set method of determining the yield point of a material.

For the majority of materials, stress-strain diagrams obtained for short compression blocks are the same as those found in tension. However, there are some notable exceptions. For example, cast iron and concrete are very weak in tension but not in compression. For these materials the diagrams differ considerably, depending on the sense of the applied force.

2-6. Deflection of Axially Loaded Rods. Equations 1-1, 2-1, and 2-2, plus a known elastic modulus for a given material, are sufficient to determine the deformations of axially loaded rods. However, the usual calculations *apply only within the elastic range of a material's behavior* inasmuch as Hooke's law (Eq. 2-2) is used. To formulate this problem in general terms, consider the *axially* loaded bar shown in Fig. 2-6a. In this bar the cross-sectional area varies along the length, and forces of various magnitudes are applied at several points. Now suppose that in this problem the change in length of the bar *between two points A and B* caused by the applied forces is sought. The quantity wanted is the sum (or accumulation) of the deformations that take place in infinitesimal

* For decreasing loads the stress-strain diagram is parallel to the straight-line portion of the original stress-strain diagram. For further details see Fig. 15-2 and the accompanying text.

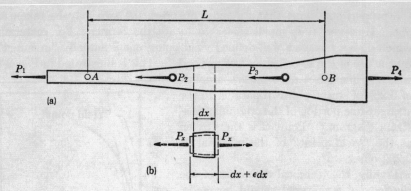

Fig. 2-6. An axially loaded bar.

lengths of the rod. Hence the amount of deformation that takes place in an arbitrary element of length dx is first formulated, then the sum or integral of this effect over the given length gives the quantity sought.

An arbitrary element cut out from the bar is shown in Fig. 2-6b. From free-body considerations, this element is subjected to a pull P_x which, in general, is a variable quantity. The infinitesimal deformation $d\Delta$ that takes place in this element upon application of the forces is equal to strain ϵ multiplied by the length dx. From Eq. 2-2, strain is equal to the stress σ_x divided by the elastic modulus E. However, in general, σ_x is a variable quantity equaling P_x divided by the *corresponding* area A_x. Hence, since $\epsilon = \sigma_x/E$ and $\sigma_x = P_x/A_x$,

$$d\Delta = \epsilon\, dx = \frac{\sigma_x}{E} dx = \frac{P_x\, dx}{A_x E}$$

Since the contribution of individual elements is now known, the total deformation between any two given points on a bar is simply their sum,[*] i.e.,

$$\Delta = \int_A^B d\Delta = \int_A^B \frac{P_x\, dx}{A_x E} \tag{2-3}$$

Three examples will now be solved to show applications of the above equations.

Example 2-1. Consider the rod AB of constant cross-sectional area A and of length L shown in Fig. 2-7a. Determine the relative displacement of the end A with respect to B when a force P is applied, i.e., find the *deflection* of the free end, caused by the application of a concentrated force P. The elastic modulus of the material is E.

SOLUTION: In this problem the rod may be treated as being weightless as only *the effect of P on the deflection* is investigated. Hence, no matter where a cut C-C is made

---

[*] The limits of integration as stated represent the range of integration. Actually, they must be expressed in terms of the values of the variable. This nonrigorous usage of the limits will often be employed in this text.

through the rod, $P_x = P$, Fig. 2-7b. The infinitesimal elements, Fig. 2-7c, are everywhere the same, subjected to a *constant* pull P. Likewise, A_x everywhere has a constant value A. Applying Eq. 2-3,

$$\Delta = \int_A^B \frac{P_x \, dx}{A_x E} = \frac{P}{AE} \int_0^L dx = \frac{P}{AE} \left. x \right|_0^L = \frac{PL}{AE} \tag{2-4}$$

It is seen from Eq. 2-4 that the deflection of the rod is directly proportional to the applied force and the length, and inversely proportional to A and E.

The equation derived will be referred to in subsequent work.

Example 2-2. Determine the relative displacement of points A and D of the steel rod of *variable* cross-sectional area shown in Fig. 2-8a when it is subjected to the four concentrated forces P_1, P_2, P_3, and P_4. Let $E = 30 \times 10^6$ psi.

SOLUTION: In attacking such a problem, a check must first be made to ascertain that the body as a whole is in equilibrium, i.e., $\Sigma F_x = 0$. Here, by inspection it may be seen that such is the case. Next, the variation of P_x along the length of the bar must be studied. This may be done conveniently with the aid of sketches as shown in Fig. 2-8b, c, and d, which show that *no matter where* a section C_1-C_1 is taken between points A and B, the force in the rod is $P_x = +40$ kips. Similarly, between B and C, $P_x = -60$ kips, and between C and D, $P_x = +20$ kips. The variation of A_x is shown in Fig. 2-8a. Both P_x and A_x, mathematically speaking, are not continuous functions along the rod. Both have "jumps" or *sudden* changes in their values. Hence, in integrating, the limits of integration must be "broken." Thus, from Eq. 2-3,

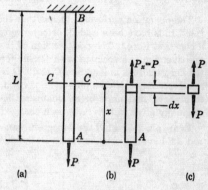

Fig. 2-7.

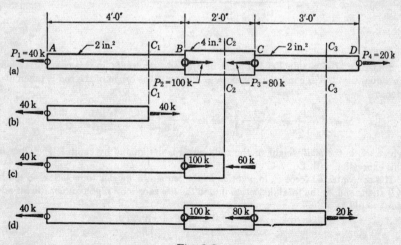

Fig. 2-8.

$$\Delta = \int_A^D \frac{P_x \, dx}{A_x E} = \int_A^B \frac{P_{AB} \, dx}{A_{AB} E} + \int_B^C \frac{P_{BC} \, dx}{A_{BC} E} + \int_C^D \frac{P_{CD} \, dx}{A_{CD} E}$$

In the last three integrals the respective P_x and A_x are constants between the limits shown. The subscripts of P and A denote the range of applicability of the function; thus P_{AB} applies in the interval AB, etc. These integrals revert to the solution of the previous example, i.e., Eq. 2-4. Applying it and substituting numerical values,

$$\Delta = \sum \frac{PL}{AE} = +\frac{40,000(4)12}{2(30)10^6} - \frac{60,000(2)12}{4(30)10^6} + \frac{20,000(3)12}{2(30)10^6}$$

$$= +0.032 - 0.012 + 0.012 = +0.032 \text{ in.}$$

The operation performed means that the individual deformations of the three "separate" rods have been added, or *superposed*. Each one of these "rods" is subjected to a constant force. The positive sign of the answer indicates that the rod *elongates*, as a positive sign is associated with tensile forces. The equality of the absolute values of the deformations in lengths BC and CD is purely accidental. Note that in spite of the relatively large stresses present in the rod, the value of Δ is small. Finally, do not fail to observe that units of all quantities have been changed to be consistent. Forces originally given in kips have been changed into pounds, lengths into inches.

Example 2-3. Find the deflection, caused by its own weight, of the free end A of the rod AB having a constant cross-sectional area A and weighing w lb per in., Fig. 2-9a.

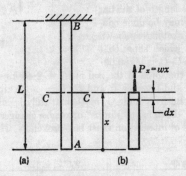

Fig. 2-9.

SOLUTION: Here again Eq. 2-3 must be applied. However, in this case P_x is a variable quantity. It is conveniently expressed as wx if the origin of the rod is taken at A. Hence

$$\Delta = \int_A^B \frac{P_x \, dx}{A_x E} = \frac{1}{AE} \int_0^L wx \, dx = \frac{w}{AE} \left| \frac{x^2}{2} \right|_0^L = \frac{(wL)L}{2AE} = \frac{WL}{2AE}$$

where wL is the *total* weight of the rod, which is designated by capital W. Compare this expression with Eq. 2-4.

If a concentrated force P, in *addition* to the bar's own weight, were acting on the bar AB at the end A, the total deflection due to the *two* causes by *superposition* (direct addition) would be

$$\Delta = \frac{PL}{AE} + \frac{WL}{2AE} = \frac{[P + (W/2)]L}{AE}$$

In problems where the area of a rod is variable, a proper *function* for it must be substituted into Eq. 2-3 to determine deflections. In practice, it is sometimes sufficiently accurate to analyze such problems by approximating the shape of a rod by a *finite* number of elements as shown in Fig. 2-10. The deflections for each one of these elements are added to obtain the total deflection.

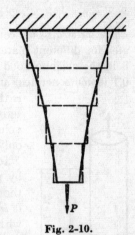

2-7. Poisson's Ratio. In addition to the deformation of materials in the direction of the applied force, another remarkable property can be observed in all solid materials, namely, that at right angles to the applied force, a certain amount of lateral (transverse) expansion or contraction takes place. This phenomenon is shown in Fig. 2-11a and b, where the deformations are greatly *exaggerated*. For clarity this physical fact may be restated thus: if a solid body is subjected to an axial tension, it contracts laterally; on the other hand, if it is compressed, the material "squashes out" sidewise. With this in mind, directions of lateral deformations are easily

Fig. 2-10.

traced, depending on the sense of the applied force. Mathematically a plus sign is usually assigned to an *increment* of lateral dimension, or vice versa.

For a general theory, as for the deformations taking place in the direction of the applied force, it is preferable to refer to lateral deformations on the basis of deformation per *unit* of length of the transverse dimension. Thus the lateral deformations on a *relative* basis can be expressed in inches

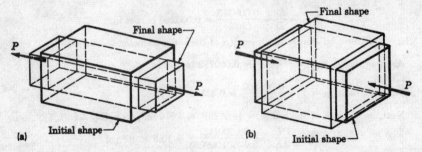

Fig. 2-11. Lateral contraction and expansion of solid bodies subjected to axial forces (Poisson effect).

per inch (or feet per foot). These relative unit lateral deformations are termed *lateral strains*. Moreover, it is known from experiments that lateral strains bear a *constant* relationship to the longitudinal or axial strains caused by an axial force, provided a material remains *elastic* and is homogeneous and isotropic.   This constant is a definite property of a material, just like the elastic modulus E, and is called *Poisson's ratio*.* It will be denoted by μ (mu) and is defined as follows:

$$\mu = \frac{lateral\ strain}{axial\ strain} \tag{2-5}$$

*where the strains are caused by **uni-axial** stress only.*   The value of μ fluctuates for different materials over a relatively narrow range.   Generally it is in the neighborhood of 0.25 to 0.35.   In extreme cases values as low as 0.1 (some concretes) and as high as 0.5 (rubber) occur.   The latter value is the *largest possible*.   It is normally attained by materials during plastic flow and signifies constancy of volume.†   In this text Poisson's ratio will be used only when materials behave elastically.

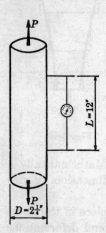

Fig. 2-12.

In conclusion, note that the Poisson effect exhibited by materials causes *no additional stresses* other than those considered earlier *unless the transverse deformation is inhibited or prevented*.   The same is found to be true with regard to thermal expansion or contraction of materials.   This topic will be treated in the chapter on statically indeterminate structures.

Example 2-4.   Consider a carefully conducted test where an aluminum bar of $2\frac{1}{4}$ in. diameter is stressed in a testing machine as shown in Fig. 2-12.   At a certain instant the applied force P is 32 kips while the measured elongation of the rod is 0.00938 in. in a 12 in. gage length and the diameter's dimension is decreased by 0.000585 in.   Calculate the two physical constants μ and E of the material.

SOLUTION: *Transverse strain:*

$$\epsilon_t = \frac{\Delta_t}{D} = \frac{0.000585}{(2.25)} = 0.000260 \text{ in. per in.}$$

where Δ_t is the *total* change in dimension of the rod's diameter.

Axial strain: $\epsilon_a = \dfrac{\Delta}{L} = \dfrac{0.00938}{12} = 0.000782$ in. per in.

Poisson's ratio: $\mu = \dfrac{\epsilon_t}{\epsilon_a} = \dfrac{0.000260}{0.000782} = 0.333$

Next, as the area of the rod $A = \frac{1}{4}\pi(2.25)^2 = 3.976$ in.², from Eq. 2-4,

$$E = \frac{PL}{A\Delta} = \frac{32,000(12)}{3.976(0.00938)} = 10.3 \times 10^6 \text{ psi}$$

In practice, when a study of physical quantities, as E and μ, is being made, it is well to work with the corresponding stress-strain diagram to be sure that the quantities determined are associated with the elastic range of the material.   Also note that it makes no difference whether the initial or the final lengths are used in computing strains.

* Named after S. D. Poisson, a French scientist who formulated this concept in 1828.
† Nadai, A., *Theory of Flow and Fracture of Solids*, vol. 1.   New York: McGraw-Hill, 1950.

This is true because changes that take place in dimensions are *very small*. Strictly speaking, the *initial* dimensions of lengths are implied.

*2-8. Generalized Hooke's Law. In the above article Poisson's ratio was defined as the ratio of lateral strain to the axial strain for an axially loaded member. This applies only to a uni-axial state of stress on an element. Now a more general state of stress acting upon an *isotropic* body will be considered, and equations relating stress to deformation will be developed.

A block whose sides are *a*, *b*, *c* respectively is acted upon by tensile stresses *uniformly* distributed on all faces as shown in Fig. 2-13a.*   This

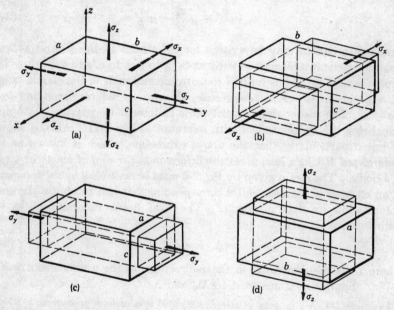

Fig. 2-13.   An element subjected to normal stresses acting in the directions of co-ordinate axes.

diagram approaches the generality of Fig. 1-3.   However, for the present, shearing stresses have been deleted, as it is a known experimental fact that the strains caused by normal stresses are *independent of small shearing deformations*.   The normal stresses are designated by σ's with appropriate subscripts referring to the directions in which the stresses act.

For the moment, attention will be directed to the change in length of the block in the *x*-direction. To find this change use is made of the *principle of superposition*, which is based upon the premise that the resultant stress or strain in a system due to several forces *is the algebraic sum of their effects when separately applied*.   This assumption is true only if

* This figure is adapted from Dreyer, G., *Festiakeitslehre und Elastizitätslehre*, p. 151 Leipzig: Jänecke.

each effect is directly and linearly related to the force causing it. It is only approximately true when the deflections or deformations due to one force cause an abnormal change in the effect of another force. Fortunately the magnitudes of deflections are relatively small in most engineering structures. Hence, by proceeding on the basis of the above principle, the separate effects shown in Figs. 2-13b, c, and d may be summed. The stress in the x-direction causes a positive strain $\epsilon_x' = \sigma_x/E$. Each of the stresses in the y- and z-directions causes a negative strain *in the x-direction* as a result of Poisson's effect. These strains are $\epsilon_x'' = -\mu\sigma_y/E$ and $\epsilon_x''' = -\mu\sigma_z/E$, respectively. Thus the net strain in the x-direction is

$$\epsilon_x = \frac{\sigma_x}{E} - \mu\frac{\sigma_y}{E} - \mu\frac{\sigma_z}{E} \qquad (2\text{-}6)$$

Similar expressions may be written for the strains in the y- and z-directions by cyclic interchange of subscripts (x to y, y to z, z to x, etc.). The application of Eq. 2-6 is limited to isotropic materials in the elastic range. *If a particular stress is compressive, the sign of the corresponding term changes.* The reader should verify this statement by *physical* reasoning, visualizing the Poisson effect with reference to Fig. 2-11. Also, it should be noted particularly that the above expression, which is known as the **generalized Hooke's law,** gives the *deformation per unit of length* or strain in a body. The strain given by Eq. 2-6 *must be multiplied by the dimension* of an element or member *in the corresponding direction* to obtain the total deformation in that direction.* The *total* linear deformation in the x-direction is

$$\Delta_x = \epsilon_x L_x \qquad (2\text{-}7)$$

where L_x is the dimension in the x-direction, as the a dimension in Fig. 2-13a. Similar relations exist for Δ_y and Δ_z.

Example 2-5. A 2 in. cube of steel is subjected to a uniform pressure of 30,000 psi acting on all faces. Determine the change in dimension between two parallel faces of the cube. Let $E = 30 \times 10^6$ psi and $\mu = \frac{1}{4}$.

SOLUTION: Using Eq. 2-6 and noting that pressure is a compressive stress,

$$\epsilon_x = \frac{(-30{,}000)}{(30)10^6} - \left(\frac{1}{4}\right)\frac{(-30{,}000)}{(30)10^6} - \left(\frac{1}{4}\right)\frac{(-30{,}000)}{(30)10^6}$$

$$= -(5)10^{-4} \text{ in. per in.}$$

$$\Delta_x = \epsilon_x L_x = -(5)10^{-4} \times 2 = -10^{-3} \text{ in.} \quad \text{(contraction)}$$

In this case $\Delta_x = \Delta_y = \Delta_z$.

2-9. Shearing Stresses on Mutually Perpendicular Planes. Article 2-8 dealt with a general case of deformations caused by normal stresses. Now the effect of shearing stresses on deformation will be considered. This requires some preparatory remarks. First, return to Fig. 1-3 and simplify it to the case shown in Fig. 2-14a. In this figure only the τ_{xy}

* The stresses must remain constant in the interval considered.

and τ_{yz} shearing stresses are shown. As before, the first subscript of τ associates the shearing stress with a plane *perpendicular* to a given axis and the second specifies its *direction* relative to another axis. The dimensions of the *infinitesimal* element considered are $(dx)(dy)(dz)$. For any such element, as with normal stresses, the shearing stresses on *parallel*

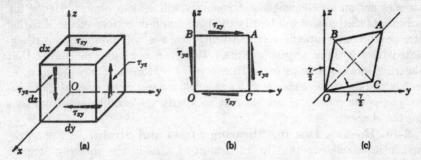

Fig. 2-14. An element of a body in pure shear.

planes are numerically equal. This follows directly from the equilibrium of an element. Thus, multiplying stresses by their respective areas and applying $\Sigma F_z = 0$,

$$(\tau_{yz})_{\text{left-hand face}}\,dx\,dz = (\tau_{yz})_{\text{right-hand face}}\,dx\,dz$$

Hence, the shearing stress τ_{yz} on the left- and the right-hand face of an infinitesimal element is numerically the same, but is *opposite in direction*. Similar reasoning applies to τ_{zy}.

Although the three-dimensional aspect of the problem should not be forgotten, it is customary, for the sake of convenience, to deal with a plane representation of the problem as shown in Fig. 2-14b. Using this representation and summing the moments of *forces* about axis O,

$$\Sigma M_O = 0 \circlearrowright +, \qquad +(\tau_{zy})(dy\,dx)(dz) - (\tau_{yz})(dx\,dz)(dy) = 0$$

where the bracketed expressions correspond respectively to stress, area, and moment arm. Simplifying,

$$\tau_{zy} = \tau_{yz} \tag{2-8}$$

Similarly it can be shown that $\tau_{xz} = \tau_{zx}$, and $\tau_{yx} = \tau_{xy}$. Hence the subscripts for the shearing stresses are commutative, i.e., their order may be interchanged.

The implication of Eq. 2-8 is very significant. The fact that subscripts are commutative signifies that *shearing stresses on mutually perpendicular planes of an infinitesimal element are numerically equal.* (Note that the mutually perpendicular planes referred to contain shearing stresses which act only toward or away from the intersection of such planes.) Moreover, it is possible to have an element in equilibrium only when **shearing** *stresses occur on four sides of an element simultaneously.* That is, in any stressed body where shearing stresses exist, *two* pairs of such stresses act on the mutually perpendicular planes. Hence $\Sigma M_O = 0$ is not satisfied by a single pair of shearing stresses.

In the subsequent work situations where more than two pairs of shearing stresses act on an element simultaneously will seldom occur. Hence the subscripts used above to identify the planes and directions of the shearing stresses become superfluous. Shearing stresses will normally be designated by τ without any subscripts. However, one must remember that shearing stresses always occur in *two pairs.* Moreover, on diagrams, as in Fig. 2-14b, *the arrowheads of the shearing stresses must meet at diametrically opposite corners* of an element to satisfy the equilibrium conditions for the element.

2-10. Hooke's Law for Shearing Stress and Strain. In the above article it was shown that in *an element* of a body the shearing stresses must occur in two pairs acting on mutually perpendicular planes. When *only* these stresses occur, the element is said to be in *pure shear*. Such a system of stresses distorts an element of an elastic body in the fashion shown in Fig. 2-14c. Of course such a distortion is true only for a perfectly homogeneous, isotropic body having equal properties in all directions. The diagonals OA and BC are axes of symmetry for a distorted element.

If attention is confined to the study of *small* deformations, and further, if the behavior of an element is considered only in its elastic range, it is again found experimentally that there is a *linear* relationship between the shearing stress and the angle γ (gamma) shown in Fig. 2-14c. Hence, *if γ is defined as the **shearing strain,*** mathematically the extension of Hooke's law for shearing stress and strain is

$$\tau = G\gamma \qquad (2\text{-}9)$$

where G is a constant of proportionality called *the shearing modulus of elasticity* or the modulus of rigidity. Like E, G is a constant for a given material. It is measured in the same units as E (psi), while γ is measured in *radians*, a dimensionless quantity. (The shearing strain γ can be stated in percent, in the same way as ϵ).

For convenience, Fig. 2-14c is redrawn with a different set of axes so that the complete angle* γ appears on only one side of the distorted element, Fig. 2-15. Note that the shearing strains considered, numerically given by γ, are *always small*. It is sufficiently accurate to as-

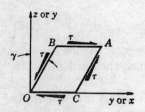

Fig. 2-15. Distortion due to pure shear.

---

* Shearing strain is independent of the individual angles made with the co-ordinate axes.

sume that tan γ, sin γ, or γ in *radian* measure are numerically equal. Likewise, the linear dimensions of a distorted element do not change appreciably.   For example, in Fig. 2-15, $OB \cos \gamma \doteq OB$.

The best arrangement available for direct experimental verification of Eq. 2-9 is a *thin* tube subjected to a twist or torque.   As will be explained in the next chapter, in this arrangement there is *uniform* shearing stress throughout the walls of the tube.   From such experiments it is known that the appearance of τ-γ diagrams is similar to that of the σ-ϵ diagrams of a tension test for the same material.   Similar points for the elastic limit in *shear*, yield point, and ultimate shearing stress may be obtained. However, *for the same material, the numerical values of the shearing stresses are generally much lower than* (approximately one-half) *the corresponding values for the normal stress.*

In Art. 8-11 it will be shown that the three elastic constants E, μ, and G are not independent of each other for homogeneous materials.   In fact,

$$G = \frac{E}{2(1 + \mu)} \tag{2-10}$$

Thus, for example, in the tension experiment described in Example 2-4,

$$G = (10.3)10^6/2(1 + 0.333) = 3.86 \times 10^6 \text{ psi}$$

*2-11. Stress Concentrations.** The first fundamental formulas of stress analysis, Eqs. 1-1 and 1-2, were discussed in Chapter 1, and from the preceding articles of this chapter it is seen that stresses are accompanied by deformations.   If such deformations take place at the same uniform rate in *adjoining* elements, no additional stresses other than those given by the above equations exist in isotropic materials.   However, if the *uniformity* of the cross-sectional area of an axially loaded member is interrupted, or if the applied force is actually applied over a very small area, a perturbation in stresses takes place.   This is caused by the fact that the adjoining elements must be physically *continuous* in a distorted state.   They must stretch or contract equal amounts at the adjoining sides of all particles.   These deformations result from linear and angular deformations involving the properties of materials E, G, and μ and the applied forces.   Methods of obtaining this disturbed stress distribution are beyond the scope of this text.   Such problems are treated in the Mathematical Theory of Elasticity.   Even by those advanced methods only the simpler cases have been solved.   The mathematical difficulties become too great for many practically significant problems. For the group of problems that are not tractable mathematically, special experimental techniques (mainly Photoelasticity, briefly discussed in Art. 9-4) have been developed to determine the actual stress distribution.

In this text it seems significant to examine qualitatively the results of more advanced investigations. For example, in Fig. 2-16a a short block is shown loaded by a concentrated force P.   This problem could be solved by using Eq. 1-1, i.e., $\sigma = P/A$.   But is this answer really correct?   Reasoning in a qualitative way, it is apparent that the strains must be maximum in the *vicinity* of the applied force, hence the corresponding stresses must also be maximum.   That indeed is the answer given by the Theory of Elasticity.*   The end results for normal stress distribution at various sections are shown in the adjoining stress distribution diagrams, Fig. 2-16b, c, and d.   For present purposes, physical intuition is sufficient to justify these results.   Note particularly the high peak of the normal stress at a section close to the applied force.†   Also note how rapidly this peak smoothes out to a nearly uniform stress distribution at a section below

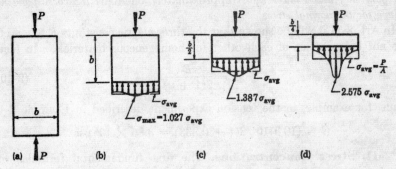

Fig. 2-16.   Stress distribution near a concentrated force.

the top equal to the width of the bar.   This illustrates the famed *Saint Venant's principle* of rapid dissipation of *localized* stresses.   This principle asserts that the effect of forces or stresses applied over a small area may be treated as a statically equivalent system which, at a distance approximately equal to the width or thickness of a body, causes stress distribution which follows a simple law.   Hence Eq. 1-1 is nearly true at a distance equal to the width of the member from the point of application of a concentrated force.   Note also that at every level where the stress is investigated accurately, the *average* stress is still correctly given by Eq. 1-1. This follows, since the equations of statics *must always be satisfied*.   No matter how irregular the nature of the stress distribution at a given section through a member, an integral (or sum) of σdA over the whole area *must be equal to the applied force.*

Because of the great difficulty encountered in solving for the above-mentioned "peak" or *local* stresses, a convenient scheme has been developed in practice.   This scheme consists simply of calculating the stress by the elementary equations (as Eqs. 1-1 or 1-2) and then multiplying the

* Timoshenko, S., and Goodier, J. N., *Theory of Elasticity*, p. 52.   New York: McGraw-Hill, 1951, Second Edition.   Fig. 2-16 is adopted from this source.

† In a purely elastic material the stress is infinite right under a "concentrated" force.

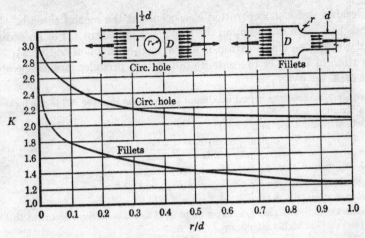

Fig. 2-17.   Stress-concentration factors for flat bars in tension.

stress so computed by a number which is called the **stress-concentration factor.**   In this text this number will be designated by K.   The values of the stress-concentration factor depend *only* on the *geometrical proportions* of the member.   These factors are available in technical literature in various tables and graphs* as a function of the geometrical proportions of members.   Using this scheme, Eq. 1-1 may now be rewritten as

$$\sigma_{max} = K\frac{P}{A} \qquad (2\text{-}11)$$

where K is the stress-concentration factor.   From Fig. 2-16d, at a depth below the top equal to one-quarter of the width of the member, $K = 2.575$.   Hence $\sigma_{max} = 2.575\ \sigma_{av}$.

Two other particularly significant stress-concentration factors for *flat* axially loaded members are shown in Fig. 2-17.†   The corresponding factors which may be read from this graph represent a *ratio* of the peak stress of the actual stress in the *net* or small section of the member as shown in Fig. 2-18 to the average stress in the net section given by Eq. 1-1.   A

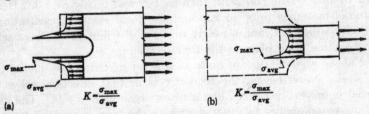

Fig. 2-18.   Meaning of the stress-concentration factor K.

* Roark, R. J., *Formulas for Stress and Strain.*   New York: McGraw-Hill, 1943.
† Frocht, M. M., "Factors of Stress Concentration Photoelastically Determined." *Trans., ASME*, 1935, vol. 57, p. A-67.

considerable stress concentration also occurs at the root of threads. This depends to a large degree upon the sharpness of the cut. For an ordinary thread the stress-concentration factor is in the neighborhood of $2\frac{1}{2}$. The application of Eq. 2-11 presents no difficulties, provided proper graphs or tables of K are available.

Example 2-6. Find the actual maximum stress in the member AB in the forked end at A in Example 1-3.

SOLUTION: *Geometrical proportions:*

$$\frac{\text{radius of the hole}}{\text{net width}} = \frac{3/16}{1/2} = 0.375$$

From Fig. 2-17:* $K \doteq 2.2$ for $r/d = 0.375$.

Average stress from Example 1-3: $\sigma_{\text{av}} = P/A_{\text{net}} = 11.9$ ksi.

Maximum stress, Eq. 2-11: $\sigma_{\text{max}} = K\sigma_{\text{av}} = 2.2(11.9) = 27$ ksi

This answer indicates that actually a large local increase in stress occurs at this hole, a fact that may be highly significant.

In considering stress-concentration factors in design, it must be remembered that their theoretical or photoelastic determination is based on the use of Hooke's law. If members are *gradually* stressed beyond the proportional limit of the material, these factors lose their significance. For example, consider a flat bar of *mild steel*, of the proportions shown in Fig. 2-19, that is subjected to a gradually increasing force P. The stress distribution will be geometrically similar to that shown in Fig. 2-18 until σ_{max} reaches the yield point of the material. However, with a further increase in the applied force, σ_{max} *remains* the same, as a great deal of deformation can

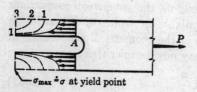

$\sigma_{\text{max}} \doteq \sigma$ at yield point

Fig. 2-19. Behavior of a flat bar of mild steel when stressed beyond the yield point.

take place while the material yields. Therefore the stress at A remains virtually "frozen" at the same value. Nevertheless, for equilibrium, stresses acting over the net area must be high enough to resist P. As a result of this, the stress distribution begins to look something like that shown by line 1-1 in Fig. 2-19; then as 1-2, and finally as 1-3. Hence, for *ductile* materials prior to rupture, the local stress concentration is practically wiped out, and a nearly uniform distribution of stress across the net section takes place at the time of fracture.

The above argument is not quite as true for materials less ductile than mild steel. Nevertheless, the tendency is in that direction unless the material is unusually brittle, like glass or some alloy steels. The argument presented applies to situations where the force is gradually applied or is static in character. *It is not applicable for fluctuating loads as found*

* Strictly speaking the stress concentration depends on the condition of the hole, whether it is empty, or filled with a bolt or pin. For further details see Spotts, M. F., *Design of Machine Elements*. New York: Prentice-Hall, 1948.

in some machine parts. There the working stress level that is actually reached *locally* determines the fatigue behavior of the member. The maximum permissible stress is set from an *S-N* diagram (Art. 1-8). *Failure of most machine parts can be traced to progressive cracking originating at points of high stress.* In machine design, then, stress concentrations are of paramount importance, although some machine designers feel that the theoretical concentrations are somewhat high. Apparently some tendency is present to smooth out the stress peaks even in members subjected to dynamic loads.

From the above discussion and accompanying charts it should be apparent why a trained machine designer tries to "streamline" the juncture and transition of parts that make up a structure.

Problems for Solution

2-1. A standard steel specimen of $\frac{1}{2}$ in. diameter elongated 0.0087 in. in an 8 in. gage length when it was subjected to a tensile force of 6,250 lb. If the specimen was known to be in the elastic range, what is the elastic modulus of the steel? *Ans.* 29.3 × 10⁶ psi.

2-2. A steel rod 30 ft long used in a control mechanism must transmit a tensile force of 980 lb without stretching more than $\frac{1}{8}$ in., nor exceeding an allowable stress of 20,000 psi. What must the diameter of the rod be? Give the answer to the nearest eighth of an inch. $E = 30 \times 10^6$ psi. *Ans.* $\frac{3}{8}$ in.

2-3. A solid cylinder of 2 in. diameter and 36 in. length is subjected to a tensile force of 30 kips. One part of this cylinder, L_1 long, is of steel; the other part, fastened to steel, is aluminum and is L_2 long. (a) Determine the lengths L_1 and L_2 so that the two materials elongate an equal amount. (b) What is the total elongation of the cylinder? $E_{St} = 30 \times 10^6$ psi; $E_{Al} = 10 \times 10^6$ psi.

2-4. Revise the data in Example 2-2 to read as follows: $P_1 = 10$ kips; $P_3 = 100$ kips; $P_4 = 30$ kips, cross-sectional area of the rod from A to B is 1 in.² Then find (a) the force P_2 necessary for equilibrium and (b) the total elongation of the rod AD. *Ans.* 0.020 in.

2-5. In Example 2-2 what two additional (equal and opposite) forces applied at the ends will bring the total deformation back to zero?

2-6. A $\frac{1}{4}$ in. by 3 in. plate, hanging vertically, consists of an aluminum portion 6 ft long fastened to a steel portion 8 ft long. At the lower end a load of 6,000 lb is suspended. Neglecting the weight of the plate, calculate the deflection of the lower end. $E_{St} = 30 \times 10^6$ psi; $E_{Al} = 10 \times 10^6$ psi.

2-7. A round steel bar having a cross-section of 0.5 in.² is attached at the top and is subjected to three axial forces, as shown in the figure. Find the deflection of the free end caused by these forces. $E = 30 \times 10^6$ psi. *Ans.* 0.040 in.

2-8. A bar of steel and a bar of aluminum have the dimensions shown in the figure. Calculate the magnitude of the force P that will cause the total length of the two bars to decrease 0.010 inches. Assume a uniform stress distribution over all cross-sections of both bars and that the bars are prevented from buckling sidewise. E_{St} and E_{Al} are the same as in Prob. 2-6. *Ans.* 51.6 k.

2-9. In one of the California oil fields a very long steel drill pipe got stuck in hard clay (see figure). It was necessary to determine at what depth this occurred. The engineer on the job ordered the pipe subjected to a large upward tensile force. As a result of this operation the pipe came up elastically 2 ft. At the same time the pipe elongated 0.0014 in. in an 8 in. gage length.   Approximately where was the pipe stuck? Assume that the cross-sectional area of the pipe was constant and that the media surrounding the pipe hindered elastic deformation of the pipe in a static test very little. *Ans.* 11,400 ft.

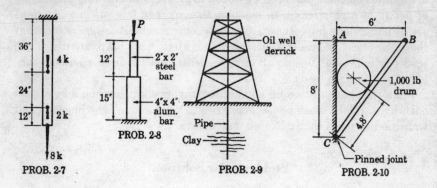

PROB. 2-7 . PROB. 2-8 PROB. 2-9 PROB. 2-10

2-10. A wall bracket is constructed as shown in the figure.   All joints may be considered pin-connected.   The steel rod *AB* has a cross-sectional area of 0.20 in.^{2} The member *BC* is a rigid beam.   If a 38.4 in. diameter drum weighing 1,000 lb is placed in the position shown, what will the elongation of the rod *AB* be?   *Ans.* 0.012 in.

2-11. For the truss shown in the figure determine the total elongation of the member *BC* due to the application of the force $P = 100$ kips.   The member *BC* is made from steel and is 2.5 in.^{2} in cross-sectional area. $E = 30 \times 10^6$ psi.   *Ans.* −0.02 in.

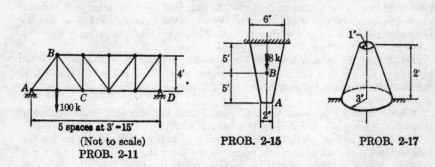

(Not to scale)
PROB. 2-11   PROB. 2-15   PROB. 2-17

2-12. If the deformation of any one member in Prob. 2-11 can not exceed 0.1% of its length, which member requires the largest cross-sectional area and what is this area?

2-13. If in Example 2-3 the rod is a 1 in. square aluminum bar weighing 1.17 lb/ft, what should its length be for the free end to elongate 0.250 in. under its own weight. $E = 10 \times 10^6$ psi.

2-14. What will the deflection of the free end of the rod in Example 2-3 be if, instead of Hooke's law, the stress-strain relationship is $\sigma^n = E\epsilon$, where n is a number dependent on the properties of the material?

2-15. The tapered steel bar shown in the figure is cut out from a steel plate 1 in. thick and is welded at the top to a rigid structure.   Find the deflection of the end *A* caused by the force of 8 kips applied at *B*.   Consider the origin of the coordinate axes at the point of intersection of the sloping lines. $E = 30 \times 10^6$ psi.   *Ans.* 0.00324 in.

2-16. Rework Prob. 2-15 taking the origin at point *B*.

2-17.* The dimensions of a frustum of a right circular cone supported at the large end on a rigid structure are shown in the figure. Determine the deflection of the top due to the weight of the body. The unit weight of material is γ; the elastic modulus is E. (*Hint:* consider the origin of the coordinate axes at the vertex of the extended cone.)

2-18.* Find the total elongation Δ of the narrow elastic bar of constant cross-sectional area A shown in the figure if it is rotated in a horizontal plane with an angular velocity of ω radians per second. The unit weight of the material is γ. Neglect the small amount of material shown in the figure to the left of the small pin. (*Hint:* first find the stress at a section a distance r from the pin by integrating the effect of the inertia forces between r and L, see Example 1-6.) *Ans.* $\gamma\omega^2L^3/3gE$.

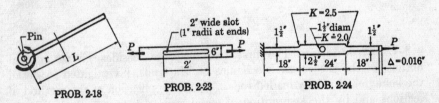

PROB. 2-18   PROB. 2-23   PROB. 2-24

2-19. A cast brass rod 2.25 in. in diameter and 6 in. long is compressed axially by a uniformly distributed force of 45,000 lb. Determine the increase in diameter caused by the applied force. $E = 12.5 \times 10^6$ psi; $\mu = 0.30$.

2-20. Determine the change in thickness occurring in a 2 in. by 10 in. by $\frac{1}{2}$ in. steel bar when it is subjected to two equal and opposite longitudinal forces of 20 kips each and two equal and opposite transverse forces of 40 kips each. The applied forces are tensile and are uniformly distributed along the outside edges of the bar. $E = 30 \times 10^6$ psi; $\mu = 0.25$.

2-21. A rectangular steel block, such as shown in Fig. 2-13a, has the following dimensions: $a = 2$ in., $b = 3$ in., and $c = 4$ in. The faces of this block are subjected to uniformly distributed forces of 36 kips (tension) in the x-direction, 40 kips (tension) in the y-direction, and 48 kips (compression) in the z-direction. Determine the magnitude of a single system of forces acting only in the y-direction which would cause the same deformation in the y-direction as the initial forces. Let $\mu = \frac{1}{4}$. *Ans.* 50.0 kips.

2-22. A $\frac{1}{4}$ in. by 3 in. plate 24 in. long has a circular hole of 1 in. diameter located in its center. Find the axial tensile force that may be applied to this plate in the longitudinal direction without exceeding an allowable stress of 32,000 psi.

2-23. A long slot is cut out from a 1 in. by 6 in. steel bar 10 ft long as shown in the figure. (a) Find the maximum stress if an axial force $P = 50$ kips, is applied to the bar. Assume that the upper curve in Fig. 2-17 is applicable. (b) For the same case determine the total elongation of the rod. Neglect local effects of stress concentrations and assume that the reduced cross-sectional area extends for 2 ft. (c) Estimate the elongation of the same rod if $P = 160$ kips. Assume that steel yields 0.020 in. per in. at a stress of 40 ksi. *Ans.* 28.7 ksi, 0.0367 in., and 0.56 in.

2-24. The bar shown in the figure is cut from a 1 in. thick piece of steel. At the changes in section, approximate stress concentration factors are as indicated. A force P is applied producing a total change of length in the bar of 0.016 inches. Determine the *maximum* stress in the bar caused by this force. Neglect the effect of the hole and stress concentrations on the axial deformation. *Ans.* $\sigma_{max} = 28,400$ psi.

Chapter Three

TORSION

3-1. Introduction. The first two chapters, besides giving general notions of the subject of Mechanics of Materials, investigated in detail the behavior of axially loaded rods. By the application of the method of sections and by the assumption of equal strains in longitudinal fibers, a formula for stress in an axially loaded rod was developed. Then an expression was established for obtaining the axial deformation of members. In this chapter, similar relations for statically determinate members subjected only to torque about their longitudinal axes will be determined. Thus *the investigation will be confined to the effect of a single type of action, i.e., of a torque causing twist or torsion in a member.* Members subjected simultaneously to torque and bending, frequently occurring in practice, will be treated in Chapter 9. Statically indeterminate cases are discussed in Chapter 12.

A major part of this chapter is devoted to the treatment of members with circular, or tubular cross-sectional areas. Noncircular sections are only briefly discussed. In practice, members that transmit torque, such as shafts of motors, torque tubes of power equipment, etc., are predominantly circular or tubular in cross-section. Thus, although mainly a special case of the torsion problem will be treated, the majority of important applications fall within the scope of the formulas developed.

Shaft couplings are briefly considered at the end of the chapter, since their analysis is related to the method of analysis used for circular shafts.

3-2. Application of Method of Sections. In analyzing members subjected to torque, the basic approach outlined in Art. 1-10 is followed. First, the system as a whole is examined for equilibrium, and then the method of sections is applied by passing a *cutting plane perpendicular to the axis of the member.* *Everything* to either side of a cut is then removed, and the *internal or resisting torque* necessary to maintain equilibrium of the isolated part is determined. For finding this internal torque in *statically determinate* members, *only one* equation of statics, $\Sigma M_z = 0$, where the z-axis is directed along the member, is required. By applying this equation to *an isolated part* of a shaft, it may be found that the externally applied torques* are *balanced* by the internal resisting torque developed in the material.   Hence *the external and internal torques are numerically equal,* but act in opposite directions.

In this chapter, shafts will be assumed "weightless" or supported at frequent enough intervals to make the effect of bending negligible.   Axial forces that may also act simultaneously on the member are excluded for the present.

Example 3-1. Find the internal torque at section *x-x* for the shaft shown in Fig. 3-1a and acted upon by the three torques indicated.

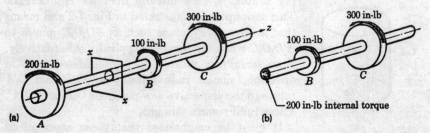

Fig. 3-1.

SOLUTION: The 300 in.-lb torque at *C* is balanced by the two torques of 200 in.-lb and 100 in.-lb at *A* and *B*, respectively.   Therefore, the body as a whole is in equilibrium.   Next, by passing a cutting plane *x-x* perpendicular to the axis of the rod *anywhere* between *A* and *B*, a free body of a part of the shaft, shown in Fig. 3-1b, is obtained. Whereupon, from $\Sigma M_z = 0$, or

$$externally\ applied\ torque = internal\ torque$$

the conclusion is reached that the internal or resisting torque developed in the shaft between *A* and *B* is 200 in.-lb.   Similar considerations lead to the conclusion that the internal torque resisted by the shaft between *B* and *C* is 300 in.-lb.

It may be seen intuitively that for a member of constant cross-sectional area the maximum internal torque causes the maximum stress and imposes the most severe condition on the material.   Hence, in investigating a torsion member, several sections may have to be examined to determine the largest internal torque.   A section where the largest internal torque is developed is the *critical section*.   In Example 3-1 the critical section is anywhere between points *B* and *C*.   If the torsion member varies in size, it is more difficult to decide where the material is critically stressed.   Several sections may have to be investigated and *stresses computed* to determine the critical section.   These situations are analogous to the case of an axially loaded rod, and means must be developed to determine stresses as a function of the internal torque and the size of the member. In the next several articles the necessary formulas are derived.

* If *two* planes are used to isolate a portion of a body, the internal torque at one end of the *isolated body* must be treated as an external torque when the other section is considered.

3-3. Basic Assumptions. To establish a relation between the internal torque and the stresses it sets up in members with *circular and tubular cross-sections*, it is necessary to make several assumptions, the validity of which will be justified further on.   These, in addition to homogeneity of material, are as follows:

1. A plane section of material perpendicular to the axis of a circular member remains *plane* after the torques are applied, i.e., no *warpage* or distortion of parallel planes normal to the axis of a member takes place.*

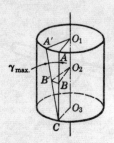

Fig. 3-2. Variation of strain in a circular member subjected to torque.

2. In a circular member subjected to torque, *shearing strains*, γ, vary **linearly** *from the central axis*. This assumption is illustrated in Fig. 3-2 and means that an imaginary plane such as AO_1O_3C moves to $A'O_1O_3C$ when the torque is applied.   Alternatively, if an imaginary radius O_3C is considered fixed in direction, similar radii initially at O_2B and O_1A rotate to the respective new positions O_2B' and O_1A'. These radii *remain* straight.

It must be emphasized that these assumptions *hold only for circular and tubular members*.   For this class of members these assumptions work so well that they *apply beyond the limit of the elastic behavior of a material*.   These assumptions will be used again in Art. 3-8 where stress distribution beyond the proportional limit is discussed.   However, if attention is confined to the *elastic* case, Hooke's law applies, hence

3. Shearing stress is proportional to shearing strain.

In the interior of a member it is difficult to justify the first two assumptions directly.   However, after deriving stress and deformation formulas based on them, unquestionable agreement is found between measured and computed quantities.   Moreover, their validity may be rigorously demonstrated by the methods of the Theory of Elasticity based on the generalized Hooke's law.

3-4. The Torsion Formula. In the elastic case, on the basis of the above assumptions, since stress is proportional to strain, and the latter varies linearly from the center, *stresses vary linearly from the central axis of a circular member*.   The stresses induced by the assumed distortions are *shearing* stresses and lie in the plane parallel to the section taken normal to the axis of a rod.   The variation of shearing stress is illustrated in Fig. 3-3.   Unlike the case of an axially loaded rod, this stress is *not* of uniform

---

* Actually it is also implied that parallel planes perpendicular to the axis *remain a constant* distance apart.   This is not true if deformations are unusually large.   However, since the usual deformations are very small, stresses not considered here are negligible.   For details see Timoshenko, S., *Strength of Materials*, Part II, Advanced Theory and Problems, Chapter VI.   New York: Van Nostrand. 1941.

intensity. The maximum shearing stress occurs at points most remote from the center O and is designated τ_{max}. These points, such as point A in Fig. 3-3, lie at the periphery of a section at a distance c from the center. While, by virtue of a linear stress variation, at *any* arbitrary point at a distance ρ from O, the shearing stress is $(\rho/c)\tau_{max}$.

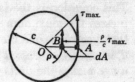

Once the stress distribution at a section is established, the resistance to torque in terms of stress can be expressed. The resistance to the torque so developed must be *equivalent* to the internal torque discussed previously. Hence an equality may be formulated thus:

Fig. 3-3. Variation of stress in a circular member in the elastic range.

$$\underbrace{\underbrace{\int_A \underbrace{\frac{\rho}{c}\tau_{max}}_{\text{(stress)}}\ \underbrace{dA}_{\text{(area)}}}_{\text{(force)}}\ \underbrace{\rho}_{\text{(arm)}}}_{\text{(torque)}} = T$$

where the integral sums up all torques developed on the cut by the infinitesimal forces acting at a distance ρ from a member's axis, O in Fig. 3-3, over the whole area A of the cross-section, and where T is the resisting torque.

At any given section τ_{max} and c are constant, hence the above relation may be written as

$$\frac{\tau_{max}}{c}\int_A \rho^2\, dA = T \tag{3-1}$$

However, $\int_A \rho^2\, dA$, *the polar moment of inertia* of a cross-sectional area, is also a constant for a particular cross-sectional area. It will be designated by J in this text. For a circular section, $dA = 2\pi\rho\, d\rho$, where $2\pi\rho$ is the circumference of an annulus* with a radius ρ of width $d\rho$. Hence

$$J = \int_A \rho^2\, dA = \int_O^c 2\pi\rho^3\, d\rho$$

$$= 2\pi\left.\frac{\rho^4}{4}\right|_O^c = \frac{\pi c^4}{2} = \frac{\pi d^4}{32} \tag{3-2}$$

where d is the diameter of a solid circular shaft. If c, or d, is measured in inches, J has the units of inches.[4]

By using the symbol J for the polar moment of inertia of a circular area, Eq. 3-1 may be written more compactly as

* An annulus is an area contained between two concentric circles.

$$\tau_{\max} = \frac{Tc}{J} \qquad (3\text{-}3)$$

This equation is the famed **torsion formula*** for circular shafts which expresses the maximum shearing stress in terms of the resisting torque and the dimensions of a member. In applying this formula the internal torque T is usually expressed in inch-pounds, c in inches, and J in inches.[4] Such usage makes the units of the torsional shearing stress,

$$\frac{[\text{in.-lb}]\,[\text{in.}]}{[\text{in.}^4]} = [\text{lb per in.}^2], \quad \text{or } psi.$$

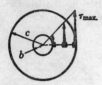

Fig. 3-4. Variation of stress in a hollow circular member in the elastic range.

A more general relation than Eq. 3-3 for a shearing stress, τ, at *any* point a distance ρ from the center of a section is

$$\tau = \frac{\rho}{c}\,\tau_{\max} = \frac{T\rho}{J} \qquad (3\text{-}3a)$$

Equations 3-3 and 3-3a *are applicable* with equal rigor *to circular tubes*, since the same assumptions as used in the above derivation apply. It is necessary, however, to modify J. For a tube, as may be seen from Fig. 3-4, the limits of integration for Eq. 3-2 extend from b to c. Hence for a *circular tube*,

$$J = \int_A \rho^2\, dA = \int_b^c 2\pi\rho^3\, d\rho = \frac{\pi c^4}{2} - \frac{\pi b^4}{2} \qquad (3\text{-}4)$$

or stated otherwise: J for a circular tube equals J for a solid shaft, using the outer diameter, minus J for a solid shaft, using the inner diameter.

For *thin* tubes, if b is nearly equal to c, and $c - b = t$, the thickness of the tube, J reduces to a simple approximate expression:

$$J \doteq 2\pi c^3 t \qquad (3\text{-}4a)$$

which is sufficiently accurate in many applications.

The concepts used in deriving the torsion formula are summarized below:

1. *Statics* is used to determine the internal or resisting torque.

2. *Geometry* is used by assuming linear variation of strain in a circular shaft.

3. *Properties of materials* are used to relate the assumed strain variation to stress.

3-5. Remarks on the Torsion Formula. So far the shearing stresses as given by Eqs. 3-3 and 3-3a have been thought of as being in the plane

---

* It was developed by Coulomb, a French engineer, in about 1775 in connection with his work on electric instruments. His name has been immortalized by its use for a practical unit of quantity in electricity.

of a cut perpendicular to the axis of the shaft. There indeed they are acting to form a couple resisting the externally applied torques. However, to understand the problem further, an element,* shown in Fig. 3-5b, is isolated from the member of Fig. 3-5a.

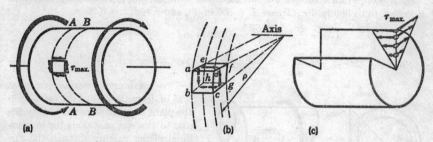

Fig. 3-5. Existence of shearing stresses on mutually perpendicular planes in a shaft subjected to torque.

The shearing stresses acting in the planes perpendicular to the axis of the rod are known from Eq. 3-3a. *Their directions coincide with the direction of the internal resisting torque.* (This should be clearly visualized by the reader.) On adjoining parallel planes of a disklike element these stresses act in opposite directions. However, these shearing stresses acting in the plane of the cuts taken normal to the axis of a rod *cannot exist alone*, as was shown in Art. 2-9. Numerically equal shearing stresses must act on the axial planes (such as the planes *adfe* and *bcgh* in Fig. 3-5b) to fulfill the requirements of static equilibrium for an element.†

Shearing stresses acting in the axial planes follow the same variation in intensity as do the shearing stresses in the planes perpendicular to the axis of the rod. This variation of shearing stresses on the mutually perpendicular planes is shown in Fig. 3-5c, where a portion of the shaft has been removed for the purposes of illustration.

In homogeneous materials it makes little difference in which direction the shearing stresses act. However, not all materials used in construction are homogeneous. For example, wood exhibits drastically different properties of strength in different directions. The shearing strength of wood on planes parallel to the grain is much less than on planes perpendicular to the grain. Hence, although equal intensities of shearing stress exist on mutually perpendicular planes, wooden shafts of inadequate size fail

---

* Two planes perpendicular to the axis of the rod, two planes through the axis, and two surfaces at different radii are used to isolate this element. Properties of such an element are expressible mathematically in cylindrical co-ordinates.

† Note that maximum shearing stresses as shown diagrammatically in Fig. 3-5a actually act on planes perpendicular to the axis of the rod and on planes passing through the axis of the rod. The representation shown is purely schematic. The free *surface* of a shaft is *free* of all stresses.

longitudinally along axial planes. Wooden shafts are occasionally used in the process industries.

Example 3-2. Find the maximum torsional shearing stress in the shaft AC shown in Fig. 3-1a. Assume the shaft from A to C to be of $\frac{1}{2}$ in. diameter.

SOLUTION: From Example 3-1 the maximum internal torque resisted by this shaft is known to be 300 in.-lb. Hence $T = 300$ in.-lb, and $c = d/2 = 0.25$ in.

From Eq. 3-2: $J = \pi \dfrac{d^4}{32} = \dfrac{\pi(0.5)^4}{32} = 0.00614$ in.^{4}

From Eq. 3-3: $\tau_{max} = \dfrac{Tc}{J} = \dfrac{(300)(0.25)}{0.00614} = 12{,}200$ psi

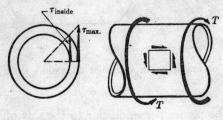

Fig. 3-6.

This maximum shearing stress at 0.25 in. from the axis of the rod acts in the plane of a cut perpendicular to the axis of the rod *and* along the longitudinal planes passing through the axis of the rod (Fig. 3-5c).

Example 3-3. Consider a long tube of 1 in. outside diameter, d_o, and of 0.9 in. inside diameter, d_i, twisted about its longitudinal axis with a torque T of 400 in.-lb. Determine the shearing stresses at the outside and the inside of the tube, Fig. 3-6.

SOLUTION: *From Eq. 3-4:*

$$J = \frac{\pi(c^4 - b^4)}{2} = \frac{\pi(d_o^4 - d_i^4)}{32}$$

$$= \frac{\pi(1^4 - 0.9^4)}{32} = 0.0337 \text{ in.}^4$$

From Eq. 3-3: $\tau_{max} = \dfrac{Tc}{J} = \dfrac{(400)(1/2)}{0.0337} = 5{,}930$ psi

From Eq. 3-3a: $\tau_{inside} = \dfrac{T\rho}{J} = \dfrac{400(0.9/2)}{0.0337} = 5{,}330$ psi

Note that for a tube less material is required to transmit a given torque at the same stress than for a solid shaft, since no material operates at a low stress. By making the wall thickness small and the diameter large, nearly uniform shearing stress τ is obtained in the wall. This fact makes thin tubes suitable for experiments where a uniform "field" of pure shearing stress is wanted (Art. 2-10). To avoid local crimping or buckling, the wall thickness, however, cannot be excessively thin.

3-6. Design of Circular Members in Torsion. In designing members for strength, allowable shearing stresses must be selected. These depend on the information available from experiments and on the intended application. Accurate information on the capacity of materials to resist shearing stresses comes from tests on thin-walled tubes. Solid shafting is employed in routine tests. Moreover, as torsion members are so often used in power equipment, many fatigue experiments are done. Characteristically, the shearing stress that a material can withstand is lower than the normal stress. The ASME (American Society of Mechanical Engineers) code of recommended practice for transmission shafting gives an allowable value in shearing stress of 8,000 psi for ordinary steel.* In practical designs, suddenly applied and shock loads warrant special considerations.

Once the torque to be transmitted by the shaft is known and the maximum shearing stress is selected, the proportions of the member become fixed. Thus from Eq. 3-3,

$$\frac{J}{c} = \frac{T}{\tau_{max}} \qquad (3\text{-}5)$$

where J/c is the *parameter* on which the elastic strength of a shaft depends. For an axially loaded rod it corresponds to the area of a member. For a *solid* shaft, $J/c = \pi c^3/2$, where c is the outside radius. By using this expression and Eq. 3-5, the required radius of a shaft may be determined. For a *hollow* shaft, a number of tubes can provide the same numerical value of J/c, so the problem has an infinite number of possible solutions.

Rotating shafts transmitting power are very widely used. Hence, before proceeding with design examples, a formula will be established for the conversion of horsepower into torque acting through the shaft.

By definition, *one* horsepower does work of 550 ft-lb per second, or 550(12)60 in.-lb per minute. Likewise, it will be recalled from dynamics that work is equal to the torque multiplied by the angle, measured in radians, through which the torque rotates per unit of time. For a shaft rotating at N rpm, the angle is $2\pi N$ radians per minute. Hence, if a shaft were transmitting a *constant* torque T measured in *inch-pounds*, it would do $2\pi NT$ in.-lb of work per minute. Equating this to the horsepower (Hp) supplied,

$$\text{Hp } (550)12(60) \text{ [in.-lb per min]} = 2\pi NT \text{ [in.-lb per min]}$$

or
$$T[\text{in.-lb}] = \frac{63{,}000 \text{ Hp}}{N} \qquad (3\text{-}6)$$

where N is the number of revolutions of the shaft transmitting the horsepower (Hp) per minute. This equation converts the horsepower delivered to the shaft into a constant torque acting through it as the power is applied.

Example 3-4. Select a solid shaft for a 10 Hp motor operating at 1,800 rpm. The maximum shearing stress is limited to 8,000 psi.

SOLUTION: *From Eq. 3-6:* $T = \dfrac{63{,}000 \text{ Hp}}{N} = \dfrac{63{,}000(10)}{1{,}800} = 350$ in.-lb

From Eq. 3-5: $\dfrac{J}{c} = \dfrac{T}{\tau_{max}} = \dfrac{350}{8{,}000} = 0.0438$ in.^{3}

$$\frac{J}{c} = \frac{\pi c^3}{2}, \quad \text{or} \quad c^3 = \frac{2}{\pi}\frac{J}{c} = \frac{2(0.0438)}{\pi} = 0.0279 \text{ in.}^3$$

Hence, $c = 0.303$ in.   or $d = 2c = 0.606$ in.

For practical purposes a $\frac{5}{8}$ in. shaft would probably be selected.

* Extensive recommendations for other materials may be found in machine design books. For example, see Spotts, M. F., *Design of Machine Elements*. New York: Prentice-Hall, 1948.

Example 3-5. Select solid shafts to transmit 200 Hp each without exceeding a shearing stress of 10,000 psi. One of these shafts operates at 20 rpm and the other at 20,000 rpm.

SOLUTION: Subscript 1 applies to the low-speed shaft; 2 to the high-speed shaft.

From Eq. 3-6: $T_1 = \dfrac{(\text{Hp})(63,000)}{N_1} = \dfrac{200(63,000)}{20}$

$$= 630,000 \text{ in.-lb}$$

Similarly, $T_2 = 630 \text{ in.-lb}$

From Eq. 3-5: $\dfrac{J_1}{c} = \dfrac{T_1}{\tau_{max}} = \dfrac{630,000}{10,000} = 63 \text{ in.}^3$

$$\frac{J_1}{c} = \frac{\pi d_1{}^3}{16} \quad \text{or} \quad d_1{}^3 = \frac{16}{\pi}(63) = 322 \text{ in.}^3$$

and $d_1 = 6.85 \text{ in.}$

Similarly, $d_2 = 0.685 \text{ in.}$

This example illustrates the reason for the modern tendency to use high-speed machines in mechanical equipment. The difference in size of the two shafts is striking. Further saving in the weight of the material may be effected by making use of hollow tubes.

*3-7. Stress Concentrations. Equations 3-3, 3-3a, and 3-5 apply only to solid and tubular shafts while the material behaves elastically. Moreover, the cross-sectional areas along the shaft should remain reasonably constant. If a *gradual* variation in the diameter takes place, the above equations give satisfactory solutions. On the other hand, for stepped shafts where the diameters of the adjoining portions change abruptly, large perturbations of shearing stresses take place. In such a case, at the juncture of the two parts near the center of a shaft, shearing stresses remain about the same as previously discussed. On the other hand, at extreme points from the center, high *local* shearing stresses occur. Methods of determining these local concentrations of stress are beyond the scope of this text. However, by forming a ratio of the true maximum shearing stress to the maximum stress given by Eq. 3-3, a torsional-stress-concentration factor may be obtained. An analogous method was used for obtaining the stress-concentration factors in axially loaded members (Art. 2-11). The stress-concentration factors depend only on the geometry of the member. Stress-concentration factors for various proportions of stepped round shafts are shown in Fig. 3-7.*

To obtain the actual stress at a geometrical discontinuity of a stepped shaft, a curve for a particular D/d is selected in Fig. 3-7. Then, corresponding to the given r/d ratio, the stress-concentration factor K is read off. Lastly, from the definition of K, the actual maximum shearing stress is obtained from the modified Eq. 3-3, i.e.,

---

* This figure is adapted from a paper by Jacobsen, L. S., "Torsional-Stress Concentrations in Shafts of Circular Cross-section and Variable Diameter," *Trans. ASME*, 1926, vol. 47, p. 632.

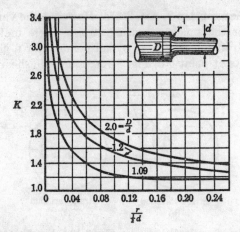

Fig. 3-7. Torsional stress-concentration factors in circular shafts of two diameters.

$$\tau_{max} = K\frac{Tc}{J} \tag{3-3b}$$

where the shearing stress Tc/J is determined for the smaller shaft.

A study of stress-concentration factors shown in Fig. 3-7 emphasizes the need for a generous fillet radius r at all sections where a transition in the shaft diameter is made.

Considerable stress raisers also occur in shafts at oil holes and keyways. The latter usually is a necessary evil for attaching pulleys and gears to the shaft. A shaft prepared for a key, Fig. 3-8, is no longer a circular member. However, according to the procedure suggested by the ASME, computations for shafts with keyways are made using Eq. 3-3 or 3-5, but the allowable shearing stress is *reduced* by 25%. This supposedly compensates for the stress concentration and reduction in cross-sectional area.

Fig. 3-8.
Circular
shaft with
a keyway.

*3-8. Shearing Stresses in the Inelastic Range; Modulus of Rupture. The torsion formula for circular sections is based upon Hooke's law. Therefore it applies only up to the point where the proportionaly limit of the material in shear is reached in the outer annulus of a shaft. Figure 3-9 shows a section of a circular shaft which has been subjected to a torque just large enough to cause the proportional-limit stress τ_{pl} to occur at the outside of the shaft. Shearing stresses and strains both vary linearly from the center to the outer edge of the section.

The same section is shown in Fig. 3-10 after it has been subjected to a larger torque causing shearing stresses which exceed the proportional limit of the material. Here, the variation of strain from center to outer edge *remains linear* (Assumption 2, Art. 3-3). However, the variation of stress is linear only for the smaller shearing strains where material is elastic, for a distance Oa in Fig. 3-10b. Beyond point a, for a given amount of shearing strain, as at point b in Fig. 3-10a, a definite shearing stress must

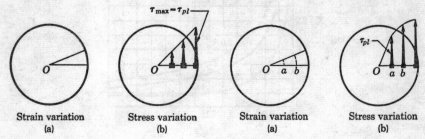

| Strain variation | Stress variation | Strain variation | Stress variation |
| (a) | (b) | (a) | (b) |

Fig. 3-9. Variation of strain and stress in the elastic case.   **Fig. 3-10.** Variation of strain and stress in the inelastic case.

be obtained from an experimentally determined shearing stress-strain diagram. Beyond point a the shearing stress does not vary linearly.

Although the shearing-stress distribution after the elastic limit is exceeded is nonlinear, and the elastic torsion formula does not apply, sometimes it is used to calculate a fictitious stress at the outer edge of a shaft for the ultimate torque. The computed stress using the *ultimate* torque in the elastic torsion formula, Eq. 3-3, is called the *modulus of rupture*. It serves as a rough index of the ultimate strength of a material in torsion.

Example 3-6. Determine the torque carried by a solid circular shaft of mild steel when shearing stresses above the proportional limit are reached nearly everywhere.

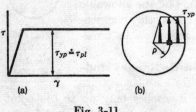

(a)   (b)

Fig. 3-11.

For mild steel, the shearing stress-strain diagram is to be idealized to that shown in Fig. 3-11a. (This idealization is reasonable as on a *relative* basis a *very small* amount of elastic deformation takes place in comparison with the amount of ductile or plastic deformation.) The shearing yield-point stress τ_{yp} is to be taken as being the same as the proportional limit in shear τ_{pl}.

SOLUTION: If a large torque is imposed on a member, large strains take place everywhere except near the center. Corresponding to the large strains for the idealized material considered, the yield-point shearing stress will be reached everywhere except near the center. However, the resistance to the applied torque offered by the material located near the center of the shaft is negligible, as the corresponding ρ's are small, Fig. 3-11b. Hence, with sufficient accuracy it can be assumed that a constant shearing stress τ_{yp} is acting *everywhere* on the section considered. The torque corresponding to this condition may be considered the ultimate torque, since an enormous amount of twist takes place as the material yields. Thus

$$T_{\text{ult}} = \int_A \tau_{\text{yp}}\, dA\, \rho = \int_0^c 2\pi\rho^2\, \tau_{\text{yp}}\, d\rho$$

$$= \frac{2\pi}{3}\frac{c^3}{}\tau_{\text{yp}} = \frac{4}{3}\frac{\tau_{\text{yp}}}{c}\frac{\pi c^4}{2} = \frac{4}{3}\frac{\tau_{\text{yp}}J}{c}$$

The reader can trace the intermediate steps used above by referring to a similar derivation for Eq. 3-3.

Note that from Eq. 3-3 the maximum elastic torque capacity of a solid shaft is $T = \tau_{\text{yp}}J/c$. Therefore since T_{ult} is $\frac{4}{3}$ times this value, *only* $33\frac{1}{3}\%$ of the torque capacity remains after τ_{yp} is reached at the extreme fibers of a shaft. However, it must be further noted that in machine members, because of the fatigue properties of materials, the ultimate *static capacity* of the shafts evaluated above is of minor importance. For this reason the elastic analysis of shafts is usually used.

3-9. Angle of Twist of Circular Members.

So far in this chapter, methods of determining stresses in solid and hollow circular shafts subjected to torque have been discussed. Now attention will be directed to the method of finding the angle of twist for shafts subjected to torsional loading. The interest in this problem is at least three-fold. First, it is important to predict the twist of a shaft *per se*, since at times it is not sufficient to design it to be only strong enough: it must also not deform excessively. Then, magnitudes of angular rotations of shafts are needed in the torsional vibration analysis of machinery, although this subject is not treated here. Finally, the angular twist of members is needed in dealing with statically indeterminate torsional problems which are discussed in Chapter 12.

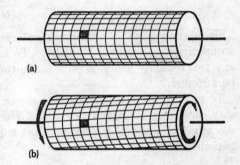

Fig. 3-12. Circular shaft (a) before, and (b) after torque is applied.

According to Assumption 1 stated in Art. 3-3, planes perpendicular to the axis of a circular rod do not warp. The elements of a shaft undergo deformation of the type shown in Fig. 3-12b. The shaded element in the latter figure is also shown in its undistorted form in Fig. 3-12a. From such a shaft an element of length dz as shown in Fig. 3-13 is isolated. Any other element of the shaft will behave similarly.

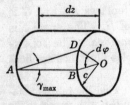

Fig. 3-13. An element of a circular shaft subjected to torque.

In the element shown a line or "fiber" such as AB initially is parallel to the axis of the shaft. After the torque is applied, it assumes a new position AD. At the same time, by virtue of Assumption 2, Art. 3-3, radius OB remains straight and rotates through a small angle $d\varphi$ to a new position OD.

Denoting the small angle DAB by γ_{max}, from geometry:

$$\text{arc } BD = \gamma_{max}\, dz \qquad \text{or} \qquad \text{arc } BD = d\varphi\, c$$

where both angles are small and are measured in *radians*. Hence

$$\gamma_{max}\, dz = d\varphi\, c \tag{3-7}$$

γ_{max} applies only in the zone of an infinitesimal "tube" of uniform maximum shearing stress τ_{max}. In the elastic range according to Hooke's law, Eq. 2-9, this angle is proportional to τ_{max}, i.e., $\gamma_{max} = \tau_{max}/G$. Moreover, by Eq. 3-3 $\tau_{max} = Tc/J$, hence $\gamma_{max} = Tc/(JG)$. Whence upon substituting the latter expression into Eq. 3-7 and cancelling out c,

$$d\varphi = \frac{T\, dz}{JG}$$

This relation gives* the *relative* angular rotation of two adjoining sections an infinitesimal distance dz apart. To find the total rotation φ between any two sections A and B on a shaft, the rotations of the elements must be summed.

In general, the internal torque T, as well as the polar moment of inertia J, may *vary along the length of a shaft.* Hence in the general expression for the angle of twist of a circular shaft subscripts z are attached to these two quantities, i.e.,

$$\varphi = \int_A^B d\varphi = \int_A^B \frac{T_z\, dz}{J_z G} \tag{3-8}$$

This relation is valid for both solid and hollow circular shafts, which follows from the assumptions used in its derivation.

Note the great similarity of this relation to Eq. 2-3 for the deformation of axially loaded rods. Here T_z replaces P_x, J_z replaces A_x, and G is used in place of E. The angle φ is measured in *radians*. The following two examples illustrate applications of Eq. 3-8.

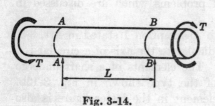

Fig. 3-14.

Example 3-7. Find the relative rotation of the section B-B with respect to the section A-A of the solid shaft shown in Fig. 3-14 when a constant torque T is being transmitted through it. The polar moment of inertia of the cross-sectional area J is constant.

SOLUTION: In this case $T_z = T$ and $J_z = J$, hence from Eq. 3-8,

---

* The foregoing argument can be carried out in terms of any γ, which progressively becomes smaller as the axis of the rod is approached. The only difference in derivation consists in taking an arc corresponding to BD an *arbitrary* distance ρ from the center, and using $T\rho/J$ instead of Tc/J for τ.

$$\varphi = \int_A^B \frac{T_z\,dz}{J_z G} = \int_0^L \frac{T\,dz}{JG} = \frac{T}{JG}\int_0^L dz = \frac{TL}{JG} \tag{3-9}$$

Equation 3-9 is a very important relation. It can be used in the design of shafts for stiffness, i.e., for limiting the amount of twist that may take place in their length. For such an application T, L, and G are known quantities, and the solution of Eq. 3-9 yields J. This fixes the size of the required shaft (see Eqs. 3-2 and 3-4). Note that for stiffness requirements, J, rather than J/c of the strength requirement, is the significant parameter.

Another application of Eq. 3-9 is found in the laboratory. There a shaft may be subjected to a known torque T, J may be computed from the dimensions of the specimen, and the relative angular rotation φ between two planes a distance L apart may be measured. Then, by using Eq. 3-9, the shearing modulus of elasticity in the elastic range can be computed, i.e., $G = TL/J\varphi$.

In using this relation, or Eq. 3-9, note particularly that the angle φ must be expressed in *radians*. Also observe the similarity of Eq. 3-9 to Eq. 2-4, $\Delta = PL/AE$, formerly derived for axially loaded rods.

Example 3-8. Consider the stepped shaft shown in Fig. 3-15 attached to a wall at E, and determine the rotation of the end A when the two torques at B and at D are applied. Assume the shearing modulus G to be 12×10^6 psi, a typical value for steels.

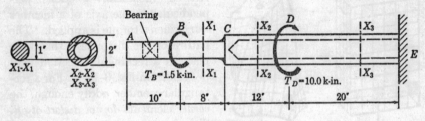

Fig. 3-15.

SOLUTION: *From Eq. 3-2:* $J_{AB} = J_{BC} = \dfrac{\pi d^4}{32} = \dfrac{\pi 1^4}{32} = 0.0982$ in.^{4}

From Eq. 3-4: $J_{CD} = J_{DE} = \dfrac{\pi}{32}(d_o{}^4 - d_i{}^4) = \dfrac{\pi}{32}(2^4 - 1^4) = 1.47$ in.^{4} where subscripts indicate the range of applicability of a given value. Then by passing arbitrary sections X_1-X_1, X_2-X_2, and X_3-X_3, and considering a portion of the shaft each time *to the left* of such sections, the internal torques for the various intervals are found to be

$$T_{AB} = 0, \quad T_{BD} = T_{BC} = T_{CD} = 1.5 \text{ kip-in.}, \quad T_{DE} = 11.5 \text{ kip-in.}$$

To find the rotation of the end A, Eq. 3-8 is applied with the limits of integration "broken" at points where T or J change their values abruptly.

$$\varphi = \int_A^E \frac{T_z\,dz}{J_z G} = \int_A^B \frac{T_{AB}\,dz}{J_{AB}G} + \int_B^C \frac{T_{BC}\,dz}{J_{BC}G} + \int_C^D \frac{T_{CD}\,dz}{J_{CD}G} + \int_D^E \frac{T_{DE}\,dz}{J_{DE}G}$$

In the last group of integrals T's and J's are constant between the limits considered, so each integral reverts to a known solution, Eq. 3-9. Hence

$$\varphi = \frac{T_{AB}L_{AB}}{J_{AB}G} + \frac{T_{BC}L_{BC}}{J_{BC}G} + \frac{T_{CD}L_{CD}}{J_{CD}G} + \frac{T_{DE}L_{DE}}{J_{DE}G}$$

$$= 0 + \frac{1{,}500(8)}{0.0982(12)10^6} + \frac{1{,}500(12)}{1.47(12)10^6} + \frac{11{,}500(20)}{1.47(12)10^6}$$

$$= 0.0102 + 0.0010 + 0.0130$$
$$= 0.0242 \text{ radians} \quad \text{or} \quad (360/2\pi)(0.0242) = 1.39°$$

The part AB of the shaft contributes nothing to the value of the angle φ as no internal torque acts through it. It rotates as much as the section at B. Little is contributed to φ by the shaft from C to D. This is so because a small internal torque and a large J are associated with this segment. No doubt there is a stress concentration at the step, but this local effect plays a small role in the over-all rotation.

The angle computed would hold equally true for a *relative* rotation of sections for an analogous problem of a rotating shaft.

In some torsion problems the applied torque or J may vary *continuously* in a mathematical sense along the shaft. Such problems can be solved by applying Eq. 3-8 in a manner analogous to that used in Example 2-3 of the preceding chapter.

*3-10. Solid Non-circular Members. The analytical treatment of solid non-circular members in torsion is beyond the scope of this book.

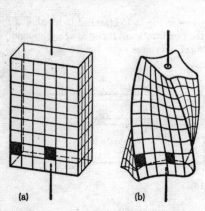

(a)   (b)

Fig. 3-16. Rectangular shaft (a) before, and (b) after a torque is applied.

Mathematically the problem is complicated.* *The first two assumptions stated in Art. 3-3 do not apply* for non-circular members. Sections perpendicular to the axis of a member *warp* when a torque is applied. The nature of the distortions that take place in a rectangular section may be seen from Fig. 3-16.† For a rectangular member, oddly enough, the *corner* elements *do not distort at all.* Shearing stresses at the corners are *zero*, while they are maximum at the mid-point of the *long* sides. Figure 3-17 shows the shearing-stress distribution along three radial lines emanating from the center. Note particularly the difference in this stress distribution compared with that of a circular section. For the latter, the stress is a maximum at the most remote point, while for the former the stress is *zero* at the most remote point.‡ The maximum shearing

---

* This problem remained unsolved until the time when a famous French elastician, B. de St. Venant, developed a solution for such problems in 1853. The general torsion problem is sometimes referred to as the St. Venant Problem.

† An experiment with a rubber eraser on which a rectangular grating is ruled can demonstrate the same type of distortions.

‡ This situation can be explained by considering a corner element as shown in Fig 3-A. *If* a shearing stress τ existed at the corner, it could be resolved into two components parallel to the edges of the bar. However, as shears always occur in pairs acting on mutually perpendicular planes, these components would have to be met by shears lying *in the plane of the outside surfaces.* The latter situation is impossible as outside surfaces are *free* of all stresses. Hence τ must be zero. Similar considerations can be applied to other points on the boundary. All shearing stresses in the plane of a cut near the boundaries act parallel to them.

stress and the rotation for a rectangular section subjected to a constant torque can be expressed respectively as

$$\tau_{max} = \frac{T}{\alpha bc^2} \quad \text{and} \quad \varphi = \frac{TL}{\beta bc^3 G}$$

where b is the long, and c is the short side of the section. The values of α and β are parameters dependent upon the ratio* b/c. For thin sections, when b is much greater than c, α and β approach the value of $\frac{1}{3}$.

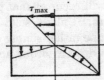

Fig. 3-17. Shearing-stress distribution in a rectangular shaft subjected to a torque.

Fig. 3-A. The shearing stress shown cannot exist. (See ‡, p. 62.)

Formulas as above are available for many other types of cross-sectional areas in more advanced books. For cases which cannot be conveniently solved mathematically, a remarkable method has been devised.† It so happens that the solution of the partial differential equation which must be solved in a torsion problem is automatically satisfied by a thin membrane, such as a soap film, *lightly* stretched over a hole. This hole must be geometrically similar to the cross-section of the shaft being studied. Light air pressure must be kept on one side of the membrane. Then it can be shown that

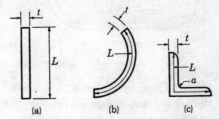

Fig. 3-18. Members with equal cross-sectional areas of the same thickness carrying the same torque. (This does not apply to tubular members.)

1. The shearing stress at any point is proportional to the greatest *slope* of the stretched membrane at the same point.

2. The direction of a particular shearing stress at a point is tangent to the contour‡ of the membrane at the same point.

3. Twice the volume enclosed by the membrane is proportional to the torque carried at that section.

* For values of α and β see Timoshenko, S., *Strength of Materials*, Part I, p. 270 New York: Van Nostrand, 1940.

† This analogy was introduced by a famous German engineering scientist, L. Prandtl, in 1903.

‡ A line connecting points of *equal* elevation.

The foregoing analogy is called the *membrane analogy*. In addition to its value in experimental applications, it is a very useful *mental* tool for visualizing stresses and torque capacities of members. For example, all the sections shown in Fig. 3-18 can withstand approximately the same torque at the same maximum shearing stress (same maximum slope of the membrane) since the volume enclosed by the membranes would be nearly the same in all three cases. However, a little imagination will convince the reader that the contour lines of a soap film will "pile up" at *a* for the angular section. Hence high *local* stresses will occur at that point.

*3-11. Thin-Walled Hollow Members. Unlike solid noncircular members, *thin-walled* tubes of *any shape* can be rather simply analyzed for the magnitude of the shearing stresses caused by a torque applied to the

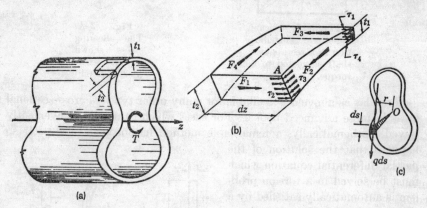

Fig. 3-19. Thin-walled member of variable thickness.

tube. Thus, consider a tube of an arbitrary shape with varying wall thickness, such as shown in Fig. 3-19a, subjected to a torque T. Then isolate an element from this tube, as shown to an enlarged scale in Fig. 3-19b. This element must be in equilibrium under the action of the *forces* F_1, F_2, F_3, and F_4. These forces are equal to the shearing stresses acting on the cut planes multiplied by the respective areas.

From $\Sigma F_z = 0$, $F_1 = F_3$; but $F_1 = \tau_2 t_2\, dz$, and $F_3 = \tau_1 t_1\, dz$, where τ_2 and τ_1 are shearing stresses acting on the respective areas $t_2\, dz$ and $t_1\, dz$. Hence, $\tau_2 t_2\, dz = \tau_1 t_1\, dz$, or $\tau_1 t_1 = \tau_2 t_2$. However, since the longitudinal cutting planes were taken an *arbitrary* distance apart, it follows from the above relations that the product of the shearing stress by the wall thickness is the same, i.e., *constant*, on *any* such planes. This constant will be denoted by q, and if the shearing stress is measured in pounds per square inch and the thickness of the tube in inches, q is measured in pounds per inch (lb per in.).

In Art 2-9, Eq. 2-8, it was established that shearing stresses on mutually perpendicular planes are equal at a corner of an element. Hence at a corner such as A in Fig. 3-19b, $\tau_2 = \tau_3$; similarly, $\tau_1 = \tau_4$. Therefore $\tau_4 t_1 = \tau_3 t_2$, or in general, q is constant *in the plane of a cut perpendicular to the axis of a member*. On this basis an analogy may be formulated. The inner and outer *boundaries* of the wall can be thought of as being the boundaries of a channel. Then one can imagine a constant quantity of water steadily circulating in this channel. In this arrangement the quantity of water flowing through a plane across the channel is constant. Because of this analogy the quantity q has been termed the *shear flow*.

Next consider the cross-section of the tube as shown in Fig. 3-19c. The force *per inch* of the perimeter of this tube, by virtue of the previous argument, is constant and is the shear flow q. This shear flow multiplied by the length ds of the perimeter gives a force $q\,ds$ per differential length. The product of this infinitesimal force $q\,ds$ by r around some convenient point such as O, Fig. 3-19c, gives the contribution of an element for resisting the applied torque T. Adding or integrating these,

$$T = \int_0^s rq\,ds$$

where the integration process is carried around the tube *along the line of the perimeter*, i.e., a line integral.

Instead of carrying out the actual integration, a simple interpretation of the above integral is available. From Fig. 3-19c it can be seen that $r\,ds$ is *twice* the value of the shaded area of an infinitesimal triangle whose area is one-half the base times the altitude. Hence, inasmuch as q is a constant, the complete integral is *twice* the **whole** area A *bounded by the center line of the perimeter of the tube*. Therefore

$$T = 2Aq \qquad \text{or} \qquad q = \frac{T}{2A} \tag{3-10}$$

This equation* applies only to *thin*-walled tubes. The area A is approximately an *average* of the two areas enclosed by the inside and the outside surfaces of a tube, or, as noted above, it is an area **enclosed** by the center line of the wall's contour. Equation 3-10 is not applicable at all if the tube is slit.

Since for any tube the shear flow q given by Eq. 3-10 is constant, from the definition of shear flow, the shearing *stress* at any point of a tube where the wall thickness is t is

$$\tau = \frac{q}{t} \tag{3-11}$$

Equations 3-10 and 3-11 are applicable to any shape of tube. They are widely used in aircraft work.

---

* Equation 3-10 is sometimes called Bredt's formula in honor of the German engineer who developed it.

Example 3-9. Rework Example 3-3, using Eqs. 3-10 and 3-11. The tube has outside and inside radii of 0.5 in. and 0.45 in., respectively, and the applied torque is 400 in-lb.

SOLUTION: The *mean* radius of the tube is 0.475 and the wall thickness is 0.05 in. Hence

$$\tau = \frac{q}{t} = \frac{T}{2At} = \frac{400}{2\pi(0.475)^2(0.05)} = 5,640 \text{ psi}$$

Note that by using Eqs. 3-10 and 3-11 only one shearing stress is obtained and that it is just about the average of the two stresses computed in Example 3-3. The thinner the walls, the more accurate the answer, or vice versa.

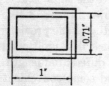

It is interesting to note that a *rectangular* tube, shown in Fig. 3-20, with a wall thickness of 0.05 in., for the same torque will have nearly the same shearing stress as the above circular tube. This is so because its enclosed area of 0.71 in.^{2} is about the same as $\pi(0.475)^2$, the A of the circular tube. However, some local stress concentrations will be present at the corners of a square tube.

Fig. 3-20.

3-12. Shaft Couplings. Frequently situations arise where the available lengths of shafting are not long enough. Likewise, often, for maintenance or assembly reasons, it is desirable to make up a long shaft from several pieces. To join the pieces of the shaft together, the so-called flanged shaft couplings of the type shown in Fig. 3-21 are used. When bolted together, such couplings are termed *rigid*, to differentiate them from another type called *flexible* which provides for misalignment of adjoin-

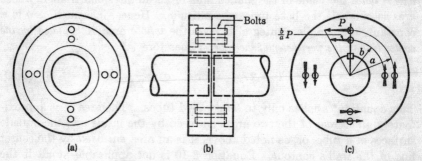

Fig. 3-21. Flanged shaft coupling.

ing shafts. The latter type is almost universally used to join the shaft of a motor to driven equipment. Here only the rigid type couplings are considered. The reader is referred to machine design texts and manufacturer's catalogues for the other type.

For rigid couplings it is customary to assume that shearing strains in the bolts vary directly (linearly) as their distance from the axis of the shaft. Friction between the flanges is neglected. Therefore, analogous to the torsion problem of circular shafts, if the bolts are of the same material, elastic shearing **stresses** in the bolts also vary linearly as their respective distances from the center of a coupling. The shearing stress in any one bolt is assumed to be *uniform* and is governed by the distance from its center to the center of the coupling. Then, if the shearing stress in a bolt is multiplied by its cross-sectional area, the force in a bolt is found. On this basis, for example, for bolts of *equal size* in two "bolt circles," the forces on the bolts located by the respective radii a and b are as shown in Fig. 3-21c. The moment of the forces developed by the bolts around the axis of a shaft gives the torque capacity of a coupling.

The above reasoning is the same as that used in deriving the torsion formula for circular shafts, except that, instead of a continuous cross-section, a discrete number of points is considered. This analysis is crude since stress concentrations are undoubtedly present at the points of contact of the bolts with the flanges of a coupling. A conversion of the torsion formula for this use and for analyzing more difficult cases than couplings is discussed in Chapter 14.

The above method of analysis is valid only for the case of a coupling in which the bolts act primarily in shear. However, in some couplings the bolts are tightened so much that the coupling acts in a different fashion. The initial tension in the bolts is great enough to cause the entire coupling to act in friction. Under these circumstances the above analysis is not valid, or is valid only as a measure of the ultimate strength of the coupling should the stresses in the bolts be reduced. However, if high tensile strength bolts are used, there is little danger of this happening, and the strength of the coupling may be greater than it would be if the bolts had to act in shear.*

Example 3-10. Estimate the torque-carrying capacity of a steel coupling forged integrally with the shaft, shown in Fig. 3-22, as controlled by an allowable shearing stress of 6,000 psi in the eight bolts. The bolt circle is 9 in. in diameter.

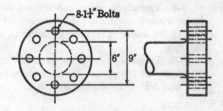

Fig. 3-22.

SOLUTION: *Area of one bolt:* $A = \frac{1}{4}\pi(1.25)^2 = 1.227$ in.^{2}

Allowable force for one bolt: $P_{\text{allow}} = A\tau_{\text{allow}} = 1.227(6) = 7.37$ kips

Since eight bolts are available at a distance of 4.5 in. from the central axis,

$$T_{\text{allow}} = 7.37(4.5)8 = 265 \text{ kip-in.}$$

Problems for Solution

3-1. Find the shearing stress developed in the extreme fibers of a 3 in. diameter steel shaft due to an applied torque of 4,000 ft-lb. Assuming that the torque is applied in the direction shown in Fig. 3-5a, indicate on a suitable sketch the directions of the computed stress.

* See "Symposium on High-Strength Bolts," Part I, by Wyly, L. T., and Part II by Ruble, E. J., *Proceedings AISC*, 1950.

3-2. A hollow shaft is of 4 in. outside diameter and 3 in. inside diameter. If the allowable shearing stress is 8,000 psi, what torque can it transmit? What is the stress at the inner surface of the shaft when the allowable torque is applied? *Ans.* 68,600 in.-lb.

3-3. A shaft of Douglas Fir is to be used in a certain process industry. If the allowable shearing stress parallel to the grain of the wood is 120 psi, calculate the maximum torque which can be transmitted by an 8 in. round shaft with the grain of the wood parallel to the axis.

3-4. A 6 in. diameter core, i.e., an axial hole of 3 in. radius, is bored out from a 9 in. diameter solid circular shaft. What percentage of the torsional strength is lost by this operation? *Ans.* 19.6%.

3-5. Determine the maximum shearing stress in the shaft subjected to the torques shown in the figure. *Ans.* 900 psi.

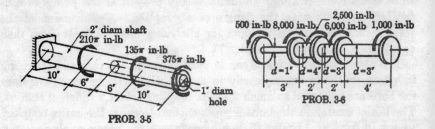

PROB. 3-5   PROB. 3-6

3-6. The solid cylindrical shaft of variable size shown in the figure is acted upon by the torques indicated. What is the maximum torsional stress in the shaft, and between what two pulleys does it occur?

3-7. A 6 in. diameter solid steel shaft is transmitting 600 Hp at 80 rpm. Compute the maximum shearing stress. Find the change which would occur in the shearing stress if the speed were increased to 320 rpm.

3-8. Two shafts, one a hollow steel shaft with an outside diameter of 3.5 in. and an inside diameter of 1.2 in., the other a solid shaft with a diameter of 3.5 in., are to transmit 75 Hp each. Compare the shearing stresses in the two shafts if both operate at 200 rpm.

3-9. The solid 2 in. diameter steel line shaft shown in the figure is driven by a 30 Hp motor at 180 rpm. Find the maximum torsional stresses in the sections *AB*, *BC*, *CD*, and *DE* of the shaft. *Ans.* 0, 1,114 psi, 5,570 psi, and 2,230 psi.

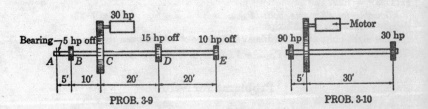

PROB. 3-9   PROB. 3-10

3-10. A motor, through a set of gears, drives a line shaft as shown in the figure, at 630 rpm. 30 Hp are delivered to a machine on the right; 90 Hp on the left. Select a solid round shaft of the same size throughout. The allowable shearing stress is 5,750 psi. *Ans.* 2 in. diam.

3-11. Design a hollow steel shaft to transmit 300 Hp at 75 rpm without exceeding a shearing stress of 6,000 psi. Use 1.2 as the ratio of the outside diameter to the inside diameter.

3-12. A solid circular shaft of 6 in. diameter is machined down to a 3 in. diameter along a part of the shaft. If at the transition point of the two diameters the fillet radius is $\frac{1}{2}$ in., what maximum shearing stress is developed when a torque of 2,000 ft-lb is applied to the shaft? What will the maximum shearing stress be if the fillet radius is reduced to $\frac{1}{8}$ in.?

3-13. Find the required fillet radius for the juncture of a 6 in. diameter shaft with a 4 in. diameter segment if the shaft transmits 110 Hp at 100 rpm and the maximum shearing stress is limited to 8,000 psi.

3-14. A specimen of an SAE 1060 steel bar of $\frac{3}{4}$ in. diameter and 18 in. in length failed at a torque of 7,620 in.-lb. What is the modulus of rupture of this steel in torsion?

3-15. What must the length of a 0.2 in. diameter aluminum wire be so that it could be twisted through one complete revolution without exceeding a shearing stress of 6,000 psi? $G = 3.84 \times 10^6$ psi.

3-16. A hollow steel rod 6 in. long is used as a torsional spring. The ratio of inside to outside diameters is $\frac{1}{2}$. The required stiffness for this spring is $\frac{1}{12}$ of a degree per one inch-pound of torque. Determine the outside diameter of this rod. $G = 12 \times 10^6$ psi. *Ans.* 0.25 in.

3-17. A solid aluminum shaft 40 in. long and of 2 in. outside diameter is to be replaced by a tubular steel shaft of the same length and the same outside diameter so that either shaft could carry the same torque and have the same angle of twist over the total length. What must the inner radius of the tubular steel shaft be? $G_{St} = 12 \times 10^6$ psi and $G_{Al} = 4 \times 10^6$ psi. *Ans.* 0.903 in.

3-18. A 100 Hp motor is driving a line shaft through gear A at 26.3 rpm. Bevel gears at B and C drive rubber-cement mixers. If the power requirement of the mixer driven by gear B is 25 Hp and that of C is 75 Hp, what are the required shaft diameters? The allowable shearing stress in the shaft is 6,000 psi. A sufficient number of bearings is provided to avoid bending. If G is 12×10^6 psi, what is the angle of twist under load in the left-hand section of the shaft? State answer in degrees. *Ans.* $d_1 = 3.71$ in., $d_2 = 5.34$ in., and $\varphi = 3.72°$.

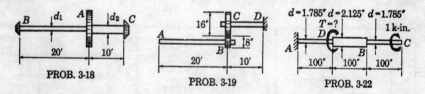

PROB. 3-18   PROB. 3-19   PROB. 3-22

3-19. Two gears are attached to two 2 in. diameter steel shafts as shown in the figure. The gear at B has an 8 in. pitch diameter; the gear at C a 16 in. pitch diameter. Through what angle will the end A turn if at A a torque of 5,000 in.-lb is applied, and the end D of the second shaft is prevented from rotating? $G = 12 \times 10^6$ psi. *Ans.* 11°.

3-20. In Example 3-8 find the magnitude of a torque which applied alone at A would cause the same angular rotation at A as do the two torques applied at B and D.

3-21. Find the total angle of twist between A and E for the shaft in Prob. 3-9. $G = 12 \times 10^6$ psi. *Ans.* 8.3°.

3-22. The shaft shown in the figure is subjected to a known torque of 1,000 in.-lb at bearing C. It is desired that the angle of twist at C be 0.6°. What torque is required at D to fulfill this condition? (There is a sufficient number of bearings so that bending of the shaft need not be considered.) $G = 12 \times 10^6$ psi. *Ans.* 1,240 in.-lb.

3-23. The stepped steel shaft shown in the figure is subjected to a torque T at the free end and a torque $2T$ in the opposite direction at the junction of the two sizes. What is the total angle of twist at the free end C if the maximum shearing stress is limited to 10,000 psi? Neglect the weight of the shaft and the effect of stress concentrations. $G = 12 \times 10^6$ psi. *Ans.* 0.0575 radians.

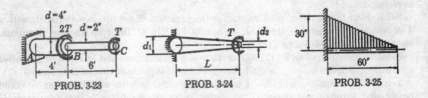

PROB. 3-23   PROB. 3-24   PROB. 3-25

3-24.* A solid tapered steel shaft is rigidly fastened to a fixed support at one end and is subjected to a torque T at the other end. Find the angular rotation of the free end if $d_1 = 6$ in.; $d_2 = 2$ in.; $L = 20$ in.; and $T = 27,000$ in.-lb. Assume that the usual assumptions of strain in prismatic circular shafts subjected to torque apply and let $G = 12 \times 10^6$ psi. *Ans.* 0.263°.

3-25.* A series of reeds is attached to a small circular tube as shown in the figure. Determine the angle of twist of the free end if a wind of 1 psi intensity is acting normal to the reeds. Neglect the aerodynamic effect on edges and suction on the back of the reeds. The deflection of the tubular cantilever is not wanted, only its rotation. Let $G = 12 \times 10^6$ psi and assume $J = 0.6$ in.⁴ for the tube.

3-26. Compare the maximum shearing stress and angle of twist for members of equal length having a square section, a rectangular section, and a circular section of equal area. All members are subjected to the same torque. The circular section is 4 in. in diameter and the rectangular section is one inch wide. For the square section, $\alpha = 0.208$ and $\beta = 0.141$; for the rectangular section, $\alpha \doteq \beta \doteq \frac{1}{3}$.

3-27 through 3-29. Find the maximum shearing stresses developed in members having the cross-sections shown in the figures due to an applied torque of 500 in.-lb in each case. Neglect stress concentrations.

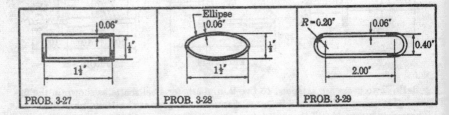

PROB. 3-27   PROB. 3-28   PROB. 3-29

3-30. Compare the maximum shearing stress for a thin tube of 2 in. diameter having a wall thickness of 0.049 in. subjected to a torque with that of a similar tube having a narrow slot through the wall parallel to the axis subjected to the same torque.

3-31. A rigid coupling with six 1 in. diameter bolts in an 8 in. diameter bolt circle is subjected to a torque of 175 kip-in. Compute the shearing stress in the bolts.

3-32. A coupling is made with eight $\frac{3}{4}$ in. diameter high strength bolts located on a 10 in. diameter bolt circle. (a) Calculate the torque which may be transmitted by this coupling if the allowable stress in the bolts is 10,500 psi. (b) Find the Hp which can be transmitted when the shaft and couplings are rotating at 250 rpm.

3-33. The drive shaft for a certain marine engine has a coupling with six 1 in. diameter bolts in the outer bolt circle of 6 in. radius and six 1 in. diameter bolts in the inner bolt circle of 4 in. radius. For an applied torque of 400 kip-in., calculate the maximum shearing stress in the bolts. What is the shearing stress in the bolts in the inner circle?

3-34. A flange coupling has 6 bolts having a cross-sectional area of 0.2 in.^{2} each in an 8 in. diameter bolt circle, and 6 bolts having a cross-sectional area of 0.5 in.^{2} each in a 5 in. diameter bolt circle. If the allowable shearing stress in the bolts is 16 ksi, what is the torque capacity of this coupling? *Ans.* 152 k-in.

3-35. * Six $\frac{3}{4}$ in. diameter bolts in the outer bolt circle of 7 in. radius are aluminum and six $\frac{3}{4}$ in. diameter bolts in the inner bolt circle of 5 in. radius are steel. What is the torque capacity of the coupling? Assume the allowable shearing stress for both materials at 6,000 psi and use $G_{Al} = 4 \times 10^6$ psi and $G_{St} = 12 \times 10^6$ psi.

Chapter Four

AXIAL FORCE—SHEAR—AND BENDING MOMENT

4-1. Introduction. The effect of axial forces on straight members was treated in Chapters 1 and 2. Torsion of straight members was discussed in Chapter 3. It should be intuitively clear to the reader that these are not the only types of forces to which a member may be subjected. In fact, in many engineering structures members resist forces applied laterally or transversely to their axes. This type of member is termed a *beam*. Numerous applications of beams may be found in structural and machine parts. The main members supporting floors of buildings are beams, just as an axle of a car is a beam. Many shafts of machinery act simultaneously as torsion members and as beams. With modern materials, the beam is a dominant member of construction. The determination of the system of forces at a section of a beam necessary for equilibrium of its segment will be the main objective of this chapter.

Beams may be straight or curved, but the major attention of this chapter will be directed toward a study of straight beams. Straight beams occur more frequently in practice; moreover, the system of forces at a section of a straight beam is the same as in a curved one. Hence, if the behavior of a straight beam is understood, little needs to be added regarding curved beams. To simplify the work of this chapter,† the forces applied to the beams will be assumed to lie in the same plane, i.e., a "planar" beam problem will be discussed exclusively. Further, although in actual installations a straight beam may be vertical, inclined, or horizontal, for *convenience*, the beams discussed here will be shown in a horizontal position. All beams considered will be statically determinate, i.e., reactions can always be determined by applying the equations of static equilibrium.

For the axially loaded or torsion members previously considered, only one internal force was required at a section to satisfy the conditions of equilibrium. However, at a section of a beam, in general, a system of *three* internal forces is required. These quantities will be determined in this

---

* The contents of this chapter may be familiar to some students. Nevertheless, it is well to review the material presented here. A thorough knowledge of this material must be had prior to the study of the chapters that follow.

† See Chapter 7 for treatment of the more general problem.

chapter by isolating segments of a beam and applying the equilibrium conditions to them. The analysis relating these forces to the stresses which they cause in the beam will be discussed in the next two chapters.

4-2. Diagrammatic Conventions for Supports. In studying beams it is imperative to adopt diagrammatic conventions for their supports and loadings inasmuch as several kinds of supports and a great variety of loads are possible. A thorough mastery of and *adherence* to such conventions avoids much confusion and minimizes the chances of making mistakes. These conventions form the pictorial language of engineers. As stated in the introduction, for *convenience*, the beams will usually be shown in a horizontal position.

Three types of supports are recognized for beams loaded with forces acting in the same plane. These are identified by the kind of resistance they offer to the forces. One type of support is physically realized by a

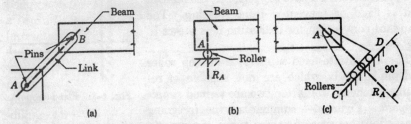

Fig. 4-1. Link and roller type of support. (The only possible line of action of the reaction is shown by the dashed lines.)

roller or a *link*. It is capable of resisting a force in only *one specific line of action*. The link shown in Fig. 4-1a can resist a force only in the direction of line AB. The roller in Fig. 4-1b can resist only a vertical force, while the rollers in Fig. 4-1c can resist only a force which acts perpendicular to the plane CD. This type of support will be usually represented in this text by rollers as shown in Figs. 4-1b and c, and it will be understood that *a roller support is capable of resisting a force in either direction** along the line of action of the reaction. To avoid this ambiguity, a schematic link will be occasionally employed (see Fig. 4-4). A reaction of this type corresponds to a single unknown when equations of statics are applied. For inclined reactions the *ratio* between the two components is fixed (see Example 1-3).

Another type of support that may be used for a beam is a *pin*. In construction such a support is realized by using a detail as shown in Fig. 4-2a. In this text such supports will be represented diagrammatically as shown in Fig. 4-2b. A pinned support is capable of resisting a force acting in *any* direction of the plane. Hence, in general, the reaction at

---

* This implies that in the actual design a link must be provided if the reaction acts away from the beam.

such a support may have two components, one in the horizontal and one in the vertical direction.   Unlike the ratio applying to the roller support,

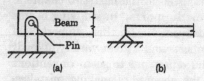

that between the reaction components for the pinned support is *not fixed*.   To determine these two components, two equations of statics must be used.

Fig. 4-2. Pinned support, (a) actual, (b) diagrammatic.

The third type of support used for beams is capable of resisting a force in any direction *and is also capable of resisting a couple or a moment*.   Physically such a support is obtained by building-in a beam into a brick wall, casting it into concrete, or welding an end of a beam to the main structure.   A system of *three* forces can exist at such a support, two components of force and a moment.   Such a support is called a *fixed support*, i.e., the built-in end is fixed or prevented from rotating.   The standard convention for indicating it is shown in Fig. 4-3.

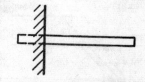

To differentiate fixed supports from the roller and pin supports, which are not capable of resisting moment, the latter two are termed *simple supports*.   Figure 4-4 summarizes the foregoing

Fig. 4-3. Fixed support.

distinctions between the three types of supports, and the kind of resistance offered by each type is shown.   Practicing engineers normally assume the supports to be of one of the three types by "judgment," although in actual construction supports for beams do not always clearly fall into these classifications.   A more refined investigation of this aspect of the problem is beyond the scope of this text.

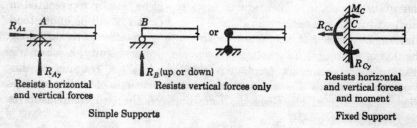

Resists horizontal and vertical forces

Resists vertical forces only

Resists horizontal and vertical forces and moment

Simple Supports

Fixed Support

Fig. 4-4. The three common types of support.

4-3. Diagrammatic Conventions for Loading. Beams are called upon to support a variety of loads.   Frequently a force is delivered to the beam through a post, a hanger, or a riveted detail as shown in Fig. 4-5a.   Such arrangements apply the force over a very limited portion of the beam and are idealized for the purposes of beam analysis as *concentrated* forces.

These are shown diagrammatically in Fig. 4-5b. On the other hand, in many instances the forces are applied over a considerable portion of the

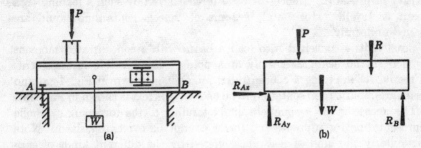

Fig. 4-5.   Concentrated loading on a beam, (a) actual, (b) idealized.

beam. For example, in a warehouse goods may be piled up along the length of a beam. Such forces are termed *distributed* loads.

Many types of distributed loads occur. Among these, two kinds are particularly important: the *uniformly distributed* loads and the *uniformly*

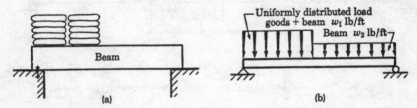

Fig. 4-6.   Distributed loading on a beam, (a) actual, (b) idealized.

varying loads. The first could easily be an idealization of the warehouse load just mentioned, where the same kind of goods are piled up to the same height along the beam. Likewise the beam itself, if of constant cross-sectional area, is an excellent illustration of the same kind of loading. A realistic situation and a diagrammatic idealization are shown in Fig. 4-6. This load is usually expressed in pounds per lineal foot (or inch) of the beam, unless specifically noted otherwise, and is abbreviated as lb per ft or lb/ft.

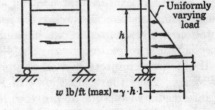

Fig. 4-7.   Hydrostatic loading on a vertical wall.

Uniformly varying loads act on the vertical and inclined walls of a vessel containing liquid. This is illustrated in Fig. 4-7 where it is assumed that the vertical beam is *one foot wide* and γ (lb/ft^3) is the unit weight of the liquid. For this type of loading, it should be carefully noted that the maximum intensity of the load of w lb per ft is applicable only to an *infinitesimal length* of the beam. It is twice as large as the average intensity of pressure. Hence the total force exerted by such a loading on a beam is $\frac{1}{2}wh$ lb. Horizontal bottoms of vessels containing liquid are loaded uniformly.

Finally, it is conceivable to load a beam with a concentrated moment applied to the beam essentially at a point. One possible arrangement, of many, for applying a concentrated moment is shown in Fig. 4-8a, and its diagrammatic representation to be used in this text is shown in Fig. 4-8c.

The necessity for a complete understanding of the foregoing symbolic representation for supports and forces cannot be overemphasized. Note particularly the kind of resistance offered by the different kinds of supports and the manner of representation of the forces at such supports. These notations will be used to construct free-body diagrams for beams.

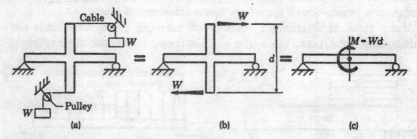

Fig. 4-8. A method of applying a concentrated moment to a beam.

4-4. Classification of Beams. Beams are classified into several groups, depending primarily on the kind of support used. Thus if the supports are at the ends and are either pins or rollers, the beams are *simply supported* or *simple* beams, Fig. 4-9a and b. The beam becomes a *fixed* beam or *fixed-ended* beam, Fig. 4-9c, if the ends have fixed supports. Likewise, following the same scheme of nomenclature, the beam shown in Fig. 4-9d is a beam fixed at one end and simply supported at the other. Such beams are also called *restrained* beams as an end is "restrained" from rotation. A beam fixed at one end and completely free at the other has a special name, a *cantilever* beam, Fig. 4-9e.

If the beam projects beyond a support, the beam is said to have an *overhang*. Thus the beam shown in Fig. 4-9f is an overhanging beam. If intermediate supports are provided for a physically continuous member acting as a beam, Fig. 4-9g, the beam is termed a *continuous* beam.

For all beams the distance L between supports is called a *span*. In a continuous beam there are several spans which may be of varying lengths.

In addition to classifying beams on the basis of supports, descriptive clauses pertaining to the loading are often used. Thus the beam shown in Fig. 4-9a is a simple beam with a concentrated load, while the one in

Fig. 4-9b is a simple beam with a uniformly distributed load. Other types of beams are similarly described.

For most of the work in Mechanics of Materials it is also meaningful to further classify beams into statically determinate and statically indeterminate beams. If the beam, loaded in a plane, is statically determinate, the number of unknown reaction components does not exceed three. These unknowns may always be determined from the equations of static equilibrium. The next article will briefly review the methods of statics for com

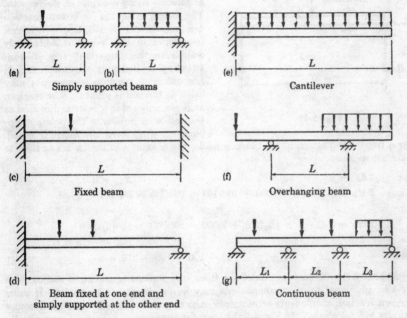

(a) (b) L L Simply supported beams
(e) L Cantilever
(c) L Fixed beam
(f) L Overhanging beam
(d) L Beam fixed at one end and simply supported at the other end
(g) L_1 L_2 L_3 Continuous beam

Fig. 4-9.   Types of beams.

puting reactions for statically determinate beams. An investigation of statically indeterminate beams will be postponed until Chapter 12.

4-5. Calculation of Beam Reactions. All subsequent work with beams will begin with determination of the reactions. When all of the forces are applied in one plane, three equations of static equilibrium are available for this purpose. These are $\Sigma F_x = 0$, $\Sigma F_y = 0$, and $\Sigma M_z = 0$, and they have already been discussed in Chapter 1. For straight beams in the horizontal position, the x-axis will be taken in a horizontal direction, the y-axis in the vertical direction, and the z-axis normal to the plane of the paper. The application of these equations to several beam problems is illustrated below and is intended to serve as a review of this important procedure. The deformation of beams, being small, can be neglected when the above equations are applied. For stable beams the small amount of deformation that does take place changes the points of application of the forces imperceptibly.

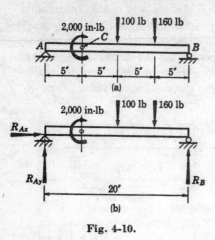

(a)

(b)

Fig. 4-10.

Example 4-1. Find the reactions at the supports for a simple beam loaded as shown in Fig. 4-10a. Neglect the weight of the beam.

SOLUTION: The loading of the beam is already given in diagrammatic form. The nature of the supports is examined next and the unknown components of these reactions are *boldly indicated on the diagram.* The beam, with the unknown reaction components and *all* of the applied forces, is redrawn in Fig. 4-10b to deliberately emphasize this important step in constructing a free-body diagram. At A, *two* unknown reaction components may exist, as the end is pinned. The reaction at B can only act in a vertical direction as the end is on a roller. The points of application of all forces are carefully noted.

After a free-body diagram of the beam is made, the equations of statics are applied to obtain the solution.

$$\Sigma F_x = 0 \qquad\qquad\qquad\qquad R_{Ax} = 0$$
$$\Sigma M_A = 0 \circlearrowright +, \qquad 2,000 + 100(10) + 160(15) - R_B(20) = 0$$
$$R_B = +270 \text{ lb} \uparrow$$
$$\Sigma M_B = 0 \circlearrowright +, \qquad R_{Ay}(20) + 2,000 - 100(10) - 160(5) = 0$$
$$R_{Ay} = -10 \text{ lb} \downarrow$$

Check: $\qquad \Sigma F_y = 0 \uparrow +, \qquad -10 - 100 - 160 + 270 = 0$

Note that $\Sigma F_x = 0$ uses up one of the three independent equations of statics, thus only two additional reaction components may be determined from statics. If more unknown reaction components or moments exist at the support, the problem becomes statically indeterminate. In Fig. 4-9 the beams shown in parts c, d, and g are statically

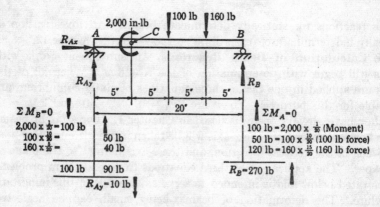

Fig. 4-11.

indeterminate beams as may be proved by examining the number of unknown reaction components (verify this statement).

Note that the concentrated moment applied at C enters only into the expressions for the summation of moments. The positive sign of R_B indicates that the direction of R_B has been correctly assumed in Fig. 4-10b. The inverse is the case for R_{Ay}, and the vertical reaction at A is downward. Note that a check on the arithmetical work is available if the calculations are made as shown.

ALTERNATE SOLUTION: In computing reactions some engineers prefer to make calculations in the manner indicated in Fig. 4-11. Fundamentally this involves the use of the same principles. Only the details are different. The reactions for every force are determined one at a time. The total reaction is obtained by summing these reactions. This procedure permits a running check of the computations *as they are performed*. For every force the sum of its reactions is equal to the force itself. For example, for the 160 lb force, it is easy to see that the upward forces of 40 lb and 120 lb total 160 lb. On the other hand, the concentrated moment at C, being a couple, is resisted by a couple. It causes an *upward* force of 100 lb at the right reaction and a *downward* force of 100 lb at the left reaction.

Example 4-2. Find the reactions for a partially loaded beam with a uniformly varying load, shown in Fig. 4-12a. Neglect the weight of the beam.

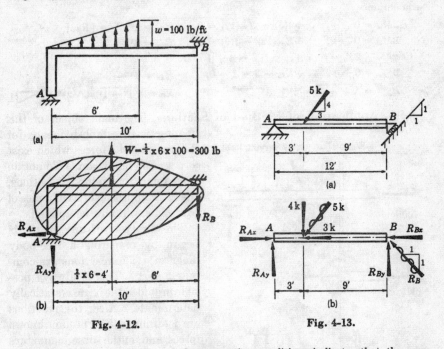

Fig. 4-12.   Fig. 4-13.

SOLUTION: An examination of the supporting conditions indicates that there are three unknown reaction components, hence the beam is statically determinate. These and the applied load are shown in Fig. 4-12b. Note particularly that, for computing the reactions the configuration of the member is not important. A crudely shaped outline bearing no resemblance to the actual beam is indicated to emphasize this point. However, this new body is supported at points A and B in the same manner as the original beam.

For calculating the reactions the distributed load is replaced by an equivalent concentrated force. This force is equal to the sum of the distributed forces acting on the beam. It acts through the centroid of the distributed forces. These pertinent quantities are marked on the working sketch, Fig. 4-12b. *After* a free-body diagram is prepared the solution follows by applying the equations of static equilibrium.

$$\Sigma F_x = 0 \qquad\qquad\qquad\qquad\qquad R_{Ax} = 0$$
$$\Sigma M_A = 0 \circlearrowright +, \qquad +300(4) - R_B(10) = 0, \qquad R_B = 120 \text{ lb} \downarrow$$
$$\Sigma M_B = 0 \circlearrowright +, \qquad -R_{Ay}(10) + 300(6) = 0, \qquad R_{Ay} = 180 \text{ lb} \downarrow$$

Check: $\qquad\qquad \Sigma F_y = 0 \uparrow +, \qquad -180 + 300 - 120 = 0$

Example 4-3. Determine the reactions at A and B for the "weightless" beam shown in Fig. 4-13a.

SOLUTION: A free-body diagram is shown in Fig. 4-13b. At A there are *two* unknown reaction components, R_{Ax} and R_{Ay}. At B the reaction R_B acts normal to the supporting plane and constitutes a *single* unknown. It is expedient to replace this force by the two components R_{By} and R_{Bx}, which in this particular problem are numerically equal (see Example 1-3). Similarly, it is best to replace the inclined force with the two components shown. These steps reduce the problem to one where *all* forces are either horizontal or vertical. This is of great convenience in applying the equations of static equilibrium.

$$\Sigma M_A = 0 \circlearrowright +, \qquad +4(3) - R_{By}(12) = 0, \qquad R_{By} = 1^{\text{kip}} \uparrow \; = | R_{Bx} |$$
$$\Sigma M_B = 0 \circlearrowright +, \qquad +R_{Ay}(12) - 4(9) = 0, \qquad R_{Ay} = 3^{\text{kip}} \uparrow$$

Check: $\quad \Sigma F_y = 0 \uparrow +, \qquad +3 - 4 + 1 = 0$

$$\Sigma F_x = 0 \rightarrow +, \qquad +R_{Ax} - 3 - 1 = 0, \qquad R_{Ax} = 4^{\text{kip}} \rightarrow$$

$$R_A = \sqrt{4^2 + 3^2} = 5^{\text{kip}} \qquad R_B = \sqrt{1^2 + 1^2} = \sqrt{2}^{\text{kip}}$$

4-6. Application of Method of Sections.

The main object of this chapter is to establish means for determining the forces which exist at a section of a beam. To obtain these forces the method of sections, the basic approach of Mechanics of Materials, will now be applied.

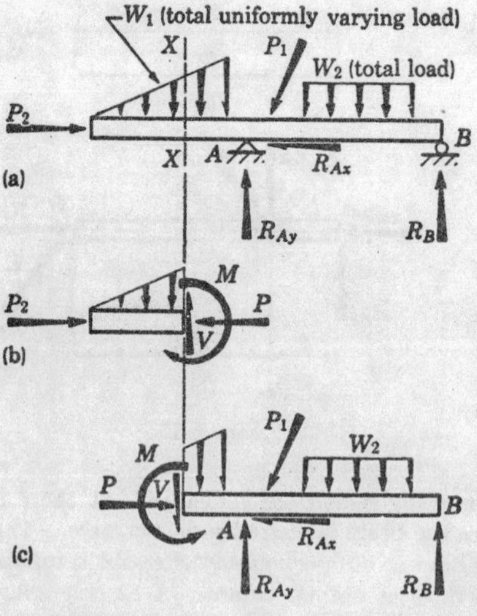

The analysis of any beam is begun by preparing a free-body diagram. The reactions are computed next. This is always possible provided the beam is statically determinate. After the reactions are determined, they become known forces, and, in the subsequent steps of beam analysis, *no distinction need be made between the applied and reactive forces.* Then, to apply the method of sections to any beam, the previously used dictum is employed, i.e., if a whole body is in

Fig. 4-14. An application of the method of sections to a statically determinate beam.

equilibrium, *any part* of it is likewise in equilibrium. As before, the practice of making imaginary cuts *perpendicular* to the axis of the member is continued.

For concreteness consider a beam, such as shown in Fig. 4-14a, with certain concentrated and distributed forces acting on it together with reactions presumed to be known. Any part of this beam to either side of an imaginary cut, as X-X, can be treated as a free body. Separating this beam at the section X-X, two segments, shown in Fig. 4-14b and c, are obtained. Note particularly that the imaginary section goes through the distributed load and separates it too. Either one of these beam segments is in equilibrium. However, for such segments the equations of statics are usually not satisfied by the external forces alone, although reactions are a part of the external force system. The fulfillment of *the necessary conditions of static equilibrium requires the existence of a system of forces at the cut section of the beam.* In general, at a section of a beam a vertical force, a horizontal force, and a moment are necessary to maintain the part of the beam in equilibrium. These quantities take on a special significance in beams and therefore will be discussed separately.

4-7. Shear in Beams. To maintain a segment of a beam such as shown in Fig. 4-14b in equilibrium there must be an internal vertical force V at the cut to satisfy the equation $\Sigma F_y = 0$. This internal force V, acting *at right angles* to the axis of the beam, is called the *shear* or the *shearing force. The shear is numerically equal to the algebraic sum of all the vertical components of the external forces acting on the isolated segment,* but it is opposite in direction. Given the qualitative data shown in Fig. 4-14b, V is opposite in direction to the downward load to the left of the section. Similarly, the shear at the same section is also equal numerically, and is opposite in direction, to the sum of all vertical forces to the *right* of the section, Fig. 4-14c. The latter sum of forces must, of course, include the vertical reaction components. Whether the right-hand segment or the left is used to determine the shear at a section is immaterial—arithmetical simplicity governs. Shears at *any other section* may be computed similarly.

At this time a significant observation must be made. The *same* shear shown in Figs. 4-14b and c at the section X-X is opposite in direction in the two diagrams. For that *part* of the downward load W_1 to the left of section X-X, the beam at the section provides an upward support to maintain vertical forces in equilibrium. Conversely, the loaded portion of the beam exerts a downward force *on* the beam as in Fig. 4-14c. At a section "two directions" of shear must be differentiated, depending upon *which segment* of the beam is considered. This follows from the familiar action-reaction concept of statics and has occurred earlier in the case of an axially loaded rod, and again in the torsion problem.

The direction of the shear at section X-X would be reversed in *both* diagrams if the distributed load W_1 were acting upward. Frequently a similar reversal in the direction of shear takes place at one section or another along a beam for reasons which will become apparent later. The adoption of a sign convention is necessary to differentiate between the two possible directions of shear. The definition of positive shear is illus-trated in Fig. 4-15a. To cause positive shear, the forces on the left-hand side of a section sum up to an *upward* resultant force *tend-ing* to produce the displacement shown at the section.

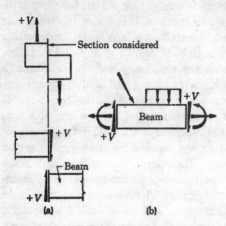

Fig. 4-15. The definition of a positive shear.

On a segment isolated from a beam by two sections, Fig. 4-15b, an *upward* force on the left-hand side or a *downward* force on the right-hand side corresponds to positive shear. The shear at sec-tion X-X of Fig. 4-14a is a negative shear since it acts up on the right-hand edge of the *left segment*.

4-8. Axial Force in Beams. In addition to the shear V, a hori-zontal force such as P, shown in Fig. 4-14b or c, may be necessary at a sec-tion of a beam to satisfy the conditions of equilibrium. The magnitude and sense of this force follows from a particular solution of the equation $\Sigma F_x = 0$. If the horizontal force P acts toward the cut, it is called a *thrust;* if away from the cut, it is termed *axial tension*. In referring to either of these forces the term *axial force* is used, as was done in Chapter 1.

The effect of an axial force on a section of a member has already been discussed in Chapter 1. It was shown there that it is imperative to apply this force through the *centroid* of the cross-sectional area of a member to avoid bending. Similarly, here *the line of action of the axial force will always be directed through the **centroid of the beam's cross-sectional area**.*

Any section along a beam may be examined for the magnitude of the axial force in the above manner. The tensile force at a section is custom-arily taken positive. The axial force (thrust) at section X-X in Fig. 4-14b and c is equal to the horizontal force P_2.

4-9. Bending Moment in Beams. The determination of the shear and axial force at a section of a beam completes two of the requirements of statics which a segment must fulfill. These forces satisfy the equations $\Sigma F_x = 0$ and $\Sigma F_y = 0$. The remaining condition of static equilibrium for a planar problem is $\Sigma M_z = 0$. This, in general, can be satisfied only by developing a couple or an *internal resisting moment* within the cross-sectional area of the cut to counteract the moment caused by the external forces. The internal resisting moment must act in a direction opposite to the external moment to satisfy the governing equation $\Sigma M_z = 0$.   Likewise it follows from the same equation that *the magnitude of the internal resisting moment equals the external moment*.   These moments tend to bend a beam in the plane of the loads and are usually referred to as *bending moments*.

The internal bending moment M is indicated in Fig. 4-14b.   It can be developed only within the cross-sectional area of the beam and is equivalent to a couple.   To determine this moment necessary to maintain the equilibrium of a segment, the sum of the moments caused by the forces may be made around any point in the plane; of course, *all* forces times their arms must be included in the sum.   The internal forces V and P form *no* exception. To exclude the moments caused by these forces from the sum, it is usually most convenient in numerical problems to *select the point of intersection of these two internal forces as the point around which the moments are summed*.   Both V and P have arms of zero length at this point, which is located *on the centroid of the cross-sectional area* of the beam.

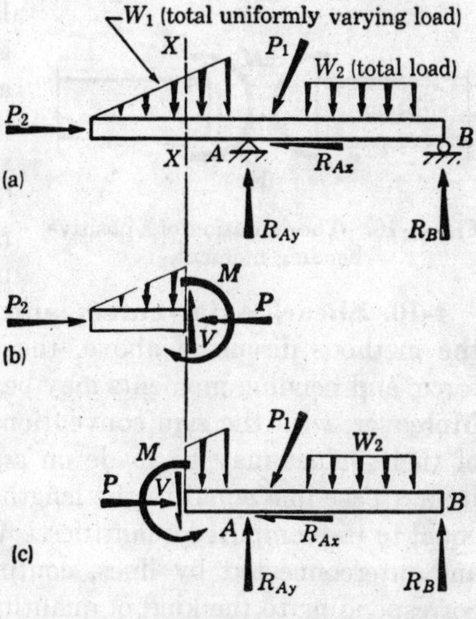

Fig. 4-14.   An application of the method of sections to a statically determinate beam.   (Repeated.)

Instead of considering the segment to the left of section X-X, the right-hand segment of the beam, Fig. 4-14c, may also be used to determine the internal bending moment. As explained above, this internal moment is equal to the external moment of the applied forces (including reactions), provided the summation of moments is made around the *centroid* of the section *at* the cut.   In Fig. 4-14b the resisting moment may be physically interpreted as a pull on the top fibers of the beam and a push on the lower ones.   The same interpretation applies to the same moment shown in Fig. 4-14c.

If the load W_1 in Fig. 4-14a were acting in the opposite direction, the resisting moments in Figs. 4-14b *and* c would reverse.   This and similar situations require a sign convention for the bending moments.   This convention is associated with a definite physical action of the beam.   For example, in Figs. 4-14b and c the internal moments shown pull on the top portion of the beam and compress the lower.   This tends to increase the length of the top surface of the beam and to contract the lower surface. A continuous occurrence of such moments along the beam makes the beam deform convex upwards, i.e., "shed water." Such bending moments are assigned a *negative sign*. Conversely, a positive moment is defined as one that produces compression in the top part and tension in the lower part of a beam's cross-section. Under such circumstances the beam as-

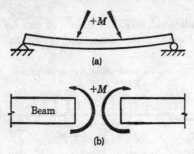

(a)

(b)

Fig. 4-16. The definition of a positive bending moment.

sumes a shape that "retains water." For example, a simple beam supporting a group of downward forces deflects down as shown in *exaggerated* form in Fig. 4-16a, a fact immediately suggested by physical intuition. In such a beam a detailed investigation of bending moments along the beam shows that all of them are positive. The sense of a positive bending moment at a section of a beam is defined in Fig. 4-16b.

4-10. Shear, Axial-Force, and Bending-Moment Diagrams. By the methods discussed above, the magnitude and sense of shear, axial force, and bending moments may be obtained at many sections of a beam. Moreover, with the sign conventions adopted for these quantities, a plot of their values may be made on *separate* diagrams. On such diagrams, from a base line equal to the length of a beam, ordinates may be laid off equal to the computed quantities. When these ordinate points are plotted and interconnected by lines, continuous plots result. These diagrams, corresponding to the kind of quantities they depict, are called respectively *the shear diagram, the axial-force diagram, or the bending-moment diagram.* With the aid of such diagrams, the magnitudes and locations of the various quantities become immediately apparent. It is convenient to make these plots directly below the free-body diagram of the beam, using the same horizontal scale for the length of the beam. Draftsmanlike precision in making such diagrams is usually unnecessary, although the significant ordinates are generally marked with their numerical value.

The axial-force diagrams are not as commonly used as the shear and the bending-moment diagrams. This is so because the majority of beams investigated in practice are loaded by forces which act perpendicular to the axis of the beam. For such loadings of a beam, there are no axial forces at any section.

Shear and moment diagrams are exceedingly important. From them a designer sees at a glance the kind of performance that is desired from a beam at every section. In Chapter 10 on the design of members, methods of constructing these diagrams in a rapid manner will be discussed. However, the procedure discussed above of sectioning a beam and finding the system of forces at the section is the most fundamental approach. It will be used in the following illustrative examples.

Example 4-4. Construct shear, axial-force, and bending-moment diagrams for the weightless beam shown in Fig. 4-17a subjected to the inclined force $P = 5$ kips.

SOLUTION: A free-body diagram of the beam is shown in Fig. 4-17b. Reactions follow from inspection after the applied force is resolved into the two components. Then several sections through the beam are investigated, as shown in Figs. 4-17c, d, e, f, and g. In every case the same question is posed: *What are the necessary internal forces to keep the segment of the beam in equilibrium?* The corresponding quantities are recorded on the respective free-body diagrams of the beam segment. The ordinates for these quantities are indicated by heavy dots in Figs. 4-17h, i, and j, with due attention paid to their sign.

Note that the free bodies shown in Figs. 4-17d and g are alternates, as they furnish the same information, and normally both would not be made. Note that a section *just to the left* of the applied force has one sign of shear, Fig. 4-17e, while *just to the right*, Fig. 4-17f, it has another. This indicates the importance of determining shears on either side of a concentrated force. For the condition shown, the beam *does not resist* a shear which is equal to the whole force. The bending moment in both cases is the same.

In this particular case, after a few individual points have been established on the three diagrams in Figs. 4-17h, i, and j, the behavior of the respective quantities across the whole length of the beam may be reasoned out. Thus, although the segment of the beam shown in Fig. 4-17c is 2 ft long, it may vary in length anywhere from zero to *just to the left* of the applied force, and *no change in the shear and the axial force occurs.* Hence the ordinates in Figs. 4-17h and i *remain* constant for this segment of the beam. On the other hand, the bending moment depends directly on the distance from the supports, hence it varies linearly as shown in Fig. 4-17j. Similar reasoning applies to the segment shown in Fig. 4-17d, enabling one to complete the three diagrams on the right-hand side. The use of the free body of Fig. 4-17g for completing the diagram to the right of center yields the same result.

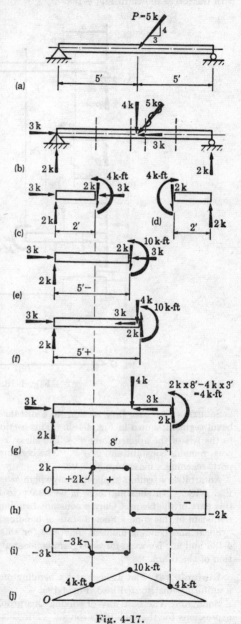

Fig. 4-17.

Example 4-5. Construct shear and bending-moment diagrams for the beam loaded with the forces shown in Fig. 4-18a.

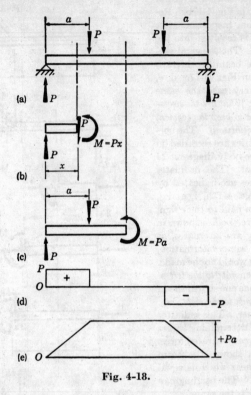

Fig. 4-18.

SOLUTION: An arbitrary section at a distance x from the left support isolates the beam segment shown in Fig. 4-18b. This section is applicable for any value of x just to the left of the applied force P. The shear, regardless of the distance from the support, remains constant and is $+P$. The bending moment varies linearly from the support, reaching a maximum of $+Pa$.

An arbitrary section applicable anywhere *between* the two applied forces is shown in Fig. 4-18c. No shearing force is necessary to maintain equilibrium of a segment in this part of the beam. Only a constant bending moment of $+Pa$ must be resisted by the beam in this zone. Such a state of bending or flexure is called *pure* bending.

Shear and bending-moment diagrams for this loading condition are shown in Figs. 4-18d and e. No axial-force diagram is necessary, as there is no axial force at any section of the beam.

Example 4-6. Plot a shear and a bending-moment diagram for a simple beam with a uniformly distributed load, Fig. 4-19a.

SOLUTION: The best way of solving this problem consists of writing down algebraic expressions for the quantities sought. For this purpose an arbitrary section taken at a distance x from the left support is used to isolate the segment shown in Fig. 4-19b. Since the applied load is continuously distributed along the beam, this section is typical and applies to *any section* along the length of the beam. In more difficult cases several zones of a beam may have to be investigated if *different* functions for the quantities

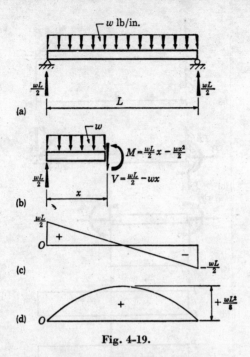

Fig. 4-19.

sought apply. In some instances it is even advisable to resort to several origins of x to simplify the form of the algebraic functions.

The shear V is equal to the left upward reaction *less* the load to the left of the section. The internal bending moment M resists the moment caused by the reaction on the left *less* the moment caused by the forces to the left of the same section. The summation of moments is performed around an axis *at the section.* Although it is customary to isolate the left-hand segment, similar expressions may be obtained by considering the right-hand segment of the beam, with due attention paid to sign conventions. The plot of the V and M functions is shown in Fig. 4-19c and d.

Example 4-7. Determine shear, axial-force, and bending-moment diagrams for the cantilever loaded with an inclined force at the end, Fig. 4-20a.

SOLUTION: First the inclined force is replaced by the two components shown in Fig. 4-20b and the reaction is determined. The *three* unknowns at the reaction follow from the familiar equations of statics. This completes the free-body diagram shown in Fig. 4-20b. *Completeness in indicating all of these forces is of the utmost importance.*

A segment of the beam is shown in Fig. 4-20c; from this segment it may be seen that the shearing force and the axial force remain the same regardless of the distance x. On the other hand, the bending moment is a variable quantity. A summation of moments around C gives $(PL - Px)$ acting in the direction shown. This represents a *negative* moment. The moment at the support is likewise a *negative* bending moment as it tends to pull on the *upper* fibers of the beam. The three diagrams are plotted in Figs. 4-20d, e, and f.

Example 4-8. Given a curved beam whose centroidal axis is bent into a semicircle of 10 in. radius as shown in Fig. 4-21a. If this member is being pulled by the 1,000 lb forces shown, find the axial force, the shear, and the bending moment at the section A-A, $\alpha = 45°$. The centroidal axis and the applied forces all lie in the same plane.

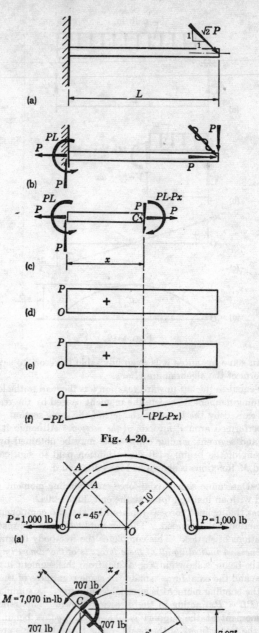

Fig. 4-20.

Fig. 4-21.

SOLUTION: There is no essential difference in the method of attack in this problem compared with that in a straight beam problem. The body as a whole is examined for conditions of equilibrium. From the conditions of the problem here, such is already the case. A segment of the beam is isolated next. This is shown in Fig. 4-21b. *Section A-A is taken perpendicular to the axis of the beam.* Before determining the quantities wanted at the cut, the applied force P is resolved into components parallel and perpendicular to the cut. These directions are taken respectively as the y- and x-axes. This resolution replaces P by the components shown in Fig. 4-21b. From $\Sigma F_x = 0$, the axial force at the cut is $+707$ lb. From $\Sigma F_y = 0$, the shear is 707 lb in the direction shown. The bending moment at the cut may be determined in several different ways. For example, if $\Sigma M_O = 0$ is used, note that the lines of action of the applied force P and the shear at the section pass through O. Therefore only the axial force at the centroid of the cut times the radius needs to be considered, and the *resisting* bending moment is $707(10) = 7,070$ in.-lb acting in the direction shown. An alternative solution may be obtained by applying $\Sigma M_C = 0$. At C, a point lying on the centroid, the axial force and the shear intersect. The bending moment is then the product of the applied force P and the 7.07 in. arm. In both of these methods of determining bending moment, use of the components of the force P is avoided as this is more involved arithmetically.

It is suggested that the student complete this problem in terms of a general angle α. Several interesting observations may be made from such a general solution. The moments at the ends will vanish for $\alpha = 0°$ and $\alpha = 180°$. For $\alpha = 90°$ the shear vanishes and the axial force becomes equal to the applied force P. Likewise the maximum bending moment is associated with $\alpha = 90°$.

4-11. Step-by-Step Procedure. In beam analysis it is exceedingly important to be able to determine the shear, the axial force, and the bending moment at any section of the beam. The technique of obtaining these quantities is unusually clear cut and systematic. To lend further emphasis, the steps used in all such problems are summarized. This summary is intended to aid the student in an orderly analysis of problems. Sheer memorization of this procedure is discouraged.

1. Make a good sketch of the beam on which *all* of the applied forces are clearly noted and located by dimension lines from the supports.

2. Boldly indicate the unknown reactions (colored pencil may be used to advantage). Remember that a roller support has *one* unknown, a pinned support has *two* unknowns, and a fixed support has *three* unknowns.

3. Replace all of the inclined forces (known and unknown) by components acting parallel and perpendicular to the beam.*

4. Apply the equations of statics to obtain the reactions.† A check on the reactions computed in the manner indicated in Examples 4-1, 4-2, and 4-3 is highly desirable.

5. Pass a section at the desired location through the beam perpendicular to its axis. This imaginary section cuts *only the beam* and isolates the forces which act on the segment.

6. Select a segment to either side of the proposed section and *redraw*

---

* More ingenuity may be required for curved beams.

† This step may be avoided in cantilevers by proceeding from the free end.

this segment, indicating *all* external forces acting on it. This must include all of the reaction components.

7. Indicate the three possible unknown quantities at the cut sections, i.e., show V, P, and M, assuming their directions.

8. Apply the equations of static equilibrium to the segment and solve for the quantities sought. Revise the assumed directions for V, P, and M if these were originally shown in an incorrect direction.

This procedure enables one to determine the shear, the axial force, and the bending moment at any section of a beam. Signs for these quantities follow from the definitions given earlier. If diagrams for this system of internal forces are wanted, several sections may have to be investigated. Do not fail to determine the abrupt change in shear at concentrated forces and the *abrupt change in bending-moment value* at points where concentrated moments are introduced. Algebraic expressions for the same quantities sometimes are also very useful.

At this time it is suggested that Art. 1-10 on the basic approach of Mechanics of Materials be reviewed, as a better appreciation may now be had of the contents of that article.

Problems for Solution

(*Note:* In addition to beams, simple frames are included in the following problems. For the quantities asked, the analysis of these frames is analogous to that of beams.)

4-1. Show that the effect on a structure of the tensile forces acting in a flexible cable going over a frictionless pulley is the same as that of the same two forces applied at the center of the axle.

4-2 through 4-11. For the planar structures loaded as shown in the figures determine the reactions or all reaction components. All structures are to be assumed weightless. *A correctly drawn free-body diagram is an essential part of each problem. Ans.* Upward reaction component for the left reaction is given in parentheses by each figure in the units of the applied loads.

4-12. For the beam loaded as shown in the figure, find the shear and the bending moment at the center of the span caused by the applied load. *Ans.* $V = -1\text{k}$, $M = -13.5$ k-ft.

4-13. A chain block used for raising 10 ton weights by means of a spreader beam is shown in the figure. The chain AB is 6 ft long; chain BC is 8 ft long. Neglecting the weight of the assembly, find the components of all forces acting parallel and perpendicular to the beam when in use.

4-14. Two 3 lb weights are attached to a shaft by means of rigid arms as shown in the figure. Neglecting the weight of the shaft and the arms, find the reactions at the bearings if the shaft rotates at 600 rpm.

4-15. Determine the bending moment at the support B in Prob. 4-3. *Ans.* -25 k-ft.

4-16. Determine the shear and the bending moment at a section midway between C and D in the beam AB of Prob. 4-7. *Ans.* $+60$ k; $+900$ k-ft.

4-17 through 4-24. For the planar structures shown in the figures, determine the axial force, the shear, and the bending moment at sections a-a, b-b, c-c, and d-d, wherever

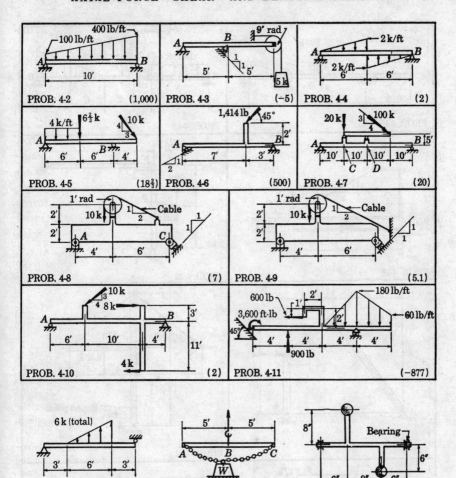

PROB. 4-2   (1,000)

PROB. 4-3   (-5)

PROB. 4-4   (2)

PROB. 4-5   (18⅔)

PROB. 4-6   (500)

PROB. 4-7   (20)

PROB. 4-8   (7)

PROB. 4-9   (5.1)

PROB. 4-10   (2)

PROB. 4-11   (-877)

PROB. 4-12

PROB. 4-13

PROB. 4-14

they apply. Neglect the weight of members. *In every case, draw a free-body of the isolated part of the structure and clearly show on it the sense of the computed quantities.* Some of the sections are shown close together. In these cases, determine the quantities asked just to the left and just to the right of the point in question. *Ans.* The answers are given in the following order: axial force, shear, and moment. The signs of shear and moment apply only for horizontal members.

Prob. 4-17. At *a-a:* −28 k, −152 k-ft. At *b-b:* −8 k, −152 k-ft. At *c-c:* −8k, −176 k-ft. At *d-d:* −8 k, +24 k-ft.

Prob. 4-18. At *a-a:* 0, +44.4 k, +77.2 k-ft. At *b-b:* +50 k, −5.6 k, −222.8 k-ft. At *c-c:* +50 k, +17.4 k, +111.6 k-ft.

Prob. 4-19. At *a-a:* −3.43 k, −1.71 k, +61.7 k-in.

Prob. 4-20. At *a-a:* +4 k, 8 k, 16 k-ft. At *b-b:* +4 k, 8 k, 72 k-ft. At *c-c:* +8 k, −4 k, +72 k-ft.

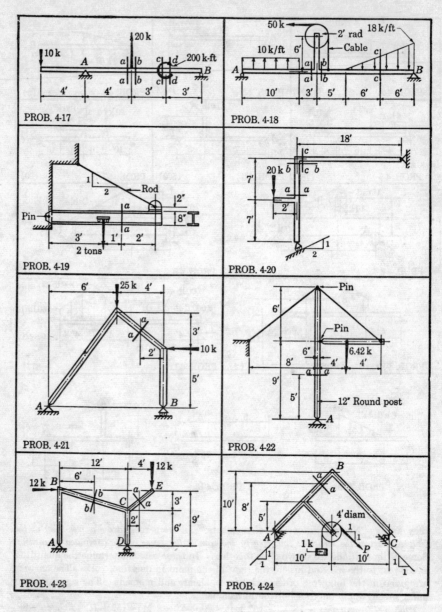

PROB. 4-17

PROB. 4-18

PROB. 4-19

PROB. 4-20

PROB. 4-21

PROB. 4-22

PROB. 4-23

PROB. 4-24

Prob. 4-21. At *a-a:* −14 k, 2 k, 5 k-ft.

Prob. 4-22. At *a-a:* −7.71 k, 1.72 k, 8.60 k-ft.

Prob. 4-23. At *a-a:* −7.2 k, 9.6 k, 24 k-ft.   At *b-b:* −3.15 k, 12.6 k, 30 k-ft.

Prob. 4-24. At *a-a:* +1.21 k, 0, 17.1 k-ft.

4-25 through 4-27. Plot the shear and moment diagrams for the beams loaded as shown in the figures. *Ans.* Max. moment in parentheses by the figure.

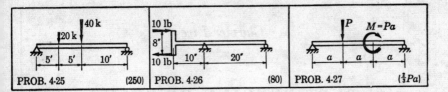

PROB. 4-25   (250)   PROB. 4-26   (80)   PROB. 4-27   ($\frac{2}{3}Pa$)

4-28. Establish general algebraic equations for the axial force, shear, and bending moment for the curved beam of Example 4-8.

4-29 through 4-31. For beams loaded as shown in the figures, express the shear and bending moments by algebraic expressions for the interval AB.

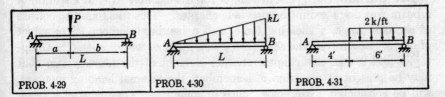

PROB. 4-29   PROB. 4-30   PROB. 4-31

(*Note:* for additional problems see Chapter 10.)

Chapter Five

PURE BENDING OF BEAMS

5-1. Introduction. The system of forces that may exist at a section of a beam was discussed in the previous chapter. This was found to consist of an axial force, a shearing force, and a bending moment. The effect of one of these forces, the axial force, on a member was discussed in Chapters 1 and 2. In this chapter another element of the force system that may be present at a section of a member, the internal bending moment, will be considered. Moreover, since in some cases a segment of a beam may be in equilibrium under the action of a moment alone, a condition called *pure bending or flexure*, this in itself represents a complete problem. It is the purpose of this chapter to relate the internal bending moment to the stresses it causes in a beam. If, in addition to the internal bending moment, an axial force and a shear also act simultaneously, complex stresses arise. These will be treated in Chapters 7, 8, and 9. The deflection of beams due to bending will be discussed in Chapter 11.

A major part of this chapter will be devoted to methods for determining the stresses in straight homogeneous beams caused by bending moments. Topics on beams made from two or more different materials and curved beams are also included.

5-2. Some Important Limitations of the Theory. Just as in the case of axially loaded rods and in the torsion problem, all forces applied to a beam will be assumed to be steady and delivered to the beam without shock or impact. Shock or impact problems will be considered in Chapter 15. Moreover, all of the beams will be assumed to be stable under the applied forces. A similar point was brought out in Chapter 1, where it was indicated that a rod acting in compression cannot be too slender, or its behavior will not be governed by the usual compressive strength criterion. In such cases the *stability* of the member becomes important. As an example, consider the possibility of using a sheet of paper on edge as a beam. Such a beam has a substantial depth, but even if it is used to carry a force over a small span, it will buckle sidewise and collapse. The same phenomenon may take place in more substantial members which may likewise collapse under an applied force. Such unstable beams do not come within the scope of this chapter. All of the beams considered here will be assumed to be sufficiently stable laterally by virtue of their proportions, or to be thoroughly braced in the transverse direction. A better understanding of this important phenomenon will result after the study of the chapter on columns, where this matter will be discussed in more detail (see Art. 13-11). It is indeed fortunate that the majority of beams used in structural framing and machine parts are such that the flexural theory to be developed here is applicable, as the theory governing the stability of a member is more involved.

5-3. Basic Assumptions. For the present it is assumed that only *straight* beams having constant cross-sectional areas *with an axis of symmetry* are to be included in the discussion. Moreover, it is assumed that the applied bending moments lie in a plane containing this axis of symmetry and the beam axis. Let it be further agreed that for the sake of simplicity in making sketches, the axis of symmetry will be taken vertically.

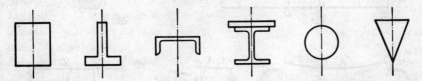

Fig. 5-1.   Beam cross-sections with a vertical axis of symmetry.

Several cross-sectional areas of beams satisfying these conditions are shown in Fig. 5-1. A generalization of this problem will be made in Art. 5-7.

A segment of a beam fulfilling the above requirements is shown in Fig. 5-2a, and its cross-section is shown in Fig. 5-2b. For such a beam a line through the centroid of all cross-sections will be referred to as the axis of the beam. Next, imagine that two planes are passed through the beam perpendicular to its axis. The intersections of these planes with a longitudinal plane passing through the beam axis and the axis of symmetry is shown by lines AB and CD. Then it is not difficult to imagine that when this segment is subjected to the bending moments M at its ends as shown in Fig. 5-2c, the beam bends, and the planes perpendicular to the beam axis tilt slightly. Moreover, the lines AB and CD *remain* straight.[*] This can be satisfactorily verified experimentally.[†]   Generalizing this

---

[*] A rubber model with a ruled grating on it may be used to illustrate this behavior.

[†] Rigorous solutions from the Mathematical Theory of Elasticity show that slight warpage of these lines may take place. This warpage is greatest if a beam carries a shear in addition to a bending moment. However, the warpage of the *adjoining sections* is exceedingly similar in shape. Thus the distance between any two points such as A and C on the adjoining sections remains practically the same whether warped or straight lines AB and CD are considered. And since the distance between the adjoining sections is the basis for establishing the elementary flexure theory, the foregoing assumption forms an excellent working hypothesis for all cases. Moreover, a conclusion of far-reaching importance is that the existence of a shear at a section does not invalidate the expressions to be derived in this chapter. This will be implied in the subsequent work.

observation for the whole beam, one obtains the **most fundamental hypothesis** of the flexure theory, based on the geometry of deformations. It may be stated thus:

1. Plane sections through a beam, taken normal to its axis, **remain plane** after the beam is subjected to bending.

This means that in a bent beam two planes normal to the beam axis and initially parallel cease to be parallel. In a side view the behavior of two such planes corresponds to the behavior of lines AB and CD of Figs. 5-2a and c. An element of the beam contained between these planes is

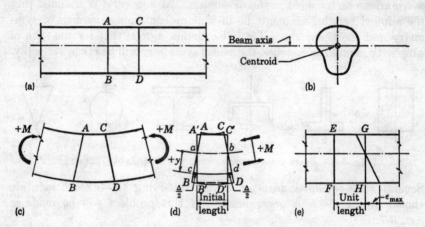

Fig. 5-2. Behavior of a beam in bending.

shown in Fig. 5-2d. Under the action of the moments of the sense shown, the distance AC becomes smaller than BD. Further, since the internal moment can be thought of as a couple, shown next to the side CD in Fig. 5-2d, a push must exist on the upper part of the beam and a pull on the lower. Hence, the undistorted beam element must be related to the distorted one, as $A'C'D'B'$ is to $ACDB$, Fig. 5-2d. From this diagram it is seen that the fibers or "filaments" of the beam along the surface* ab do not change in length. Hence, *the fibers in the surface ab are not stressed at all*, and, as the element selected was an arbitrary one, fibers free of stress exist continuously over the whole length and width of the beam. These fibers lie in a surface which is called the *neutral surface* of the beam. Its intersection with a right section through the beam is termed the *neutral axis* of the beam. Either term implies a location of *zero stress* in the member subjected to bending.

The precise location of the neutral surface in a beam will be determined in the next article. First, a study of the nature of the strains in fibers

---

* A rigorous solution shows that this surface is slightly cylindrical in two directions. In the present treatment this surface is assumed to be curved only in the direction shown.

parallel to the neutral surface will be made. Thus consider a fiber such
as *cd* parallel to the neutral surface and located at a distance* y from it.
During bending it elongates an amount Δ. If this elongation is divided
by the initial length L of the fiber, the *strain* ϵ in that fiber is obtained.
Next, note that from the geometrical assumption made earlier, elongations
of different fibers vary *linearly* from the neutral axis since these elongations
are fixed by the triangles aBB', bDD', aAA', and bCC'. On the other
hand, the initial length of all fibers is the same. Hence the original
fundamental assumption may be restated† thus:

1a. In a beam subjected to bending, strains in its fibers vary linearly
or directly as their respective distances from the neutral surface.

This situation is analogous to the one found earlier in the torsion problem where the *shearing* strains vary linearly from the axis of a circular
shaft. In a beam, strains vary linearly from the *neutral surface*. This
variation is represented diagrammatically in Fig. 5-2e. These *axial*
strains are associated with stresses which act **normal** to the section of a
beam. The above corollary to the original assumption is applicable in
the elastic as well as in the inelastic range of the material's behavior.‡
For the present this generality will be limited by introducing the second
fundamental assumption of the flexure theory:

2. Hooke's law is applicable to the individual fibers, i.e., stress is proportional to strain. The same elastic modulus E is assumed to apply to
material in tension as well as in
compression. The Poisson effect
and the interference of the adjoining differently stressed fibers
are ignored.

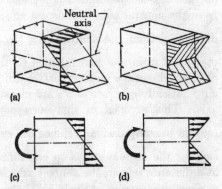

Combining the foregoing assumptions, the basis for establishing the flexural theory for the
elastic case is obtained:

*On a section of a beam, normal
stresses resulting from bending vary
linearly as their respective distances
from the neutral axis.*

That these stresses act normal
to the section of a beam should be

Fig. 5-3.   Stress distribution at a section of a
beam resisting a bending moment.

firmly fixed in the reader's mind. They are the result of *axial* elongation
or contraction of the various beam fibers. That they vary linearly from
the neutral axis, to repeat, is due to the linear variation of the strains and
to the proportionality of stress to strain. The distance to the various

---

* Positive direction of y is taken downward from the neutral axis.
† Experimentally, this assumption may be more easily verified than assumption (1).
‡ Beams stressed beyond the elastic limit are treated in Art. 5-9.

fibers of the beam is measured *vertically* from the neutral axis. Figures 5-3a and b illustrate the nature of the stress distribution in a beam resisting a bending moment. Two alternative schemes of representing this three-dimensional problem in a plane are shown in Figs. 5-3c and d. In subsequent work these will be the usual forms for showing the flexural stress distribution at a section of a beam.

5-4. The Flexure Formula. After the nature of the stress distribution in the elastic range at a section of a beam is understood, quantitative expressions relating bending moment to stress may be established. For this purpose the neutral surface is first located from considerations of static equilibrium.

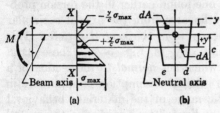

Fig. 5-4. A beam in pure flexure.

Consider a beam segment subjected to a positive bending moment M as shown in Fig. 5-4a. At section X-X this applied moment is resisted by stresses which vary linearly from the neutral axis. The highest stresses occur at the points most remote from the neutral axis. For the beam shown this occurs along the line ed, Fig. 5-4b. This stress, being a normal stress, is designated by σ_{max}, Fig. 5-4a. Any other normal stress acting on the cross-sectional area is related to this stress by a ratio of distances from the neutral axis. Thus, on an infinitesimal area dA, Fig. 5-4b, at a distance y from the neutral axis, the stress is $\frac{y}{c}\sigma_{max}$, where distance c is measured from the neutral axis to the most remote fiber of the beam. Stresses above the neutral surface are given by a similar relation; the sign automatically reverses as y's are measured positive down from the neutral axis. This reversal of sign corresponds to the reversal in stress from tension to compression. Hence the expression $\frac{y}{c}\sigma_{max}$ is a general expression for the normal stress on *any* infinitesimal area of the beam's section at a distance y from the neutral axis.

Since the segment of the beam shown in Fig. 5-4a must be in equilibrium, the sum of all forces in the x-direction, which is taken horizontally, must vanish, i.e., $\Sigma F_x = 0$. Therefore as the beam's segment resists only a couple, the sum (or integral) of all forces acting *on the section* of the beam must vanish. Thus

$$\underbrace{\underbrace{\int_A \left(\frac{y}{c}\sigma_{max}\right)}_{(stress)} \underbrace{dA}_{(area)} = 0}_{(force)}$$

where the subscript A of the integral indicates that the summation must be carried out over the entire cross-sectional area of the beam. At a section, however, σ_{max} and c are constants, so the integral may be rewritten as

$$\frac{\sigma_{max}}{c}\int_A y\, dA = 0$$

Since in a stressed beam neither c nor σ_{max} can be zero, it follows that $\int_A y\, dA = 0$. But by definition $\int_A y\, dA = \bar{y}A$, where $\bar{y}$ is the distance from a base line (neutral axis in the case considered) to the centroid of the area A, so $\bar{y}A = 0$. Then since A is not zero, $\bar{y}$ must be. Therefore the distance from the neutral axis to the centroid of the area must be zero, and *the neutral axis passes through the centroid of the cross-sectional area of the beam.* Hence the neutral axis may be quickly and easily determined for any beam by simply finding the centroid of the cross-sectional area.

Next, the remaining significant equation of static equilibrium will be applied to the beam segment shown in Fig. 5-4a to evaluate the magnitudes of the normal stresses. This equation is $\Sigma M_z = 0$, which for the present purpose is more conveniently stated as: *The external moment M is resisted by or equal to the internal bending moment developed by the flexural stresses at a section.* The latter quantity is determined by summing forces acting on infinitesimal areas dA, Fig. 5-4b, multiplied by their respective arms from the neutral axis. By formulating these statements mathematically, the following equality is obtained:

$$M = \int_A \underbrace{\underbrace{\left(\frac{y}{c}\sigma_{max}\right)}_{\text{(stress)}}\quad \underbrace{dA}_{\text{(area)}}}_{\text{(force)}\qquad\text{(arm)}} \qquad y = \frac{\sigma_{max}}{c}\int_A y^2\, dA$$

(moment)

where as before, σ_{max}/c is a constant, hence it appears outside the integral sign. The integration must be performed over the entire cross-sectional area A of the beam.

The integral $\int_A y^2\, dA$ depends only on the geometric properties of the cross-sectional area. In Mechanics this integral is called the *moment of inertia* of the cross-sectional area about the centroidal axis, when y is measured from such an axis. It is a definite constant for any particular area, and in this text it will be designated by I. With this notation the foregoing expression may be written more compactly as

$$M = \frac{\sigma_{max}}{c}I \qquad \text{or} \qquad \sigma_{max} = \frac{Mc}{I} \qquad (5\text{-}1)$$

Equation 5-1 is the *flexure formula** for beams. It gives the *maximum* normal stress in a beam subjected to a bending moment M. Moreover, since stress σ on any point of a cross-section is $\frac{y}{c}\sigma_{max}$, a more general form of Eq. 5-1 is

$$\sigma = \frac{My}{I} \qquad (5\text{-}1a)$$

These formulas are of unusually great importance in Mechanics of Materials and should be memorized. In these formulas, M is the internal or resisting bending moment, which is equal to the external moment at the section where the stresses are sought. It is best to express the bending moment in *inch-pound* units for use in these formulas. The distance y from the neutral axis of the beam to the point on a section where the normal stress σ is wanted is measured perpendicular to the neutral axis and should be expressed in inches. When it reaches its maximum value (measured either up or down) it corresponds to c, and as y approaches this maximum value, the normal stress σ approaches σ_{max}. In this equation I is the moment of inertia of the *whole* cross-sectional area of the beam *about its neutral axis*. To avoid confusion with the *polar* moment of inertia, I is sometimes referred to as the *rectangular* moment of inertia. It has the dimensions of inches⁴. Its evaluation for various areas will be discussed in the next article. The use of units as indicated above makes the units of stress σ, [in.-lb][in.]/[in.⁴] = [lb per in.²], or *psi*.

Inasmuch as stress is a vectorial quantity, it is often of considerable importance to determine its sense in addition to its magnitude as given by the above equations. If the *resisting* moment is positive and y is measured positive down from the neutral axis, a positive answer signifies a tensile stress on an elementary area, and vice versa. A negative resisting moment at a section, with the same sign convention for y, likewise leads to consistent results. However, it is much simpler to determine the sense of the normal stress by inspection. *The normal stresses must build up a couple statically equivalent to the resisting bending moment.* The sense of both couples must naturally coincide. By this simple expedient, the tensile zone to one side of the neutral axis of the beam is differentiated from the compression zone. This is the usual practice, and all quantities substituted into Eqs. 5-1 and 5-1a are treated as being positive.

The student is urged to reflect on the meanings of the terms used in the derived equations. The stresses given by these equations indicate that they act perpendicular to the section and vary linearly from the neutral

* It took nearly two centuries to develop this seemingly simple expression. The first attempts to solve the flexure problem were made by Galileo in the seventeenth century. In the form in which it is used today the problem was solved in the early part of the nineteenth century. Generally, Navier of France is credited for this accomplishment. However, some maintain that credit should go to Coulomb, who also derived the torsion formula.

axis. These facts are very significant. Likewise, the three-dimensional aspect of the problem must be kept in mind.

The foregoing discussion applies only to cases where the material behaves *elastically*. The important concepts used in deriving the flexure formula may be summarized as follows:

1. *Geometry* was used to establish the linear variation of strains from the neutral axis.

2. *Properties of materials* were used to relate stress to strain.

3. *Statics* was used to locate the neutral axis and to determine the internal resisting moment.

These are the *same* concepts as were used to derive the torsion formula.

5-5. Computation of the Moment of Inertia. In applying the flexure formula, the moment of inertia I of the cross-sectional area about the neutral axis must always be determined. Its value is defined by the integral of $y^2\,dA$ over the entire particular area, and it must be emphasized that for the flexure formula the moment of inertia *must be computed around the neutral axis of the cross-sectional area*. This axis, according to the previous article, is synonymous with an axis passing through the centroid of the cross-sectional area perpendicular to the axis of symmetry. Such an axis is one of the *principal axes** of the cross-sectional area. Most readers should already be familiar with the method of determining the moment of inertia I. However, the necessary procedure is reviewed below.

The first step in evaluating I for an area consists in finding the centroid of the area. An integration of $y^2\,dA$ is then performed with respect to the horizontal axis passing through the area's centroid. Actual integration over areas is necessary for only a few elementary shapes, such as rectangles, triangles, etc. After this is done, most cross-sectional areas used in practice may be broken down into a combination of these simple shapes. Values of moments of inertia for some simple shapes may be found in any standard civil or mechanical engineering handbook (also see Table 2 in Appendix). To find I for an area composed of several simple shapes, the *parallel-axis theorem* (sometimes called the *transfer formula*) is necessary, the development of which follows.

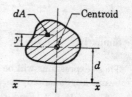

Fig. 5-5. Shaded area used in deriving the parallel-axis theorem.

The area shown in Fig. 5-5 has a moment of inertia I_o around the horizontal axis passing through its *own centroid*, i.e., $I_o = \int y^2\,dA$, where y is measured from the centroidal axis. The moment of inertia I_{xx} of the same area around another horizontal axis x-x by definition is

---

* By definition the principal axes are those about which the rectangular moment of inertia is a maximum or a minimum. *Such axes are always mutually perpendicular.* The product of inertia, defined by $\int yz\,dA$, where y has the meaning as above and z is a horizontal distance to the elementary area, vanishes for the principal axes (see Fig. 5-11). An axis of symmetry of a cross-section is always a principal axis. For further details see any book on mechanics, such as Higdon, A., and Stiles, W. B., *Engineering Mechanics*. New York: Prentice-Hall, 1949.

$$I_{xx} = \int_A (d + y)^2 \, dA$$

where as before y is measured from the axis through the centroid. Squaring the quantities in the parentheses and placing the constants outside the integral signs,

$$I_{xx} = d^2 \int_A dA + 2d \int_A y \, dA + \int_A y^2 \, dA = Ad^2 + 2d \int_A y \, dA + I_o$$

However, since the axis from which y is measured passes through the centroid of the area, $\int_A y \, dA$ or $\bar{y} A$ is zero. Hence

$$I_{xx} = I_o + Ad^2 \qquad (5\text{-}2)$$

This is the parallel-axis theorem. It can be stated as follows: The moment of inertia of an area around any axis is equal to the moment of inertia of the same area around a parallel axis passing through the area's centroid, plus the product of the same area and the square of the distance between the two axes.

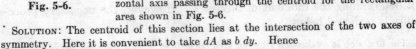

The following examples illustrate the method of computing I directly by integration for two simple areas. Then an application of the parallel-axis theorem to a composite area is given. Values of I for commercially fabricated steel beams, angles, and pipes are given in Tables 3 to 8 of the Appendix.

Example 5-1. Find the moment of inertia around the horizontal axis passing through the centroid for the rectangular area shown in Fig. 5-6.

Fig. 5-6.

SOLUTION: The centroid of this section lies at the intersection of the two axes of symmetry. Here it is convenient to take dA as $b \, dy$. Hence

$$I_{xx} = I_o = \int_A y^2 \, dA = \int_{-h/2}^{+h/2} y^2 b \, dy = b \left| \frac{y^3}{3} \right|_{-h/2}^{+h/2} = \frac{bh^3}{12} \qquad (5\text{-}3)$$

Similarly, $I_{yy} = \dfrac{b^3 h}{12}$

These expressions will be employed frequently, as rectangular beams are commonly used in practice.

Example 5-2. Find the moment of inertia about a diameter for a circular area of radius c, Fig. 5-7.

SOLUTION: Since there is some chance of confusing I with J for a circular section, it is well to refer to I as the *rectangular* moment of inertia of the area in this case.

To find I for a circle, first note that $\rho^2 = x^2 + y^2$, as may be seen from the figure. Then using the definition of J, noting the symmetry around both axes, and using Eq. 3-2,

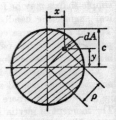

Fig. 5-7.

$$J = \int_A \rho^2 \, dA = \int_A (x^2 + y^2) \, dA = \int_A x^2 \, dA + \int_A y^2 \, dA$$

$$= I_{yy} + I_{xx} = 2I_{xx}$$

$$I_{xx} = I_{yy} = \tfrac{1}{2} J = \tfrac{1}{4} \pi c^4 \qquad (5\text{-}4)$$

In mechanical applications circular shafts often act as beams, hence Eq. 5-4 will be found useful.   For a tubular shaft, the moment of inertia of the hollow interior must be subtracted from the above expression.

Example 5-3. Determine the moment of inertia I around the horizontal axis for the area shown in Fig. 5-8, for use in the flexure formula.

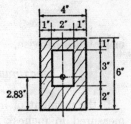

Fig. 5-8.

SOLUTION: As the moment of inertia wanted is for use in the flexure formula, it must be obtained around the axis through the centroid of the area.   Hence the centroid of the area must be found first.   This is most easily done by treating the entire outer section and deducting from it the hollow interior.   For convenience, the work is carried out in tabular form.   Then the parallel-axis theorem is used to obtain I.

Part of area	A [in.^{2}]	y [in.] (from bottom)	Ay
Entire area	$4(6) = 24$	3	72
Hollow interior	$-2(3) = -6$	3.5	-21
	$\Sigma A = 18$ in.^{2}		$\Sigma Ay = 51$ in.^{3}

$$y = \frac{\Sigma Ay}{\Sigma A} = \frac{51}{18} = 2.83 \text{ in. from bottom}$$

For entire area:

$$I_o = \frac{bh^3}{12} = \frac{4(6)^3}{12} \quad = 72.00 \text{ in.}^4$$

$$Ad^2 = 24(3.00 - 2.83)^2 = \underline{0.69 \text{ in.}^4}$$

$$I_{xx} = 72.69 \text{ in.}^4$$

For hollow interior:

$$I_o = \frac{bh^3}{12} = \frac{2(3)^3}{12} \quad = 4.50 \text{ in.}^4$$

$$Ad^2 = 6(3.50 - 2.83)^2 = \underline{2.69 \text{ in.}^4}$$

$$I_{xx} = 7.19 \text{ in.}^4$$

For composite section: $I_{xx} = 72.69 - 7.19 = 65.50$ in.^{4}

Note particularly that in applying the parallel-axis theorem, *each element* of the composite area contributes *two* terms to the total I.   One term is the moment of inertia of an area around its *own* centroidal axis, the other term is due to the transfer of its axis to the centroid of the whole area.   Methodical work is the prime requisite in solving such problems correctly.

5-6. Remarks on the Flexure Formula. The bending stress at any point of a beam's section is given by Eq. 5-1a, $\sigma = My/I$.   The maximum stress at the same section follows from this relation by making y a maximum, which leads to Eq. 5-1, $\sigma_{max} = Mc/I$.   In most practical problems the maximum stress given by Eq. 5-1 is the quantity sought; thus it is desirable to make the process of determining σ_{max} as simple as possible. This can be accomplished by noting that both I and c are constants for a given section of a beam.   Hence I/c is a constant.   Moreover, since this ratio is only a function of the cross-sectional dimensions of a beam's section, it can be uniquely determined for any cross-sectional area.   This ratio is called the *section modulus* of a section and will be designated* by Z. With this notation Eq. 5-1 becomes

$$\sigma_{max} = \frac{Mc}{I} = \frac{M}{I/c} = \frac{M}{Z} \qquad (5\text{-}5)$$

or stated otherwise,

$$maximum\ bending\ stress = \frac{bending\ moment}{section\ modulus}$$

If the moment of inertia I is measured in inches[4] and c in inches, Z is measured in inches[3]. Likewise, if M is measured in inch-pounds, the units of stress, as before, become pounds per square inch. It bears repeating that the distance c as used here is measured from the neutral axis to the *most remote fiber* of the beam. This makes $I/c = Z$ a minimum, and consequently M/Z gives the maximum stress. The efficient sections for resisting bending have as large a Z as possible for a given amount of material. This is accomplished by locating as much of the material as possible far from the neutral axis.

The use of the section modulus term in Eq. 5-5 somewhat corresponds to the use of the area term A in Eq. 1-1 ($\sigma = P/A$). However, only the *maximum* flexural stress on a section is obtained from Eq. 5-5, while the stress computed from Eq. 1-1 holds true across the whole section of a member.

Equation 5-5 is widely used in practice because of its simplicity. To facilitate its use, section moduli for rolled cross-sections are tabulated in handbooks. Values for a few sections are given in Tables 3 to 8 in the Appendix. Equation 5-5 is particularly convenient for the design of beams. Once the maximum bending moment for a beam is determined, and an allowable stress is decided upon, Eq. 5-5 may be solved for the required section modulus. This information is sufficient to select a beam. However, a detailed consideration of beam design will be delayed until Chapter 10. This is necessary inasmuch as a shearing force, which in turn causes stresses, usually also acts at a beam's section. The interaction of the various kinds of stresses must first be considered to gain a complete picture of the problem.

Although the use of the flexure formula is limited to the *elastic* case, it is customary for laboratories to report the ratio of the *ultimate* bending moment resisted by a beam to the section modulus of the beam's section. This ratio gives the *nominal* maximum fiber stress reached in a beam. It is not the true stress. This ratio is called the *rupture modulus* of the material in bending. As will be explained in Art. 5-9, this stress always exceeds the true stress that has been reached in the material at the time of failure.

* Many handbooks designate the section modulus by S.

The application of the flexure formulas to particular problems should cause little difficulty, if the meaning of the various terms occurring in them has been thoroughly understood. The following two examples illustrate investigations of bending stresses at specific sections.

Example 5-4. A 12 in. by 16 in. (full-sized) wooden cantilever beam weighing 50 lb per ft carries an upward concentrated force of 4,000 lb at the end, as shown in Fig. 5-9a. Determine the maximum bending stresses at a section 6 ft from the free end.

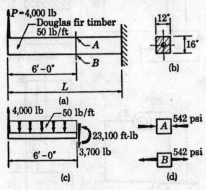

Fig. 5-9.

SOLUTION: A free-body diagram for a 6 ft segment of the beam is shown in Fig. 5-9c. To keep this segment in equilibrium requires a shear of $4,000 - 50(6) = 3,700$ lb and a bending moment of $4,000(6) - 50(6)3 = 23,100$ ft-lb at the cut section. Both of these quantities are shown with their proper sense in Fig. 5-9c. By inspecting the cross-sectional area, the distance from the neutral axis to the extreme fibers is seen to be 8 in., hence $c = 8$ in. This is applicable to both the tension and compression fibers.

From Eq. 5-3: $I_{zz} = \dfrac{bh^3}{12} = \dfrac{12(16)^3}{12} = 4,095$ in.^{4}

From Eq. 5-1: $\sigma_{max} = \dfrac{Mc}{I} = \dfrac{23,100(12)8}{4,095} = \pm 542$ psi

From the sense of the bending moment shown in Fig. 5-9c the top fibers of the beam are seen to be in compression, while the bottom ones are in tension. In the answer given, the positive sign applies to the tensile stress, the negative sign applies to the compressive stress. Both of these stresses decrease at a linear rate toward the neutral axis where the bending stress is zero. The normal stresses acting on infinitesimal elements at A and B are shown in Fig. 5-9d. It is important to learn to make such a representation of an element as it will be frequently used in Chapters 7, 8, and 9.

ALTERNATE SOLUTION: If only the maximum stress is desired, the equation involving the section modulus may be used. The section modulus for a rectangular section in algebraic form is

$$Z = \frac{I}{c} = \frac{bh^3}{12}\frac{2}{h} = \frac{bh^2}{6} \tag{5-6}$$

In this problem, $Z = (\tfrac{1}{6})12(16)^2 = 512$ in.^{3}, and by Eq. 5-5

$$\sigma_{max} = \frac{M}{Z} = \frac{23,100(12)}{512} = 542 \text{ psi}$$

In either solution, do not fail to notice that the bending moment substituted into the equations has the units of inch-pounds.

Example 5-5. Find the maximum tensile and compressive stresses normal to the section A-A of the machine bracket shown in Fig. 5-10a caused by the applied force of 8 kips.

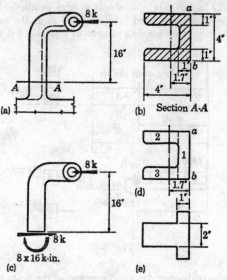

Fig. 5-10.

SOLUTION: The shear and bending moment of proper magnitude and sense to maintain the segment of the member in equilibrium are shown in Fig. 5-10c. Next the neutral axis of the beam must be located. This is done by locating the centroid of the area shown in Fig. 5-10b (also see Fig. 5-10d). Then the moment of inertia about the neutral axis is computed. In both of these calculations the legs of the cross-section are assumed rectangular, neglecting fillets. Finally, keeping in mind the sense of the resisting bending moment and applying Eq. 5-1, the desired values are obtained.

Area number	A [in.²]	y [in.] (from ab)	Ay
1	4.0	0.5	2.0
2	3.0	2.5	7.5
3	3.0	2.5	7.5
	$\Sigma A = 10.0$ in.²		$\Sigma Ay = 17.0$ in.³

$$y = \frac{\Sigma Ay}{\Sigma A} = \frac{17.0}{10.0} = 1.70 \text{ in. from the line } ab$$

$$I = \Sigma(I_o + Ad^2) = \frac{4(1)^3}{12} + 4(1.2)^2 + \frac{(2)1(3)^3}{12} + 2(3)(0.8)^2$$

$$= 14.43 \text{ in.}^4$$

$$\sigma_{max} = \frac{Mc}{I} = \frac{(8)16(2.3)}{14.43} = 20.4 \text{ ksi} \qquad \text{(compression)}$$

$$\sigma_{max} = \frac{Mc}{I} = \frac{(8)16(1.7)}{14.43} = 15.1 \text{ ksi} \quad \text{(tension)}$$

These stresses vary linearly toward the neutral axis and vanish there. If for the same bracket the direction of the force P were reversed, the sense of the above stresses would also reverse. The results obtained would be the same if the cross-sectional area of the bracket were made T-shaped as shown in Fig. 5-10e. The properties of this section about the significant axis are the same as those of the channel. Both of these sections have an axis of symmetry.

The above example shows that members resisting flexure may be proportioned so as to have a different maximum stress in tension than in compression. This is significant for materials having different strengths in tension and compression. For example, cast iron is strong in compression and weak in tension. Thus, the proportions of a cast-iron member may be so set as to have a low maximum tensile stress. The potential capacity of the material may thus be better utilized. This matter will be further considered in the chapter on the design of beams.

*5-7. Pure Bending of Beams with Unsymmetrical Section. Pure bending of elastic beams having an axis of symmetry was discussed in the preceding articles. The applied moments were assumed to act in the plane of symmetry. These limitations, while expedient in developing the flexural theory, are too severe and may be partly relaxed. The same formulas can be used for any beam in *pure* bending, provided the bending moments are applied in a plane parallel to *either principal axis* of the cross-sectional area. The previous derivation could be repeated identically. Stresses vary linearly from the neutral axis passing through the centroid. As

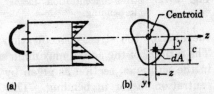

Fig. 5-11. A beam with an unsymmetrical cross-sectional area.

before, the stress on any elementary area dA, Fig. 5-11, is $\frac{y}{c}\sigma_{max}$. Hence $\frac{y}{c}\sigma_{max}\,dA$ is a force on an element. The sum of the moments of these internal forces around the z-axis develops the internal moment. However, as symmetry is lacking, these internal forces *may* build up a moment around the y-axis. This must be reconciled.

The arms of forces acting on infinitesimal areas around the y-axis are equal to z. Thus a possible moment M_y around the y-axis is

$$M_y = \int_A \frac{y}{c}\sigma_{max}\,dA\,z = \frac{\sigma_{max}}{c}\int_A yz\,dA$$

The last integral represents the product of inertia of the cross-sectional area. It is equal to zero if the axes selected are the *principal axes* of the area. Since these axes are used here, $M_y = 0$, and thus the usual formulas do apply to a beam with any shape of cross-section.

If a pure bending moment is applied without being parallel to either principal axis, the techniques discussed in Chapter 7 must be followed.

*5-8. Stress Concentrations. The flexure theory developed in the preceding articles applies only to beams of constant cross-sectional area. Such beams may be referred to as *prismatic* beams. If the cross-sectional area of the beam varies gradually, no significant deviation from the stress pattern discussed earlier takes place. However, if notches, grooves, rivet holes, or an abrupt change in the cross-sectional area of the beam occur, high *local* stresses arise. This situation is analogous to the ones discussed earlier for axial and torsion members.

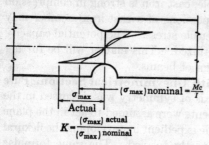

$(\sigma_{max})\text{nominal} = \dfrac{Mc}{I}$

σ_{max}

Actual

$$K = \frac{(\sigma_{max})\text{ actual}}{(\sigma_{max})\text{ nominal}}$$

Fig. 5-12. Stress-concentration factor in bending.

Again it is very difficult to obtain analytical expressions for the actual stress. Most of the information regarding the actual stress distribution comes from accurate photoelastic experiments.

Fortunately, as in the other cases discussed, only the geometric proportions of the member affect the local stress pattern. Moreover, since interest is in the maximum stress, the idea of the stress-concentration factor may be used to advantage. The ratio K of the actual maximum stress to the nominal maximum stress in the *minimum* section as given by Eq. 5-1 is defined as the stress-concentration factor in bending. This concept is illustrated in Fig. 5-12. Hence, in general,

$$(\sigma_{max})_{\text{actual}} = K\,\frac{Mc}{I} \tag{5-7}$$

Figures 5-13 and 5-14 are plots of stress-concentration factors for two representative cases.* The factor K, depending on the proportions of the member, may be obtained from these diagrams. A study of these graphs indicates the desirability of generous fillets and the elimination of sharp notches to reduce local stress concentrations. These remedies are highly desirable in machine design. In structural work, particularly where ductile materials are used and the applied forces are not fluctuating, stress concentrations are ignored.

If the cross-sectional area of a beam is irregular itself, stress concentrations also occur. This becomes particularly significant if the cross-sectional area has re-entrant angles. For example, high localized stresses

---

* These figures are reproduced from a paper by Frocht, M. M., "Factors of Stress Concentration Photoelastically Determined," *Trans. ASME*, 1935, vol. 57, p. A-67.

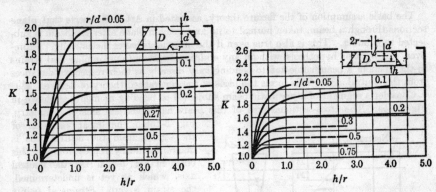

Fig. 5-13. Stress-concentration factors in pure bending for flat bars with various fillets.

Fig. 5-14. Stress-concentration factors in bending for grooved flat bars.

occur at the point where the flange* and the web of an I-beam meet. To minimize these, commercially rolled shapes have a generous fillet at all such points.

In addition to stress concentrations caused by changes in the cross-sectional area of a beam, another effect is significant. Forces often are applied over a limited area of a beam. Moreover, the reactions act only locally on a beam at the points of support. In the previous treatment, all such forces were idealized as concentrated forces. In practice the average bearing pressure between the member delivering such a force and the beam are computed at the point of contact of such forces with the beam. This bearing pressure or stress acts normal to the neutral surface of a beam and is at *right angles to the bending stresses discussed in this chapter.* A more detailed study of the effect of such forces shows that they cause a disturbance of all stresses on a local scale, and the bearing pressure as normally computed is a crude approximation. The stresses at right angles to the flexural stresses behave more nearly as shown in Fig. 2-16. An investigation of the disturbance caused in the bending-stress distribution by the bearing stresses is beyond the scope of this book.†

The reader must remember that the stress-concentration factors apply only while the material behaves elastically.

*5-9. Inelastic Bending of Beams. The flexure formula derived earlier is valid only while stress is proportional to strain. This is known to be true only in the elastic range. A more general theory will now be discussed where the material does not follow Hooke's law.

* The *web* is a thin vertical part of a beam. Thin horizontal parts of a beam are called *flanges.*

† By virtue of St. Venant's principle (Art. 2-11), at distances away from the concentrated forces comparable with the cross-sectional dimensions of a member, the formulas developed in this text are accurate, but the usual formulas are not applicable for short, stubby beams such as gear teeth.

The basic assumption of the flexure theory, as stated in Art. 5-3, asserts that plane sections through a beam, taken normal to its axis, remain plane after the beam is subjected to bending. This is also true even if the material behaves inelastically. Moreover, this working hypothesis, without any additional assumptions, implies that strains in the fibers of a beam subjected to bending vary directly as their respective distances from the neutral axis. This forms the basis of the generalized theory of flexure.

Consider a segment of a prismatic beam subjected to bending moments as shown in Fig. 5-15a. The cross-sectional area of this beam has a vertical axis of symmetry,

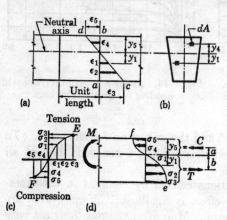

(a)   (b)

(c)   (d)

Fig. 5-15. Inelastic bending of a beam.

Fig. 5-15b. The linear variation of the strains from the neutral axis is diagrammatically represented on this beam in Fig. 5-15a. At the neutral axis, which as yet is undetermined, the strain is zero. Strains at points away from the neutral axis correspond to the horizontal distance from the line ab to cd. For example, the strain of a fiber at a distance y_1 from the neutral axis is ϵ_1. These distances give the axial strain of every fiber in a beam.

Next, attention will be directed to a general stress-strain curve. To make the argument general, the material will be assumed to have a different stress-strain curve in tension and compression. A possible curve for a material is shown in Fig. 5-15c. Such curves may always be constructed on the basis of data from axial loading tests.

If the Poisson effect is neglected, the longitudinal fibers or "filaments" of a beam in bending behave independently. Each one of these may be thought of as an infinitesimal axially loaded rod, stressed to a level dependent upon its strain. Since the variation of the strain in a beam is set by the assumption, the stress pattern may be formulated from the stress-strain curve, Fig. 5-15c. Corresponding to the tensile* strain ϵ_1, at a distance y_1 from the neutral axis, a tensile stress σ_1 acts in the beam. Similarly, ϵ_4 is associated with σ_4, a compressive stress. The same thing applies to any other fiber of the beam. This determines the stress distribution shown in Fig. 5-15d, which resembles the shape of the stress-strain curve (compare EF with ef by turning it clockwise through 90°).

Since the beam acts in pure bending, the same equations of statics will be used here as were used in establishing the elastic flexure formula. Thus two relations follow (see Art. 5-4):

$$\Sigma F_x = 0 \quad \text{or} \quad \int_A \sigma \, dA = 0 \tag{5-8}$$

$$\Sigma M_z = 0 \quad \text{or} \quad \int_A \sigma \, y \, dA = M \tag{5-9}$$

where σ is a normal stress acting on an infinitesimal element dA of the cross-sectional area A of the beam, and y is the distance from the neutral axis to an element dA. In the last expression the external bending moment M is equated to the internal resisting moment.

* This is judged by the sense of the resisting bending moment.

The solution of the most general problem in inelastic bending, i.e., the satisfaction of the equilibrium Eqs. 5-8 and 5-9, requires a trial-and-error procedure. Initially the location of the neutral axis is unknown. A possible method consists of assuming a strain distribution, thus locating a trial neutral axis and giving the stress distribution shown in Fig. 5-15d. Such trials must be continued until the sum of the forces C on the compression side of the beam is equal to the sum of the forces T on the tension side of the beam. When such a condition is fulfilled, the neutral axis of the beam is located. Note particularly that *in inelastic flexure the neutral axis of a beam may not coincide with the centroidal axis of the cross-sectional area.* It does so only if the cross-sectional area has two axes of symmetry and the stress-strain diagram is identical in tension and compression.

After the neutral axis is located and the magnitudes of C and T are known, their line of action may be determined. This is possible since the stress distribution on the cross-sectional area is known. Finally, the resisting moment is $T(a + b)$ or $C(a + b)$. The foregoing process is equivalent to the integration indicated in Eq. 5-9. However, the resisting moment so computed, based upon *assumed* strains, may not be equal to the applied moment. Hence, the process must be repeated by initially assuming

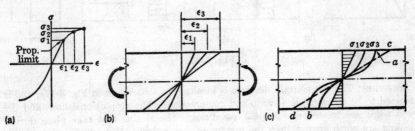

Fig. 5-16. Rectangular beam in bending exceeding the proportional limit of the material.

greater or smaller strain at the extreme fibers until the resisting moment becomes equal to the applied moment.

The foregoing method of solving a general problem is tedious, and accelerated techniques for arriving at a solution have been developed.* However, the above discussion should be sufficient to give a visual picture of the behavior of a beam in flexure beyond the elastic limit. As a simple example, consider a beam of rectangular cross-section subjected to bending. Let the stress-strain diagram of the beam's material be *alike* in tension and compression as shown in Fig. 5-16. Then, as progressively increasing bending moments are applied to the beam, the strains will increase as exemplified by ϵ_1, ϵ_2, and ϵ_3 in Fig. 5-16b. Corresponding to these strains and their linear variation from the neutral axis, the stress distribution will look as shown in Fig. 5-16c. The neutral axis coincides with the centroidal axis in this case, as the section has two axes of symmetry and the stress-strain diagram is alike in tension and compression.

If σ_3 corresponds to the ultimate strength of the material in axial tension, the ultimate bending moment which the beam is capable of resisting may be predicted. It is associated with the stress distribution given by the curved line ab shown in Fig. 5-16c. An equivalent resistance to the bending moment based on the assumption of linear stress distribution from the neutral axis is shown by the line cd in Fig. 5-16c. Since both of these stress distributions supposedly resist the *same* moment, and in the latter

* Nadai, A., *Theory of Flow and Fracture of Solids*, vol. I. New York: McGraw-Hill, 1950

case lower stresses act near the neutral axis, higher stresses must act near the outer fibers. The stress in the extreme fibers, computed on the basis of the *elastic* flexure formula for the experimentally determined ultimate bending moment, is the *rupture modulus* of the material in bending (see Art. 5-6). That it is higher than the true stress may now be understood. For materials whose stress-strain diagrams approach a straight line all the way up to the ultimate strength, the discrepancy between the true maximum stress and the rupture modulus is small. On the other hand, the discrepancy is very large for materials with a pronounced curvature in the stress-strain curve. Mild steel is one of the materials belonging to the latter group.

Example 5-6. Determine the ultimate capacity in flexure of a mild steel beam of rectangular cross-section.

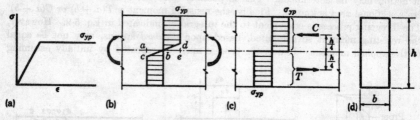

Fig. 5-17.

SOLUTION: The stress-strain diagram is idealized to that shown in Fig. 5-17a, and is assumed to be the same in tension and compression. The proportional limit and the yield point are treated as identical quantities. The strains that take place during yielding are much greater than the maximum *elastic* strain (15 to 20 times the latter quantity). Moreover, the deformations that would take place beyond the yield "plateau" would make the beam deform so severely that they would not be tolerated in any engineering structure. Hence the diagram as shown in Fig. 5-17a will be accepted as a *complete* diagram for the purpose of determining the ultimate capacity of the beam.

The stress distribution shown in Fig. 5-17b applies after a large amount of deformation takes place. In computing the resisting moment the stresses corresponding to the triangular areas *abc* and *bde* may be neglected without unduly impairing the accuracy. They contribute little resistance to the applied bending moment, owing to their short moment arms. Hence the idealization of the stress distribution to that shown in Fig. 5-17c is permissible and has a simple physical meaning. The whole upper half of the beam is subjected to a uniform compressive stress σ_{yp}, while the lower half is all under a uniform tension σ_{yp}. That the beam is divided *evenly* into a tension and a compression zone follows from symmetry. Numerically,

$$C = T = \sigma_{yp}\,\frac{bh}{2} \quad \text{i.e., (stress)} \times \text{(area)}$$

Each one of these forces acts at a distance $h/4$ from the neutral axis. Hence the ultimate resisting moment of the beam is

$$M_{\text{ult}} = C\left(\frac{h}{4} + \frac{h}{4}\right) = \sigma_{yp}\,\frac{bh^2}{4}$$

where b is the breadth of the beam and h is its height.

The same solution may be obtained by directly applying Eqs. 5-8 and 5-9. Noting the sign of stresses, it is found that Eq. 5-8 is satisfied by taking the neutral axis through the middle of the beam. By taking $dA = b\,dy$, Eq. 5-9 becomes

$$M_{\text{ult}} = \int_{-h/2}^{+h/2} \sigma_{\text{yp}}\, yb\, dy = b\sigma_{\text{yp}} \left.\frac{y^2}{2}\right|_{-h/2}^{+h/2} = \sigma_{\text{yp}} \frac{bh^2}{4}$$

The resisting bending moment of a beam of rectangular section when the outer fibers just reach σ_{yp}, as given by the elastic flexure formula, is

$$M_{\text{yp}} = \sigma_{\text{yp}} \frac{I}{c} = \sigma_{\text{yp}} \frac{bh^2}{6}$$

It is seen from this expression that M_{yp} may be exceeded by 50% before the ultimate capacity of a rectangular beam is reached. There is much agitation* to adopt the method of ultimate capacity calculations for the design of beams. This method is called the *limit design* of members. It is reasonably satisfactory for beams which carry a steady load, as in buildings. It is unacceptable for the design of machine parts, where fatigue properties of the material are important.

*5-10. Beams of Two Materials. So far, the beams analyzed were assumed to be of one homogeneous material. Important uses of beams made of several different materials occur in practice. Beams of two materials are especially common. Wooden beams are often reinforced by metal straps, and concrete beams are reinforced with steel rods. The fundamental theory underlying the analysis of such beams in the *elastic* range will be discussed in this article.

Consider a symmetrical beam of two materials with a cross-section as shown in Fig. 5-18a. The outer material 1 has an elastic modulus E_1, and the modulus of the inner material 2 is E_2. If such a beam is subjected to bending, the assumption repeatedly used in the flexure theory is again valid. Plane sections at right angles to the axis of a beam remain plane. Therefore the strains must vary linearly from the neutral axis, as shown in Fig. 5-18b. Then since the *elastic* case is considered, stress is proportional to strain, and the stress distribution, assuming $E_1 > E_2$, is as shown in Fig. 5-18c. Note particularly that at the surfaces of contact of the two materials a break in the intensity of stress is indicated. Although the strain in both materials at such surfaces is equal, a greater stress exists in the stiffer material. The stiffness of a material is measured by the elastic modulus E. The foregoing information is sufficient to solve any beam problem of two (or more) materials by using a trial and error solution similar to the one discussed in the previous article. However, a considerable simplification over the former procedure is possible. In formally applying $\Sigma F_x = 0$ to locate the neutral axis and $\Sigma M_z = 0$ to obtain the resisting moment, only the correct magnitudes and locations of the resisting *forces* (not stresses) are significant. The new technique consists of constructing a section of *one* material on which the *resisting forces* are the same as on the original section. Such a section is termed an

* Van den Broek, J. A., *Theory of Limit Design*. New York: Wiley, 1948.

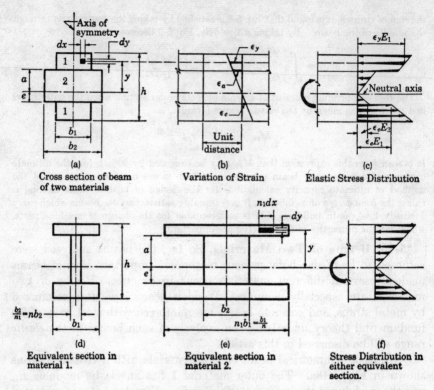

Fig. 5-18. Beam of two materials.

equivalent or *transformed cross-sectional area*. After a beam of several materials is reduced to an equivalent beam of one material, the usual elastic flexure formula applies.

The transformation of a section is accomplished by changing the dimensions *perpendicular to the axis of symmetry* of the various materials in the ratio of their elastic moduli. For example, if the equivalent section is wanted in material 1, the dimensions corresponding to material 1 do not change. The horizontal dimensions of material 2 are changed by a ratio n, where $n = E_2/E_1$, Fig. 5-18d. On the other hand, if the transformed section is to be of material 2, the horizontal dimension of the other material is changed by a ratio $n_1 = E_1/E_2$, Fig. 5-18e. The ratio n_1 is the reciprocal of n.

The legitimacy of transforming sections is seen by comparing the forces acting on the original and on the equivalent sections. The force from a known strain ϵ_y acting on an elementary area $dx\,dy$ in Fig. 5-18a is $\epsilon_y E_1\,dx\,dy$. The same element of area in Fig. 5-18e is $n_1\,dx\,dy$. The force acting on it is $\epsilon_y E_2 n_1\,dx\,dy$. However, from the definition of n_1, $E_1 = n_1 E_2$. So the forces acting on both elements are the same, and both, by virtue of their location, contribute equally to the resisting moment.

In a beam with a transformed area, strains and stresses vary linearly from its neutral axis. The stresses calculated in the usual manner are correct for the material *of which the transformed section is made*. For the other material the computed stress must be multiplied by the ratio n or n_1 of the transformed to the actual area. For example, the force acting on $n_1\, dx\, dy$ in Fig. 5-18e *actually acts* on $dx\, dy$ of the real material.

Example 5-7. Consider a composite beam of the cross-sectional dimensions shown in Fig. 5-19a. The upper 6 in. by 10 in. (full sized) part is wood, $E_w = 1.5 \times 10^6$ psi; the bottom $\frac{1}{2}$ in. by 6 in. strap is steel, $E_s = 30 \times 10^6$ psi. If this beam is subjected to a bending moment of 20,000 ft-lb around a horizontal axis, what are the maximum stresses in the steel and wood?

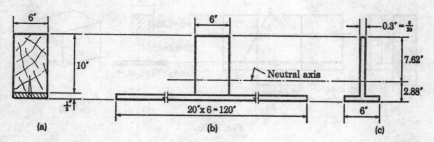

Fig. 5-19.

SOLUTION: The ratio of the elastic moduli $E_s/E_w = 20$. Hence, using a transformed section of wood, the width of the bottom strip is $6(20) = 120$ in. The transformed area is shown in Fig. 5-19b. Its centroid and moment of inertia around the centroidal axis are

$$y = \frac{6(10)5 + (0.5)120(10.25)}{6(10) + (0.5)120} = 7.62 \text{ in. from the } top$$

$$I_{zz} = \frac{6(10)^3}{12} + (6)10(2.62)^2 + \frac{120(0.5)^3}{12} + (0.5)120(2.63)^2 = 1,328 \text{ in.}^4$$

The maximum stress in the wood is

$$(\sigma_w)_{max} = \frac{Mc}{I} = \frac{(20,000)12(7.62)}{1,328} = 1,380 \text{ psi}$$

The maximum stress in the steel is

$$(\sigma_s)_{max} = n\sigma_w = 20\,\frac{(20,000)12(2.88)}{1,328} = 10,400 \text{ psi}$$

ALTERNATE SOLUTION: A transformed area in terms of steel may be used instead. Then the equivalent width of wood is $b/n = 6/20$, or 0.3 in. This transformed area is shown in Fig. 5-19c.

$$y = \frac{(0.3)10(5.5) + 6(0.5)(0.25)}{(0.3)10 + 6(0.5)} = 2.88 \text{ in. from the } bottom$$

$$I_{zz} = \frac{(0.3)10^3}{12} + (0.3)10(2.62)^2 + \frac{6(0.5)^3}{12} + (0.5)6(2.63)^2 = 66.5 \text{ in.}^4$$

$$(\sigma_s)_{max} = \frac{(20,000)12(2.88)}{66.5} = 10,400 \text{ psi}$$

$$(\sigma_w)_{max} = \frac{\sigma_s}{n} = \left(\frac{1}{20}\right)\frac{(20,000)12(7.62)}{66.5} = 1,380 \text{ psi}$$

Note that if the transformed section is an equivalent wooden section, the stresses in the actual wooden piece are obtained directly. Conversely, if the equivalent section is steel, stresses in steel are obtained directly. The stress in a material stiffer than the material of the transformed section is increased, since to cause the same unit strain a higher stress is required.

Example 5-8. Determine the maximum stress in the concrete and steel for a reinforced-concrete beam with the section shown in Fig. 5-20a if it is subjected to a *positive* bending moment of 50,000 ft-lb. Assume the ratio of E for steel to that of concrete to be 15, i.e., $n = 15$.

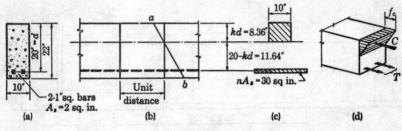

Fig. 5-20.

SOLUTION: Plane sections are assumed to remain plane in a reinforced-concrete beam. Strains vary linearly from the neutral axis as shown in Fig. 5-20b by the line ab. A transformed section in terms of concrete is used to solve this problem. However, concrete is so *weak* in tension that there is no assurance that minute cracks will not occur in the tension zone of the beam. *For this reason no credit is given to concrete for resisting tension.* On the basis of this assumption, concrete in the tension zone of a beam "only holds the reinforcing steel in place." * Hence in this analysis it virtually "does not exist at all," and the transformed section assumes the form shown in Fig. 5-20c. The cross-section of concrete has its own true shape above the neutral axis; below it no concrete is shown. Steel, of course, can resist tension, so it *is* shown as the transformed concrete area. For computation purposes, the steel is located by a single dimension from the neutral axis to its centroid. There is a negligible difference between this distance and the true distances to the various steel fibers. The crude placement of rods on the job concurs with this practice.

So far the idea of the neutral axis has been used, but its location is unknown. However, it is known that this axis coincides with the axis through the centroid of the trans-formed section. It is further known that the first (or statical) moment of the area on one side of a centroidal axis is equal to the first moment of the area on the other side. Thus, let kd be the distance from the top of the beam to the centroidal axis as shown in Fig. 5-20c, where k is an unknown ratio† and d is the distance from the top of the beam to the center of the steel. An algebraic restatement of the foregoing locates the neutral axis, about which I is computed and stresses are determined as in the preceding example.

* Actually it is used to resist shear and provide fireproofing for the steel.

† This conforms with the usual notation used in books on reinforced concrete. In this text h is generally used to represent the height or depth of the beam.

$$\underbrace{10(kd)}_{\substack{\text{concrete}\\\text{area}}} \quad \underbrace{\left(\frac{kd}{2}\right)}_{\text{arm}} \quad = \quad \underbrace{30}_{\substack{\text{transformed}\\\text{steel area}}} \quad \underbrace{(20 - kd)}_{\text{arm}}$$

$$5(kd)^2 = 600 - 30(kd)$$

$$(kd)^2 + 6(kd) - 120 = 0$$

Hence: $kd = 8.36$ in., and $20 - kd = 11.64$ in.

$$I = \frac{10(8.36)^3}{12} + 10(8.36)\left(\frac{8.36}{2}\right)^2 + 0 + 30(11.64)^2 = 6{,}020 \text{ in.}^4$$

$$(\sigma_c)_{\max} = \frac{Mc}{I} = \frac{(50{,}000)12(8.36)}{6{,}020} = 833 \text{ psi}$$

$$\sigma_s = n\frac{Mc}{I} = \frac{15(50{,}000)12(11.64)}{6{,}020} = 17{,}400 \text{ psi}$$

ALTERNATE SOLUTION: *After kd* is determined, instead of computing *I*, a procedure evident from Fig. 5-20d may be used. The resultant force developed by the stresses acting in a "hydrostatic" manner on the compression side of the beam must be located $\frac{1}{3} kd$ below the top of the beam. Moreover, if *b* is the width of the beam, this resultant force $C = \frac{1}{2} b(kd)(\sigma_c)_{\max}$, (*average* stress times area). The resultant tensile force *T* acts at the center of the steel and is equal to $A_s\sigma_s$, where A_s is the cross-sectional area of the steel. Then if *jd* is the distance between *T* and *C*, and since $T = C$, the applied moment *M* is resisted by a couple equal to *Tjd* or *Cjd*.

$$jd = d - \frac{1}{3}kd = 20 - \frac{8.36}{3} = 17.21 \text{ in.}$$

$$M = Cjd = \frac{1}{2} b(kd)(\sigma_c)_{\max}(jd)$$

$$(\sigma_c)_{\max} = \frac{2M}{b(kd)(jd)} = \frac{2(50{,}000)12}{10(8.36)(17.21)} = 833 \text{ psi}$$

$$M = T(jd) = A_s\sigma_s jd$$

$$\sigma_s = \frac{M}{A_s(jd)} = \frac{(50{,}000)12}{2(17.21)} = 17{,}400 \text{ psi}$$

Both methods naturally give the same answer. The second method is more convenient in practical applications. Since steel and concrete have different allowable stresses, the beam is said to have *balanced reinforcement* when it is designed so that the respective stresses are at their allowable level simultaneously. Finally, it must be noted that the above analyses are based on the elastic behavior of materials. The applicability of Hooke's law to concrete over a considerable range is questionable. Note that the beam shown would become virtually worthless if the bending moments were applied in the opposite direction.

*5-11. Curved Beams. The flexure theory for curved bars is developed in this article. Attention is confined to beams having an axis of symmetry of the cross-section, with this axis lying in one plane along the length of the beam. Only the elastic case is treated, with the usual proviso that the elastic modulus is the same in tension and compression.

Consider a curved member such as shown in Figs. 5-21a and b. The outer fibers are at a distance of r_o from the center of curvature O. The inner fibers are at a distance of r_i. The distance from O to the centroidal axis is $\bar{r}$. The solution* of this problem is again based on the familiar assumption: Sections perpendicular to the axis of the beam remain plane after a bending moment M is applied. This is diagrammatically represented by the line ef in relation to an element of the beam $abcd$. The element is defined by the central angle ϕ.

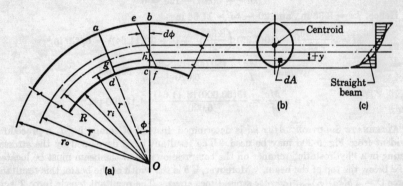

Fig. 5-21. Curved bar in pure bending.

Although the basic assumption is the same as for straight beams, and, from Hooke's law, the normal stress $\sigma = E\epsilon$, a difficulty is encountered. The initial length of a beam fiber such as gh depends upon the distance r from the center of curvature. Thus, although the total deformation of beam fibers (described by the small angle $d\phi$) follows a linear law, *strains* do not. The elongation of an arbitrary fiber gh is $(R - r)\,d\phi$, where R is the distance from O to the *neutral surface* (not yet known), while its initial length is $r\phi$. The *strain* ϵ of any arbitrary fiber is $\dfrac{(R - r)\,d\phi}{r\phi}$, and the normal stress σ on an element dA of the cross-sectional area is

$$\sigma = E\epsilon = E\,\frac{(R - r)\,d\phi}{r\phi} \tag{5-10}$$

For future use note also that

$$\frac{\sigma r}{R - r} = \frac{E\,d\phi}{\phi} \tag{5-10a}$$

Equation 5-10 gives the *normal* stress acting on an element of area of the cross-section of a curved beam. The location of the neutral axis follows from the condition that the summation of the forces acting *perpendicular* to the section must be equal to zero, i.e.,

$$\Sigma F_n = 0, \qquad \int_A \sigma\,dA = \int_A \frac{E(R - r)\,d\phi}{r\phi}\,dA = 0$$

---

* This approximate solution was developed by E. Winkler in 1858. The exact solution of the same problem by the methods of the Mathematical Theory of Elasticity is due to H. Golovin, who solved it in 1881.

However, since E, R, ϕ, and $d\phi$ are constant at any one section of a stressed beam, they may be taken outside the integral sign and a solution for R obtained. Thus:

$$\frac{E\,d\phi}{\phi}\int_A \frac{R-r}{r}\,dA = \frac{E\,d\phi}{\phi}\left[R\int_A \frac{dA}{r} - \int_A dA\right] = 0$$

$$R = \frac{A}{\displaystyle\int_A \frac{dA}{r}} \qquad (5\text{-}11)$$

where A is the cross-sectional area of the beam, and R locates the neutral axis. Note that the neutral axis so found **does not coincide with the centroidal axis**. This differs from the situation found to be true for straight elastic beams.

Now that the location of the neutral axis is known, the equation for the stress distribution is obtained by equating the external moment to the internal resisting moment built up by the stresses given by Eq. 5-10. The summation of moments is made around the z-axis, which is normal to the plane of the figure shown in Fig. 5-21a.

$$\Sigma M_z = 0, \qquad M = \underbrace{\int_A \sigma\,dA}_{\text{(force)}} \quad \underbrace{(R-r)}_{\text{(arm)}} = \int_A \frac{E(R-r)^2\,d\phi}{r\phi}\,dA$$

Again remembering that E, R, ϕ, and $d\phi$ are constant at a section, by using Eq. 5-10a and performing the algebraic steps indicated, the following is obtained:

$$M = \frac{E\,d\phi}{\phi}\int_A \frac{(R-r)^2}{r}\,dA = \frac{\sigma r}{R-r}\int_A \frac{(R-r)^2}{r}\,dA$$

$$= \frac{\sigma r}{R-r}\int_A \frac{R^2 - Rr - Rr + r^2}{r}\,dA$$

$$= \frac{\sigma r}{R-r}\left[R^2\int_A \frac{dA}{r} - R\int_A dA - R\int_A dA + \int_A r\,dA\right]$$

Here, since R is a constant, the first two integrals vanish as may be seen from the bracketed expression appearing just before Eq. 5-11. The third integral is A, and the last integral, by definition, is $\bar{r}A$. Hence

$$M = \frac{\sigma r}{R-r}(\bar{r}A - RA)$$

whence the normal stress acting on a curved beam at a distance r from the center of curvature is

$$\sigma = \frac{M(R-r)}{rA(\bar{r}-R)} \qquad (5\text{-}12)$$

If positive y is measured down *from the neutral axis*, and $\bar{r} - R = e$, Eq. 5-12 may be written in a form which more closely resembles the flexure formula for straight beams,

$$\sigma = \frac{My}{Ae(R - y)} \qquad (5\text{-}12a)$$

These equations indicate that the stress distribution in a curved bar follows a *hyperbolic* pattern. The maximum stress is always on the inside (the concave) side of the beam. A comparison of this result with the one that follows from the formula for straight bars is shown in Fig. 5-20c. Note particularly that in the curved bar the neutral axis is "pulled toward the center" of the beam's curvature. This results from the higher stresses developed below the neutral axis. The theory developed of course applies only to elastic stress distribution and *only to beams in pure bending*. For a consideration of situations where an axial force is also present at a section see Art. 7-2.

Example 5-9. Compare stresses in a 2 in. by 2 in. rectangular bar subjected to end couples of 13,333 in.-lb in three special cases: (a) straight beam, (b) beam curved to a radius of 10 in. along the centroidal axis, i.e., $\bar{r} = 10$ in., Fig. 5-22a, and (c) beam curved to $\bar{r} = 3$ in.

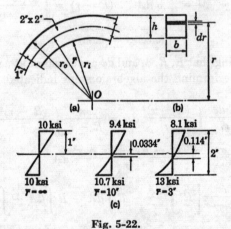

(a)   (b)

(c)

Fig. 5-22.

SOLUTION: *Case* (a) follows directly by applying Eqs. 5-6 and 5-5 in the order named.

$$Z = \frac{bh^2}{6} = \frac{2(2)^2}{6} = 1.33 \text{ in.}^3$$

$$\sigma_{max} = \frac{M}{Z} = \frac{13,333}{1.33} = \pm 10,000 \text{ psi or 10 ksi}$$

This result is shown in Fig. 5-22c. $\bar{r} = \infty$, since a straight bar has an infinite radius of curvature.

To solve parts (b) and (c) the neutral axis must be first located. This is found in general terms by integrating Eq. 5-11. For the rectangular section, the elementary area is taken as $b \, dr$, Fig. 5-22b. The integration is carried out between the limits r_i and r_o, the inner and outer radii, respectively.

$$R = \frac{A}{\int_A \frac{dA}{r}} = \frac{bh}{\int_{r_i}^{r_o} \frac{b \, dr}{r}} = \frac{h}{\int_{r_i}^{r_o} \frac{dr}{r}}$$

$$= \frac{h}{\left| \ln r \right|_{r_i}^{r_o}} = \frac{h}{\ln \left(\frac{r_o}{r_i} \right)} = \frac{h}{2.3026 \log \left(\frac{r_o}{r_i} \right)} \tag{5-13}$$

where h is the depth of the section, ln is the natural logarithm, and log is a logarithm with a base of 10 (common logarithm).

For *Case* (b), $h = 2$ in., $\bar{r} = 10$ in., $r_i = 9$ in., and $r_o = 11$ in. The solution is obtained by evaluating Eqs. 5-13 and 5-12. Subscript i refers to the normal stress σ of the inside fibers; o of the outside fibers.

$$R = \frac{2}{2.3026 \log \frac{11}{9}} = \frac{2}{2.3026 \, (\log 11 - \log 9)} = 9.9666 \text{ in.}$$

$$e = \bar{r} - R = 10 - 9.9666 = 0.0334 \text{ in.}$$

$$\sigma_i = \frac{M(R - r_i)}{r_i A(\bar{r} - R)} = 13{,}333 \, \frac{9.9666 - 9}{9(4)(0.0334)} = 10{,}700 \text{ psi}$$

$$\sigma_o = \frac{M(R - r_o)}{r_o A(\bar{r} - R)} = 13{,}333 \, \frac{9.9666 - 11}{11(4)(0.0334)} = -9{,}400 \text{ psi}$$

The negative sign of σ_o indicates a compressive stress. These quantities and the corresponding stress distribution are shown in Fig. 5-22c, $\bar{r} = 10$ in.

Case (c) is computed in the same way. Here $h = 2$ in., $\bar{r} = 3$ in., $r_i = 2$ in., and $r_o = 4$ in. Results of the computation are shown in Fig. 5-22c.

$$R = \frac{2}{\ln \frac{4}{2}} = \frac{2}{\ln 2} = \frac{2}{0.6931} = 2.886 \text{ in.}$$

$$e = 3 - 2.886 = 0.114 \text{ in.}$$

$$\sigma_i = 13{,}333 \, \frac{0.886}{2(0.114)4} = 13{,}000 \text{ psi}$$

$$\sigma_o = 13{,}333 \, \frac{-1.114}{4(0.114)4} = -8{,}140 \text{ psi}$$

Several important conclusions, generally true, may be reached from the above example. First, *the usual flexure formula is reasonably good for beams of considerable curvature.* Only 7% error in the maximum stress occurs in *Case* (b) for $\bar{r}/h = 5$, an error tolerable for most applications. For greater ratios of $\bar{r}/h$ this error diminishes. As the curvature of the beam increases, the stress on the concave side rapidly increases over the one given by the usual flexure formula. When $\bar{r}/h = 1.5$ a 30% error occurs.

Second, the evaluation of the integral for R over the cross-sectional area may become very complex. Finally, calculations of R must be *very accurate* since differences between R and numerically comparable quantities are used in the stress formula.

The last two difficulties prompted the development of other methods of solution. One such method consists of expanding certain terms of the solution into a series,* another of building up a solution on the basis of a special transformed section. Yet another device consists of working "in reverse." Curved beams of various cross-sections, curvatures, and applied moments are analyzed for stress; then these quantities are divided by a flexural stress that would exist for the same beam *if it were straight.* These ratios are then tabulated.† Hence, conversely, if stress in a curved beam is wanted, it is given as

$$\sigma = K \frac{Mc}{I} \tag{5-14}$$

where the coefficient K is obtained from a table or a graph and Mc/I is computed as in the usual flexure formula.

An expression for the distance from the center of curvature to the neutral axis of a curved beam of circular cross-sectional area is given below for future reference:

$$R = \frac{\bar{r} + \sqrt{\bar{r}^2 - c^2}}{2} \tag{5-15}$$

where $\bar{r}$ is the distance from the center of curvature to the centroid and c is the radius of the circular cross-sectional area.

Problems for Solution

5-1 through 5-5. For the cross-sectional areas with the dimensions shown in the figures, determine the moment of inertia for each section with respect to the horizontal centroidal axis.

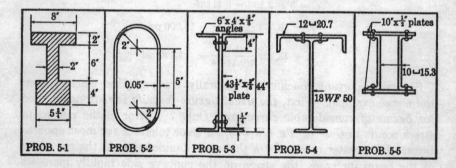

| PROB. 5-1 | PROB. 5-2 | PROB. 5-3 | PROB. 5-4 | PROB. 5-5 |

5-6 through 5-10. The beams having the cross-sectional dimensions shown in the figures are each subjected to a positive bending moment of 40,000 ft-lb acting around the horizontal neutral axis. For each case, determine the bending stress acting on each of the three infinitesimal areas shown by the heavy dots.

---

* Timoshenko, S., *Strength of Materials*, Part II. New York: Van Nostrand, 1941.
† Roark, R. J., *Formulas for Stress and Strain*. New York: McGraw-Hill, 1943, Second Edition.

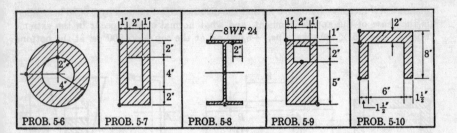

| PROB. 5-6 | PROB. 5-7 | PROB. 5-8 | PROB. 5-9 | PROB. 5-10 |

5-11. Verify the section moduli given in the Appendix for 12 I 40.8, 10 WF 112, and 12 $\sqsubset$ 20.7.

5-12. Determine the allowable bending moment for a rectangular wooden beam having a full-sized cross-section of 2 in. by 4 in. for an allowable bending stress of 1,200 psi, (a) if bent around a neutral axis parallel to the 2 in. side, (b) if bent around a neutral axis parallel to the 4 in. side. *Ans.* 6.4 k-in., 3.2 k-in.

5-13. If a pure bending moment of 23 kip-ft is to be resisted by a WF section without exceeding a 20,000 psi stress, (a) what size section should be used if the moment acts around the X-X axis, (b) around the Y-Y axis?

5-14. The cast iron machine part, a section through which is shown in the figure, acts as a beam resisting a positive bending moment. If the allowable stress in tension is 3,000 psi and in compression 12,000 psi, what moment may be applied to this beam? *Ans.* 69,500 in.-lb.

5-15. A beam having a solid rectangular cross-section with the dimensions shown in the figure is subjected to a positive bending moment of 12,000 ft-lb acting around the horizontal axis. (a) Find the compressive force acting on the shaded area of the cross-section developed by the bending stresses. (b) Find the tensile force acting on the cross-hatched area of the cross-section.

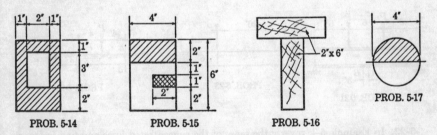

| PROB. 5-14 | PROB. 5-15 | PROB. 5-16 | PROB. 5-17 |

5-16. Two 2 in. by 6 in. full sized wooden planks are glued together to form a tee section as shown in the figure. If a positive bending moment of 2,270 ft-lb is applied to such a beam acting around a horizontal axis, (a) find the stresses at the extreme fibers ($I = 136$ in.^{4}), (b) calculate the total compressive force developed by the normal stresses above the neutral axis due to the bending of the beam, (c) find the total force due to the tensile bending stresses at a section and compare with the result found in (b). *Ans.* (b) 5,000 lb.

5-17.* By integration, determine the force developed by the bending stresses and its position acting on the shaded area of the cross-section of the beam shown in the figure if the beam is subjected to a negative bending moment of 30,000 in.-lb acting around the horizontal axis.

5-18. A gray cast iron channel-shaped member, as shown in the figure, acts as a horizontal beam in a machine. When vertical forces are applied to this member, the distance AB increases by 0.0010 in. and the distance CD decreases by 0.0090 in.   What is the sense of the applied moment, and what normal stresses occur in the extreme fibers? $E = 15 \times 10^6$ psi.   *Ans.* +5,620 psi at the top, −22,500 psi at the bottom.

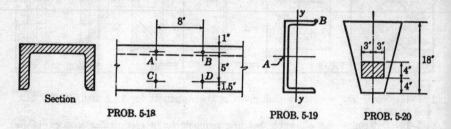

Section

PROB. 5-18   PROB. 5-19   PROB. 5-20

5-19. A 12 ⊔ 20.7 steel beam is bent around the y-y axis as shown in the figure. Due to this bending, a measurement in a 12 in. longitudinal gage distance (corresponding in the figure to a line at A perpendicular to the plane of the paper) indicated a contraction of 0.00323 in.   What is the stress at B? $E = 29 \times 10^6$ psi.   *Ans.* 25 ksi.

5-20. A solid steel beam having the cross-sectional dimensions partially shown in the figure was loaded in the laboratory in pure bending.   Bending took place around a horizontal neutral axis.   Strain measurements showed that the top fibers contracted 0.0003 in./in. longitudinally; the bottom fibers elongated 0.0006 in./in. longitudinally. Determine the total normal force in pounds which acted on the shaded area indicated in the figure at the time the strain measurements were made. $E = 30 \times 10^6$ psi. *Ans.* +216 k.

5-21. When two concentrated forces were applied to an 18 WF 50 steel beam as shown in the figure, an elongation of 0.0050 in. was observed between the gage points A and B.   What was the magnitude of the applied forces? $E = 30 \times 10^6$ psi.

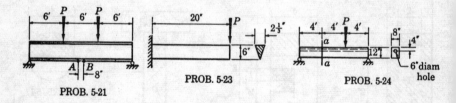

PROB. 5-21

PROB. 5-23   PROB. 5-24   6" diam hole

5-22. In Example 5-4, reverse the sense of the concentrated force and find the maximum bending stresses in the beam at the built in end if $L = 8$ ft.

5-23. Find the maximum flexural stress at a section 10 in. from the support for the cantilever beam loaded as shown in the figure.   Show the result on an isolated element alongside the beam.   The beam weighs approximately 24 lb/ft of length and $P = 100$ lb.   *Ans.* 314 psi.

5-24. At section a-a for the beam, loaded as shown in the figure, find: (a) the maximum normal stress; (b) the normal stress midway between the top and the bottom fibers.   The beam weighs 230 lb/ft and $P = 2,100$ lb.   *Ans.* (a) −572 psi.

5-25.* Find the largest bending moment which an 8 in. by 6 in. by 1 in. angle may carry without exceeding a stress of 20 ksi.   (*Hint:* the minimum radius of gyration for the angle is given in Table 7 of the Appendix.   From definition, Art. 13-5, $I_{min} = Ar_{min}^2$, where A is the cross-sectional area.   Moreover $I_{min} + I_{max} = I_{XX} + I_{YY}$, hence I_{max} may be obtained.)

5-26. Show that the maximum bending stress for a beam of rectangular cross-section is $\sigma_{max} = \dfrac{Mc}{I}\dfrac{(2n+1)}{3n}$ if, instead of Hooke's law, the stress-strain relationship is $\sigma^n = E\epsilon$, where n is a number dependent on the properties of the material.

5-27 through 5-31. Find the ratios M_{ult}/M_{yp} for mild steel beams resisting bending around the horizontal axes and having the cross-sectional dimensions shown in the figures. Assume the idealized stress-strain diagram used in Example 5-6. *Ans. Prob. 5-27: 1.7. Prob. 5-29: 1.11. Prob. 5-31: 1.8.*

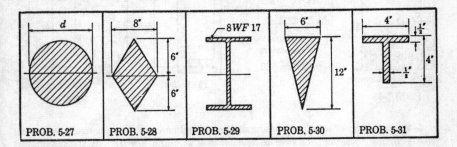

PROB. 5-27   PROB. 5-28   PROB. 5-29   PROB. 5-30   PROB. 5-31

5-32 through 5-34. Composite beams having the cross-sectional dimensions shown in the figures are subjected to positive bending moments of 60 kip-ft each. Materials are fastened together so that the beams act as a unit. Determine the maximum bending stress in each material. $E_{St} = 30 \times 10^6$ psi; $E_{Al} = 10 \times 10^6$ psi; $E_{CI} = 15 \times 10^6$ psi. (*Hint for Prob. 5-34:* for an ellipse with semi-axes a and b, $I = \pi\,ab^3/4$ around the major centroidal axis.)

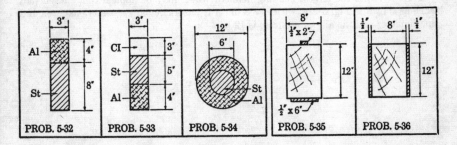

PROB. 5-32   PROB. 5-33   PROB. 5-34   PROB. 5-35   PROB. 5-36

5-35 and 5-36. Determine the allowable bending moment around horizontal neutral axes for the composite beams of wood and steel having the cross-sectional dimensions shown in the figures. Materials are fastened together so that they act as a unit. $E_{St} = 30 \times 10^6$ psi; $E_w = 1.2 \times 10^6$ psi. The allowable bending stresses are $\sigma_{St} = 20{,}000$ psi and $\sigma_w = 1{,}200$ psi.

5-37. A 6 in. by 12 in. rectangular section is subjected to a positive bending moment of 180,000 ft-lb around the "strong" axis. The material of the beam is nonisotropic and is such that the modulus of elasticity in tension is $1\frac{1}{2}$ times as great as in compression. If the stresses do not exceed the elastic limit, find the maximum tensile and compressive stresses in the beam.

5-38. A reinforced concrete beam having a cross-section as shown in the figure is subjected to a positive bending moment of 8,000 ft-lb. Determine the maximum compressive stress in the concrete and the maximum stress in the steel. Assume $n = 15$.

5-39. A 5 in. thick concrete slab is longitudinally reinforced with steel bars as shown in the figure. Determine the allowable bending moment per one foot width of this slab. Assume $n = 12$ and the allowable stresses for steel and concrete as 18,000 psi and 900 psi, respectively.

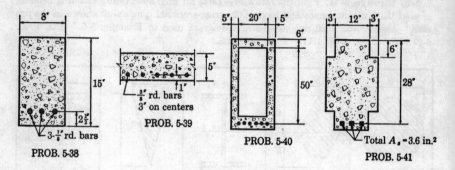

PROB. 5-38

PROB. 5-39

PROB. 5-40

PROB. 5-41

5-40. A section of a hollow rectangular reinforced concrete beam is made as shown in the figure. The area of steel in tension is 9 in.², and $n = 10$. If the maximum compression stress in the concrete caused by bending is known to be 1,000 psi, what is the stress in the steel and what bending moment is applied to the section?

5-41. A beam has a cross-section as shown in the figure, and is subjected to a positive bending moment which causes a tensile stress in the steel of 18,000 psi. If $n = 10$, what is the value of the bending moment? *Ans.* 131.6 k-ft.

5-42. Rework Example 5-9 by changing h to 4 in.

5-43.* Derive Eq. 5-15.

5-44. What is the largest bending moment which may be applied to a curved bar, such as shown in Fig. 5-21a, with $\bar{r} = 3$ in., if it has a circular cross-sectional area of 2 in. diameter and the allowable stress is 12 ksi?

Chapter Six

SHEARING STRESSES IN BEAMS

6-1. Introduction. It was shown in Chapter 4 that in a planar problem three elements of a force system may be necessary at a section of a beam to maintain the segment in equilibrium. These were an axial force, a shearing force, and a bending moment. The stress caused by an axial force was investigated in Chapter 1. In Chapter 5 the nature of the stresses caused by a bending moment in a beam was discussed. The stresses in a beam caused by the shearing force will be investigated in this chapter.

In all of the previous derivations of the stress distribution in a member, the same sequence of reasoning was employed. First, the equations of statics were applied to a segment of the member. Then a strain distribution was assumed at the cut section. Finally, using the elastic properties of the material in conjunction with the above steps, the stress distribution was determined. However, the development of the expression linking the shearing force and the cross-sectional area of a beam to the stress in a beam follows a different path. In the problem at hand the same procedure cannot be employed, as no simple assumption for the strain distribution due to the shearing force can be made. Instead, an indirect method of approach is used. *The stress distribution caused by flexure, as determined in the preceding chapter, is assumed, and together with the laws of statics, fixes invariably the whole problem related to the shearing force.*

First it will be necessary to establish that the shearing force is *IN-SEPARABLY* linked with a *change* in the bending moment at adjoining* sections through a beam. Thus, if a shear and a bending moment are present at one section through a beam, it will be shown that a *different* bending moment will exist at an adjoining section, although the shear may remain constant. This will lead to the establishment of the shearing stresses on the imaginary longitudinal planes through the member which are parallel to its axis. Then finally, since at a point equal shearing stresses exist on the mutually perpendicular planes, the shearing stresses whose direction is coincident with the shearing force at a section will be determined.

---

* Adjoining sections are parallel sections taken perpendicular to the axis of the beam a small distance apart.

Elastic behavior of material will be assumed throughout this chapter. The investigation will be limited to straight beams, and in the early part of this chapter only beams with a symmetrical cross-section will be considered. The applied forces will be assumed to act in the plane containing such an axis of symmetry and the axis of the beam. The analysis of shearing stresses in curved beams is beyond the scope of this text.

6-2. Relation between Shear and Bending Moment. As stated above, the interrelation of the bending moment and the shearing force must be established first. Later this will lead to the establishment of an expression for the shearing stresses in a beam.

Consider an element dx long, isolated from a beam by two adjoining sections taken perpendicular to the axis of the beam. Such an element is

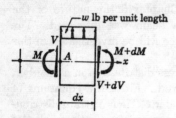

Fig. 6-1. An element cut from a beam by two adjoining sections dx apart.

shown as a free body in Fig. 6-1. At the sections shown the shearing forces and bending moments act on the element as indicated. The elements of this force system are shown with a positive *sense* (for sign conventions see Figs. 4-15 and 4-16). Moreover, since the shear and the moment may each change from one section to the next, on the right-hand end of the element they are respectively noted as $V + dV$ and $M + dM$. The external force acting on the element is indicated by an upward distributed load of w lb per unit length. The reason for selecting an upward direction for the applied load as positive will become apparent after the study of Chapter 10. As axial forces have no bearing on the problem considered they are not shown.

The element of a beam shown in Fig. 6-1 must be in equilibrium. Hence the summation of moments around the axis through point A perpendicular to the plane of the figure must be zero, i.e., $\Sigma M_A = 0$. Noting that from point A the arm of the distributed force is $dx/2$,

$$\Sigma M_A = 0 \curvearrowleft +, \qquad (M + dM) - M - (V + dV)\, dx + w\, dx\, \frac{dx}{2} = 0$$

By simplifying and ignoring* the infinitesimals of higher order, one can reduce this to $dM - V\, dx = 0$. Hence,

* This is legitimate and is *not* an approximation. Thus, consider an element of a beam Δx long, instead of dx. Then all quantities on successive faces vary by an amount Δ. Summing moments around the right-hand end, and simplifying the results,

$$\frac{\Delta M}{\Delta x} = V + \frac{w(x)}{2}\, \Delta x$$

whence by definition, $\lim\limits_{\Delta x \to 0} \dfrac{\Delta M}{\Delta x} \equiv \dfrac{dM}{dx} = V$

Note that the applied load $w(x)$ may vary in the interval considered.

$$dM = V\, dx \qquad \text{or} \qquad \frac{dM}{dx} = V \qquad\qquad (6\text{-}1)$$

Equation 6-1 means that if a shear is acting at a section, there will be a *different* bending moment at an adjoining section. When shear is pres-

ent, the difference between the bending moments on the adjoining sections is equal to $V\, dx$. If no shear acts at the adjoining sections of a beam, *no change in the bending moment occurs.* Conversely, the rate of change of the bending moment along the beam is equal to the shear. Thus although shear is treated in this chapter as an independent action on a beam, it is *INSEPARABLY* linked with a change in the bending moment along the beam's length.

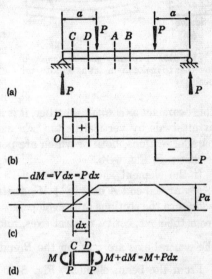

As an illustration of the meaning of Eq. 6-1, the problem discussed in Example 4-5 for which the shear and bending moment diagrams were established is reproduced in Fig. 6-2. At any two sections such as A and B taken through the beam

Fig. 6-2.   Relation between shear and bending-moment diagrams for the loading shown.

anywhere between the applied forces P, the bending moment is the same. *No shear* acts at these sections.   On the other hand, at any two sections such as C and D near the support, a change in the bending moment does take place. Shearing forces act at these sections. These shears are shown acting on an element of the beam in Fig. 6-2d. Note that in this zone of the beam the *change* in the bending moment in a distance dx is $P\, dx$ as the shear V is equal to P. The rate of change of the bending moment along the beam, dM/dx, is equal to the shear and is represented by the slope of the moment diagram. For subsequent discussion, the possibility of equal, as well as of different, bending moments on two adjoining sections through a beam must be appreciated.

6-3. Shear Flow. Before proceeding with the development of the expression for the shearing stresses in a beam caused by a shearing force, a related problem will be considered. Thus consider a wooden plank placed on top of another as is shown in Figs. 6-3a and b. If these planks act as a beam and are *not interconnected*, sliding at the surfaces of their contact will take place. The tendency for this sliding may be visualized by considering the two loaded planks shown in Fig. 6-3b. The interconnection of these planks with nails or glue is necessary to make them act as an integral beam. An equation will be derived for determination of the required interconnection between the component parts of a beam to make them act

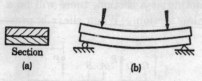

Section
(a)   (b)

Fig. 6-3. Separate planks fastened together to make them act as an integral beam.

as a unit. In the next article this equation will be modified to yield shearing stresses.

Consider a beam made from *several* continuous planks whose cross-section is shown in Fig. 6-4a. For simplicity the beam shown has a rectangular cross-section, but such a limitation is *not* implied. To make this beam act as a *single* member, it is assumed that the planks are fastened at intervals by vertical bolts. An element of this beam isolated by two parallel sections, both of which are perpendicular to the axis of the beam, is shown in Fig. 6-4b.

If the element shown in Fig. 6-4b is subjected to a bending moment $+M_A$ at the end A and to $+M_B$ at the end B, bending stresses which act *normal* to the sections are developed. These bending stresses vary linearly from their respective neutral axes, and at any point at a distance y from the neutral axis are $\dfrac{M_B y}{I}$ on the B end, and $\dfrac{M_A y}{I}$ on the A end.

From the beam element, Fig. 6-4b, isolate the top (or bottom) plank as is shown in Fig. 6-4c. The fibers of this plank *nearest* the neutral axis are located by the distance y_1. Then, since stress times area is equal to a

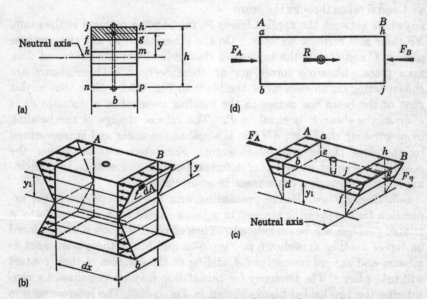

Fig. 6-4. Deriving an expression for the shear flow in a beam.

force, the forces acting *perpendicular* to the ends A and B of *this* plank may be determined. At the end B the force acting on an infinitesimal area dA at a distance y from the neutral axis is $\dfrac{M_B y}{I} dA$. Hence the force on the area $fghj$ is the sum, or an integral, of these forces over this area. Denoting the total force acting *normal* to the area $fghj$ by F_B, and remembering that at a section, M_B and I are constants, one obtains the following relation:

$$F_B = \int_{\substack{\text{area} \\ fghj}} \frac{M_B y}{I} dA = \frac{M_B}{I} \int_{\substack{\text{area} \\ fghj}} y \, dA$$

Similarly, at the end A the total force acting *normal* to the area $abde$ is

$$F_A = \frac{M_A}{I} \int_{\substack{\text{area} \\ abde}} y \, dA$$

If a given beam has a constant cross-sectional area, an area such as $fghj$ is equal to the area $abde$. Likewise, the moment of inertia I of the **whole** cross-sectional area is constant. Hence *if* the moment at A *were equal* to the moment at B, i.e., $M_A = M_B$, it follows that $F_A = F_B$. The element shown in Fig. 6-4c *would be in equilibrium*. The bolt shown in the figure would perform a nominal function of keeping the planks together and would *not* be needed to resist any known forces.

On the other hand, *if M_A is not equal to M_B*, which is *always* the case when shears are present at the adjoining sections, F_A is *not* equal to F_B. More push (or pull) develops on one end of a "plank" than on the other, as different *normal* stresses act on the section from the two sides. Thus if $M_A \neq M_B$, equilibrium of the horizontal forces in Fig. 6-4c may only be attained by developing a horizontal resisting force R in the bolt. If M_B is assumed to be greater than M_A, F_B is greater than F_A, and $F_A + R = F_B$, Fig. 6-4d. The force $F_B - F_A = R$ tends to shear the bolt *in the plane of the plank edfg*.* If the shearing force acting on the bolt at the level km, Fig. 6-4a, were to be investigated, the *two* upper planks should be considered as one unit.

If $M_A \neq M_B$ and the element of the beam is only dx long, the bending moments on the adjoining sections change by an infinitesimal amount. Thus if the bending moment at A is M_A, the bending moment at B is $M_B = M_A + dM$. Likewise, in the same distance dx the longitudinal forces F_A and F_B change by an infinitesimal force dF, i.e., $F_B - F_A = dF$. By substituting these relations into the expressions for F_B and F_A found earlier, remembering that in a prismatic member areas $fghj$ and $abde$ are

---

* The forces $(F_B - F_A)$ and R are not collinear, but the element shown in Fig. 6-4c is in equilibrium. To avoid ambiguity, shearing forces acting in the vertical cuts are omitted from the diagram.

equal, an expression for the differential longitudinal push (or pull) dF is obtained.

$$dF = F_B - F_A = \frac{M_A + dM}{I} \int_{\substack{\text{area} \\ fghj}} y\,dA - \frac{M_A}{I} \int_{\substack{\text{area} \\ abde}} y\,dA$$

$$= \frac{dM}{I} \int_{\substack{\text{area} \\ fghj}} y\,dA$$

Note that in the simplified expression for dF the *actual* bending moments at the adjoining sections are *eliminated*. Only the **difference** in the bending moments dM at the adjoining sections remains in the equation.

Instead of working with a force dF which is developed in a distance dx, it is more significant to obtain a similar force **per unit of the beam's length.** This quantity is obtained by dividing dF by dx. Physically this quantity represents the difference between F_B and F_A for an element of the beam one inch long.* The quantity dF/dx will be designated by q and will be referred to as the *shear flow*. Since force is usually measured in pounds, shear flow q has units of *pounds per inch*. Thus, remembering that by Eq. 6-1 $dM/dx = V$, one obtains the following expression for the shear flow in beams:

$$q = \frac{dF}{dx} = \frac{dM}{dx} \frac{1}{I} \int_{\substack{\text{area} \\ fghj}} y\,dA = \frac{V}{I} \int_{\substack{\text{area} \\ fghj}} y\,dA \qquad (6\text{-}2)$$

In this equation I stands for the moment of inertia of the beam's **entire** cross-sectional area *around the neutral axis*, just as it does in the flexure formula from which it came. The *total shearing force* at the section investigated is represented by V, and the integral of $y\,dA$ extends *only* over the cross-sectional area of the beam *to one side* of the surface at which q is investigated. In the example considered the integration of $y\,dA$ extends *only* over the area† $fghj$, y being measured from the neutral axis. This integral represents the first or the statical moment of area $fghj$ *around the neutral axis*. Moreover, from the definition of the centroid of an area, this integral is equal to the same area $fghj$ multiplied by the distance from *its* centroid to the neutral axis of the beam. This interpretation of the integral is convenient in applications to problems. For further brevity, the same integral is usually designated by Q. In Fig. 6-4a Q is equal to the area $fghj$ multiplied by $\bar{y}$, i.e., $Q = A_{fghj}\bar{y}$. In terms of these notations the equation for the shear flow in a beam may be rewritten as

---

* In aircraft practice an approximate expression for this quantity is often obtained by calculating the force F_B, using M_B, moving *one inch* along the beam, finding the new moment M_A, and calculating F_A. The difference between F_B and F_A is the desired quantity.

† Area $fgpn$ may be used instead. See Prob. 6-1.

$$q = \frac{V A_{fghj}\bar{y}}{I} = \frac{VQ}{I} \tag{6-2a}$$

where

$$Q = \int_{\substack{\text{area} \\ fghj}} y \, dA.$$

In retrospect, note carefully that Eqs. 6-2 and 6-2a *were derived on the basis of the flexure formula*, but no term for a bending moment appears in the final expressions. This resulted from the fact that only the *change* in the bending moments at the adjoining sections had to be considered, and the latter quantity is *inseparably* linked with the shear V. The shear V was substituted for dM/dx and this masks the origin of the established relations. Equations 6-2 and 6-2a are very useful in determining the necessary interconnection between the continuous parts of a beam. This will be illustrated by examples.

Example 6-1. Two long wooden planks form a *T*-section of a beam as shown in Fig. 6-5a. If this beam carries a constant vertical shear* of 690 lb at all sections, find the necessary spacing of the nails between the two planks to make the beam act as a unit. Assume that the allowable shearing force per nail is 150 lb.

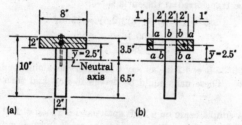

Fig. 6-5.

SOLUTION: This problem may be solved by applying Eq. 6-2a to determine the shear flow in the plane of contact of the two planks. For this purpose the neutral axis of the *whole* section and its moment of inertia around the neutral axis must be found. Then as V is known and Q is defined as the statical moment of the *area of the upper plank* around the neutral axis, q may be determined. The distance y_c from the top to the neutral axis is

$$y_c = \frac{2(8)1 + 2(8)6}{2(8) + 2(8)} = 3.5 \text{ in.}$$

$$I = \frac{8(2)^3}{12} + (2)8(2.5)^2 + \frac{2(8)^3}{12} + (2)8(2.5)^2 = 291 \text{ in.}^4$$

$$Q = A_{fghj}\bar{y} = (2)8(3.5 - 1) = 40 \text{ in.}^3$$

$$q = \frac{VQ}{I} = \frac{690(40)}{291} = 95 \text{ lb per in.}$$

---

* This would occur if this beam were a cantilever and a downward force of 690 lb were applied at the end. The weight of the beam itself is neglected.

This means that a force of 95 lb must be transferred from one plank to the other in every lineal inch along the length of the beam. However, from the data given, each nail is capable of resisting a force of 150 lb, hence one nail can take care of 150/95 = 1.59 linear inches along the length of the beam. As shear remains constant at various sections of the beam, the nails may be spaced throughout at 1.59 in. intervals. In a practical problem a 1.5 in. spacing would probably be used.

SOLUTION FOR AN ALTERNATE ARRANGEMENT OF PLANKS: If instead of the two planks used above, a beam of the same cross-section were made from five pieces, Fig. 6-5b, a different nailing schedule would be required.

First, the shear flow between *one* of the 1 in. by 2 in. pieces and the remainder of the beam will be found, and although the contact surface *a-a* is vertical, the procedure is the same as before. The push or pull on an element is built up in the same manner as was formerly discussed:

$$Q = A_{fghj}\bar{y} = (1)2(2.5) = 5 \text{ in.}^3$$

$$q = \frac{VQ}{I} = \frac{690(5)}{291} = 11.8 \text{ lb per in.}$$

If the same nails as before are used to join the 1 in. by 2 in. piece to the 2 in. by 2 in. piece, they may be 150/11.8 = 12.7 in. apart. This nailing applies to *both* sections *a-a*.

To determine the shear flow between the 2 in. by 10 in. vertical piece and either one of the 2 in. by 2 in. pieces, the whole 3 in. by 2 in. area must be used to determine Q. It is the difference of pushes (or pulls) on this whole area that causes the unbalanced force which must be transferred at the surface *b-b*:

$$Q = A_{fghj}\bar{y} = (3)2(2.5) = 15 \text{ in.}^3$$

$$q = \frac{VQ}{I} = \frac{690(15)}{291} = 35.6 \text{ lb per in.}$$

Space nails at 150/35.6 = 4.2 in., or say 4 in. intervals along the length of the beam in *both* sections *b-b*. These nails could be driven in first and then the 1 in. by 2 in. pieces put on.

Example 6-2. A simple beam on a 20 ft span carries a load of 200 lb per ft including its own weight. The beam's cross-section is to be made from several full-sized wooden pieces as is shown in Fig. 6-6a. Specify the spacing of the $\frac{1}{2}$ in. lag screws shown which is necessary to fasten this beam together. Assume that one $\frac{1}{2}$ in. lag screw, as determined by laboratory tests, is good for 500 lb when transmitting lateral load parallel to the grain of the wood. For the *entire* section I is equal to 6,060 in.[4]

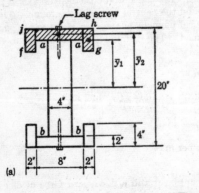
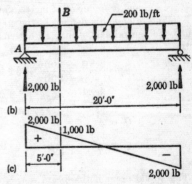

Fig. 6-6.

SOLUTION: To find the spacing of the lag screws, the shear flow at section a-a must be determined. The loading on the given beam is shown in Fig. 6-6b, and to show the variation of the shear along the beam, the shear diagram is constructed in Fig. 6-6c (Example 4-6). Next, to apply the shear flow formula, $\int_{\substack{area \\ fghj}} y \, dA = Q$ must be determined. This is done by considering the *shaded* area to one side of the cut a-a in Fig. 6-6a. The statical moment of this area is most conveniently computed by multiplying the area of the *two* 2 in. by 4 in. pieces by the distance from their centroid to the neutral axis of the beam and adding to this product a similar quantity for the 2 in. by 8 in. piece. The largest shear flow occurs at the supports, as the largest vertical shears V of 2,000 lb act there:

$$Q = A_{fghj}\bar{y} = 2A_1\bar{y}_1 + A_2\bar{y}_2$$
$$= 2(2)4(8) + 2(8)9 = 272 \text{ in.}^3$$
$$q = \frac{VQ}{I} = \frac{2,000(272)}{6,060} = 90 \text{ lb per in.}$$

At the supports the spacing of the lag screws must be $500/90 = 5.56$ in. apart. This spacing of the lag screws applies only at a section where the shear V is equal to 2,000 lb. Similar calculations for a section where $V = 1,000$ lb gives $q = 45$ lb per in., and the spacing of the lag screws becomes $500/45 = 11.12$ in. Thus it is proper to specify the use of $\frac{1}{2}$ in. lag screws at $5\frac{1}{2}$ in. on centers for a distance of 5 ft nearest both of the supports and 11 in. spacing of the same lag screws for the middle half of the beam. A greater refinement in making the transition from one spacing of fastenings to another may be desirable in some problems. The *same* spacing of lag screws should be used at the section b-b as at the section a-a.

In a manner analogous to the above, the spacing of rivets in composite beams made from continuous angles and plates, Fig. 6-7, may be deter-

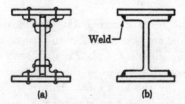

Fig. 6-7. Typical beam sections consisting of component parts, (a) plate girder, (b) *I*-beam reinforced with plates.

mined. The capacity of a rivet is based either on its resistance in shear or bearing on the plates, whichever governs. The *nominal* shearing stress in a rivet is determined by dividing the total shearing *force* transmitted by the rivet (shear flow times spacing of the rivets) by the cross-sectional area of the rivet. For a detailed analysis of rivets and welds see Chapter 14.

6-4. The Shearing Stress Formula for Beams. The shearing stress formula for beams may be obtained by modifying the shear flow formula. Thus, analogous to the earlier procedure, an element of a beam may be isolated between two adjoining sections taken perpendicular to the axis of the beam. Then by passing *another imaginary section* through this element parallel to the axis of the beam, a new element is obtained, which corresponds to the element of one "plank" used in the earlier derivations. A side view of such an element is shown in Fig. 6-8a where the imaginary

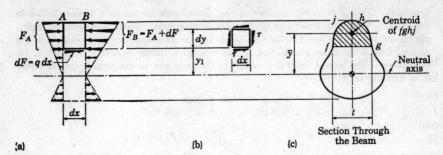

Fig. 6-8. Deriving the shearing stress formula for beams.

longitudinal cut is made at a distance y_1 from the neutral axis. The cross-sectional area of the beam is shown in Fig. 6-8c.

If shearing forces exist at the sections through the beam, a different bending moment acts at section A than at B. Hence more push or pull is developed on one side of the *partial* area *fghj* than on the other, and, as before, this *longitudinal* force in a distance dx is

$$dF = \frac{dM}{I} \int_{\substack{\text{area} \\ fghj}} y \, dA = \frac{dM}{I} A_{fghj}\bar{y} = \frac{dM}{I} Q$$

In a *solid* beam the force resisting dF may be developed only *in the plane* of the longitudinal cut taken parallel to the axis of the beam. Therefore, assuming that the shearing stress τ is *uniformly distributed* across the cut of width t, the shearing stress in the *longitudinal plane* may be obtained by dividing dF by the area $t \, dx$. However, as for an *infinitesimal* element numerically equal shearing stresses act on the mutually perpendicular planes, Fig. 6-8b, a relation giving **simultaneously** the longitudinal shearing stress and the shearing stress *in the plane of the vertical section at the longitudinal* cut follows.*

---

* The appearance of $\bar{y}$ in this relation may be explained differently. If the shear is present at a section through a beam, the moments at the adjoining sections are M and $M + dM$. The magnitude of M is irrelevant for determination of the shearing stresses. Hence alternately, *no* moment need be considered at one section *if at the adjoining section a bending moment dM is assumed to act*. Then on a partial area of the section, such as the shaded area in Fig. 6-8c, this bending moment dM will cause an *average normal stress* $(dM)\bar{y}/I$ as given by the flexure formula. In the latter relation $\bar{y}$ locates the fiber which is at an *average* distance from the neutral axis in the *partial* area of a section. Multiplying $(dM)\bar{y}/I$ by the partial area of the section leads to the same expression for dF as above.

$$\tau = \frac{dF}{dx\,t} = \frac{dM}{dx}\frac{A_{fghj}\bar{y}}{It}$$

This equation may be simplified, since according to Eq. 6-1 $dM/dx = V$ and by Eq. 6-2a $q = VQ/I$, hence

$$\tau = \frac{VA_{fghj}\bar{y}}{It} = \frac{VQ}{It} = \frac{q}{t} \qquad (6\text{-}3)$$

Equation 6-3 is the important formula for the shearing stresses in a beam.* It gives the shearing stresses *at* the longitudinal cut. It is related to the shear flow formula, and V, Q, and I have the same or analogous meanings. As before, V is the *total* shearing force at a section, and I is the moment of inertia of the **whole** cross-sectional area about the neutral axis. Both V and I are constant at a section through a beam. Here Q is the statical moment of the **partial** area of the cross-section *to one side* of the imaginary longitudinal cut around the neutral axis, and $\bar{y}$ is the distance from the neutral axis of the beam to the centroid of the partial area A_{fghj}. Finally, t is the width of the imaginary longitudinal cut, which is usually equal to the thickness or width of the member. The shearing stress at different longitudinal cuts through the beam assumes different values as the values of Q and t for such cuts differ.

Care must be exercised in making the longitudinal cuts preparatory for use in Eq. 6-3. The proper sectioning of some cross-sectional areas of

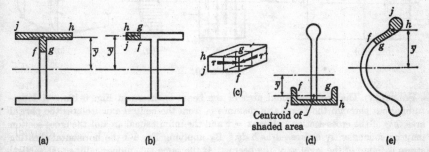

(a)   (b)   (c)   (d)   (e)

Fig. 6-9. Proper sectioning for partial areas of the cross-section for computing the shearing stresses in beams.

beams is shown in Figs. 6-9a, b, d, and e. The use of inclined cutting planes should be avoided *unless* the cut is made across a small thickness.† When the axis of symmetry of the cross-sectional area of the beam is vertical and in the plane of the applied forces, the longitudinal cuts are usually made horizontal. In such cases the solution of Eq. 6-3 gives

---

* This formula was derived by D. I. Jouravsky in 1855. Its development was prompted by observing horizontal cracks in wood ties on several of the railroad bridges between Moscow and St. Petersburg.

† Rigorous solutions of the problem indicate that *wide* inclined cuts through the section may lead to inconsistencies.

simultaneous values of *horizontal and vertical* shearing stresses, as such planes are mutually perpendicular. The latter stresses act in the plane of the transverse section through the beam. Collectively, these shearing stresses resist the shearing force at the same section, thus satisfying the relation of statics $\Sigma F_y = 0$. The validity of this statement for a special case will be proved in Example 6-3.

For thin members only, Eq. 6-3 may be used to determine the shearing stresses, as in the cut *f-g* of Fig. 6-9b. These shearing stresses act in a vertical plane and are directed perpendicularly to the plane of the paper. Matching shearing stresses act horizontally, Fig. 6-9c. These shearing stresses act in *entirely different directions* than those obtained by making horizontal cuts, such as *f-g* in Figs. 6-9a and d. As these shearing stresses do not contribute directly to the resistance of the vertical shear V, they are not of immediate interest. Such stresses will be discussed in Art. 6-6.

The application of Eq. 6-3 to two *particularly important* types of cross-sectional areas of beams will now be illustrated.

Example 6-3. Derive an expression for the shearing-stress distribution in a beam of solid rectangular cross-section transmitting a vertical shear V.

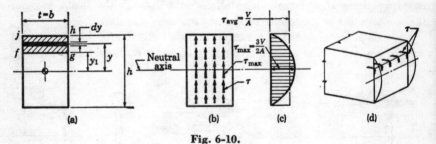

Fig. 6-10.

SOLUTION: The cross-sectional area of the beam is shown in Fig. 6-10a. A longitudinal cut through the beam at a distance y_1 from the neutral axis isolates the partial area *fghj* of the cross-section. Here $t = b$ and the infinitesimal area of the cross-section may be conveniently expressed as $b\,dy$. By applying Eq. 6-3 the horizontal shearing stress is found *at* the level y_1 of the beam. *At* the same cut, numerically equal vertical shearing stresses act *in the plane of the cross-section*.

$$\tau = \frac{VQ}{It} = \frac{V}{It}\int_{\substack{\text{area}\\ fghj}} y\,dA = \frac{V}{Ib}\int_{y_1}^{h/2} by\,dy$$

$$= \frac{V}{I}\left.\frac{y^2}{2}\right|_{y_1}^{h/2} = \frac{V}{2I}\left[\left(\frac{h}{2}\right)^2 - y_1^2\right]$$

This equation shows that in a beam of rectangular cross-section both the horizontal and the vertical shearing stresses vary parabolically. The maximum value of the shearing stress is obtained when y_1 is equal to zero. *In the plane of the cross-section*, Fig. 6-10b, this is diagrammatically represented by τ_{max} at the neutral axis of the beam. At increasing distances from the neutral axis, the shearing stresses gradually diminish. At the upper and lower boundaries of the beam, the shearing stresses cease to exist, as

$y_1 = h/2$. These values of the shearing stresses at the various levels of the beam may be represented by the parabola shown in Fig. 6-10c. An isometric view of the beam with horizontal and vertical shearing stresses is shown in Fig. 6-10d.

To satisfy the condition of statics $\Sigma F_y = 0$, at a section of the beam the sum of all the vertical shearing stresses τ times their respective areas dA must be equal to the vertical shear V. That this is the case may be shown by integrating $\tau\, dA$ over the *whole* cross-sectional area A of the beam, using the general expression for τ found above.

$$\int_A \tau\, dA = \frac{V}{2I} \int_{-h/2}^{+h/2} \left[\left(\frac{h}{2}\right)^2 - y_1^2 \right] b\, dy_1 = \frac{Vb}{2I} \left[\left(\frac{h}{2}\right)^2 y_1 - \left(\frac{y_1^3}{3}\right) \right]_{-h/2}^{+h/2}$$

$$= \frac{Vb}{\left(2\,\dfrac{bh^3}{12}\right)} \left[\left(\frac{h}{2}\right)^2 h - \frac{2}{3}\left(\frac{h}{2}\right)^3 \right] = V$$

As the derivation of Eq. 6-3 was indirect, this proof showing that the shearing stresses integrated over the section equal the vertical shear is reassuring. Moreover, since an agreement in signs is found, this result indicates that *the direction of the shearing stresses at the section through a beam is the same as that of the shearing force V*. This fact may be used to determine the sense of the shearing stresses.

As noted above, the maximum shearing stress in a rectangular beam occurs at the neutral axis, and for this case the general expression for τ_{max} may be simplified, as $y_1 = 0$.

$$\tau_{max} = \frac{Vh^2}{8I} = \frac{Vh^2}{8\,\dfrac{bh^3}{12}} = \frac{3}{2}\frac{V}{bh} = \frac{3}{2}\frac{V}{A} \tag{6-4}$$

where V is the total shear and A is the *entire* cross-sectional area. The same result may be obtained more directly if it is noted that to make $VQ/(It)$ a maximum, Q must attain its largest value, as in this case V, I, and t are constants. From the property of the statical moments of areas around a centroidal axis, the maximum value of Q is obtained by considering one-half the cross-sectional area around the neutral axis of the beam. Hence, alternately,

$$\tau_{max} = \frac{VQ}{It} = \frac{V\left(\dfrac{bh}{2}\right)\left(\dfrac{h}{4}\right)}{\left(\dfrac{bh^3}{12}\right)b} = \frac{3}{2}\frac{V}{A} \tag{6-4a}$$

Since beams of rectangular cross-sectional area are used frequently in practice, Eq. 6-4a is very useful. It is widely used in the design of wooden beams as the shearing strength of wood on planes parallel to the grain is small. Thus, although equal shearing stresses exist on mutually perpendicular planes, wooden beams have a tendency to split longitudinally along the neutral axis. Note that the maximum shearing stress is $1\frac{1}{2}$ times as great as the *average* shearing stress* V/A.

Example 6-4. An *I*-beam is loaded as shown in Fig. 6-11a. If it has the cross-section shown in Fig. 6-11c, determine the shearing stresses at the levels indicated. Neglect the weight of the beam.

SOLUTION: A free-body diagram of a segment of the beam is shown in Fig. 6-11b. It is seen from this diagram that the vertical shear at every section is 50 kips. Bending moments do not enter directly into the present problem. The shear flow at the various levels of the beam is computed using Eq. 6-2a in the table below. Since $\tau = q/t$,

---

* Application of the expression $\tau = V/A$ is permissible only for rivets and bolts and must not be used in the design of beams.

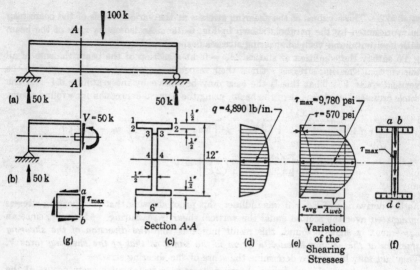

Fig. 6-11.

Eq. 6-3, the shearing stresses are obtained by dividing the shear flows by the respective widths of the beam.

$$I = \frac{6(12)^3}{12} - \frac{(5.5)(11)^3}{12} = 254 \text{ in.}^4$$

For use in Eq. 6-2a $V/I = 50,000/254 = 197$ lb/in.^{4}

Level	A_{fghj}*		$\bar{y}$**	$Q = A_{fghj}\bar{y}$	$q = VQ/I$	t	τ, psi
1-1	0		6	0	0	6.0	0
2-2	(0.5)6	= 3.00	5.75	17.25	3,400	6.0 0.5	570 6,800
3-3	(0.5)6 (0.5)(0.5)	= 3.00 = 0.25	5.75 5.25	17.25 ⎫ 1.31 ⎬ 18.56	3,650	0.5	7,300
4-4	(0.5)6 (0.5)(5.5)	= 3.00 = 2.75	5.75 2.75	17.25 ⎫ 7.56 ⎬ 24.81	4,890	0.5	9,780

* A_{fghj} is the partial area of the cross-section above a given level in in.^{2}
** $\bar{y}$ is the distance from the neutral axis to the centroid of the partial area in inches.

Note that for convenience rectangular parts of the partial areas are used in computing Q. At the level 2-2 *two* widths are used to determine the shearing stress, one *just above* the line 2-2, and one *just below*. A width of 6 in. corresponds to the first case, and 0.5 in. to the second. This transition point will be discussed in the next article. The results obtained, which by virtue of symmetry are also applicable to the lower half of the section, are plotted in Fig. 6-11d and e. By a method similar to the one used in the preceding example, it may be shown that the curves in Fig. 6-11e are parts of a second-degree parabola.

The variation of the shearing stress indicated by Fig. 6-11e may be diagrammatically interpreted as is shown in Fig. 6-11f. The maximum shearing stress occurs at the neutral axis. Moreover, the shearing stresses in the *web** of the beam are *nearly* of the same magnitude. The shearing stresses occurring in the flanges are very small. For this reason the maximum shearing stress in an *I*-beam is often approximated by dividing the total shear V by the *cross-sectional area of the web* (area *abcd* in Fig. 6-11f). Hence

$$(\tau_{\max})_{\text{approx}} = \frac{V}{A_{\text{web}}} \qquad (6\text{-}5)$$

In the example considered this gives

$$(\tau_{\max})_{\text{approx}} = \frac{50,000}{(0.5)12} = 8,330 \text{ psi}$$

This stress differs by about 15% from the one found by the accurate formula. In many practical investigations such accuracy is sufficient, and codes specify the allowable shearing stress in *I*-beams with this particular type of stress distribution in mind.† It should be clear from the above that division of V by the *whole* cross-sectional area of the beam to obtain the shearing stress is *not permissible*.

The direction of the shearing stresses acting *on* the section through the *I*-beam coincides with the direction of the shearing force V. This conclusion follows, as in the preceding example, by considering $\int_{A} \tau \, dA$, which must be equal to V. An element of the beam *at the neutral axis* is shown in Fig. 6-11g. The shearing stress on the *right-hand face* of this element acts in the same direction as the vertical shear V.‡ The diagram shown in Fig. 6-11g is complete. At levels 3-3 and 2-2, bending stresses, in addition to the shearing stresses, act on the vertical faces of the elements. No shearing stresses and only bending stresses act on the elements at the level 1-1.

The maximum shearing stress was found to be at the neutral axis in both of the above examples. This is always so if the sides of the cross-sectional area are parallel. For this case, Q becomes the only variable in the shearing stress equation, and it attains its maximum value at the neutral axis. If the sides of the cross-sectional area are not parallel, τ becomes a function of Q and t, and the maximum shearing stress may not be at the neutral axis. For example, the maximum shearing stress occurs midway between the apex and the base in a symmetrical triangular cross-section, while the neutral axis is at one-third the height from the base.

The same procedure as above applies to the investigation of the longitudinal joints in beams in which such contact surfaces are glued. A knowledge of the shearing stresses in the glued joint aids in the selection of a glue of proper strength. If beams of two materials are investigated, transformed sections must be used to obtain a solution. In reinforced-concrete beams, concrete between the neutral axis and the reinforcing

---

* The *web* is a thin vertical part of a beam. Thin horizontal parts of a beam are called *flanges*.

† For most cross-sections a much closer approximation to the true maximum shearing stress may be obtained by dividing the shear by the web area *between* the flanges only. For the above example this procedure gives a stress of 9,091 psi, which is only about 8% in error.

‡ If a section *A-A* is taken to the right of the applied force, the direction of the shearing stresses must be reversed as V acts upward there.

steel, as well as that above the neutral axis, is assumed to resist the shearing stresses.

*6-5. Limitations of the Shearing Stress Formula. The shearing stress formula for beams is based on the flexure formula. Hence all of the limitations imposed on the flexure formula apply. The material is assumed to be elastic with the same elastic modulus in tension as in compression. The theory developed applies only to straight beams. More-

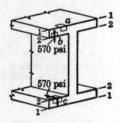

over, there are additional limitations which are not present in the flexure formula. Some of these will be discussed now.

Consider a section through the *I*-beam analyzed in Example 6-4. Some of the results of this analysis are reproduced in Fig. 6-12. The shearing stresses computed earlier for the level 1-1 apply to the infinitesimal element *a*. The vertical shearing stress is zero for this element. Likewise, *no* shearing stresses exist *on* the top plane of the beam. This is as it should be, since the top *surface* of the beam is a *free* surface. In mathematical phraseology this means that the conditions at the boundary are sat-

Fig. 6-12. Boundary conditions are not satisfied by the flange elements at the levels 2-2.

isfied. Similarly, for beams of rectangular cross-section the situation at the boundaries is correct.*

A different situation is discovered when the shearing stresses determined for the *I*-beam at the levels 2-2 are scrutinized. The shearing stresses were found to be 570 psi for the elements such as *b* or *c* shown in the figure. This requires matching horizontal shearing stresses on the inner planes of the flanges. However, the latter planes *must be free* of the shearing stresses as they are *free boundaries* of the beam. This leads to a contradiction which cannot be resolved by the methods of Mechanics of Materials. The more advanced techniques of the Mathematical Theory of Elasticity must be used to obtain a correct solution.

Fortunately, the above defect of the shearing stress formula for beams is not too serious. The shearing stresses in the flanges which were considered† are small. The significant shearing stresses occur in the web and, for all practical purposes, are correctly given by Eq. 6-3. *No appreciable error is involved by using the relations derived in this chapter for thin-walled members*, and the majority of beams belong to this group. Moreover, as stated earlier, the solution for the shearing stresses for a beam with a rectangular cross-section is satisfactory.

---

* Rigorously some error may be shown to exist even in this case. Stresses given by Eq. 6-3 were established on the basis of equilibrium conditions of an element without reference to the conditions of compatibility of all components of strain (Poisson effect, etc.). For more details see Love, A. E. H., *Mathematical Theory of Elasticity*. New York: Dover, 1944, Fourth Edition, Chapter XV.

† Other shearing stresses will be discussed in the next article.

In mechanical applications circular shafts frequently act as beams. Hence beams having a solid circular cross-section form an important class. These beams are not "thin-walled." An examination of the boundary conditions for circular members, Fig. 6-13a, leads to the conclusion that when shearing stresses are present they must act parallel to the boundary. As no matching shearing stress can exist *on* the free sur-

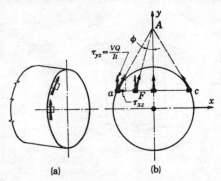

<table>
<tr><td>(a)</td><td>(b)</td></tr>
</table>

Fig. 6-13. Modification of a solution based on the shearing stress formula to satisfy the boundary conditions.

face of the beam, no shearing stress component can act normal to the boundary. However, according to Eq. 6-3, *vertical* shearing stresses of *equal* intensity act at every level such as ac in Fig. 6-13b. This is incompatible with the boundary conditions for the elements as a and c at the boundary, and the solution indicated by Eq. 6-3 is inconsistent.[*] Fortunately, the *maximum* shearing stresses occurring at the neutral axis satisfy the boundary conditions and are very near their true value (within about 5%).[‡]

*6-6. Further Remarks on the Distribution of the Shearing Stresses.

In an I-beam the existence of shearing stresses lying in a longitudinal cut as c-c in Fig. 6-14a was indicated in Art. 6-4. These shearing stresses act perpendicular to the plane of the paper. Their magnitude may be found by applying Eq. 6-3, and their sense follows by considering the bending moments at the adjoining sections through the beam. For example, if for the beam shown in Fig. 6-14b *positive* bending moments increase toward the reader, larger *normal* forces act on the *nearer* cross-section. For the elements shown, $\tau t\, dx$ or $q\, dx$ must aid the smaller force acting on the partial area of the cross-section. This fixes the sense of the shearing stresses in the longitudinal cuts. However, numerically equal shearing stresses act on the mutually perpendicular planes of an *infinites-*

[*] The exact solution of this problem is beyond the scope of this text. However, a better approximation of the true stresses may be obtained rather simply. First an assumption is made that the shearing stress as found by Eq. 6-3 gives a true *component* of the shearing stress acting in the *vertical direction*. Then, since at every level the shearing stresses at the boundary must act tangent to the boundary, the lines of action of these shearing stresses intersect at some point as A in Fig. 6-13b. Thus a second assumption is made that all shearing stresses at a given level act in a direction toward a single point as A in Fig. 6-13b. Whence the shearing stress at any point such as F becomes equal to $\tau_{yz}/\cos \phi$. The stress system found in the above manner is consistent.

[‡] Love, *op. cit.*, p. 348.

imal element, and the shearing stresses on such planes either meet or part with their directional arrowheads at a corner. Hence the sense of the shearing stresses in the plane of the cross-section becomes known also.

The magnitude of the shearing stresses varies for the different vertical cuts. For example, if the cut *c-c* in Fig. 6-14a is at the edge of the beam,

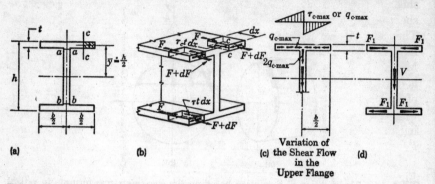

Fig. 6-14. Existence of shearing forces in the flange of an *I*-beam which act perpendicularly to the axis of symmetry.

the *shaded* area of the beam's cross-section is zero. However, if the thickness of the flange is constant, and the cut *c-c* is made progressively closer to the web, the shaded area increases from zero at a linear rate. Moreover, as $\bar{y}$ remains constant for any such area, Q also increases linearly from zero toward the web. Therefore, since V and I are constant at any section through the beam, the shear flow $q_c = VQ/I$ follows the same variation. If the thickness of the flange remains the same, the shearing stress $\tau_c = VQ/It$ varies similarly. The same variation of q_c and τ_c applies on both sides of the axis of symmetry of the cross-section. However, as may be seen from Fig. 6-14b, these quantities in the plane of the cross-section act in *opposite* directions on the two sides. The variation of these shearing stresses or shear flows is represented in Fig. 6-14c, where for simplification it is assumed that the web is very thin.

In common with all stresses, the shearing stresses shown in Fig. 6-14c, when integrated over the area on which they act, are equivalent to a force. The magnitude of the horizontal force F_1 for **one-half** of the flange, Fig. 6-14d, is equal to the *average* shearing stress multiplied by *one-half of the whole area of the flange*, i.e.,

$$F_1 = \left(\frac{\tau_{c\text{-max}}}{2}\right)\left(\frac{bt}{2}\right) \quad \text{or} \quad F_1 = \left(\frac{q_{c\text{-max}}}{2}\right)\left(\frac{b}{2}\right)$$

If an *I*-beam transmits a vertical shear, these horizontal forces act in the upper and lower flanges. However, because of the *symmetry* of the cross-section, these equal forces occur in pairs and *oppose* each other, and cause no apparent external effect.

To determine the shear flow at the juncture of the flange and the web (cut *a-a* in Fig. 6-14a), the *whole* area of the flange times $\bar{y}$ must be used in computing the value of Q. However, since in finding $q_{c\text{-}max}$ *one-half* the flange area times the same $\bar{y}$ has already been used, the *sum* of the *two horizontal shear flows* coming in from opposite sides gives the *vertical* shear flow* at the cut *a-a*. Hence, figuratively speaking, the horizontal shear flows "turn through 90° and merge to become the vertical shear flow." Thence the shear flows at the various horizontal cuts through the web may be determined in the manner explained in the preceding articles. Moreover, as the resistance to the vertical shear V in thin-walled *I*-beams is developed mainly in the web, it is so shown in Fig. 6-14d. The sense of the shearing stresses and shear flows *in the web* coincides with the direction of the shear V. Note that the vertical shear flow "splits" upon reaching the lower flange. This is represented in Fig. 6-14d by the two forces F_1 which are the result of the horizontal shear flows in the flanges.

The shearing forces which act at a section of an *I*-beam are shown in Fig. 6-14d, and, for equilibrium, *the applied vertical forces must act through the centroid of the cross-sectional area* to be coincident with V. If the forces are so applied, *no torsion* of the member will occur. This is true for all sections having cross-sectional areas with an axis of symmetry. To avoid torsion of such members, the applied forces must act in the plane of symmetry of the cross-section and the axis of the beam. A beam with an unsymmetrical section will be discussed next.

*6-7. Shear Center. Consider a beam whose cross-section is a channel, Fig. 6-15a. The walls of this channel are assumed to be so thin that all computations may be based on the dimensions to the *center line* of the

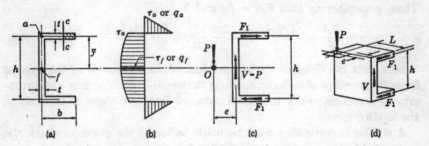

Fig. 6-15. Deriving the location of the shear center for a channel.

walls. Bending of this channel takes place around the horizontal axis, and although this cross-section does not have a vertical axis of symmetry, it will be **assumed** that the bending stresses are given by the usual flexure formula. Assuming further that this channel resists a vertical shear, the bending moments will vary from one section through the beam to another.

---

* The same statement can*not* be made with regard to the shearing stresses as the thickness of the flange may differ from that of the web.

By taking an arbitrary cut as $c\text{-}c$ in Fig. 6-15a, q and τ may be found in the usual manner. Along the horizontal legs of the channel, these quantities vary linearly from the free edge, just as they do for one side of the flange in an I-beam. The variation of q and τ is parabolic along the web. The variation of these quantities is shown in Fig. 6-15b, where they are plotted along the center line of the channel's section.

The *average* shearing stress $\tau_a/2$ multiplied by the area of the flange gives a force $F_1 = (\tau_a/2)bt$, and the sum of the vertical shearing stresses over the area of the web is the shear $V = \displaystyle\int_{-h/2}^{+h/2} \tau t\, dy.$* These shearing forces acting in the plane of the cross-section are shown in Fig. 6-15c and indicate that a force V *and a couple* F_1h are developed at the section through the channel. Physically there is a tendency for the channel to twist around some longitudinal axis. To prevent twisting and thus maintain the applicability of the initially assumed bending stress distribution, the externally applied forces must be applied in such a manner as to *balance the internal couple* F_1h. For example, consider the segment of a cantilever beam of negligible weight, shown in Fig. 6-15d, to which a vertical force P is applied parallel to the web at a distance e from the web's *center line*. To maintain this applied force in equilibrium, an *equal and opposite* shearing force V must be developed in the web. Likewise, to cause *no twisting of the channel*, the couple Pe must *equal* the couple F_1h. At the same section through the channel, the bending moment PL is resisted by the *usual* flexural stresses (these are not shown in the figure).

An expression for the distance e, locating the plane in which the force P must be applied so as to cause *no twist* in the channel, may now be obtained. Thus, remembering that $F_1h = Pe$ and $P = V$,

$$ e = \frac{F_1h}{P} = \frac{(1/2)\tau_a bth}{P} = \frac{bth}{2P}\frac{VQ}{It} = \frac{bth}{2P}\frac{Vbt(h/2)}{It} = \frac{b^2h^2t}{4I} \qquad (6\text{-}6) $$

Note that the distance e is independent of the magnitude of the applied force P, as well as of its location along the beam. The distance e is a property of a section and is measured outward from the *center* of the web to the applied force.

A similar investigation may be made to locate the plane in which the horizontal forces must be applied so as to cause no twist in the channel. However, for the channel considered, by virtue of symmetry, it may be seen that this plane coincides with the neutral plane of the former case. The intersection of these two mutually perpendicular planes with the plane

---

* When the thickness of a channel is variable, it is more convenient to find F_1 and V by using the respective shear flows, i.e., $F_1 = (q_a/2)b$ and $V = \displaystyle\int_{-h/2}^{+h/2} q\, dy$. Since the flanges are thin, the vertical shearing force carried by them is negligible.

of the cross-section locates a point which is called the *shear center*. The shear center is designated by the letter O in Fig. 6-15c. The shear center for any cross-section lies on a longitudinal line parallel to the axis of the beam. *Any transverse force* applied through the shear center causes no torsion of the beam.* A detailed investigation of this problem shows that when a member of any cross-sectional area *is* twisted, the twist takes place around the shear center, which remains fixed. For this reason, the shear center is sometimes called the *center of twist*.

For cross-sectional areas having one axis of symmetry, the shear center is always located on the axis of symmetry. For those which have two axes of symmetry, the shear center coincides with the centroid of the cross-sectional area. This is the case for the I-beam which was considered in the previous article.

The exact location of the shear center for unsymmetrical cross-sections of thick material is difficult to obtain and is known only in a few cases. If the material is *thin*, as has been assumed in the preceding discussion, relatively simple procedures may always be devised to locate the shear center of the cross-section. The usual method consists of determining the shearing forces, as F_1 and V above, at a section, and then finding the location of the external force necessary to keep these forces in equilibrium.

Example 6-5. Find the approximate location of the shear center for a beam with the cross-section of the channel shown in Fig. 6-16.

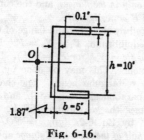

Fig. 6-16.

SOLUTION: Instead of using Eq. 6-6 directly, some further simplifications may be made. The moment of inertia of a thin-walled channel around its neutral axis may be found with sufficient accuracy by neglecting the moment of inertia of the flanges *around their own axes* (only!). This expression for I may then be substituted into Eq. 6-6 and, after simplifications, a formula for e of channels is obtained.

$$I \doteq I_{\text{web}} + (Ad^2)_{\text{flanges}} = \frac{th^3}{12} + 2bt\left(\frac{h}{2}\right)^2 = \frac{th^3}{12} + \frac{bth^2}{2}$$

$$e = \frac{b^2h^2t}{4I} = \frac{b^2h^2t}{4\left(\frac{bth^2}{2} + \frac{th^3}{12}\right)} = \frac{b}{2 + \frac{h}{3b}} \tag{6-6a}$$

---

* See Art. 7-6 for the method of analysis of the lateral forces which do not lie in a plane parallel to one of the principal planes of the cross-sectional area.

Equation 6-6a shows that when the width of flanges b is very large, e approaches its maximum value of $b/2$. When h is very large, e approaches its minimum value of zero. Otherwise, e assumes an intermediate value between these two limits. For the numerical data given in Fig. 6-16,

$$e = \frac{5}{2 + \frac{10}{3(5)}} = 1.87 \text{ in.}$$

Hence the shear center O is $1.87 - 0.05 = 1.82$ in. from the outside vertical face of the channel. The answer would not be improved if Eq. 6-6 were used in the calculations.

Example 6-6. Find the approximate location of the shear center for the cross-section of the I-beam shown in Fig. 6-17a. Note that the flanges are unequal.

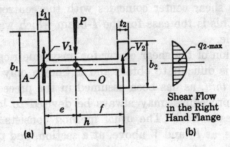

Shear Flow
in the Right
Hand Flange

(a)   (b)

Fig. 6-17.

SOLUTION: This cross-section has a horizontal axis of symmetry, and the shear center is located on it; where remains to be answered. The applied force P causes significant bending and shearing stresses *only in the flanges*, and the contribution of the web to the resistance of the applied force P is negligible.

Let the shearing force resisted by the left-hand flange of the beam be V_1, and by the right-hand flange, V_2. For equilibrium, $V_1 + V_2 = P$. Likewise, to have no twist of the section, from $\Sigma M_A = 0$, $Pe = V_2h$ (or $Pf = V_1h$). Thus only V_2 remains to be determined to solve the problem. This may be done by noting that the right-hand flange is actually an ordinary rectangular beam. The shearing stress (or shear flow) in such a beam is distributed parabolically, Fig. 6-17b, and since the area of a parabola is two-thirds of the base times the maximum altitude, $V_2 = \frac{2}{3}b_2(q_2)_{\text{max}}$. However, since the total shear $V = P$, by Eq. 6-2a $(q_2)_{\text{max}} = VQ/I = PQ/I$, where Q is the statical moment of the *upper half of the right-hand flange* and I is the moment of inertia of the *whole* section. Hence

$$Pe = V_2h = \frac{2}{3}b_2(q_2)_{\text{max}}\, h = \frac{\frac{2}{3}hb_2PQ}{I}$$

$$e = \frac{2hb_2}{3I}Q = \frac{2hb_2}{3I}\frac{b_2t_2}{2}\frac{b_2}{4} = \frac{h}{I}\frac{t_2b_2^3}{12} = \frac{hI_2}{I} \qquad (6\text{-}7)$$

where I_2 is the moment of inertia of the *right-hand flange* around the neutral axis. Similarly, it may be shown that $f = hI_1/I$, where I_1 applies to the *left-hand flange*. If the web of the beam is thin, as originally assumed, $I \doteq I_1 + I_2$, and $e + f = h$, as is to be expected.

A similar analysis leads to the conclusion that the shear center for a symmetrical angle is located at the intersection of the center lines of its legs, as shown in Figs. 6-18a and b. This follows since the shear flow at every section, as c-c, is directed along the center line of a leg. These

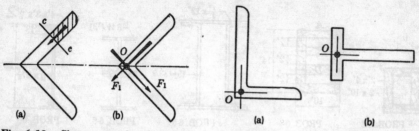

Fig. 6-18.   Shear center for a symmetrical angle (equal legs) located by O.

Fig. 6-19.   Shear center for the sections
shown located by O.

shear flows yield two identical forces F_1 in the legs. The vertical components of these forces equal the vertical shear applied through O. An analogous situation is also found for any angle or T-section as shown in Fig. 6-19a and b. The location of the shear center for various members is particularly important in aircraft applications, and for further details the reader is referred to books on this subject.*

Problems for Solution

6-1. Assuming that a member consists of five 2 in. by 6 in. full-sized wooden planks bolted together, as shown in the cross-sectional view in Fig. 6-4a, show that $A_{fghj}\bar{y}_1 = A_{fgpn}\bar{y}_2$, where $\bar{y}_1$ is the distance from the centroid of the whole area to the area A_{fghj}, and $\bar{y}_2$ the corresponding distance for the area A_{fgpn}.

6-2. A cantilever 10 ft long is fabricated from five full-sized 2 in. by 6 in. wooden planks. Its cross-section is similar to the one shown in Fig. 6-4a. The planks are fastened together by $\frac{3}{4}$ in. diameter vertical bolts spaced 5 in. apart. This beam carries a uniformly distributed load including its own weight of 200 lb/ft. Find the shearing stresses in a bolt which is located 5 ft from the support. Make this investigation at all four planes of contact of the planks. *Ans.* 1,090 psi and 1,640 psi.

6-3. A hollow wooden beam is to be made from full-sized planks as shown in the figure. At the section considered, the total vertical shear in the beam will be 930 lb and the bending moment 50 ft-lb. The nailing is to be done with 16 d (16 penny) box nails that are good for 50 lb each in shear. What must the spacing of nails be? *Ans.* 2 in.

6-4. A beam has the cross-sectional dimensions shown in the figure. It is made up of full-sized 2 in. thick boards nailed together with nails which have a shear resistance of 96 lb each. If the moment of inertia of the whole cross-sectional area around the neutral axis is approximately 1,900 in.^{4} and the shear V at the section considered is 3,800 lb; (a) what should be the longitudinal spacing of the nails connecting board A with boards B and C; (b) what should be the longitudinal spacing of the nails connecting board D with boards B and C? *Ans.* (a) 0.8 in.; (b) 4 in.

6-5. A beam is fabricated from two channels and two cover plates as shown in the figure. If at the section investigated this member transmits a vertical shear of 150 kips and a moment of 450 kip-in., what must the spacing of $\frac{7}{8}$ in. rivets be in each row? Assume that one $\frac{7}{8}$ in. rivet is good for 9.02 kips in shear. *Ans.* $I = 1345$ in.^{4}; 3.48 in.

* Bruhn, E. F., *Analysis and Design of Airplane Structures.* Cincinnati, Ohio: Tri-State Offset Co., 1950.

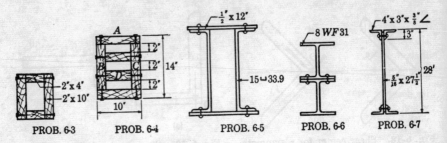

PROB. 6-3　　　PROB. 6-4　　　PROB. 6-5　　　PROB. 6-6　　　PROB. 6-7

6-6. Two 8 WF 31 beams are to be adequately fastened together with two rows of rivets, as shown in the figure, so as to make the two beams act as a unit. At the section considered, the total vertical shear is 40 kips and the bending moment is 2,700 ft-lb. Using $\frac{3}{4}$ in. rivets, which in single shear are good for 6.63 kips each, specify the proper rivet spacing. *Ans.* 4.66 in.

6-7. A plate girder is made up of four equal angles and a web plate as shown in the figure. For the girder around the neutral axis, I is 2,283 in.[4] For a total vertical shear of 81,400 lb and a bending moment of 211,000 ft-lb, determine the required rivet spacing of $\frac{3}{4}$ in. rivets. One rivet is good for 13,250 lb in double shear and 9,380 lb in bearing on $\frac{5}{16}$ in. plate. *Ans.* 4 in.

6-8. A plate girder is made up from two 14 in. by $\frac{1}{2}$ in. cover plates, four 6 in. by 4 in. by $\frac{5}{8}$ in. angles, and a $39\frac{1}{2}$ in. by $\frac{3}{8}$ in. web plate as shown in the figure. If at the section considered a total vertical shear of 150 kips is transmitted, what must the spacing of rivets A and B be? For the girder around the neutral axis, I is 16,132 in.[4] Assume $\frac{3}{4}$ in. rivets and note that one rivet is good for 6.63 kips in single shear, 13.25 kips in double shear and 11.3 kips in bearing on $\frac{3}{8}$ in. plate. *Ans.* Rivets A, 3.3 in. apart.

6-9. A simply supported beam has a cross-section consisting of a 12 ⌐ 20.7 and an 18 WF 50 fastened together by $\frac{3}{4}$ in. diameter rivets spaced longitudinally 6 in. apart in each row as shown in the figure. If this beam is loaded with a downward concentrated force of 112 kips in the middle of the span, what is the shearing stress in the rivets? Neglect the weight of the beam. Of the whole member around the neutral axis, I is 1,120 in.[4] *Ans.* 12.4 ksi.

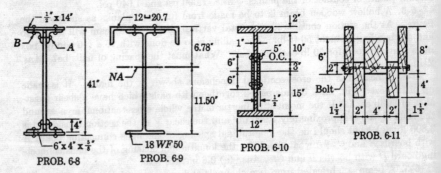

PROB. 6-8　　　PROB. 6-9　　　PROB. 6-10　　　PROB. 6-11

6-10. A T-flange girder is used to support a 200 kip load in the middle of a 24 ft simple span. The dimensions of the girder are given in the figure in a cross-sectional view. If the $\frac{7}{8}$ in. diameter rivets are spaced 5 in. apart longitudinally, what shearing stress will be developed in the rivets by the applied loading? The moment of inertia of the girder around the neutral axis is approximately 11,000 in.[4] *Ans.* 15.8 ksi.

6-11.* A beam is made up from five separate timbers bolted together, as shown in the cross-sectional view. The bolts have a cross-sectional area of 0.5 in.² each and are spaced longitudinally 6 in. apart. If this beam spans 8 ft and supports a load of 1,250 lb/ft including its own weight, what is the maximum shearing stress developed in the bolts? The moment of inertia of the beam's section is 608 in.⁴ *Ans.* 2,380 psi.

6-12. If the allowable shearing stress for Douglas Fir is 100 psi, determine the capacity of a beam having a full-sized cross-section of 2 in. by 4 in. to resist a vertical shear when placed with the 4 in. dimension vertical; when placed with the 2 in. dimension vertical.

6-13. A beam has a cross-sectional area in the form of an isosceles triangle for which the base b is equal to one-half its height h. Using calculus, show that the maximum shearing stress caused by a vertical shear occurs at mid-height, i.e., at $\frac{1}{2}h$ from the base.

6-14. Show that a formula, analogous to Eq. 6-4, for beams having a solid circular cross-section of area A is $\tau_{max} = \frac{4}{3}\frac{V}{A}$.

6-15. Show that a formula, analogous to Eq. 6-4, for thin-walled circular tubes acting as beams having a net cross-sectional area A is $\tau_{max} = 2\frac{V}{A}$.

6-16. A beam having the cross-section of an isosceles triangle with a base $b = 6$ in. and a height $h = 18$ in. is subjected to a shear of 6,000 lb at a section. Find the horizontal shearing stress at the neutral axis and at mid-height. Extrapolate the results and show them on a plot similar to Fig. 6-10c. (*Hint:* see Prob. 6-13.)

6-17. A cast iron beam has a T-section as shown in the figure ($I = 136$ in.⁴). If this beam transmits a vertical shear of 54.4 kips, find the shearing stresses at the levels indicated. Report the results on a plot similar to the one shown in Fig. 6-11e. *Ans.* $\tau_{max} = 5,000$ psi.

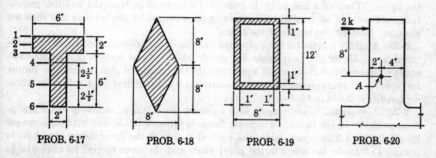

PROB. 6-17   PROB. 6-18   PROB. 6-19   PROB. 6-20

6-18. A beam has a rhombic cross-section as shown in the figure. Assume that this beam transmits a vertical shear of 1,000 lb, and investigate the shearing stresses at levels 2 in. apart beginning with the apex. Report the results on a plot similar to the one shown in Fig. 6-10c. *Ans.* $\tau_{max} = 17.60$ psi.

6-19. A box section having the dimensions shown in the figure is used for a beam on simple supports. In a certain region along the beam there is a constant, linear change in moment of 1,000 in.-lb per in. along the axis of the beam. What is the maximum shearing stress at a section in this region?

6-20. A machine bracket having a rectangular cross-section of $1\frac{1}{2}$ in. by 6 in. is subjected to a horizontal centrally applied force of 2 kips as shown in the figure. Determine the shearing stresses acting on infinitesimal elements located on a line perpendicular to the plane of the paper at A. Show the results on an isolated element. Since this element is also subjected to a bending stress, without computing this stress, indicate the normal stresses of proper sense acting on the element.

6-21. Determine the maximum shearing stress at section A-B for the beam in Example 5-4. Show the result on an infinitesimal element. Does bending stress also act on this element?

6-22. Determine the maximum shearing stress at section A-A for the machine bracket in Example 5-5. Show the results on an infinitesimal element drawn near a free body of the bracket. Does bending stress also act on this element?

6-23. A 14 WF 87 beam supports a uniformly distributed load of 4 kips/ft, including its own weight as shown in the figure. Using Eq. 6-3, determine the shearing stresses acting on the elements at A and B. Show the sense of the computed quantities on infinitesimal elements. If bending stresses also act on these elements, without additional computations, indicate the normal stresses of proper sense acting on the elements.

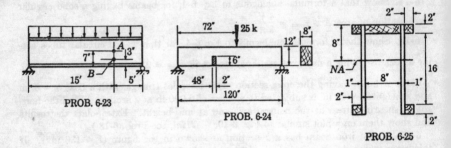

PROB. 6-23   PROB. 6-24

PROB. 6-25

6-24. * A solid beam having an 8 in. by 12 in. cross-section is loaded as shown in the figure. From this beam remove a segment 2 in. by 6 in. by 8 in. shown shaded in the figure. Then on a free-body diagram of this segment indicate the location, magnitude, and sense of all resultant forces acting on it caused by the bending and shearing stresses. Neglect the weight of the beam.

6-25. A girder fabricated from plywood has the cross-sectional dimensions shown in the figure. All longitudinal joints are glued. At a critical section this girder must resist a total vertical shear of 4.0 kips. Specify the quality of glue required by stating its capacity to resist shearing stress as controlled by the critical joint. For the whole section $I_{NA} = 3,648$ in.[4] *Ans.* 30.7 psi.

6-26. A wooden I-beam is made with a narrow lower flange because of space limitations as shown in the figure. The lower flange is fastened to the web with nails spaced longitudinally 1.5 in. apart, while the vertical boards in the lower flange are glued in place. Determine the stress in the glued joints and the force carried by each nail in the nailed joint if the beam is subjected to a vertical shear of 6 kips. Around the neutral axis for the whole section, I is 2,640 in.[4] *Ans.* 60 psi, 565 lb.

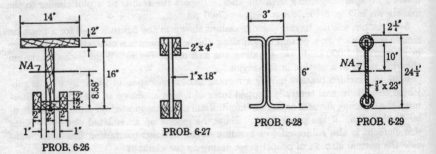

PROB. 6-26   PROB. 6-27   PROB. 6-28   PROB. 6-29

6-27. A beam is made up of four 2 in. by 4 in. full-sized Douglas Fir pieces which are glued to a 1 in. by 18 in. Douglas Fir plywood web as shown in the figure. Determine the maximum allowable shear and the maximum allowable bending moment which this section can carry if the allowable bending stress is 1,500 psi; the allowable shearing stress in wood is 80 psi and the allowable shearing stress in the glued joints is 40 psi.

6-28. The AISI (American Iron and Steel Institute), in the Design Manual for Light Gage Steel, lists a beam section having the dimensions shown in the figure. Such beams are available in several gages of steel. (a) If the channels are made from No. 10 gage (0.135 in. thick) and the allowable bending stress is 18,000 psi, what is the maximum allowable bending moment for this section? (b) What is the maximum allowable shear for the same beam if the allowable shearing stress is 12,000 psi? In computations disregard the small curvature of the plates at the corners. *Ans.* (a) 67.2 k-in., (b) 15.8 k.

6-29.* A beam is fabricated by slotting 4 in. standard steel pipes longitudinally and then securely welding them to a 23 in. by $\frac{3}{8}$ in. web plate as shown in the figure. I of the composite section around the neutral axis is 1,018 in.[4] If at a certain section this beam transmits a vertical shear of 40 kips, determine the shearing stress in the pipe and in the web plate at a level 10 in. above the neutral axis. *Ans.* 1,500 psi, 634 psi.

6-30. Determine the shearing stress along the section A shown in the figure for a 10 WF 21 beam resisting a vertical shear of 20 kips and a bending moment of 30 kip-in. *Ans.* 1,800 psi.

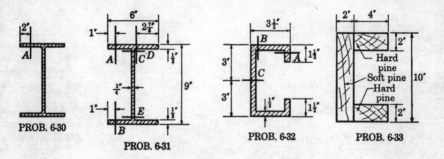

PROB. 6-30   PROB. 6-31   PROB. 6-32   PROB. 6-33

6-31.* A beam having a cross-section with the dimensions shown in the figure is in a region where there is a constant, positive vertical shear of 24 kips. (a) Calculate the shear flow q acting at each of the five sections indicated in the figure. (b) Assuming a positive bending moment of 240 kip-in. at one section and a larger moment at the adjoining section one inch away, draw isometric sketches of each segment of the beam isolated by the sections one inch apart and the five sections (A,B,C,D, and E) shown in the figure, and on the sketches indicate all forces acting on the segments. Neglect vertical shearing stresses in the flanges.

6-32. A beam having the cross-section with the dimensions shown in the figure transmits a vertical shear $V = 7$ kips applied through the shear center. Determine the shearing stresses at sections A, B, and C. I around the neutral axis is 35.7 in.[4] The thickness of the material is $\frac{1}{2}$ in. throughout. *Ans.* 392 psi; 2,000 psi; 2,900 psi.

6-33. A cantilever beam 4 ft long is built up of two kinds of pine planks glued together as shown in the figure. An upward concentrated force of 1,000 lb is to be applied to this beam in such a manner as not to cause any torsional stresses. Where must the force be applied? Assume that the planks may be considered thin. For hard pine $E = 1.5 \times 10^6$ psi; for soft pine $E = 1.0 \times 10^6$ psi. (*Hint:* transform the section into an equivalent section of one material.)

6-34 through 6-37.* Determine the location of the shear center for the beams having the cross-sectional dimensions shown in the figures. In Prob. 6-36 assume that the cross-sectional area of the plate is negligible in comparison with the cross-sectional areas A of the flanges.

Ans. *Prob. 6-36:* $e = \dfrac{\alpha}{\sin \alpha}\, a$ from 0. *Prob. 6-37:* $I = a^3 t\, (\alpha - \sin \alpha \cos \alpha)$ and

$$e = 2a \frac{\sin \alpha - \alpha \cos \alpha}{\alpha - \sin \alpha \cos \alpha}.$$

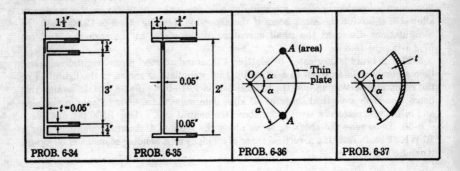

PROB. 6-34   PROB. 6-35   PROB. 6-36   PROB. 6-37

Chapter Seven

COMPOUND STRESSES

7-1. Introduction. All fundamental formulas used in this text for determining stresses resulting from a single element of a force system acting at a section of a stable member have been established in the previous chapters. Of these formulas, those which apply while a material behaves elastically are deemed to be the most significant ones, as nearly all design is based on their use. There are four formulas for straight members and an additional one for curved beams which are particularly important. These formulas may be classified into two groups. The first group gives the *normal* stresses at a point in a section through a member, while the second group gives the *shearing* stresses. The three important formulas belonging to the first group are: $\sigma = P/A$, the normal stress due to an axial force; $\sigma = My/I$, the normal stress for straight members due to bending; and $\sigma = \dfrac{My}{Ae(R-y)}$, the normal stress for curved beams due to bending. In the second group, $\tau = T\rho/J$ gives the shearing stress in a circular shaft due to torque and $\tau = VQ/(It)$ gives the shearing stress caused by a shearing force in a beam.

Next, attention will be directed to the fact that to maintain the equilibrium of a segment of a member, *several elements of a force system may be present simultaneously at a section through the member*. This was repeatedly pointed out in the earlier chapters. In general, at a section through a member, an axial force, a bending moment, a torque, and a shear may be present. If all of these forces occur simultaneously at a section of a member, the general problem of stress analysis results. The treatment of such problems is one of the objectives of this text. However, the purpose of this chapter will be limited to combinations of normal stresses with normal stresses, and shearing stresses with shearing stresses. The first three formulas enumerated earlier give the *normal* stresses on an element of a member. The nature of these stresses, regardless of their cause, is precisely the same. Their addition or superposition will be considered in the first part of this chapter. This will provide the means of obtaining the *normal* stresses caused by an axial force and a bending moment when they act simultaneously. A similar combination of the *shearing* stresses

155

given by the last two equations mentioned above will be discussed in the remainder of the chapter.

7-2. The Basic Approach. When stresses caused by several elements of a force system are to be investigated at a section through a member, the usual method of attack is employed (Art. 1-10). A section is taken normal to the axis of the member under investigation, a segment is isolated to either side of the section, and the system of forces acting at the section is determined (Chapters 1, 3, and 4). The stresses are then calculated *separately* for each element of the force system acting at the section, using one of the formulas summarized in Art. 7-1. Once these stresses are determined, it makes no difference whether the member is straight or curved. Only the *magnitude*, *sense*, and *kind* (i.e., normal or shearing) of stress are significant. Normal stresses, regardless of their cause, are precisely the same kind of stresses. If these stresses act in the same direction on the *same* elementary area of the cross-section, they may be added; if they act in opposite directions they must be subtracted from each other. The resultant of two (or more) shearing stresses may be obtained in an analogous manner.

The above technique of algebraic addition of the same kind of stresses to obtain the resultant or the *compound* stress, as it will be called in this text, is justified by the principle of *superposition*. This principle was used in Art. 2-8 when the generalized Hooke's law was discussed. It asserts that the resultant stress or strain due to *several* forces in any system is the algebraic sum of the effects caused by the individual forces. Superposition of stresses is permissible if each stress is directly and *linearly* related to the force causing the stress. The principle of superposition will be repeatedly used in the remainder of the book. However, it cannot be used if deformations or deflections due to one force cause an abnormal change in the effect of another force, such as in columns (Chapter 13).

The determination of compound stresses using the principle of superposition will now be illustrated by several examples.

Example 7-1. A 2 in. by 3 in. (3 in. side vertical) bar of negligible weight is supported at L and R and is loaded as shown in Fig. 7-1a. Determine the maximum tensile and compressive stresses acting normal to the section through the beam, i.e., find the maximum compound normal stresses.

SOLUTION: To emphasize the method of superposition this problem is solved by dividing it into two parts. In Fig. 7-1b the bar is shown subjected *only* to the axial force, while in Fig. 7-1c the same bar is shown subjected *only* to the transverse force. For the axial force the normal stress throughout the length of the bar is

$$\sigma = \frac{P}{A} = \frac{6,000}{2(3)} = +1,000 \text{ psi} \quad \text{(tension)}$$

this result is indicated in Fig. 7-1d. The normal stresses due to the transverse force depend on the magnitude of the bending moment, and the maximum bending moment occurs at the applied force. As the left reaction is 600 lb, $M_{max} = 600(15) = 9,000$

in.-lb. From the flexure formula, the maximum stresses at the extreme fibers caused
by this moment are

$$\sigma = \frac{Mc}{I} = \frac{6M}{bh^2} = \pm 3{,}000 \text{ psi}$$

These stresses act *normal* to the section of the beam and decrease linearly toward the
neutral axis as is shown in Fig. 7-1e. Then to obtain the compound stress for any
particular element, bending stresses must be added algebraically to the direct tensile
stress. Thus, as may be seen from Fig. 7-1f, at point A the resultant *normal* stress is
2,000 psi compression, while at C it is 4,000 psi tension, Fig. 7-1g. By investigating
other sections along the beam, similar calculations will lead to the compound stresses
for these sections. Since the bending moment varies along the beam, these stresses
will be different at different sections.

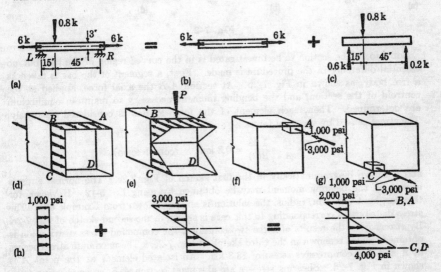

Fig. 7-1.

Instead of the isometric views, side views of the stress vectors are commonly used,
as shown in Fig. 7-1h. However, the reader should always remember the three-dimensional aspect of the problem. Note that in the final result, the line of zero stress,
which lies on the neutral axis for flexure, moves upwards. Also note that the local
stresses, caused by the concentrated force, which act normal to the top surface of the
beam, were not considered. Generally these stresses are treated independently as
local *bearing* stresses.

Although in this problem the given axial force is larger than the transverse force, bending causes higher stresses. Similar situations are found in many cases where the
stresses caused by an axial force are negligible. However, the reader is cautioned not
to regard *slender* members, particularly compression members, in the same light (see
Art. 13-10). In slender rods transversely applied forces cause considerable deflections.
These deflections, multiplied by the magnitude of an axial force, induce additional
bending moments, which for an axial compression force add to the moments considered
here. In this solution the effect on stresses caused by the deflection of the beam is
neglected. This is common practice as *usually* such deflections are very small.

*Example 7-2. A 2 in. by 2 in. bar bent into the shape of a U shown in Fig. 7-2a is acted upon by two opposing forces P of $1\frac{1}{3}$ kips each. Determine the maximum normal stress occurring at the section A-B.

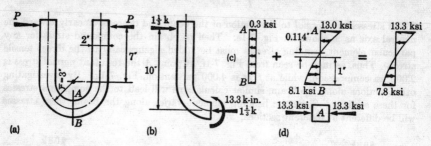

Fig. 7-2.

SOLUTION: The section to be investigated is in the curved region of the bar, but no essential difference in the procedure is made. First, a segment of the bar is taken as a free body, as shown in Fig. 7-2b. At section A-B the axial force, applied at the centroid of the section, and the bending moment necessary to maintain equilibrium are determined. Then, each element of the force system is considered separately. The stress caused by the axial forces is

$$\sigma = \frac{P}{A} = \frac{1.33}{2(2)} = 0.3 \text{ ksi} \qquad \text{(compression)}$$

and is shown diagrammatically in the first sketch of Fig. 7-2c. The normal stresses caused by the bending moment may be obtained by using Eq. 5-12. However, for this bar, bent to a 3 in. radius, the solution is already known from Example 5-9. The stress distribution corresponding to this case is shown in the second sketch of Fig. 7-2c. By *superposing* the results of these two solutions, the compound stress distribution is obtained. This is shown in the third sketch of Fig. 7-2c. The maximum stress occurs at A and is a compressive stress of 13.3 ksi. An isolated element at the point A is shown in Fig. 7-2d. Shearing stresses are absent at section A-B, as no shearing force is necessary to maintain equilibrium of the segment shown in Fig. 7-2b. The relative insignificance of the stress caused by the axial force is striking.

Problems similar to the above commonly occur in machine design. Hooks, C-clamps, frames of punch presses, etc., illustrate the variety of situations to which the foregoing methods of analysis must be applied.

Example 7-3. A small dam of triangular shape as shown in Fig. 7-3a is made from concrete, which weighs approximately 150 lb per cu ft. Find the normal stress distribution at section A-B when the water behind the dam is at the level indicated. For the purpose of calculation, consider one lineal foot of the dam in the direction perpendicular to the plane of the paper as an isolated beam. Use units of feet and kips.

SOLUTION: Pass a section at the required level* and isolate a part of the body as shown in Fig. 7-3b. The hydrostatic pressure acting on the vertical upstream face of

---

* This section is made horizontally. This departs from strict adherence to the method of sectioning discussed earlier. The axis of the dam bisects the angle ACB, and according to the procedures discussed earlier the section should be made perpendicular to this axis. However, it is customary to analyze masonry structures by taking *horizontal* sections. This follows from analogy with the section at the ground level which is horizontal.

the dam causes the horizontal force H. This force is equal to the *average* pressure acting on the dam multiplied by the contact area, and as the pressure varies linearly from the free surface of the water, it acts 3 ft above the A-B level. The unit weight of water is assumed to be 62.4 lb per cu ft.

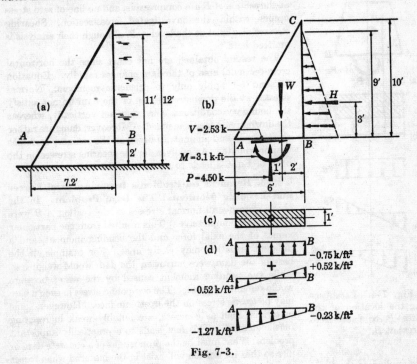

Fig. 7-3.

The weight of the "beam" W, which is the weight of a one-foot section of the dam, is equal to the volume of concrete above the A-B level multiplied by the unit weight of concrete. The resultant of this gravity force acts through the *centroid* of the concrete volume, i.e., 2 ft from the upstream face of the dam. The plan view of section A-B is shown in Fig. 7-3c. The centroid and the neutral axis of *this cross-sectional area* are midway between the upstream and the downstream faces of the dam. Thus the usual free-body diagram for a segment of the beam is completed as shown in Fig. 7-3b, where an "axial" force, a shear, and a bending moment are indicated. The problem of determining the compound normal stresses at section A-B is then solved by applying Eqs. 1-1 and 5-1 and superposing the results. This process is shown in Fig. 7-3d.

$$H = V = [(\tfrac{1}{2})9(62.4)](9)1 = 2,530 \text{ lb} = 2.53 \text{ kips}$$

$$W = P = [(\tfrac{1}{2})6(10)1]150 = 4,500 \text{ lb} = 4.50 \text{ kips}$$

$$M = H(3) - W(1) = (2.53)3 - (4.50)1 = 3.10 \text{ kip-ft}$$

$$\sigma_B = -\frac{W}{A} + \frac{Mc}{I} = \frac{4.50}{6(1)} + \frac{(3.10)3}{\tfrac{1}{12}(6)^3} = -0.75 + 0.52$$

$$= -0.23 \text{ kips per ft}^2 \quad \text{(compression)}$$

$$\sigma_A = -\frac{W}{A} - \frac{Mc}{I} = -0.75 - 0.52 = -1.27 \text{ kips per ft}^2 \quad \text{(compression)}$$

The normal stresses caused by bending vary linearly from the neutral axis of the cross-section at *A-B*. When these stresses are superposed on the uniform stress caused by the force *P* the final stress distribution shown in Fig. 7-3d results. Note that in this particular case all normal stresses at the section *A-B* are compressive, and no line of zero stress occurs within the investigated cross-section. Shearing stresses also exist at the level *A-B*, although their analysis is omitted here.

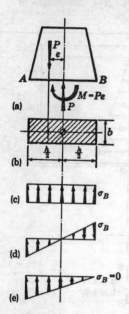

Fig. 7-4. Establishing the location of the force *P* to cause zero stress at *B*.

The results obtained are not exact since the horizontal cross-sectional area of the dam changes rapidly. Equation 1-1 and 5-1 apply only to prismatic members. Normal stresses at the downstream face of the dam do not satisfy the boundary conditions, since they act vertically, whereas the downstream face is inclined. Moreover, dams are rather *short* beams, and an analysis based on the ordinary formulas is approximate. An analysis for the shearing stresses on the basis of Eq. 6-3 leads to wrong results.*

*7-3. Remarks on Problems Involving Axial Forces and Bending Moments: The Dam Problem. In the above example all normal stresses at the section *A-B* were found to be compressive. This resulted from the particular values of the axial force and the bending moment, and a different situation may easily arise. For example, if the base of the dam were narrower, the dam would weigh less, while the bending moment caused by the water pressure would remain the same. The compound stress in such a case may be *tensile* stress on the upstream face. However, some materials, such as concrete, are notably weak in resisting tensile stresses. This fact leads to a practically important problem: What must be the proportions of a concrete dam or pier so that no tension will exist in the material when forces are applied to the structure?

To answer this question, consider a segment of a member above a section *A-B* as shown in Fig. 7-4a. The cross-sectional area at *A-B* is assumed to be rectangular as shown in Fig. 7-4b. Let the *resultant* of all of the applied forces above the section *A-B* be a vertical force, and let it act at a distance *e* from the centroid of the cross-sectional area at *A-B*. Then at the section *A-B*, to maintain this segment in equilibrium, there must be an axial force *P* and a bending moment *Pe*, Fig. 7-4a. The stress caused by the axial force is $\sigma = \dfrac{P}{A} = \dfrac{P}{bh}$, while the maximum stress caused by bending is $\sigma_{max} = \dfrac{Mc}{I}$ $= \dfrac{M}{Z} = \dfrac{6Pe}{bh^2}$, where $\dfrac{bh^2}{6}$ is the section modulus of the *rectangular* cross-section. The complete stress distributions across the section *A-B* corresponding to these two effects are shown in Figs. 7-4c and d, respectively.

To satisfy the desired condition that the stress at *B* be zero, it follows that

$$\sigma_B = -\frac{P}{bh} + \frac{6Pe}{bh^2} = 0 \quad \text{or} \quad e = \frac{h}{6}$$

which means that if the force *P* is applied at a distance of *h*/6 from the centroidal axis of the cross-section, the stress at *B* is just zero. The compound normal stress distribu-

* For further details see Timoshenko, S. and Goodier, J. N., *Theory of Elasticity*, pp. ᵥ4 and 96. New York: McGraw-Hill, 1951, Second Edition.

tion across the whole section becomes "triangular" as is shown in Fig. 7-4e. If the force P were applied closer to the centroid of the section, a smaller bending moment would be developed at the section A-B, and there would be some compression stress at B. The same argument may be repeated for the force acting to the right of the centroidal axis. Hence a practical rule, much used by designers of masonry structures may be formulated thus: *If the resultant of all vertical forces acts within the middle third of the rectangular cross-section, there is no tension in the material at that section.* It is understood that the resultant acts in a vertical plane containing one of the axes of symmetry of the rectangular cross-sectional area.

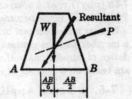

Fig. 7-5. The resultant shown acting at its extreme left-hand position to cause no tension at B.

The foregoing discussion may be generalized in order to apply to any planar system of forces acting on a member. The resultant of these forces may be made to intersect the plane of the cross-section as is shown in Fig. 7-5. At the point of intersection of this resultant with the section it may be resolved into horizontal and vertical components. If the vertical component of the resultant fulfills the conditions of the former problem, no tension will be developed at point B, as the horizontal component causes only shearing stresses. Hence, a more general "middle third" rule may be stated thus: there will be no tension at a section of a member of a *rectangular* cross-section if the resultant of the forces above this section *intersects* one of the axes of symmetry of the section within the middle third.

7-4. A Special Limitation: The Chimney Problem. At times it is impossible to achieve a situation where the resultant would pass through the "middle third" of a rectangular cross-section as discussed in the previous article. However, at some sections through a member, or between two different members, no tensile stresses may be transmitted. For example, no tensile stresses can be developed at the surface of contact of a concrete foundation for a tall chimney with the soil. On the other hand, the resultant of a horizontal force caused by the wind blowing on the chimney and the vertical force due to the weight of the chimney itself may pass outside the "middle third" of the *rectangular* foundation.

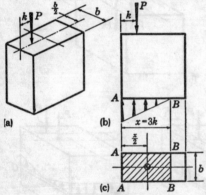

Fig. 7-6. Stress distribution between two surfaces which are unable to transmit tensile forces.

Under these circumstances the method of analysis discussed in the preceding article must be modified.

Consider the weightless rectangular block shown in Fig. 7-6a to which is applied, outside of the "middle third," a vertical force P at a distance k from one of the faces in the middle of the block's dimension b. Suppose next that at the contact surface of the block with the foundation no stresses exist to the right of the point B shown in Fig. 7-6b. Thus, it is assumed that only the portion AB of the foundation, x long by b wide, is effective in resisting the applied force P. This corresponds to the shaded area in Fig. 7-6c. The stress along the line B-B is zero by assumption. Hence the following equation for the stress at B may be written.

$$\sigma_B = -\frac{P}{xb} + P\left(\frac{x}{2} - k\right)\frac{6}{bx^2} = 0$$

where $(x/2) - k$ is the eccentricity of the applied force with respect to the centroidal axis of the shaded contact area, and $bx^2/6$ is its section modulus. Solving for x, it is found that $x = 3k$, and the pressure distribution will be "triangular" as shown in Fig. 7-6b (why?). As k decreases, the intensity of pressure on the line A-A increases; when k is zero, the block becomes unstable.

Similar reasoning can be applied to problems where a number of forces are acting on a member and the contact area is of any shape. Such problems are important in the design of foundations. However, since soil is never completely elastic and the solutions are based on a number of idealizations, they are approximate.

7-5. A Force Applied to a Prismatic Member Anywhere Parallel to Its Axis. The compound stresses considered so far were caused by an axial force and a bending moment which acts around an axis perpendicular to the plane of symmetry of the cross-section. The same procedure may be used in an analogous situation where the cross-sectional area is *un-*

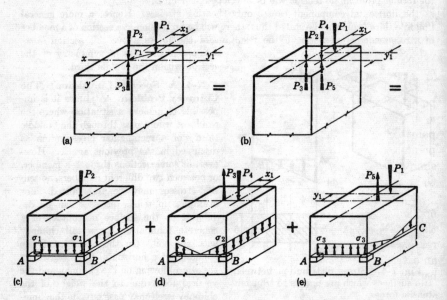

Fig. 7-7. Resolution of the given problem into three separate problems, each one of which may be solved by the methods previously discussed.

symmetrical, provided the bending moment acts around one of the *principal axes* of the cross-section (Art. 5-7). However, sometimes the bending moments are not applied in the above manner. For example, consider the force P_1 applied to a rectangular, weightless block shown in Fig. 7-7a at a distance r_1 from the centroid of the cross-section. The x- and the y-axes shown in the figure are the axes of symmetry of the block's cross-section,* and the location of the force P_1 may also be defined by the co-ordinates x_1 and y_1.

The force P_1 is not centrally applied to the block, so, to proceed, a *statically equivalent system* may be set up by introducing two equal and opposite forces P_2 and P_3 at the centroid of the section. These forces are both numerically equal to P_1, and adding them to the system does not change the problem. The force P_2 acts axially on the block, and a bending moment $P_1 r_1$ *acts in the plane of the two forces P_1 and P_3.* This bending moment does not act in the plane of either of the principal axes of the cross-section, and no adequate formula for such a condition has been derived in this text. Hence two additional equal and opposite forces, P_4 and P_5 (both equal to P_1), are introduced at a distance x_1 from the centroid of the section. The five forces shown in Fig. 7-7b still represent the initial problem from the point of view of statics. However, this equivalent problem may now be divided into the three separate problems shown in Figs. 7-7c, d, and e. In the respective diagrams, P_2 is an axial force, and $P_4 x_1$ causes only bending around the principal y-axis, and $P_1 y_1$ around the x-axis. The usual axial and flexure stress formulas are applicable for these cases. By applying these formulas and superposing the computed stresses, the net or the compound normal stress may be obtained at any point. For example, from Figs. 7-7c, d, and e it may be seen that point A in the block has a compressive stress of σ_1 and tensile stresses of σ_2 and σ_3 acting on it. This is the highest stressed point in *tension*. At point B, σ_1 and σ_2 are compressive, while σ_3 is a tensile stress. Any other point lying in the plane of the cross-sectional area of the block may be similarly examined. The highest stressed point in *compression* occurs at C, as at this point all three stresses reach their maxima in compression.

The above procedure illustrates the manner in which an eccentrically applied force may be thought of as being resisted at one of the sections through the member. For use in the known stress analysis formulas the resolved system of forces at a section through the member must consist of an *axial force* P which acts through the *centroid* of such a section, and *two* bending moments M_{xx} and M_{yy} which act respectively *around the principal* x- and y-axes of the cross-section. The expression which gives the compound normal stress at any point located by the co-ordinates x and y on the cross-section is

$$\sigma = \pm \frac{P}{A} \pm \frac{M_{xx}y}{I_{xx}} \pm \frac{M_{yy}x}{I_{yy}} \tag{7-1}$$

where A is the cross-sectional area of the member, and I_{xx} and I_{yy} are the moments of inertia of the cross-sectional area *around the respective principal axes*. In Eq. 7-1, positive signs correspond to tensile stresses, negative to compressive stresses.

* For an *unsymmetrical* cross-section these axes should be the *principal* axes.

Example 7-4. Find the stress distribution at the section $ABCD$ for the block shown in Fig. 7-8a if $P = 14.4$ kips. At the same section, locate the line of zero stress. Neglect the weight of the block.

SOLUTION: To maintain the upper part of the block in equilibrium, there are three elements of a force system at the required section. Conversely, the forces acting *on* the section $ABCD$, Fig. 7-8c, are an axial downward force $P = 14.4$ kips, a bending moment M_{yy} of $14.4(6) = 86.4$ kip-in. acting counterclockwise around the y-axis when viewed from the side AB, and a bending moment M_{xx} of $14.4(3 + 3) = 86.4$ kip-in. acting counterclockwise around the x-axis when viewed from the side BC. The cross-section of the block $A = 6(12) = 72$ in.², and the respective section moduli are $Z_{xx} =$

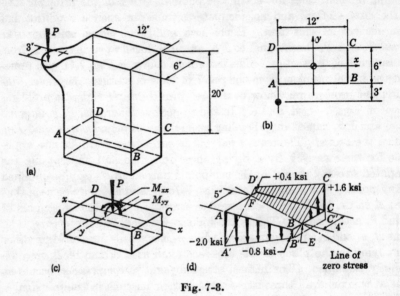

Fig. 7-8.

$12(6)^2/6 = 72$ in.³ and $Z_{yy} = 6(12)^2/6 = 144$ in.³ Hence, using a relation equivalent to Eq. 7-1, the compound normal stresses for the *corner* elements are:

$$\sigma = -\frac{P}{A} \pm \frac{M_{xx}}{Z_{xx}} \pm \frac{M_{yy}}{Z_{yy}} = -\frac{14.4}{72} \pm \frac{86.4}{72} \pm \frac{86.4}{144} = -0.2 \pm 1.2 \pm 0.6$$

where the units of stress are kips per square inch. The sense of the forces shown in Fig. 7-8c determines the signs of stresses. Therefore, if the subscript of the stress signifies its location, the corner normal stresses are:

$$\sigma_A = -0.2 - 1.2 - 0.6 = -2.0 \text{ ksi}$$
$$\sigma_B = -0.2 - 1.2 + 0.6 = -0.8 \text{ ksi}$$
$$\sigma_C = -0.2 + 1.2 + 0.6 = +1.6 \text{ ksi}$$
$$\sigma_D = -0.2 + 1.2 - 0.6 = +0.4 \text{ ksi}$$

These stresses acting at the corners of the section $ABCD$ are shown in Fig. 7-8d. The ends of these four stress vectors at A', B', C', and D' lie in the plane $A'B'C'D'$. This follows from the fact that the stress vectors normal to the section due to any one of the three effects considered in this problem terminate on a plane, and a triple superposition of such planes defines a plane. For the same reason, the vertical distance between the planes $ABCD$ and $A'B'C'D'$ defines the compound stress at any point on the cross-section. Hence the intersection of the plane $A'B'C'D'$ with the plane $ABCD$ locates the line FE where no stresses exist. This line is called the **line of zero stress**.

By drawing a line $B'C''$ parallel to BC, similar triangles $C'B'C''$ and $C'EC$ are obtained, whence the distance $CE = \dfrac{1.6}{1.6 + 0.8}$ (6) $= 4$ in. Similarly, the distance AF is found to be 5 in. Points E and F locate the line of zero stress. If the weight of the block is neglected, the stress distribution on any other section parallel to $ABCD$ is the same.

If the compound stresses at a section are all tensile or all compressive, the planes corresponding to the planes $ABCD$ and $A'B'C'D'$ may be extended beyond the actual cross-sectional area of the member until they intersect. This gives a *fictitious* line of zero stress. However, as in the former case, the stresses vary linearly from the line of zero stress as their respective perpendicular distances from this line.

*Example 7-5. Find the zone over which the vertical force P may be applied to the rectangular weightless block shown in Fig. 7-9a without causing any tensile stresses at the section A-B.

SOLUTION: The force P is placed at a general point (x, y) in the first quadrant of the x-y co-ordinate system shown. Then by employing the same reasoning as was used in the preceding example, it is seen that with this position of the force the greatest tend-

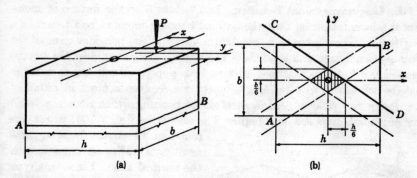

Fig. 7-9.

ency for a tensile stress exists at A. Next, an expression may be set up for the stress at point A for the chosen position of the force. Setting this equation for stress equal to zero fulfills the limiting condition of the problem, as locating the force P toward the centroid of the cross-section would certainly cause no tension at the point A. Thus

$$\sigma_A = 0 = -\frac{P}{A} + \frac{M_{xx}}{Z_{xx}} + \frac{M_{yy}}{Z_{yy}} = -\frac{P}{bh} + \frac{Py}{b^2 h/6} + \frac{Px}{bh^2/6} = 0$$

Simplifying, $\dfrac{x}{h/6} + \dfrac{y}{b/6} = 1$, which is an equation of a straight line. This equation shows that when $x = 0$, $y = b/6$; while when $y = 0$, $x = h/6$. Hence this line may be represented by the line CD in Fig. 7-9b. A vertical force may be applied to the block anywhere on this line and the stress at A will be zero. Similar lines may be established for the other three corners of the section; these are shown in Fig. 7-9b. If the force P is applied on any one of these lines, or on any line parallel to such a line *toward* the centroid of the section, there will be no tensile stress at the corresponding corner. Hence the force P may be applied anywhere *within* the shaded area shown in Fig. 7-9b without causing any tensile stress at *any* of the four corners, or anywhere else. This zone of the cross-sectional area is called the **kern** of a section. By limiting the possible location of the force to the lines of symmetry of the rectangular cross-section, the results found in this example verify the "middle third" rule discussed in Art. 7-3.

The foregoing method of analysis may also be used for tension members, but it applies only for *short* blocks in compression. Slender bars in compression require a special treatment (Chapter 13). Near the point of application of the force, the analysis used in this and the preceding example is incorrect. In the neighborhood of this point the stress distribution is somewhat similar to the one shown in Fig. 2-16. On the other hand, although the cross-sectional area of the block considered in this example was rectangular, the theory is not so limited. The same method of stress analysis may be used for a member with any cross-sectional area, provided the axes of the cross-sectional area around which bending moments are taken are the *principal axes*. By definition the principal axes are those about which the rectangular moment of inertia is a maximum or a minimum. An axis of symmetry is always a principal axis, and the principal axes are mutually perpendicular.

7-6. Unsymmetrical Bending. In Chapter 5 on the flexure of members it was emphasized that the applied bending moment had to act in a longitudinal plane parallel to one or the other of the principal axes of the cross-sectional area and the axis of the beam. Only then does the flexure formula for beams developed in this text apply. However, a member may be subjected to a bending moment which does not act in either of the above two planes. An illustration of bending which does not fulfill the limitation imposed in Chapter 5 is shown in Fig. 7-10a, where the plane in which the bending moment acts makes an angle α with the vertical axis. Since this type of bending does not occur in a plane of symmetry of the cross-section, it is called *unsymmetrical bending*. It represents the general case of flexure for which a general flexure formula may be derived. Such a formula is quite complicated and will not be discussed in this text.* However, in principle, this general problem has already been solved in Art. 7-5 by the method of superposition. There, as may be seen from Fig. 7-7a, in addition to the stresses caused by the axial force P_2, the bending stresses caused by the moment applied in the plane containing the forces P_1 and P_3 were

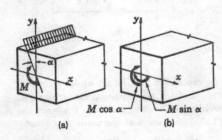

Fig. 7-10. (a) bending moment in a plane which is not coincident with either of the principal axes, and (b) components of the bending moment in the planes of the principal axes.

*See Bruhn, E. F., *Analysis and Design of Airplane Structures.* Cincinnati, Ohio: Tri-State Offset Co., 1950.

determined. This is an example of unsymmetrical bending and will be elaborated upon here.

As is known from the Principles of Mechanics, any couple, which may be a bending moment at a section of a beam, may be resolved into components. Hence a bending moment such as shown in Fig. 7-10a may be resolved into the two components shown in Fig. 7-10b. The component of the bending moment M acting around the x-axis is $M \cos \alpha$, while the one acting around the y-axis is $M \sin \alpha$.* The sense of each component follows from the sense of the total moment M. This procedure may always be used to find the bending moments which act only around the principal axes of the cross-section. Then these moments may be used *separately* in the usual flexure formula, and the compound normal stresses follow by superposition. If a member is subjected to *pure* unsymmetrical bending, this procedure gives all the stresses acting at a section through the member. On the other hand, if the bending moment is caused by a transverse force, shearing stresses will also be developed. These will be discussed later.

Example 7-6. The 4 in. by 6 in. (actual size) wooden beam shown in Fig. 7-11a is used to support a uniformly distributed load of 1,000 lb (total) on a simple span of 10 ft. The applied load acts in a plane making an angle of 30° with the vertical, as shown in Fig. 7-11b and again in Fig. 7-11c. Calculate the maximum bending stress at mid-span, and, for the same section, locate the neutral axis. Neglect the weight of the beam.

SOLUTION: The maximum bending *in the plane of the applied load* occurs at the midspan, and according to Example 4-6 it is equal to $wL^2/8$ or $WL/8$, where W is the total load on the span L. Hence

$$M = \frac{WL}{8} = \frac{1,000(10)}{8} = 1,250 \text{ ft-lb}$$

Next, this moment is resolved into components acting around the respective axes, i.e.,

$$M_{xx} = M \cos \alpha = 1,250\left(\frac{\sqrt{3}}{2}\right)12 = 13,000 \text{ in.-lb}$$

$$M_{yy} = M \sin \alpha = 1,250(0.5)12 = 7,500 \text{ in.-lb}$$

* For the reader familiar with vectorial representation of a couple, Fig. 7-A is suggested for consideration. Here the bending moment M is shown by a vector with a

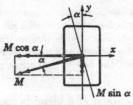

Fig. 7-A.

double-headed arrow, the sense of which coincides with the direction in which a right-hand screw would advance if turned in the direction of the sense of rotation of the moment. Thence resolution of this moment is carried out as for a force.

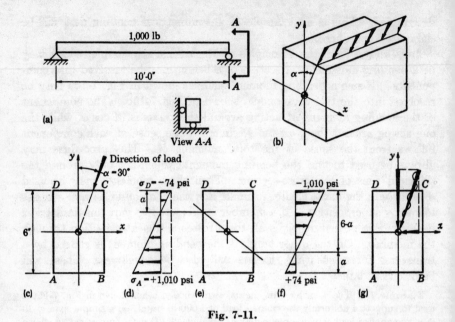

Fig. 7-11.

By considering the nature of the flexural stress distribution about both principal axes of the cross-section, it may be concluded that the maximum tensile stress occurs at A The maximum compressive stress is at C. The values of these stresses follow by super posing the stresses caused by each moment independently. Stresses at the other two corners of the cross-section are similarly determined.

$$\sigma_A = \frac{M_{xx}c_1}{I_{xx}} + \frac{M_{yy}c_2}{I_{yy}} = \frac{13,000(3)}{\dfrac{4(6)^3}{12}} + \frac{7,500(2)}{\dfrac{6(4)^3}{12}}$$

$$= +542 + 468 = +1,010 \text{ psi} \qquad \text{(tension)}$$
$$\sigma_B = +542 - 468 = +74 \text{ psi} \qquad \text{(tension)}$$
$$\sigma_C = -542 - 468 = -1,010 \text{ psi} \qquad \text{(compression)}$$
$$\sigma_D = -542 + 468 = -74 \text{ psi} \qquad \text{(compression)}$$

It is seen from this solution that the compound normal stresses at A and C are numerically equal.

The neutral axis, which is a line of zero stress in a beam, may be located in the same manner as was done in Example 7-4. However, the simplified diagrams shown in Fig. 7-11d and f serve the same purpose. From similar triangles, $a/(6 - a) = 74/1,010$, or $a = 0.41$ in. This locates the neutral axis shown in Fig. 7-11e. Note that since no axial force acts on the member, the line of zero stress passes through the centroid of the cross-sectional area.

When unsymmetrical bending of a beam is caused by applied transverse forces, another procedure equivalent to the above *is usually more convenient.* The applied forces are first resolved into components which act parallel to the principal axes of the cross-sectional area. Then the bending moments caused by these components around the respective axes are computed for use in the flexure formula. For the above example, such components of the applied load are shown in Fig. 7-11g. Note that to avoid *torsional* stresses the applied transverse forces must act through the shear center. For bilaterally symmetrical sections, e.g., a rectangle, a circle, an *I*-beam, etc., *the shear center coincides with the geometric center (centroid) of the cross-section.* For other cross-sections, such as a channel, the shear center lies elsewhere, as at *O* shown in Fig. 7-12, Art. 6-7, and it is at this point that the transverse force must be applied to prevent occurrence of torsional stresses. Single angles acting as beams must be treated similarly (see Fig. 6-19). For analysis of unsymmetrical bending, the applied forces must be resolved *at* the shear center parallel to the principal axes of the cross-section.

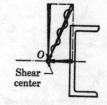

Fig. 7-12. Application of a lateral force through the shear center. No torsion is caused in the beam.

7-7. Superposition of Shearing Stresses. In some situations shearing stresses arise from torsion *and* a direct shearing force. The shearing stresses caused by each of these were discussed earlier in the text. In the chapter on torsion, only circular and thin-walled members were discussed in detail. This limits the type of problems which may be solved here. For problems where both torsional and direct shearing stresses may be determined, the compound *shearing* stress may be found by *superposition*. This procedure is analogous to the one used earlier for compound normal stresses. However, while normal stresses act only toward or away from an element of a member, shearing stresses in the plane of a cut may act in *any* direction. This results in a more difficult stress analysis problem, and the general solution is beyond the scope of this book. Attention will be directed to instances where the shearing stresses being superposed have the *same line of action*. This limitation excludes relatively few significant problems.

Example 7-7. Find the maximum shearing stress due to the applied forces in the plane *A-B* of the ½ in. diameter high-strength shaft shown in Fig. 7-13a.

SOLUTION: Since only the stresses due to the applied forces are wanted, the weight of the shaft need not be considered. The free body of a segment of the shaft is shown in Fig. 7-13b. The system of forces at the cut necessary to keep this segment in equilibrium consists of a torque, $T = 200$ in.-lb, a shear, $V = 60$ lb, and a bending moment, $M = 240$ in.-lb.

Due to the torque T, the shearing stresses in the cut A-B vary linearly from the axis of the shaft and reach the maximum value given by Eq. 3-3, $\tau_{max} = Tc/J$. These maximum shearing stresses, agreeing in sense with the *resisting* torque T, are shown at points A, B, D, and E in Fig. 7-13c.

The "direct" shearing stresses caused by the shearing force V may be obtained by using Eq. 6-3, $\tau = VQ/(It)$. For the elements A and B, Fig. 7-13d, $Q = 0$, hence $\tau = 0$. The shearing stress reaches its maximum value at the level ED. For this, Q is equal to the shaded area shown in Fig. 7-13d multiplied by the distance from its centroid to the neutral axis. The latter quantity is $\bar{y} = 4c/(3\pi)$, where c is the radius of the cross-sectional area. Hence $Q = \left(\dfrac{\pi c^2}{2}\right)\left(\dfrac{4c}{3\pi}\right) = 2c^3/3$. Moreover, since $t = 2c$, and $I = J/2 = \pi c^4/4$, the maximum direct shearing stress is

$$\tau_{max} = \frac{VQ}{It} = \frac{V}{2c}\frac{2c^3}{3}\frac{4}{\pi c^4} = \frac{4V}{3\pi c^2} = \frac{4}{3}\frac{V}{A}$$

where A is the *entire* cross-sectional area of the rod. (A similar expression was derived in Example 6-3 for a beam of rectangular section.) In Fig. 7-13d this shearing stress is shown acting down on the elementary areas at E, C, and D. This direction agrees with the direction of the shear V.

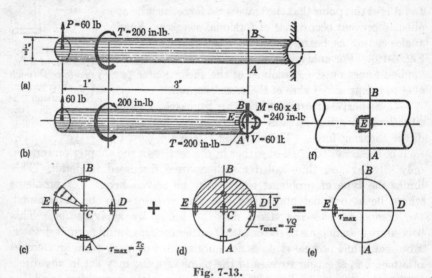

Fig. 7-13.

To find the maximum compound shearing stress in the plane A-B, the stresses shown in Figs. 7-13c and d are superposed. Inspection shows that the maximum shearing stress is at E, since in the two diagrams the shearing stresses at E act in the same direction. There are no direct shearing stresses at A and B, while at C there is no torsional shearing stress. The two shearing stresses act in *opposite* directions at D. The five points A, B, C, D, and E thus considered for the compound shearing stress are all that may be adequately treated by the methods developed in this text. However, this procedure selects the point where the maximum shearing stress acts.

$$J = \frac{\pi d^4}{32} = \frac{\pi(0.5)^4}{32} = 0.00614 \text{ in.}^4$$

$$I = \frac{J}{2} = 0.00307 \text{ in.}^4$$

$$A = \tfrac{1}{4}\pi d^2 = 0.196 \text{ in.}^2$$

$$(\tau_{max})_{torsion} = \frac{Tc}{J} = \frac{200(0.25)}{0.00614} = 8,150 \text{ psi}$$

$$(\tau_{max})_{direct} = \frac{VQ}{It} = \frac{4}{3}\frac{V}{A} = \frac{4(60)}{3(0.196)} = 408 \text{ psi}$$

$$\tau_E = 8,150 + 408 = 8,560 \text{ psi}$$

A planar representation of the shearing stress at E with the matching stresses on the longitudinal planes is shown in Fig. 7-13f. No normal stress acts on this element as it is located on the neutral axis.

7-8. Stresses in Closely Coiled Helical Springs.

Helical springs, such as the one shown in Fig. 7-14a, are often used as elements of ma-chines. With certain limitations, these springs may be analyzed for stresses by a method similar to the one used in the preceding example. The discussion will be limited * to springs manufac-tured from rods or wires of *circular cross-section.* Moreover, *any one coil of such a spring will be assumed to lie in a plane which is nearly perpendicular to the axis of the spring.* This requires the adjoining coils to be close together. With this limitation, a section taken perpendicular to the axis of the spring's rod becomes *nearly vertical.*† Hence to maintain equilibrium of a segment of the spring, only a shearing force $V = F$ and a torque $T = F\bar{r}$ are re-quired at *any* section through the rod, Fig. 7-14b.‡ Note that $\bar{r}$ is the distance from the axis of the spring to the **centroid of the rod's cross-sectional area.**

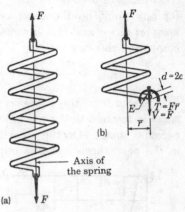

Fig. 7-14. Closely coiled helical spring.

The maximum shearing stress at an arbitrary section through the rod

* For a complete discussion on springs see Wahl, A. M., *Mechanical Springs.* Cleveland, Ohio: Penton Publishing Co., 1944.

† This eliminates the necessity of considering an axial force and a bending moment at the section taken through the spring.

‡ In previous work it has been reiterated that if a shear is present at a section, a change in the bending moment must take place along the member. Here a shear acts at every section of the rod, yet no bending moment nor a change in it appears to occur. This is so only because the rod is *curved.* An element of the rod viewed from the top

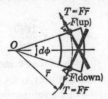

Fig. 7-B.

is shown in Fig. 7-B. At both ends of the element the torques are equal to $F\bar{r}$, and, using vectorial representation, act in the directions shown. The component of these vectors toward the axis of the spring O, resolved at the point of intersection of the vectors, $2F\bar{r}\,d\phi/2 = F\bar{r}\,d\phi$, opposes the couple developed by the vertical shears $V = F$, which are $\bar{r}\,d\phi$ apart.

could be obtained as in the preceding example, by superposing the torsional and the direct shearing stresses. This maximum shearing stress occurs at the inside of the coil at point E, Fig. 7-14b. However, in the analysis of springs it has become *customary to assume that the shearing stress caused by the direct shearing force is uniformly distributed over the cross-sectional area of the rod.* Hence, the nominal direct shearing stress for any point on the cross-section is $\tau = F/A$. Superposition of this *nominal* direct and the torsional shearing stress at E gives the maximum compound shearing stress. Thus since $T = F\bar{r}$, $d = 2c$, and $J = \pi d^4/32$,

$$\tau_{max} = \frac{F}{A} + \frac{Tc}{J} = \frac{Tc}{J}\left(\frac{FJ}{ATc} + 1\right) = \frac{16F\bar{r}}{\pi d^3}\left(\frac{d}{4\bar{r}} + 1\right) \qquad (7\text{-}2)$$

It is seen from this equation that as the diameter of the rod d becomes small in relation to the coil radius $\bar{r}$, the effect of the direct shearing stress becomes small. On the other hand, if the reverse is true, the first term in the parenthesis becomes important. However, in the latter case the

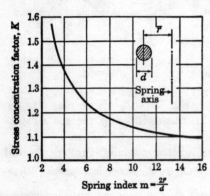

Fig. 7-15. Stress-concentration factor for helical round-wire compression or tension springs.

results indicated by Eq. 7-2 are considerably in error, and Eq. 7-2 should not be used, as it is based on the torsion formula for *straight rods*. As d becomes numerically comparable to $\bar{r}$, the length of the inside fibers of the coil differs greatly from the length of the outside fibers, and the assumptions of strain used in the torsion formula are not applicable.

The spring problem has been solved exactly* by the methods of the Mathematical Theory of Elasticity, and while these results are complicated, for any one spring they may be made to depend on a single parameter $m = 2\bar{r}/d$, which is called the *spring index*. Thus Eq. 7-2 may be rewritten as

$$\tau_{max} = K\frac{16F\bar{r}}{\pi d^3} \qquad (7\text{-}2a)$$

where K may be interpreted as a stress-concentration factor for closely coiled helical springs made from circular rods. A plot of K vs. the spring index is shown† in Fig. 7-15. For heavy springs the spring index is small,

---

* Goehner, O., "Die Berechnung Zylindrischer Schraubenfedern," *Zeitschrift des Vereins deutscher Ingenieure*, March, 1932, vol. 76:1, p. 269.

† An analytical expression which gives the value of K within 1 or 2% of the true value is frequently used. This expression in terms of the spring index m is $K_1 = \dfrac{4m - 1}{4m - 4} + \dfrac{0.615}{m}$. It was derived by A. M. Wahl on the basis of some simplifying assumptions and is known as the *Wahl correction factor* for curvature in helical springs.

hence the stress-concentration factor K becomes very important. For all cases the factor K accounts for the correct amount of direct shearing stress. Very high stresses are commonly allowed in springs because high-strength materials are used in their fabrication. For good quality spring steel, working shearing stresses range anywhere from 30,000 psi to 100,000 psi.

*7-9. Deflection of Closely Coiled Helical Springs. As the subject of closely coiled helical springs was introduced above, for completeness, their deflection will be discussed in this article. Attention will be confined to closely coiled helical springs with a large spring index, i.e., the diameter of the wire will be assumed small in comparison with the radius of the coil. This permits the treatment of an element of a spring between two closely adjoining sections through the wire as a *straight circular bar in torsion*. The effect of direct shear on the deflection of the spring will be ignored. This is usually permissible as the latter effect is small.

Consider a helical spring such as shown in Fig. 7-16. A typical element AB of this spring is subjected throughout its length to a torque $T = F\bar{r}$. This torque causes a relative rotation between the two ad-joining planes A and B, and with sufficient accuracy the amount of this rotation may be obtained by using Eq. 3-8, $d\varphi = T\,dz/(JG)$, for straight circular bars. For this equa-tion, the applied torque $T = F\bar{r}$, dz is the length of the element, G is the shearing modulus of elasticity, and J is the polar moment of inertia of the *wire's cross-sectional area*.

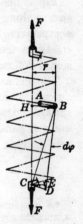

If the plane of the wire A is imagined fixed, the rotation of the plane B is given by the foregoing expression. The contribution of this element to the movement of the force F at C is equal to the distance BC multiplied by the angle $d\varphi$, i.e., $CD = BC\,d\varphi$. However, since the element AB is small, the distance CD is also small, and this distance may be considered perpendicular (although it is an arc) to the line BC. Moreover, only the vertical component of this deflection is significant, as in a spring consisting of many coils, for any element on one side of the spring there is a corresponding equivalent element on the other. The dia-metrically opposite elements of the spring balance out the horizontal component of the deflection and permit only the vertical deflection of the force F. Therefore, by finding the *vertical* increment ED of the deflection of the force F due to an element of the spring AB and summing such increments for *all* elements of the spring, the deflection of the whole spring is obtained.

Fig. 7-16. Diagram used in deriving the expression for the deflection of a helical spring.

From similar triangles CDE and CBH,

$$\frac{ED}{CD} = \frac{HB}{BC} \quad \text{or} \quad ED = \frac{CD}{BC}HB$$

However, $CD = BC\,d\varphi$, $HB = \bar{r}$, and ED may be denoted by $d\Delta$, as it represents an infinitesimal vertical deflection of the spring due to rotation of an element AB. Whence $d\Delta = \bar{r}\,d\varphi$ and

$$\Delta = \int d\Delta = \int \bar{r}\,d\varphi = \int_0^L \bar{r}\,\frac{T\,dz}{JG} = \frac{TL\bar{r}}{JG}$$

However, $T = F\bar{r}$, and for a closely coiled spring the *length L of the wire* may be taken with sufficient accuracy as $2\pi\bar{r}N$, where N is the number of *live* or active coils of the spring. Hence the deflection Δ of the spring is*

$$\Delta = \frac{2\pi F\bar{r}^3 N}{JG} \tag{7-3}$$

or if the value of J for the wire is substituted,

$$\Delta = \frac{64 F\bar{r}^3 N}{Gd^4} \tag{7-3a}$$

Equations 7-3 and 7-3a give the deflection of a closely coiled helical spring along its axis when such a spring is subjected to either a tensile or compressive force F. In these formulas the effect of the direct shearing stress on the deflection is neglected, i.e., they give only the effect of torsional deformations.

The behavior of a spring may be conveniently defined by a force required to deflect the spring one inch. This quantity is known as the **spring constant**. It is designated in this text by k and is expressed in units of pounds per inch. From Eq. 7-3a the spring constant for a helical spring made from a wire with a circular cross-section is

$$k = \frac{F}{\Delta} = \frac{Gd^4}{64\bar{r}^3 N} \qquad \left[\frac{\text{lb}}{\text{in.}}\right]$$

* A convenient set-up for deriving the deflection of a helical spring consists of imagining the spring unwound as shown in Fig. 7-C. The deflection $\bar{r}\varphi = \Delta$ of the force

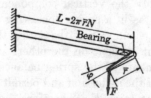

Fig. 7-C.

F due to the torsional effect on this rod is equivalent to the deflection of a helical spring with the same dimensions.

Problems for Solution

7-1. A 14 WF 61 beam is loaded with a uniformly distributed load of 2 kips/ft, including its own weight and an axial tensile force of 120 kips. Determine the maximum normal stress if the beam spans 10 ft. (*Hint:* see Example 4-6.)

7-2. A 10 WF 49 beam is subjected to a pull of 100 kips in line with the top surface of the upper flange as shown in the figure. Neglecting local stresses find the maximum normal stress.

7-3. A machine part for transmitting a pull of 3 kips is off-set as shown in the figure. Find the largest normal stress in the off-set portion of the member. *Ans.* −7 ksi.

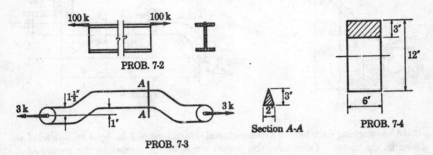

PROB. 7-2

Section A-A

PROB. 7-3

PROB. 7-4

7-4. A beam having the cross-sectional dimensions shown in the figure is subjected at a given section to the following forces: a bending moment of +144,000 in.-lb, a total vertical shear of +5,000 lb, and an axial thrust of 7,200 lb. Determine the resultant normal force on the shaded part of the cross-section.

7-5. If the 8 kip force in Example 5-5 is now applied vertically upward, what will the maximum tensile and compressive stresses be at section *A-A*? The distance from the vertical force to the right-hand face of the bracket at section *A-A* is 16 in. *Ans.* +17.5 ksi, −21.7 ksi.

7-6. A large hook fabricated from a structural steel *T* (AISC designation: ST 4B) is loaded as shown in the figure. Determine the largest normal stress at the built-in end. For this section, $A = 2.22$ in.^{2} and $I_0 = 3.29$ in.^{4} *Ans.* 20 ksi.

7-7. A cast iron frame for a punch press has the proportions shown in the figure. What force *P* may be applied to this frame controlled by the stresses in the sections such as *A-A*, if the allowable stresses are 4,000 psi in tension and 12,000 psi in compression?

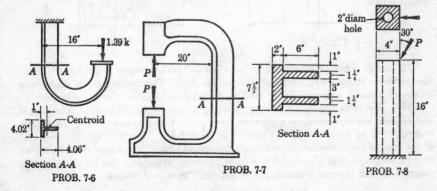

Section A-A

PROB. 7-6

Section A-A

PROB. 7-7

PROB. 7-8

7-8. A short 4 in. square steel bar with a 2 in. diameter axial hole is built in at the base and is loaded at the top as shown in the figure. Neglecting the weight of the bar, determine the value of the force P so that the maximum normal stress at the built-in end would not exceed 20 ksi.

7-9. An inclined beam having a cross-section of 6 in. by 12 in. supports a downward load as shown in the figure. Determine the maximum stress acting normal to the section A-A. Assume no eccentricity of the load or reactions and neglect the weight of the member.

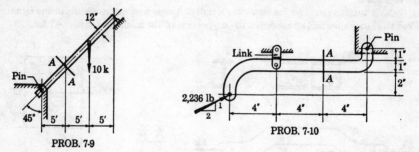

PROB. 7-9

PROB. 7-10

7-10. A machine part having cross-sectional dimensions of 1 in. by $\frac{1}{2}$ in. is loaded as shown in the figure. Determine the largest stress acting normal to the section A-A caused by the applied force. *Ans.* -16 ksi.

7-11. A member made from a one in. sq bar is shaped as shown in the figure, to support a 200 lb load. Compute the largest stress acting normal to the section A-A caused by the applied load. *Ans.* $-4{,}380$ psi.

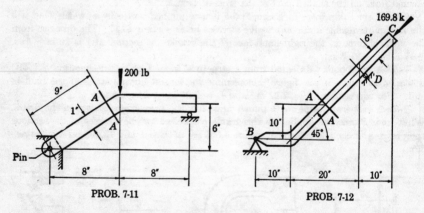

PROB. 7-11

PROB. 7-12

7-12. A force of 169.8 kips is applied to a bar BC at C as shown in the figure. Find the maximum stress acting normal to the section A-A. The member BC is made from a piece of 6 in. by 6 in. steel bar. Neglect the weight of the bar. *Ans.* -18 ksi.

7-13.* The proportions of a factory stairway are shown in the figure. The treads and landing are supported on both sides by 9 in.-13.4 lb channels. Find the largest normal stress in the channels 5 ft above the lower floor. Assume that the lower end of the stair is not anchored for resisting a horizontal force. The whole stair, including its own weight, carries a load of 400 lb/ft of *horizontal projection*. An idealized loading diagram for one channel is shown in the diagram. *Ans.* $-5{,}210$ psi.

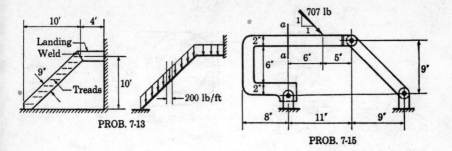

PROB. 7-13

PROB. 7-15

7-14.* Revise Prob. 7-13 by assuming that the lower end of the stairway is pinned and the top end rests against a perfectly smooth wall. *Ans.* −2,620 psi.

7-15. Calculate the maximum compressive stress acting on section *a-a* caused by the applied load for the structure shown in the figure. The cross-section at section *a-a* is that of a solid circular bar of 2 in. diameter. *Ans.* −1,114 psi.

7-16. If in Prob. 4-22 the post is a circular timber 12 in. in diameter, what is the largest tensile stress acting normal to a section 5 ft above the bottom of the post? *Ans.* 537 psi.

7-17. Compute the maximum compressive stress acting normal to the section *a-a* for the structure shown in the figure. The post *AB* has a 12 in. by 12 in. cross-section. Neglect the weight of the structure. *Ans.* −174 psi.

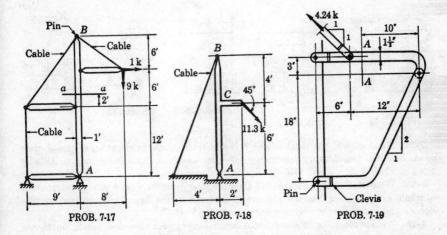

PROB. 7-17

PROB. 7-18

PROB. 7-19

7-18.* Determine the largest stress acting normal to the *critical section* through the member *AB* caused by the applied force of 11.3 kips. The joint *C* is "rigid" and the member *AB* is made of an 8 WF 31 section. (*Hint:* check sections above and below *C*.) *Ans.* 12,950 psi.

7-19. A pin-joined bracket is loaded as shown in the figure. Determine the largest stress acting normal to the section *A-A* caused by the applied force of 4.24 kips. The cross-sectional area at *A-A* is 1½ in. by 1¼ in. *Ans.* −24.2 ksi.

7-20. A steel hook, having the proportions shown in the figure, is subjected to a downward load of 19 kips. The radius of the central curved axis is 6 in. Determine the maximum stress in this hook.

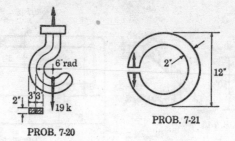

PROB. 7-21

PROB. 7-20

7-21. A steel bar of 2 in. diameter is bent into a nearly complete circular ring of 12 in. outside diameter as shown in the figure. (a) Calculate the maximum stress in this ring caused by applying two 2,000 lb forces at the open end. (b) Find the ratio of the maximum stress found in (a) to the largest compressive stress acting normal to the same section. *Ans.* (a) $+30.8$ ksi.

7-22. If a hook similar to the one shown in Prob. 7-20 has a circular cross-section of 1 in. radius and a 3 in. radius of the curved central axis, what force P may be applied to the hook without exceeding a stress of 12,000 psi?

7-23. The dimensions of a small concrete dam, retaining a water surface level with its crest, are shown in the figure. Assuming that concrete is capable of resisting some tension, determine the stresses acting normal to a horizontal section 8 ft below the top. Assume that water weighs 62.5 lb/ft³ and concrete 150 lb/ft³. *Ans.* $-2,090$ lb/ft² and $+390$ lb/ft².

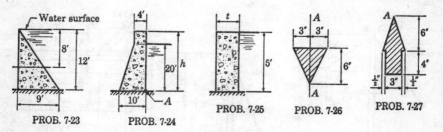

PROB. 7-23   PROB. 7-24   PROB. 7-25   PROB. 7-26   PROB. 7-27

7-24. What should the total height h of the dam shown in the cross-sectional view be so that the foundation pressure at A is just zero? Assume same unit weights as given in Prob. 7-23. *Ans.* 27.6 ft.

7-25. What must the thickness t of a rectangular concrete dam 5 ft high be in order to retain a water level even with its crest, as shown in the figure, without causing tension on the foundation at the upstream face?

7-26. A short block has cross-sectional dimensions in plan view as shown in the figure. Determine the range along the line A-A over which a downward vertical force could be applied to the top of the block without causing any tension at the base. Neglect the weight of the block. *Ans.* Between 3 in. and $4\frac{1}{2}$ in. from the apex.

7-27. The cross-sectional area in plan view of a short block is in the shape of an "arrow" as shown in the figure. Find the position of the vertical downward force on the line of symmetry of this section so that the stress at A is just zero. *Ans.* 6.944 in. from A.

7-28. Rework Example 7-4 by placing the vertical force P in line with the side AD and at a distance of 15 in. from the axis of symmetry.

7-29. If the block shown in Fig. 7-8a is made from steel weighing 0.283 lb/in.³, find the magnitude of the force P necessary to cause zero stress at D. Neglect the weight of the small bracket supporting the load. For the same condition, locate the line of zero stress at the section $ABCD$. *Ans.* 203 lb.

7-30. An 8 ft diameter steel stack, partially lined with brick on the inside, together with a 20 ft by 20 ft square concrete foundation pad weighs 160,000 lb. This stack projects 100 ft above the ground level, as shown in the figure, and is anchored to the foundation. If the horizontal wind pressure is assumed to be 20 lb/ft² of the stack's projected area and the wind blows in the direction parallel to one of the sides of the square foundation, what is the maximum foundation pressure? *Ans.* 1.21 k/ft².

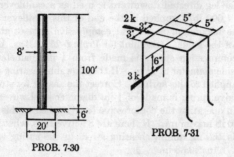

PROB. 7-30

PROB. 7-31

7-31. A cast iron block is loaded as shown in the figure. Neglecting the weight of the block, determine the stresses acting normal to a section taken 18 in. below the top and locate the line of zero stress.

7-32. A short compression member has the proportions shown in the figure; its $A = 72.9$ in.², $I_{XX} = 1,199$ in.⁴ and $I_{YY} = 633$ in.⁴ Determine the distance r along the diagonal where a longitudinal force P should be applied so that point A would lie on the line of zero stress. Neglect the weight of the member. *Ans.* 53 in.

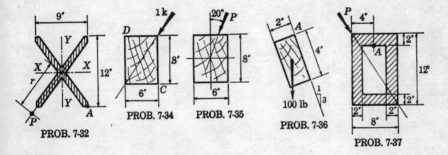

PROB. 7-32

PROB. 7-34

PROB. 7-35

PROB. 7-36

PROB. 7-37

7-33. Determine the kern for a member having a solid circular cross-section.

7-34. A 20 ft long, 6 in. by 8 in. beam is loaded in the middle of the span with an inclined concentrated force of 1 kip, as shown in the cross-sectional view. Neglecting the weight of the beam, find the maximum bending stress and locate the neutral axis. *Ans.* ±1,500 psi. NA passes through C and D.

7-35. A 20 ft long, 6 in. by 8 in. beam is to be loaded in the middle of the span with an inclined concentrated force P, as shown in the cross-sectional view. If the maximum bending stress is 1,200 psi, neglecting the weight of the beam, what may the value of the force P be? *Ans.* 917 lb.

7-36. A full-sized, 2 in. by 4 in. horizontal cantilever projects 4 ft from a concrete pier into which it is cast in a tilted position as shown in the figure. At the free end a vertical force of 100 lb is applied which acts through the centroid of the section. Determine the maximum flexural stress, caused by the applied force, in the beam at the built-in end and locate the neutral axis. Neglect the weight of the beam. *Ans.* ±1,423 psi, 3.34 in.

7-37. An inclined force P acts on a cantilever beam in the plane shown in the cross-sectional view. At the section considered, the total resisting moment in the plane of the force is 8,000 ft-lb. Find the bending stress at point A. *Ans.* 325 psi.

7-38. A 6 in. by 6 in. by $\frac{1}{2}$ in. steel angle with one of its legs placed in a horizontal position and its other leg directed downward is used as a cantilever 70.7 in. long. If an upward force of 1,000 lb is applied at the end of this cantilever through the shear center, what are the maximum tensile and compressive stresses at the built-in end? Neglect the weight of the angle. (See hint for Prob. 5-25.) *Ans.* 14.7 ksi, −18.4 ksi.

7-39. A helical compression spring is made from $\frac{1}{8}$ in. diameter phosphor-bronze wire and has an outside diameter of $1\frac{1}{4}$ in. If the allowable shearing stress is 30,000 psi, what force may be applied to this spring? Correct the answer for stress concentrations.

7-40. A helical valve spring is made of $\frac{1}{4}$ in. diameter steel wire and has an outside diameter of 2 in. In operation the compressive force applied to this spring varies from 20 lb minimum to 70 lb maximum. If there are 8 active coils, what is the valve lift (or travel), and what is the maximum shearing stress in the spring when in operation? $G = 11.6 \times 10^6$ psi. *Ans.* 0.38 in.

7-41. A helical spring is made of $\frac{1}{2}$ in. diameter steel wire by winding it on a 5 in. diameter mandrel. If there are 10 active coils, what is the spring constant? $G = 12 \times 10^6$ psi. What force must be applied to the spring to elongate it $1\frac{3}{4}$ in.?

7-42. If a helical tension spring consisting of 12 live coils of $\frac{1}{4}$ in. steel wire and of $1\frac{1}{4}$ in. outside diameter is attached to the end of another helical tension spring of 18 live coils of $\frac{1}{4}$ in. steel wire and of $1\frac{3}{4}$ in. outside diameter, what is the spring constant for this two spring system? What is the largest force that may be applied to these springs without exceeding a shearing stress of 70,000 psi? $G = 12 \times 10^6$ psi.

Chapter Eight

ANALYSIS OF PLANE
STRESS AND STRAIN

8-1. Introduction. All fundamental formulas used in this text for determining the stresses at a section of a member have already been established. In the preceding chapter these formulas were classified into two groups. One group permits the determination of the normal stresses on the elements, the other, the shearing stresses. Superposition or compounding of like stresses was discussed in the same chapter. However, in some cases normal *and* shearing stresses may act *simultaneously* on an element of a member. For example, in a circular shaft which transmits torque with an axial force, all elements except those on the axis, simultaneously experience torsional shearing stresses and axial normal stresses. In fact, if an axial force, or a bending moment, acts with a shear, or a torque, some elements are subjected to both normal *and* shearing stresses. In these cases, both shearing and normal stresses are needed to describe completely all the stresses acting on an infinitesimal element, i.e., to define its *state of stress*. For example, the state of stress for an infinitesimal element A of a beam shown in Fig. 8-1a is given in Fig. 8-1b. Using the procedures developed thus far,

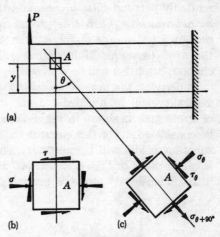

Fig. 8-1. The state of stress at a point described alternatively.

the planes which isolate this element are either parallel or perpendicular to the axis of the member. This method of isolating elements has been used throughout the text.

In this chapter it will be shown that by *changing the orientation* of an element, as defined by the angle θ for the element in Fig. 8-1c, it is possible to describe the state of stress at a point in an **infinite number of**

181

ways, which are all *equivalent.* In developing this procedure, a combination and resolution of normal and shearing stresses will be accomplished, whereas in the preceding chapter only the superposition of like stresses was treated. For this, the *laws of transformation* of stress at a point will be developed, that is, equations will be derived which transform the information given by the conventional stress formulas into *equivalent stresses* acting on any plane through a given point. The planes where the normal or the shearing stresses reach their *maximum intensity* will also be determined, as the stresses associated with these planes have a particularly significant effect on materials.

The second half of the chapter is devoted to a study of strains.

8-2. The Basic Problem. Although stresses are vectorial in nature, *they are not ordinary vectors.* Mathematically they do not obey the laws of vectorial addition and subtraction. Stresses are vectors of a higher order,* because, in addition to having a magnitude and a sense, *they are also associated with the unit of area over which they act.* Hence in combining the normal and the shearing stresses, the basic problem is solved by first converting the stresses into *forces,* which are vectors and are manipulated vectorially. To illustrate this procedure, it will first be applied to an infinitesimal wedge with particular shearing and normal stresses on two mutually perpendicular planes, and the stresses on an inclined plane will be determined. Then this procedure will be generalized, and finally a semigraphical means of solving the same problem will be discussed. In the latter technique Mohr's circle will be employed. As in the preceding chapter, attention will be confined to the elastic stresses.

In deriving the laws of transformation of stress at a point, a complete generality will be avoided. Thus, instead of treating the general state of stress such as shown in Fig. 8-2a, an element as shown in Fig. 8-2b will be considered. For this element the subscripts for the shearing stress are superfluous and will be omitted. The state of stress shown in Fig. 8-2b is called *plane* or *"two-dimensional" stress.* In practical applications this "two-dimensional" stress is particularly significant, since one face of an

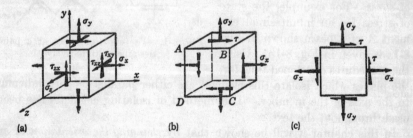

Fig. 8-2. Representation of stresses on an element of a body.

* In the Mathematical Theory of Elasticity they are termed *tensors.*

element, as $ABCD$ in Fig. 8-2b, may be selected as an *outer boundary* of a member, which usually is free of surface stresses. On the other hand, the stresses acting on the other surfaces of this element *at* the surface of a body are maximum.

Before illustrating the procedure for transforming stress at a point, certain important concepts encountered earlier need particular emphasis. First, for simplicity, the stresses acting on an element in a "two-dimensional" stress problem will be shown as in Fig. 8-2c, although an element is "three dimensional." Second, in this representation the shearing stresses of equal intensities act on mutually perpendicular planes, and their arrowheads meet at a corner to satisfy equilibrium conditions. Third, the element considered is *infinitesimal in size,* i.e., it is so small that the stresses on the faces may be regarded uniformly distributed and constant.

Example 8-1. Suppose that a certain set of computations indicates that the state of stress for an element is as shown in Fig. 8-3a. These data mean that the cuts through the body were made in the horizontal and vertical directions, and the stresses were determined by conventional formulas. The element shown is in static equilibrium. An alternate representation of the state of stress at the *same point* may be given on an infinitesimal wedge with an angle of $22\frac{1}{2}°$ as shown in Fig. 8-3b. (The rectangular element, Fig. 8-3a. and the wedge, Fig. 8-3b, are both infinitesimal elements. Their relative difference in size as shown in the diagram is of no importance.) Find the stresses which must act on the plane AB of the wedge to keep the element in equilibrium.

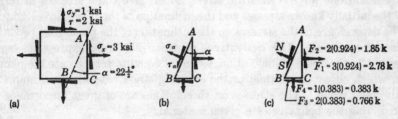

(a)   (b)   (c)

Fig. 8-3.

SOLUTION: The wedge ABC is a part of the element shown in Fig. 8-3a, therefore the stresses on the faces AC and BC are known. The unknown normal and shearing stresses acting on the face AB are designated in the figure by σ_α and τ_α, respectively. Their sense is assumed arbitrarily.

To determine σ_α and τ_α, for *convenience only,* let the area of the face defined by the line AB be one square inch. Then the area corresponding to the line AC is equal to (1) $\cos \alpha = 0.924$ in.², and to BC is equal to (1) $\sin \alpha = 0.383$ in.² (More rigorously, the area corresponding to the line AB should be taken as dA, but this quantity cancels out in the subsequent manipulations.) Next, since the stresses and their respective areas are known, a diagram showing *forces* acting on the elementary wedge may be prepared as shown in Fig. 8-3c. The forces F_1, F_2, F_3, and F_4 are obtained by multiplying the stresses by their respective areas, and the unknown equilibrant *forces* N and S act respectively normal and tangential to the plane AB. Whence by applying the equations of static equilibrium to the *forces* acting on the wedge, the forces N and S may be determined.

$$\Sigma F_N = 0, \qquad N = F_1 \cos \alpha - F_2 \sin \alpha - F_3 \cos \alpha + F_4 \sin \alpha$$
$$= 2.78(0.924) - 1.85(0.383) - 0.766(0.924) + 0.383(0.383)$$
$$= 1.29 \text{ kips}$$
$$\Sigma F_S = 0, \qquad S = F_1 \sin \alpha + F_2 \cos \alpha - F_3 \sin \alpha - F_4 \cos \alpha$$
$$= 2.78(0.383) + 1.85(0.924) - 0.766(0.383) - 0.383(0.924)$$
$$= 2.12 \text{ kips}$$

The forces N and S act on the plane defined by AB, which was initially assumed to be one square inch. Their positive signs indicate that their assumed directions were chosen correctly. Dividing these *forces* by the *area* on which they act, the stresses acting on the plane AB are obtained. Thus $\sigma_\alpha = 1.29$ ksi and $\tau_\alpha = 2.12$ ksi and act in the direction shown in Fig. 8-3b.

The foregoing procedure accomplished a remarkable thing. It *transformed* the description of the state of stress from one set of planes to another. Either system of stresses pertaining to an *infinitesimal* element describes the state of stress at the *same* point of a body, *but on different planes*.

8-3. General Equations for the Transformation of Stress. In the above example the plane AB was chosen arbitrarily at an angle of $22\frac{1}{2}°$ with the vertical axis. Another plane at *any other angle* might have been selected, and the normal and shearing stresses acting on it determined as before. This procedure is inefficient, and the problem may be solved algebraically. This results in *two* algebraic expressions, one for the normal stress and one for the shearing stress, which give these stresses in terms of the initially known stresses and the inclination of the planes investigated. The dependence of the stresses on the inclination of the plane thus becomes clearly apparent. The derivatives of these algebraic expressions with respect to the angle of inclination, when set equal to zero, locate the planes on which either the normal or the shearing stress reaches a maximum or minimum value. The stresses on these planes are of great importance in predicting the behavior of a given material.

The algebraic equations will be developed using an element, shown in Fig. 8-4a, in a state of general plane stress. All stresses shown acting on this element are *treated as having a positive sense*. The normal tensile stresses are positive, hence compressive stresses are negative. Positive shearing stress is defined as shown, i.e., acting *up* on the right-hand face

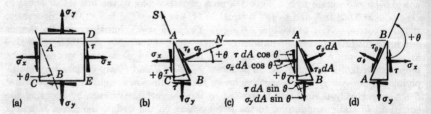

Fig. 8-4. An element used in deriving the expression for a stress on an inclined plane.

DE of the element. *This different convention of signs for shearing stress is adopted for this work only.*

By passing a plane AB through the cubic element, the wedge shown in Fig. 8-4b is isolated. The plane AB makes an angle of θ with the vertical axis, and if this plane has an area dA, the areas of the faces AC and BC are $dA \cos \theta$ and $dA \sin \theta$, respectively. *The angle θ is measured positive as shown in a counterclockwise direction.* When it exceeds 90°, the plane AB swings bodily around to the position shown in Fig. 8-4d and isolates the wedge in the lower right-hand corner of the cubic element. As in Fig. 8-4a, *all quantities shown in Figs. 8-4b, c, and d have the positive sense assumed in this convention of signs.*

Multiplying the stresses shown in Fig. 8-4b by their respective areas a diagram with the *forces* acting on the wedge is obtained, Fig. 8-4c. Then, by applying the equations of static equilibrium to the forces acting on the wedge, stresses σ_θ and τ_θ are obtained.

$$\Sigma F_N = 0, \quad \sigma_\theta \, dA = \sigma_x \, dA \cos \theta \cos \theta + \sigma_y \, dA \sin \theta \sin \theta$$
$$+ \tau \, dA \cos \theta \sin \theta + \tau \, dA \sin \theta \cos \theta$$

$$\sigma_\theta = \sigma_x \cos^2 \theta + \sigma_y \sin^2 \theta + 2\tau \sin \theta \cos \theta$$
$$= \sigma_x \tfrac{1}{2}(1 + \cos 2\theta) + \sigma_y \tfrac{1}{2}(1 - \cos 2\theta) + \tau \sin 2\theta$$

$$\sigma_\theta = \frac{\sigma_x + \sigma_y}{2} + \frac{\sigma_x - \sigma_y}{2} \cos 2\theta + \tau \sin 2\theta \qquad (8\text{-}1)$$

Similarly,

$$\Sigma F_S = 0, \quad \tau_\theta = - \frac{\sigma_x - \sigma_y}{2} \sin 2\theta + \tau \cos 2\theta \qquad (8\text{-}2)$$

Equations 8-1 and 8-2 are the general expressions for the normal and the shearing stress, respectively, on any plane located by the angle θ and caused by a known system of stresses. These equations are the equations for *transformation of stress* from one set of planes to another. Note particularly that σ_x, σ_y, and τ are initially known constants, and that *the signs of all quantities follow the conventions adopted for them in Fig. 8-4a.*

8-4. Principal Stresses. Usually interest centers in the determination of the largest possible stress as given by Eqs. 8-1 and 8-2, and the planes on which such stresses occur will be found first. To find the plane for a maximum or a minimum *normal* stress, Eq. 8-1 is differentiated with respect to θ and the derivative set equal to zero, i.e.,

$$\frac{d\sigma_\theta}{d\theta} = - \frac{\sigma_x - \sigma_y}{2} 2 \sin 2\theta + 2\tau \cos 2\theta = 0$$

Hence, $$\tan 2\theta_1 = \frac{\tau}{\tfrac{1}{2}(\sigma_x - \sigma_y)} \qquad (8\text{-}3)$$

where the subscript of the angle θ is used to designate the angle which defines the plane of the maximum or minimum normal stress. Equation

8-3 has *two roots*, since the value of the tangent of an angle in the diametrically opposite quadrants is the same. These roots are 180° apart, and,
as Eq. 8-3 is for a *double angle*, the roots of θ_1 are 90° apart. One of these
roots locates a plane on which the maximum normal stress acts, the other
locates the corresponding plane for the minimum normal stress. To determine which one of these planes is associated with the maximum or the
minimum stress, each root is substituted separately into Eq. 8-1 and the
stresses compared.

Next, carefully observe that if the location of planes on which *no* shearing stresses act is wanted, Eq. 8-2 must be set equal to zero. This yields
the *same* relation as Eq. 8-3. Hence an important conclusion is reached:
**On planes on which maximum or minimum normal stresses occur, there
are no shearing stresses.** These planes are called the *principal planes* of
stress, and the stresses acting on these planes—the maximum and minimum normal stresses—are called the ***principal stresses.*** Note again that
no shearing stresses exist on the planes of principal stresses. Thus every
state of plane stress may be transformed into principal stresses acting on
mutually perpendicular planes. If the values of both principal stresses
are different from zero, the state of stress is referred to as *biaxial stress.*
When one of the principal stresses is zero, the state of stress is *uniaxial.*

The magnitudes of the principal stresses may be obtained by substituting the values* of the sine and cosine functions corresponding to the double
angle given by Eq. 8-3 into Eq. 8-1. After this is done and the results
are simplified, the expression for the maximum normal stress denoted † by
σ_1 and the minimum normal stress denoted by σ_2 becomes

$$(\sigma_\theta)_{\substack{\text{max} \\ \text{min}}} = \sigma_{1 \text{ or } 2} = \tfrac{1}{2}(\sigma_x + \sigma_y) \pm \sqrt{[\tfrac{1}{2}(\sigma_x - \sigma_y)]^2 + \tau^2} \qquad (8\text{-}4)$$

* The tangent is defined as a ratio of the side opposite to the angle of a right triangle
to the adjacent side. Thus Eq. 8-3 may be interpreted graphically as shown in Fig.

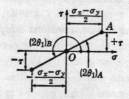

Fig. 8-A.

8-A. The side opposite one root $(2\theta_1)_A$ is $+\tau$; the adjacent side is $+\tfrac{1}{2}(\sigma_x - \sigma_y)$; and
the diagonal OA, an inherently positive quantity, is $+\sqrt{[\tfrac{1}{2}(\sigma_x - \sigma_y)]^2 + \tau^2}$. There-
fore $\sin (2\theta_1)_A = +\dfrac{\tau}{\sqrt{[\tfrac{1}{2}(\sigma_x - \sigma_y)]^2 + \tau^2}}$ and $\cos (2\theta_1)_A = +\dfrac{\tfrac{1}{2}(\sigma_x - \sigma_y)}{\sqrt{[\tfrac{1}{2}(\sigma_x - \sigma_y)]^2 + \tau^2}}$. Similar expressions, *except for sign*, correspond to the other root $(2\theta_1)_B$ of Eq. 8-3.

† In books on Photoelasticity the symbols p and q are frequently used to refer respec
tively to the maximum and minimum principal stress.

where the positive sign* in front of the radical must be used to obtain σ_1, and the negative sign to obtain σ_2. The planes on which these stresses act are defined by Eq. 8-3. Usually the principal stresses give the most significant mode of description of the state of stress at a point.

Note that the algebraic sum of the principal stresses is equal to the algebraic sum of the normal stresses acting on the mutually perpendicular planes x and y, i.e., $\sigma_1 + \sigma_2 = \sigma_x + \sigma_y$. Moreover, by considering Eq. 8-1, it may be shown that the sum of the normal stresses on any set of mutually perpendicular planes is also constant. *Thus it is said that the sum of normal stresses on any two mutually perpendicular planes remains invariant or constant.*

8-5. Principal Shearing Stresses. If σ_x, σ_y, and τ are known for an element, the shearing stress on any plane defined by an angle θ is given by Eq. 8-2, and a study similar to the one made above for the normal stresses may be made for the shearing stress. Thus similarly, to locate the planes on which the maximum or the minimum shearing stresses act, Eq. 8-2 may be differentiated with respect to θ and the derivative set equal to zero. When this is carried out and the results are simplified, the operations yield

$$tan\ 2\theta_2 = \frac{-\frac{1}{2}(\sigma_x - \sigma_y)}{\tau} \tag{8-5}$$

where the subscript 2 is attached to θ to designate the angle which defines the plane on which the shearing stress is a maximum or a minimum. Like Eq. 8-3, Eq. 8-5 has two roots. The *two* planes defined by this equation are mutually perpendicular. Moreover, the value of $\tan 2\theta_2$ given by Eq. 8-5 is a *negative reciprocal* of the value of $\tan 2\theta_1$ of Eq. 8-3. Hence the roots for the *double angles* of Eq. 8-5 are 90° apart from the corresponding roots of Eq. 8-3. This means that the angles which locate the planes of maximum or minimum shearing stress form angles of 45° with the planes of the principal stresses. A substitution of the sine and cosine functions† corresponding to the double angle given by Eq. 8-5 into Eq. 8-2 gives the maximum and the minimum values of the shearing stresses. This, after simplifications, is

$$\tau_{\substack{max \\ min}} = \pm \sqrt{\left(\frac{\sigma_x - \sigma_y}{2}\right)^2 + \tau^2} \tag{8-6}$$

It is seen from this expression that the maximum shearing stress differs

* The positive sign in front of the radical in Eq. 8-4 results from using the positive values of $\sin (2\theta_1)_A$ and $\cos (2\theta_1)_A$; the minus sign results from using the negative values of $\sin (2\theta_1)_B$ and $\cos (2\theta_1)_B$.

† A similar interpretation for the roots of Eq. 8-5 as for the roots of Eq. 8-3 may be made. However since $\tan 2\theta_2$ is given by a negative quantity, the terminal points of the diagonals lie in the second and fourth quadrants. This fact requires simultaneous use of tne sine and cosine functions with *opposite* sign.

from the minimum shearing stress only in sign.   Moreover, since the two roots given by Eq. 8-5 locate planes 90° apart, this result also means that the *numerical* value of the shearing stresses on the mutually perpendicular planes is the same.   This concept was repeatedly used after being established in Art. 2-9.   In this derivation the difference in sign of the two shearing stresses arises from the sign convention.   From the physical point of view these signs have no meaning and will not be used in subsequent work.   Either shearing stress given by Eq. 8-6 will be called the *maximum* or the *principal* shearing stress.   The definite sense of the shearing stress may always be determined by a direct substitution of the particular root of θ_2 into Eq. 8-2.   *A positive shearing stress indicates that it acts in the direction assumed in Fig. 8-4b, or vice versa.*   The determination of the maximum or the principal shearing stress is of utmost importance for materials which are weak in shearing strength.   This will be discussed further in the next chapter.

Unlike the situation found for the principal stresses for which no shearing stresses occur on the principal planes, *the planes on which the maximum shearing stresses act are not always free of normal stresses.*   Substitution of θ_2 from Eq. 8-5 into Eq. 8-1 indicates that the normal stresses which act on the planes of the principal shearing stresses are

$$\sigma' = \frac{\sigma_x + \sigma_y}{2} \tag{8-7}$$

Therefore a normal stress acts simultaneously with the principal shearing stress unless $\sigma_x + \sigma_y$ vanishes.

If σ_x and σ_y in Eq. 8-6 are the *principal* stresses, τ is zero and Eq. 8-6 simplifies into

$$\tau_{max} = \frac{\sigma_1 - \sigma_2}{2} \tag{8-8}$$

Example 8-2. For the state of stress given in Example 8-1, reproduced in Fig. 8-5a, (a) rework the previous problem for $\theta = -22\frac{1}{2}°$, using the general equations for the transformation of stress, (b) find the principal stresses and show their sense on a properly oriented element, and (c) find the maximum (principal) shearing stresses with the associated normal stresses and show the results on a properly oriented element.

SOLUTION: *Case (a)*.   As the plane on which the stresses are wanted is given by a negative angle, perhaps it is clearer to change it to a positive angle of $157\frac{1}{2}°$, as shown in Fig. 8-5b.   Then $2\theta = 315°$.   Direct substitution of all quantities into Eqs. 8-1 and 8-2 gives

$$\sigma_\theta = \frac{3+1}{2} + \frac{3-1}{2}\cos 315° + 2\sin 315° = 2 + 1(0.707) + 2(-0.707)$$

$$= +1.29 \text{ ksi}$$

$$\tau_\theta = -\frac{3-1}{2}\sin 315° + 2\cos 315° = -1(-0.707) + 2(0.707)$$

$$= +2.12 \text{ ksi}$$

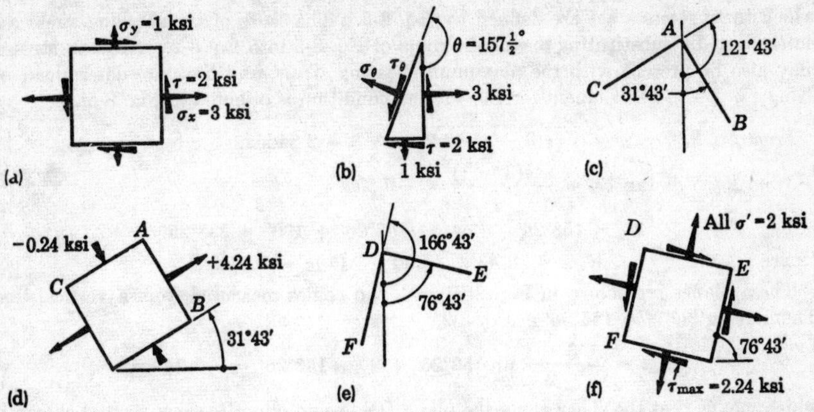

Fig. 8-5.

The positive sign of τ_θ indicates that the shearing stress acts in the same direction as that shown in Fig. 8-5b.

Case (b). The principal stresses are obtained by means of Eq. 8-4. The planes on which the principal stresses act are found by using Eq. 8-3.

$$\sigma_{1 \text{ or } 2} = \tfrac{1}{2}(3 + 1) \pm \sqrt{[\tfrac{1}{2}(3 - 1)]^2 + 2^2} = 2 \pm 2.24$$

$$\sigma_1 = +4.24 \text{ ksi (tension)}, \qquad \sigma_2 = -0.24 \text{ ksi (compression)}$$

$$\tan 2\theta_1 = \frac{\tau}{\tfrac{1}{2}(\sigma_x - \sigma_y)} = \frac{2}{\tfrac{1}{2}(3 - 1)} = 2$$

$$2\theta_1 = 63°26' \qquad \text{or} \qquad 63°26' + 180° = 243°26'$$

Hence $(\theta_1)_A = 31°43'$ and $(\theta_1)_B = 121°43'$

This locates the two principal planes *AB* and *AC*, Fig. 8-5c, on which σ_1 and σ_2 act. *Note that the angles are measured counterclockwise from a vertical line.* On which one of these planes the principal stresses act is unknown. So, by using, say, $(\theta_1)_A = 31°43'$, Eq. 8-1 is solved. The stress found by this calculation is the stress which acts on the plane *AB*. Since $2(\theta_1)_A = 63°26'$, note that

$$\sigma_1 = \frac{3+1}{2} + \frac{3-1}{2} \cos 63°26' + 2 \sin 63°26' = +4.24 \text{ ksi}$$

This result, besides giving a check on the previous calculations, shows that the *maximum* principal stress acts on the plane *AB* defined by $(\theta_1)_A = 31°43'$ (Fig. 8-5c). The *minimum* principal stress must act on the plane *AC* which is at right angles to *AB*. No shearing stresses act on either one of these planes as the stresses computed are the principal stresses.

Since the stresses acting on parallel planes infinitely close to each other are the same, it is correct to sketch a square element as shown in Fig. 8-5d and to indicate the results on it. In the element shown in Fig. 8-5d the respective sides are parallel to the planes *AB* and *AC*. *The stresses shown in Fig. 8-5d are precisely equivalent to the stresses shown in Fig. 8-5a.* However, the latter description of the state of stress at a point is much neater and more meaningful. Note that although for the original element no compressive stresses appear, in the transformed description of stress a small compressive stress is found to be present, because of shearing stresses in the original element.

Case (c). The maximum shearing stress is found by using Eq. 8-6. The planes on which these stresses act are defined by Eq. 8-5. The sense of the shearing stresses is determined by substituting one of the roots of Eq. 8-5 into Eq. 8-2. Normal stresses may also be present with the maximum shearing stress, and they are determined by using Eq. 8-7. The element for the wanted condition is oriented in Fig. 8-5f.

From Eq. 8-6: $\tau_{\max} = \sqrt{[\frac{1}{2}(3 - 1)]^2 + 2^2} = \sqrt{5} = 2.24$ ksi.

From Eq. 8-5: $\tan 2\theta_2 = -\dfrac{\frac{1}{2}(3 - 1)}{2} = -0.500.$

$$2\theta_2 = 153°26' \quad \text{or} \quad 153°26' + 180° = 333°26'$$

Hence $\qquad\qquad (\theta_2)_A = 76°43' \quad \text{and} \quad (\theta_2)_B = 166°43'$

These planes are shown in Fig. 8-5e with the angles measured from a vertical line. Then, using $2(\theta_2)_A = 153°26'$ in Eq. 8-2,

$$\tau_{\max} = -\frac{3 - 1}{2} \sin 153°26' + 2 \cos 153°26' = -2.24 \text{ ksi}$$

which means that the shear along the plane *DE* has an opposite sense to that shown in Fig. 8-4b. Since shearing stresses on mutually perpendicular planes are equal and "meet or part" at a corner of an element, the sense of all shearing stresses thus becomes fixed.

From Eq. 8-7: $\sigma' = \dfrac{3 + 1}{2} = 2$ ksi.

The results are shown in Fig. 8-5f. This description of the state of stress at the point is also *equivalent* to the one given in the original problem, Fig. 8-5a, as well as to the one shown in Fig. 8-5d.

Note that in the above example the sense of the given stresses agreed with the sense of the stresses assumed positive in Fig. 8-4a. If normal stresses or shearing stresses act in the opposite direction to that shown in Fig. 8-4a, they must be taken as *negative* quantities.

8-6. An Important Transformation of Stress. A very significant transformation of one description of a state of stress at a point to another occurs when *pure shearing stress* is converted into principal stresses. For this purpose consider an element subjected *only* to shearing stresses τ as

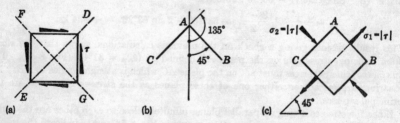

(a)   (b)   (c)

Fig. 8-6. Pure shearing stress equivalent to the tensile compressive stresses on a reoriented element.

shown in Fig. 8-6a, whence from Eq. 8-4 the principal stresses $\sigma_{1 \text{ or } 2} = \pm\tau$, i.e., **numerically σ_1, σ_2 and τ are all equal,** although σ_1 is a tensile stress and σ_2 is a compressive stress. Further, in this case, from Eq. 8-3 the principal planes are given by $\tan 2\theta_1 = \infty$, i.e., $2\theta_1 = 90°$ or $270°$. Hence $(\theta_1)_A = 45°$ and $(\theta_1)_B = 135°$, and the planes corresponding to these angles are shown in Fig. 8-6b. To determine on which plane the tensile stress σ_1 acts, a substitution into Eq. 8-1 is made with $2(\theta_1)_A = 90°$. This computation shows that $\sigma_1 = \tau \sin 90° = +\tau$, hence the tensile stress acts perpendicular to the plane AB. The principal stresses which are equivalent to the pure shearing stress are shown in Fig. 8-6c. Therefore, whenever pure shearing stress is acting on an element it may be thought of as causing tension along one of the diagonals *and* compression along the other diagonal of this element (see the diagonals DE and FG in Fig. 8-6a). The magnitude of these normal stresses is equal to the shearing stress. In subsequent work the diagonal, as DE in Fig. 8-6a, along which a tensile stress acts will be referred to as the *positive shear diagonal*. Conversely, a diagonal, as FG in Fig. 8-6a, along which the compressive stress acts will be called the *negative shear diagonal*.

From the physical point of view, the transformation of stress found completely agrees with intuition. The material "does not know" the manner in which its state of stress is described, and a little imagination should convince one that the tangential shearing stresses combine to cause a pull along the positive shear diagonal and compression along the negative shear diagonal. A clear visualization of this situation will be found helpful in subsequent work.

8-7. Determination of the Principal Stresses Using Mohr's Circle.* In this article the basic Eqs. 8-1 and 8-2 for the stress transformation at a point will be re-examined in order to devise a graphical solution for the quantities defined by them. Such a solution is quicker to apply and more easily remembered.

A careful study of Eqs. 8-1 and 8-2 shows that they represent a circle written in parametric form. That they do represent a circle is made clearer by first rewriting them as

$$\sigma_\theta - \frac{\sigma_x + \sigma_y}{2} = \frac{\sigma_x - \sigma_y}{2} \cos 2\theta + \tau \sin 2\theta \qquad (8\text{-}1a)$$

$$\tau_\theta = -\frac{\sigma_x - \sigma_y}{2} \sin 2\theta + \tau \cos 2\theta \qquad (8\text{-}2)$$

Then by squaring both of these equations, adding and simplifying,

$$\left(\sigma_\theta - \frac{\sigma_x + \sigma_y}{2}\right)^2 + \tau_\theta{}^2 = \left(\frac{\sigma_x - \sigma_y}{2}\right)^2 + \tau^2 \qquad (8\text{-}9)$$

However, in every given problem σ_x, σ_y, and τ are the three *known constants,* while σ_θ and τ_θ are the *variables.* Hence Eq. 8-9 may be written in a more compact form as

$$(\sigma_\theta - a)^2 + \tau_\theta{}^2 = b^2 \qquad (8\text{-}10)$$

where $a = \frac{1}{2}(\sigma_x + \sigma_y)$ and $b^2 = [\frac{1}{2}(\sigma_x - \sigma_y)]^2 + \tau^2$ are constants.

This equation is the familiar expression of analytical geometry,

---

* The remainder of this chapter may be omitted.

$(x - a)^2 + y^2 = b^2$, for a circle of radius b with its center at $(+a, 0)$. Hence if a circle satisfying this equation is plotted, the *simultaneous* values of a point (x, y) on this circle correspond to σ_θ and τ_θ for a particular orientation of an inclined plane. The ordinate of a point on the circle is the shearing stress τ_θ, the abscissa is the normal stress σ_θ. The circle so constructed is called a *circle of stress* or *Mohr's circle*.*

There are several alternative methods of plotting the circle defined by Eq. 8-9. It could be constructed by locating the center at $[\frac{1}{2}(\sigma_x + \sigma_y), 0]$ and using the radius $b = \sqrt{[\frac{1}{2}(\sigma_x - \sigma_y)]^2 + \tau^2}$, but this is not the best procedure for the purpose at hand. The stress data usually appear as shown in Fig. 8-7a. On any one of the faces of a given element a normal and a shearing stress appear directly, and *any two of these corresponding values of stress define **one** point on the circle*. This information, together with the knowledge that the center of the circle is located on the abscissa at $\frac{1}{2}(\sigma_x + \sigma_y)$, is sufficient to plot the circle. The circle passing through *four* co-ordinate points defined by the stresses acting on the faces of the given element is shown in Fig. 8-7b. Since the equation of the circle is

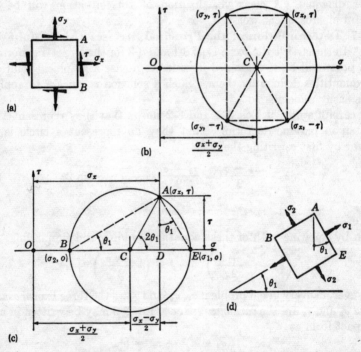

Fig. 8-7. Mohr's circle construction for determining the principal stresses.

* It is so named in honor of Professor Otto Mohr of Germany who in 1895 suggested its use in stress analysis problems.

of a simple quadratic form in y, there are two values of y of equal magnitude but of opposite sign for every value of x. For convenience the axes are shown directly in terms of σ and τ. Normal tensile stresses are considered positive, compressive negative.

After constructing the circle of stress by any one of the above methods, the magnitude and sign of the principal stresses may be found by determining the points of intersection of the circle with the abscissa. *Only normal, and no shearing stresses, correspond to these points on the circle of stress.* Positive abscissas correspond to tensile stresses, negative to compressive. In many problems, the line of action of the principal stresses is also of considerable importance. To find this directly from the graphical construction, **only one method of constructing the circle of stress is adopted in this text.** After the center of the circle is located, a governing point on the circle is determined by the values of stresses on the **right-hand face of an element** (as AB in Fig. 8-7a). By adopting this construction, Fig. 8-7c, an upward shearing stress on the *right-hand face* of the element locates a point on the circle which is above the σ-axis, or vice versa; a tensile normal stress on the *right-hand face* of the element locates a point to the right of the origin, and a compressive stress locates a corresponding point to the left.

If the recommended method of constructing the circle is used, the planes on which the principal stresses act are associated with the directions of the lines AB and AE. These lines are obtained by connecting the governing point A on the circle with the points giving the values of the principal stresses, points B and E in Fig. 8-7c. From the geometry of the figure, $\dfrac{AD}{CD} = \dfrac{\tau}{\frac{1}{2}(\sigma_x - \sigma_y)}$, which by Eq. 8-3 is equal to $\tan 2\theta_1$, hence the angle ABE is equal to θ_1.* Moreover, since the angle BAE is a right angle, the line AE is also uniquely defined by the angle θ_1. This line corresponds to the plane on which the **algebraically**† larger principal stress acts. The algebraically smaller stress acts on a plane defined by the line AB. Note particularly from Fig. 8-7c the *mechanical association* of the abscissal value of the principal stress with the plane on which it acts. The principal stress given by the abscissa of the point E acts *perpendicularly* to the line EA; while the principal stress given by the abscissa of the point B acts normally to the line BA.

By following the above procedure in constructing Mohr's circle, the complete problem of determining the magnitude, sign, and line of action of the principal stresses may be determined. The final results may be conveniently shown on an element whose sides are parallel to lines AB

* Arc AE is the same for the angle ACE and ABE.

† An algebraically larger principal stress may be a compressive stress. Under such circumstances the other principal stress is also compressive and is numerically greater than the former stress. For example, -100 psi > -200 psi.

and *AE*. A properly oriented element corresponding to the data of Fig. 8-7a is shown in Fig. 8-7d.

8-8. Determination of the Principal Shearing Stress Using Mohr's Circle. If the state of stress at a point is known, the principal or the maximum shearing stress may also be determined by using Mohr's circle, by noting the largest *ordinate* of the points on the circle, which is equal to its radius. Therefore, since the ordinates represent the shearing stress, the **radius** of the circle is equal to the principal shearing stress. The point on the circle corresponding to the maximum shearing stress lies directly above or below the *center* of the circle. Hence the value of the abscissa at the *center* of the circle gives the normal stress which acts *simultaneously* with the maximum shearing stress. In special cases the center of the circle coincides with the origin of the σ and τ-axes. *Only then* are the planes on which the maximum shearing stresses act free of normal stresses. If both of the principal stresses are equal in magnitude and sign, Mohr's circle degenerates into a point. All planes become the principal planes on which no shearing stresses act.

To complete the solution of the problem, the sense and the inclination of the planes on which the maximum shearing stresses act must be established. This phase of the solution depends on the theory developed in Art. 8-5. There it was shown that the planes on which the maximum shearing stresses act make an angle of 45° with the principal planes. Thus if the stresses σ_1 and σ_2 shown in Fig. 8-8a are the principal stresses, the planes of the element on which the maximum shearing stresses act must

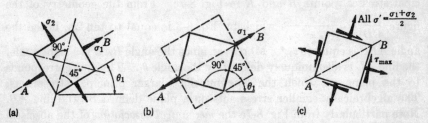

Fig. 8-8. Transformation of the principal stresses into the principal shearing stresses and the associated normal stresses.

be oriented as shown in Fig. 8-8b. In this diagram the enlarged original element is shown by the dashed lines.

Next, recall that in transforming a state of pure shearing stress into principal stresses, Art. 8-6, the tensile principal stress acts along the positive shear diagonal. The same tendency exists in a more involved case, as shown in Fig. 8-8a, and the principal shearing stresses act toward the diagonal *AB* shown in Figs. 8-8b and c. Hence in general, if algebraically $\sigma_1 > \sigma_2$, **the maximum or the principal shearing stresses act toward the** *positive shear diagonal* which corresponds to the direction of σ_1.* For the case considered, the principal shearing stresses and the corresponding normal stresses are shown in Fig. 8-8c. These normal stresses, as explained earlier, are given by the distance from the origin to the center of Mohr's circle.

8-9. Step-by-Step Procedure for Constructing Mohr's Circle. The main purpose in using Mohr's circle is to have a quick mechanical procedure for transforming a given state of stress at a point into principal stresses or into the maximum shearing stress and the associated normal stresses. To be of any value, the procedure must be rapid and simple. As an aid in applications, it is outlined below.

To determine the principal stresses, (see Fig. 8-9):

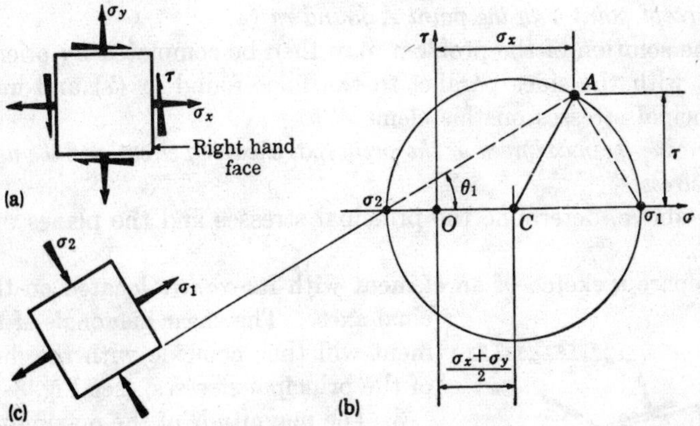

Fig. 8-9. Determination of the principal stresses by using Mohr's circle.

1. Make a sketch of the element for which the normal and shearing stresses are known and indicate on it the proper sense of these stresses.

2. Set up a rectangular co-ordinate system of axes where the horizontal axis is the *normal* stress axis, and the vertical axis is the *shearing* stress axis. Directions of positive axes are taken as usual, upward and to the right.

3. Locate the center of the circle, which is on the horizontal axis at a distance of $\frac{1}{2}(\sigma_x + \sigma_y)$ from the origin. Tensile stresses are positive, compressive are negative.

4. From the *right-hand face* of the element prepared in (1), read off the

* If $\sigma_1 > \sigma_2$ and both are tensile stresses, this means that σ_1 exercises the dominant influence in stress transformation. If $\sigma_1 > \sigma_2$ and σ_1 is a tensile stress while σ_2 is a compressive stress, the compressive stress σ_2 boosts the shearing stresses in the direction determined by σ_1. If σ_1 and σ_2 are both compressive stresses, consideration of the negative shear diagonal which is in compression along the line of action of the *numerically* larger principal stress justifies the same rule.

values for σ_x and τ and plot the controlling point A. The co-ordinate distances to this point are measured from the *origin*. The sign of σ_x is positive if tensile, negative if compressive; that of τ is positive if upward, negative if downward.

5. Connect the center of the circle found in (3) with the point plotted in (4) and determine this distance, which is the radius of the circle.

6. Draw the circle, using the radius found in (5). The two points of intersection of the circle with the σ-axis give the magnitudes and *sign* of the two principal stresses. If an intercept is found to be positive, the principal stress is tensile, and vice versa.

7. To find the direction of the principal stresses, connect the point A located in (4) with the intercepts found in (6). The principal stress given by the particular intercept found in (6) *acts normal to the line connecting this intercept point with the point A found in (4).*

8. The solution of the problem may then be completed by orienting an element with the sides parallel to the lines found in (7) and indicating the principal stresses on this element.

To determine the maximum or the principal shearing stress and the associated normal stresses:

1. As above, determine the principal stresses and the planes on which they act.

2. Prepare a sketch of an element with its *corners* located on the prin-

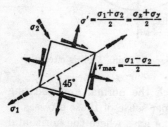

$$\sigma' = \frac{\sigma_1 + \sigma_2}{2} = \frac{\sigma_x + \sigma_y}{2}$$

$$\tau_{max} = \frac{\sigma_1 - \sigma_2}{2}$$

Fig. 8-10. Transformation of the principal stresses into the maximum shearing stresses and the associated normal stresses.

cipal axes. The shear diagonals of this element will thus coincide with the directions of the principal stresses, (see Fig. 8-10).

3. The magnitude of the maximum (principal) shearing stresses acting on mutually perpendicular planes is equal to the radius of the circle. These shearing stresses act along the faces of the element prepared in (2) toward the shear diagonal, which coincides with the direction of the *algebraically greater normal stress.*

4. The normal stresses acting on *all* faces of the element prepared in (2) are equal to the average of the principal stresses, considered algebraically. The magnitude and sign of these stresses is also given by the distance from the origin of the co-ordinate system to the center of Mohr's circle.

To solve the problems of stress transformation, the foregoing procedures may be applied graphically. However, *it is recommended that* **trigonometric computations of the critical values** *be used in conjunction with the graphical construction.* Then the work may be carried out on a crude sketch without any necessity for scaling off any of the distances or angles, and the results will be accurate. Using the Mohr's circle construction in this manner is equivalent to applying the basic equations of stress transformation. A little practice in using this aid should convince the reader that it is quicker in application than solution of the formal equations. The foregoing procedures are greatly shortened if only the magnitudes of the stresses are sought.

Example 8-3. Given the state of stress shown in Fig. 8-11a, transform it (a) into the principal stresses, and (b) into the principal shearing stresses and the associated normal stresses. Show the results for both cases on properly oriented elements.

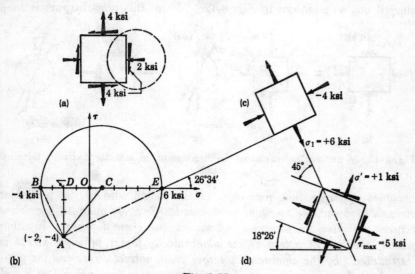

Fig. 8-11.

SOLUTION: The co-ordinate axes are set up in Fig. 8-11b. The center C of the circle is at $\frac{1}{2}(-2,000 + 4,000) = +1,000$ ksi on the σ-axis. From the *right-hand face* of the element, the required values for plotting the controlling point A on the circle are $\sigma_x = -2,000$ psi and $\tau = -4,000$ psi. Thus the distances CD and DA are 3,000 psi and 4,000 psi, respectively, and the radius of the circle is equal to $CA = \sqrt{CD^2 + DA^2} = 5,000$ psi. Hence from the diagram, $\tau_{max} = 5,000$ psi, and the associated normal stress is represented by the distance OC, i.e., $\sigma' = 1,000$ psi. The principal stresses are given by the intercepts E and B; they are respectively +6,000 psi and -4,000 psi. The angle $DEA = \tan^{-1}\frac{AD}{DE} = \tan^{-1}\frac{4,000}{8,000} = 26°34'$.

An element with its sides parallel to the lines AB and AE is shown in Fig. 8-11c. Since the faces of this element intersect at right angles, several other angles (not shown) may be used to specify its orientation. The principal stress given by the E intercept acts normal to the line EA. The principal stress given by the B intercept acts normal to the line BA.

An element oriented with its planes parallel to the maximum shearing stresses is shown in Fig. 8-11d. The maximum shearing stresses act toward the positive shear diagonal, which coincides with the direction of the algebraically larger principal stress. The associated normal stresses are also shown on the diagram. All of these are the same, and all of them are tensile in character.

It is significant to note that the approximate direction of the algebraically larger principal stress found in the above example might have been anticipated. Instead of thinking in terms of the normal and the shearing stresses as given in the original data, Fig. 8-12a, an equivalent problem shown in Fig. 8-12b may be considered. Here the shearing stresses have been replaced by the equivalent tension-compression stresses acting along the proper shear diagonals. Then, for qualitative reasoning, the outline of the original element may be obliterated, and the tensile stresses may be singled out as is shown in Fig. 8-12c. From this new diagram it then

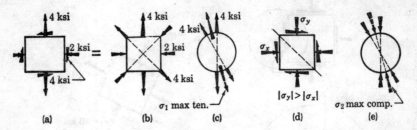

(a)   (b)   (c)   (d)   (e)

Fig. 8-12. A method for estimating the direction of the absolute maximum principal stresses.

becomes apparent that regardless of the magnitudes of the particular stresses involved, *the resultant maximum tensile stress **must** act somewhere between the given tensile stress and the positive shear diagonal.* In other words, **the line of action of the algebraically larger principal stress is "straddled" by the algebraically larger given normal stress and the positive shear diagonal.** The use of the negative shear diagonal will be found helpful in visualizing this effect for cases where both given normal stresses are compressive, Figs. 8-12d and e. This procedure provides a qualitative check on the orientation of an element for the principal stresses. This concept will be used in the next article.

8-10. Resolution of the Principal Stresses. To transform a state of stress from one set of planes to another, Eqs. 8-1 and 8-2 may be applied. This procedure was illustrated in Example 8-2. Moreover, if the original description of the state of stress is given in terms of the *principal* stresses, Eqs. 8-1 and 8-2 simplify to

$$\sigma_\theta = \frac{\sigma_1 + \sigma_2}{2} + \frac{\sigma_1 - \sigma_2}{2} \cos 2\theta \qquad (8\text{-}1b)$$

$$\tau_\theta = -\frac{\sigma_1 - \sigma_2}{2} \sin 2\theta \qquad (8\text{-}2a)$$

These equations may be used to obtain the normal and the shearing stress on any plane, *provided the angle θ is measured positive counterclockwise from the downward directed axis coinciding with the line of action of the stress σ2.* This amounts to a resolution of the principal stresses into the normal and shearing stresses acting on any plane. Strict adherence to the sign convention adopted in deriving the original equations, as shown in Fig. 8-4, must be followed, because if they are followed, the magnitude and sense of the computed quantities are uniquely determined.

Mohr's circle may also be used to resolve the principal stresses into equivalent stresses on any plane. For this purpose, using an element with principal stresses acting on it, Mohr's circle is constructed in the usual manner. Then, on this circle a diameter is located by a *double angle* 2θ from the abscissa. This double angle is equal to twice the angle θ, which locates the plane on which the stresses are sought. The angle θ may be measured either from the vertical or the horizontal line, clockwise or counterclockwise, since the co-ordinates of the terminal points of the alternate diameters, except for the sign of τ, are the same.

The two abscissas, which correspond to the terminal points on the diameter, give the normal stresses acting on planes defined either by θ or by $\theta + 90°$. The numerically equal ordinates to the same points give the shearing stresses on the mutually perpendicular planes, one of which is at an angle θ. These three quantities are all that is needed from the Mohr's circle. The line of action of these stresses is adjusted to be compatible with the given principal stresses. This is done by straddling the given algebraically larger principal stress with the positive shear diagonal of an element inclined at an angle θ and the algebraically larger normal stress found earlier. This procedure will be illustrated by an example which follows. In this manner the stresses on two mutually perpendicular planes, one of which is at the sought angle θ, are determined. *This method must not be used if the initial data are not in terms of the principal stresses.*

Example 8-4. Using Mohr's circle, transform the given principal stresses into stresses acting on the plane at an angle of $22\frac{1}{2}°$ with the vertical axis as shown in Fig. 8-13a.

SOLUTION: Mohr's circle with two alternative diameters at $2\theta = 45°$ and $135°$ is shown in Fig. 8-13b. Co-ordinates of the points C and B or A and D furnish the same information, giving a shearing stress of 2.83 ksi, and two normal stresses of -3.17 ksi and -8.83 ksi.

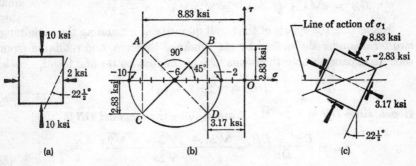

(a)   (b)   (c)

Fig. 8-13.

An element, two faces of which are oriented at an angle of $22\frac{1}{2}°$, is shown in Fig. 8-13c. The line of action of the *algebraically* larger principal stress, $\sigma_1 = -2$ ksi, is in the horizontal direction. This line is *straddled* by the positive shear diagonal, toward which the shearing stresses of 2.83 ksi act, and by the line of action of the *algebraically* larger normal stress of -3.17 ksi. The normal stress of -8.83 ksi acts at right angles to the normal stress of -3.17 ksi. The stresses acting on the element in the new orientation are as shown in Fig. 8-13c. The stresses acting on the plane at $22\frac{1}{2}°$ are thus determined.

8-11. Relation Between E, G, and μ. Having established the techniques for transforming one description of the state of stress into another, and having observed that pure shearing stresses may be converted into "pure" normal stresses, one must conclude that the deformations caused by normal stress are related to the deformations caused by shearing stress. To relate these deformations, consider the element $ABCD$ shown in Fig. 8-14a. When this element is subjected to the shearing stresses τ, it

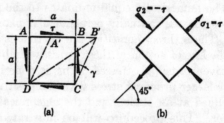

Fig. 8-14. Equivalent elements used to determine the strain along the diagonal *DB*.

deforms to $A'B'CD$. The side CB' makes a very small angle γ with the vertical, and the positive shear diagonal DB elongates an amount $DB' - DB$. The length

$$DB' = \sqrt{\overline{AD^2} + (AB + BB')^2} = \sqrt{\overline{AD^2} + (AB + BC\gamma)^2}$$

but if $AD = AB = a$,

$$DB' = a\sqrt{1 + (1 + \gamma)^2} = \sqrt{2}a\sqrt{1 + \gamma + \tfrac{1}{2}\gamma^2},$$

Neglecting the *square* of the small quantity γ, expanding the remaining two terms under the radical by the binomial theorem, and retaining from such an expansion only the terms in γ of the first power and lower,

$$DB' \doteq \sqrt{2}a(1 + \tfrac{1}{2}\gamma).$$

Hence, since $DB = \sqrt{2}a$, the *strain* ϵ_1 along the diagonal DB is

$$\epsilon_1 = \frac{DB' - DB}{DB} = \frac{\sqrt{2}a + \tfrac{1}{2}\sqrt{2}a\gamma - \sqrt{2}a}{\sqrt{2}a} = \frac{\gamma}{2}$$

However, by Eq. 2-9, which is $\tau = G\gamma$, the shearing strain γ is related to the shearing stress τ. Therefore $\epsilon_1 = \tau/2G$.

On the other hand, pure shearing stress acting on an element is equivalent to a set of normal stresses, as shown in Fig. 8-14b. Therefore the material along the diagonal DB may be said to experience a tensile stress of $\sigma_1 = \tau$ *and* a compressive stress $\sigma_2 = -\tau$ acting normal to the same diagonal. Therefore the *strain* ϵ_1 along the diagonal DB, using Eq. 2-6, is

$$\epsilon_1 = \frac{\sigma_1}{E} - \mu\,\frac{\sigma_2}{E} = \frac{\tau}{E}\,(1 + \mu)$$

Equating the two alternative relations for the strain along the positive shear diagonal, and simplifying gives

$$G = \frac{E}{2(1 + \mu)} \tag{8-11}$$

This equation shows the relation between E, G and μ. These quantities are not independent of one another. If any two are determined experimentally, the third may be computed. Note that the shearing modulus G is always less than the elastic modulus E, since the Poisson ratio μ is a positive quantity. For most materials μ is in the neighborhood of $1/4$.

8-12. Analysis of Plane Strain; Linear Strain. Up to this time the major part of this text has been devoted to a discussion of stresses. Yet, the concept of stress is a philosophical abstraction. Stress cannot be seen nor measured directly. It represents an intensity of force on an idealized material. On the other hand, deformations can be seen and measured, and in many cases the stress is estimated indirectly from the deformations. Therefore, a study of the geometry of deformations or strains is of great importance. The remainder of this chapter will be devoted to the study of deformations in a plane and their relation to stress. Since earlier only the "two-dimensional" stress problem was discussed, only the "two-dimensional" strain problem will be treated. Practically speaking, this problem is the most significant one, since the *maximum* strains usually occur on the *free* surface of a material.

In analyzing strains, a sign convention is necessary. This will be directly related to the sign convention chosen earlier for the stresses acting on an element. All stresses shown in Fig. 8-15a have a positive sense. The *strain* ϵ_x corresponding to an *elongation* in the x-direction is considered positive. Similarly, strain ϵ_y is positive if it corresponds to an *elongation* in the y-direction. Positive shearing stresses cause a distortion of an element as shown in Fig. 8-15b, thus a *decrease* in the included angle *at the lower left-hand corner* of an element is considered positive.

In studying the strains at a point, only the **relative displacement of the adjoining points is of importance.** Translation and rotation of an element as a whole is not important, since these displacements are rigid body displacements. It is the relative displacement between adjoining points that causes stresses in the material. Therefore a point A, Fig. 8-15a, of an element may be thought of as being fixed in space, and a study of the relative displacement of a point B can be made.

On an element, consider a line AB, Fig. 8-15c, whose position is defined by the angle θ measured counterclockwise from the horizontal line (x-axis). If this element is subjected to a strain of ϵ_x in the x-direction, and point A is fixed, the distance $HB = dx$ elongates an amount $\epsilon_x\,dx$, and the point B

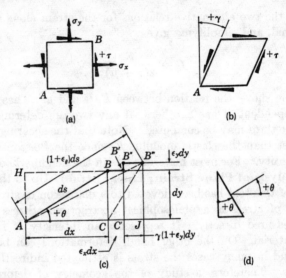

Fig. 8-15. Distortion of an element due to normal and shearing stresses which are of positive sense.

moves to B'. Similarly, owing to strain in the y-direction, the same point moves to B'' through a vertical displacement of $B'B'' = \epsilon_y\,dy$. Finally, because of angular distortion, which for small deformations causes no appreciable change in distance between parallel planes, point B'' moves to B''' through a distance of $\gamma(1 + \epsilon_y)\,dy$. No additional relative displacements would take place between the points A and B''' if, in the meantime, the element were translated or rotated bodily.

Any order of introducing the above deformations is permissible.* Moreover, their effects may be superposed, *since the deformations considered are very small.* For clarity, the diagram showing these deformations, Fig. 8-15c, *exaggerates* them to a very large degree. Also note that the angle chosen to locate the line AB is the same as was used earlier to define the direction of the normal stress *on* a plane at an angle θ with the

* See Prob. 8-34.

vertical axis. The identity of the adopted convention for the two cases may be seen by examining Fig. 8-15d.

If the linear strain in the direction of the line AB is denoted by ϵ_θ, where the subscript θ specifies the direction of this line, the elongation of a line of length ds is $\epsilon_\theta \, ds$. This elongation occurs in the direction of the normal stress located by the angle θ in Fig. 8-15d. From this it follows that the line AB''' is nearly $(1 + \epsilon_\theta) \, ds$ long, or $(AB''')^2 = [(1 + \epsilon_\theta) \, ds]^2$. However, from the geometry of the figure shown in Fig. 8-15c, $(AB''')^2$ is also equal to

$$(AJ)^2 + (JB''')^2 = [(1 + \epsilon_x) \, dx + \gamma(1 + \epsilon_y) \, dy]^2 + [(1 + \epsilon_y) \, dy]^2$$

By equating the two expressions for $(AB''')^2$ and dividing throughout by ds^2, the following is obtained

$$(1 + \epsilon_\theta)^2 = \left[(1 + \epsilon_x) \frac{dx}{ds} + \gamma(1 + \epsilon_y) \frac{dy}{ds} \right]^2 + \left[(1 + \epsilon_y) \frac{dy}{ds} \right]^2$$

This relation can be further simplified by noting from the figure that $\dfrac{dx}{ds} = \cos\theta$, and $\dfrac{dy}{ds} = \sin\theta$. Substituting these relations into the above equation, squaring, simplifying, and discarding* the terms with a square or product of strains, one obtains an expression for ϵ_θ,

$$\epsilon_\theta = \epsilon_x \cos^2\theta + \epsilon_y \sin^2\theta + \gamma \sin\theta \cos\theta \qquad \text{(8-12)}$$

Equation 8-12 is the basic expression for determining the strain in any direction defined by the angle θ. To apply this equation, ϵ_x, ϵ_y, and γ must be known. By use of the trigonometric identities already encountered in establishing Eq. 8-1, Eq. 8-12 may be rewritten as

$$\epsilon_\theta = \frac{\epsilon_x + \epsilon_y}{2} + \frac{\epsilon_x - \epsilon_y}{2} \cos 2\theta + \frac{\gamma}{2} \sin 2\theta \qquad \text{(8-12a)}$$

Note the similarity of the form of this equation to that of Eq. 8-1.

8-13. Shearing Strain. To complete the study of strains at a point, shearing strain will be discussed next. Shearing strain will be associated with the plane for which the linear strain normal to it is given by Eq. 8-12. This plane is represented by the line AD shown in Fig. 8-16 and is located by the angle θ. However, since shearing strain is defined by the change in angle that takes place between two mutually perpendicular planes, line AF at 90° from AD must be included in the discussion.

Owing to the strains ϵ_x, ϵ_y, and γ to which an element is subjected, assuming point A fixed, point F finally moves to F'''. The first movement $FF' = \epsilon_x \, dx'$ is due to the strain ϵ_x; the second, $F'F'' = \epsilon_y \, dy'$ is due to ϵ_y. The third movement $F''F'''$ is approximately equal to $\gamma \, dy'$, since

* Since strains are *very small*, their squares and higher powers or products may be neglected.

$1 + \epsilon_y \doteq 1$. The movement of the point D may be similarly established, bearing in mind the sense of the applied strains. As before, these very small movements or displacements of a point may be superposed.

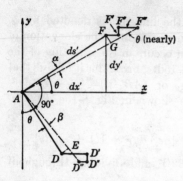

To find the shearing strain of the angle FAD caused by the various strains, the angles FAF''' and DAD''' must be found. The angle $FAF''' = \alpha$ may be found with sufficient degree of accuracy by projecting the displacements FF', $F'F''$, and $F''F'''$ onto a line FG perpendicular to the line AF, then asserting that for small angles the tangent of an angle is nearly equal to the angle itself. Hence

Fig. 8-16. Distortions due to normal and shearing stresses for determining the change in angle DAF.

$$\alpha \doteq \tan \alpha = \frac{FF' \sin \theta - F'F'' \cos \theta + F''F''' \sin \theta}{AF}$$

$$= \frac{\epsilon_x \, dx' \sin \theta - \epsilon_y \, dy' \cos \theta + \gamma \, dy' \sin \theta}{ds'}$$

where the displacements that cause a *decrease in the angle FAD* are considered positive. Next, noting that $dx'/ds' = \cos \theta$ and $dy'/ds' = \sin \theta$, the above expression is simplified to

$$\alpha = (\epsilon_x - \epsilon_y) \sin \theta \cos \theta + \gamma \sin^2 \theta$$

By similar reasoning,

$$\beta = (\epsilon_x - \epsilon_y) \sin \theta \cos \theta - \gamma \cos^2 \theta$$

Therefore the *shearing strain* associated with the angle θ, denoted by γ_θ, is

$$\gamma_\theta = \alpha + \beta = 2(\epsilon_x - \epsilon_y) \sin \theta \cos \theta - \gamma(\cos^2 \theta - \sin^2 \theta)$$

$$\gamma_\theta = (\epsilon_x - \epsilon_y) \sin 2\theta - \gamma \cos 2\theta \tag{8-13}$$

This equation is the second fundamental expression for the transformation of strains. Note that when $\theta = 90°$ the angle FAD corresponds to the interior angle at A in Fig. 8-15b. Substituting the value of this angle into Eq. 8-13 shows that $\gamma_\theta = -\gamma(-1) = +\gamma$ and indicates the consistency of the adopted sign convention.

8-14. Mohr's Circle of Strain. The equations for the transformation of strains derived in the previous two articles mathematically resemble the equations for the transformation of stresses derived in Art. 8-3. To achieve greater similarity of the new equations to the earlier ones, Eq. 8-13 is rewritten below after division throughout by two.

$$\epsilon_\theta = \frac{\epsilon_x + \epsilon_y}{2} + \frac{\epsilon_x - \epsilon_y}{2} \cos 2\theta + \frac{\gamma}{2} \sin 2\theta \qquad (8\text{-}12a)$$

$$\frac{\gamma_\theta}{2} = \frac{\epsilon_x - \epsilon_y}{2} \sin 2\theta - \frac{\gamma}{2} \cos 2\theta \qquad (8\text{-}13a)$$

These equations are mathematically similar to the stress transformation Eqs. 8-1 and 8-2, *except that the γ-terms have a coefficient of ½.* From this similarity it follows that Eqs. 8-12a and 8-13a also represent the equations of a circle in a parametric form. Hence the behavior of the corresponding variables ϵ_θ and γ_θ for the variously inclined planes at an angle θ may be conveniently studied from the plot of a circle. This circle is called *Mohr's circle of strain.* Every point on the circle gives two values, one for the linear strain, the other for the shearing strain *divided by two.* Strains corresponding to elongation are positive; for contraction they are negative. Positive shearing strains distort the element as shown in Fig. 8-15b. In plotting the circle the positive axes are taken up and to the right. This corresponds to the conventions used earlier for Mohr's circle of stress, *except* that the vertical axis is measured in terms of $\frac{1}{2}\gamma$.

As an example of Mohr's circle of strain, consider that ϵ_x, ϵ_y, and $+\gamma$ are given. Then on the $\epsilon - \frac{1}{2}\gamma$ axes shown in Fig. 8-17 the center of the circle C is at $[\frac{1}{2}(\epsilon_x + \epsilon_y), 0]$ and the governing point A for determining the circle is at $(\epsilon_x, \frac{1}{2}\gamma)$. The maximum strain is given by the intercept E. *No shearing strain is associated with this point.* The minimum strain, likewise without shearing strain, is given by the intercept B. The maximum and the minimum strains are called the *principal strains.* Analogous to the circle of stress, the direction of the principal strains may be determined by connecting the governing point A with the points E and B. In this construction, the principal strain given by the particular intercept takes place in a direction *normal* to the line connecting the intercept with the governing point A. *These directions coincide with the directions of the principal stresses.*

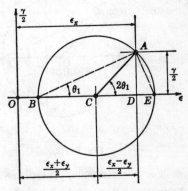

Fig. 8-17. Mohr's circle of strain.

As may be seen from the circle of strain, the analytical expression for the principal strains is

$$(\epsilon_\theta)_{\substack{\text{max} \\ \text{min}}} = \epsilon_1 \quad \text{or} \quad \epsilon_2 = \frac{\epsilon_x + \epsilon_y}{2} \pm \sqrt{\left(\frac{\epsilon_x - \epsilon_y}{2}\right)^2 + \left(\frac{\gamma}{2}\right)^2} \qquad (8\text{-}14)$$

where the positive sign in front of the radical is to be used for ϵ_1, the maximum principal strain in the *algebraic* sense. The negative sign is to be used for ϵ_2, the minimum principal strain.

The planes on which the principal strains act may also be defined analytically. From Fig. 8-17,

$$tan\ 2\theta_1 = \frac{\gamma}{\epsilon_x - \epsilon_y} \tag{8-15}$$

This equation has two roots, and to determine which of them is associated with the particular principal strain, a direct substitution into Eq. 8-12a must be made.

Other properties of strains at a point may be established by studying the circle of strain. Among these the invariance (constancy) of any two strains in two mutually perpendicular directions is notable, i.e., $\epsilon_1 + \epsilon_2 = \epsilon_x + \epsilon_y =$ constant. The behavior of shearing strains for the various orientations of an element may be studied in a manner analogous to the study of shearing stresses discussed earlier.

Example 8-5. It is observed that an element of a body contracts 0.00050 in. per inch along the x-axis, elongates 0.00030 in. per inch in the y-direction, and distorts

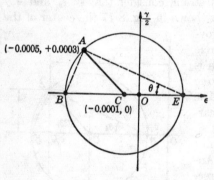

Fig. 8-18.

through an angle* of 0.00060 radians as shown in Fig. 8-15b. Find the principal strains and determine the directions in which these strains act. Use Mohr's circle of strain to obtain the solution.

SOLUTION: The data given indicate that $\epsilon_x = -0.00050$, $\epsilon_y = +0.00030$, and $\gamma = +0.00060$. Hence, on a $\epsilon - \frac{1}{2}\gamma$ system of axes, shown in Fig. 8-18, the center C of the circle is located at $\frac{1}{2}(\epsilon_x + \epsilon_y) = -0.00010$ on the ϵ-axis. The governing point A is at $(\epsilon_x, \frac{1}{2}\gamma)$ or $(-0.00050, +0.00030)$. Therefore the radius of the circle AC is equal to 0.00050. Hence $\epsilon_1 = +0.00040$ in. per in. and acts in a direction *perpendicular* to the line AE;

while $\epsilon_2 = -0.00060$ in. per inch and acts in a direction perpendicular to the line AB. From the geometry of the figure, $\theta = \tan^{-1}\dfrac{0.0003}{0.0009} = 18°25'$.

8-15. Applications of Strain Measurements; Rosettes. The above example presented no analytical difficulties; but experimentally the shearing strain measurement such as is given there is difficult to obtain. Measurements of *linear strain* are much easier to make, and therefore are more reliable. Linear strains are usually measured along several closely clustered gage lines, diagrammatically indicated in Fig. 8-19 by lines *a-a*,

---

* This measurement may be made by scribing a small square on a body, subjecting the body to the action of forces, and then measuring the change in angle which takes place. Photographic enlargements and grid techniques have been used for this purpose.

b-b, and c-c. These gage lines may be located on the member investigated with reference to some co-ordinate axes (as x and y) by the respective angles θ_1, θ_2, and θ_3. By comparing the initial distance between any two corresponding gage points with the distance in the stressed member, the elongation in the gage length is obtained. Dividing the elongation by the gage length gives the strain in the θ_1 direction, which will be designated by ϵ_{θ_1}. By performing the same operation with the other gage lines, ϵ_{θ_2} and ϵ_{θ_3} are obtained. If the distances between the gage points are small, measurements approximating the strains at a point are obtained.

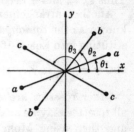

As an alternate to the foregoing experimental procedure, electric strain gages are unusually convenient to employ. These consist of very thin wires which are *glued* to the member to be investigated. As the forces are applied to a member, elongation or contraction of these wires takes place concurrently with similar changes in the material being investigated. These changes in the length of the wires alter their electrical resistance, which may be measured and calibrated to indicate the actual strain.

An arrangement of gage lines at a point in a cluster, as shown in Fig. 8-19, is known as a strain **rosette.** If three strain measurements are taken at the rosette, the information is sufficient to determine the principal strains. Thus as θ_1, θ_2, and θ_3, together with the corresponding ϵ_{θ_1}, ϵ_{θ_2}, and ϵ_{θ_3} are known, three simultaneous equations may be written from Eq. 8-12:

$$\left.\begin{aligned}
\epsilon_{\theta_1} &= \epsilon_x \cos^2 \theta_1 + \epsilon_y \sin^2 \theta_1 + \gamma \sin \theta_1 \cos \theta_1 \\
\epsilon_{\theta_2} &= \epsilon_x \cos^2 \theta_2 + \epsilon_y \sin^2 \theta_2 + \gamma \sin \theta_2 \cos \theta_2 \\
\epsilon_{\theta_3} &= \epsilon_x \cos^2 \theta_3 + \epsilon_y \sin^2 \theta_3 + \gamma \sin \theta_3 \cos \theta_3
\end{aligned}\right\} \qquad (8\text{-}16)$$

This set of equations may always be solved for ϵ_x, ϵ_y, and γ, and the determination of principal strains reverts to the case already considered.

To minimize computational work, the gages in a rosette are usually arranged in a particular pattern. For example, in Fig. 8-20a, $\theta_1 = 0°$, $\theta_2 = 45°$, and $\theta_3 = 90°$. This arrangement of gage lines is known as the

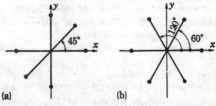

Fig. 8-20. (a) rectangular or 45° strain rosette, (b) equiangular strain rosette

rectangular or the *45° strain rosette*. By direct substitution into Eqs. 8-16, it is found that for this rosette,

$$\epsilon_x = \epsilon_{0°}, \qquad \epsilon_y = \epsilon_{90°}, \qquad \epsilon_{45°} = \tfrac{1}{2}\epsilon_x + \tfrac{1}{2}\epsilon_y + \tfrac{1}{2}\gamma_{xy}$$

or,
$$\gamma = \gamma_{xy} = 2\epsilon_{45°} - (\epsilon_{0°} + \epsilon_{90°})$$

Thus ϵ_x, ϵ_y, and γ become known.

Another arrangement of gage lines is shown in Fig. 8-20b. This is known as the *equiangular*, or the *delta*, or the *60° rosette*. Again, by substituting into Eqs. 8-16 and simplifying, $\epsilon_x = \epsilon_{0°}, \epsilon_y = \tfrac{1}{3}(2\epsilon_{60°} + 2\epsilon_{120°} - \epsilon_{0°})$, and $\gamma = \dfrac{2}{\sqrt{3}}(\epsilon_{60°} - \epsilon_{120°})$.

Other rosettes are occasionally used in experiments. The data from all rosettes may be analyzed by applying Eqs. 8-16, solving for ϵ_x, ϵ_y, and γ, and then using Mohr's circle of strain. Sometimes rosettes with more than three lines are used. An additional gage line gives a measurement which provides a check on the experimental work. For these rosettes, the invariance of the strains in the mutually perpendicular directions may be used to check the data.

The application of the rosette technique in complicated problems is almost indispensable. The principal strains may always be determined with the aid of rosettes. Moreover, since the principal strains correspond to the principal stresses, and as $\sigma_z = 0$ in a plane problem of stress, Eq. 2-6 written in terms of the principal stresses gives

$$\epsilon_1 = \frac{\sigma_1}{E} - \mu\frac{\sigma_2}{E} \qquad \text{and} \qquad \epsilon_2 = \frac{\sigma_2}{E} - \mu\frac{\sigma_1}{E}$$

By solving these equations simultaneously for the principal stresses, the following relations are obtained:

$$\sigma_1 = \frac{E}{1 - \mu^2}(\epsilon_1 + \mu\epsilon_2) \qquad \sigma_2 = \frac{E}{1 - \mu^2}(\epsilon_2 + \mu\epsilon_1) \qquad (8\text{-}17)$$

The *elastic* constants E and μ may be found for any material from some simple tests. Hence with the aid of experimental work, the principal stresses may be obtained on the surface of any stressed member. By these means, problems beyond the scope of this text and the Mathematical Theory of Elasticity may be successfully solved.*

Example 8-6. At a certain point of a steel machine part measurements with an electric rectangular rosette indicate that $\epsilon_{0°} = -0.00050$, $\epsilon_{45°} = +0.0002$, and $\epsilon_{90°} = +0.00030$. Assuming that $E = 30 \times 10^6$ psi and $\mu = 0.3$ are accurate enough. find the principal stresses at the point investigated.

SOLUTION: From the data given $\epsilon_x = -0.00050$ and $\epsilon_y = +0.00030$, while

$$\gamma = 2\,\epsilon_{45°} - (\epsilon_{0°} + \epsilon_{90°})$$
$$= 2\,(+0.0002) - (-0.00050 + 0.00030) = +0.00060$$

* See Hetényi, M., Editor-in-chief, *Handbook of Experimental Stress Analysis*, Society for Experimental Stress Analysis. New York: Wiley, 1950.

The principal strains for these data were found in Example 8-5 and are $\epsilon_1 = +0.00040$ and $\epsilon_2 = -0.00060$. Hence by Eq. 8-17 the principal stresses are

$$\sigma_1 = \frac{30(10)^6}{1 - (0.3)^2}[+0.00040 + 0.3(-0.00060)] = +7,250 \text{ psi}$$

$$\sigma_2 = \frac{30(10)^6}{1 - (0.3)^2}[-0.00060 + 0.3(+0.00040)] = -15,830 \text{ psi}$$

The tensile stress σ_1 acts perpendicularly to the line AE shown in Fig. 8-18 since that is the direction of the algebraically maximum principal strain. The compressive stress σ_2 acts in the direction perpendicular to the line AB of the same figure.

Problems for Solution

8-1 through 8-4. For the infinitesimal elements shown in the figures, find the normal and shearing stresses acting on the indicated inclined planes. Use the "wedge" method of analysis discussed in Example 8-1.

Ans. Prob. 8-1: $\sigma = 0$, $\tau = 1$ ksi; $\sigma = +4$ ksi, $\tau = 1$ ksi.

Prob. 8-2: $\sigma = -120$ psi, $\tau = 710$ psi; $\sigma = +4,120$ psi, $\tau = 710$ psi.

Prob. 8-3: $\sigma = -400$ psi, $\tau = 4,970$ psi.

Prob. 8-4: $\sigma = -13.08$ ksi, $\tau = 0$; $\sigma = -7$ ksi, $\tau = 6.08$ ksi.

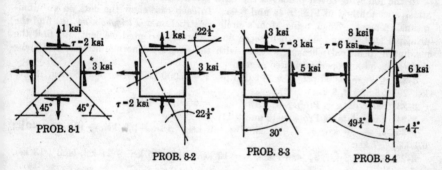

PROB. 8-1   PROB. 8-2   PROB. 8-3   PROB. 8-4

8-5. Derive Eq. 8-2.

8-6. Using Eqs. 8-1 and 8-2, rework Prob. 8-1.

8-7. Using Eqs. 8-1 and 8-2, rework Prob. 8-2.

8-8. Using Eqs. 8-1 and 8-2, rework Prob. 8-4.

8-9. Using the equations derived in Art. 8-4, find the principal stresses and show their sense on a properly oriented element for the following data: $\sigma_x = +8,000$ psi; $\sigma_y = +2,000$ psi; and $\tau = +4,000$ psi. The sign convention of the stresses given follows that illustrated in Fig. 8-4a. *Ans.* 10 ksi, 0, $\theta = 26°34'$.

8-10. Rework Prob. 8-9 changing the data to $\sigma_x = -3$ ksi; $\sigma_y = +1$ ksi; $\tau = -2$ ksi. *Ans.* 1.83 ksi, -3.83 ksi, $22\frac{1}{2}°$.

8-11. Using the equations derived in Art. 8-5, find the maximum (principal) shearing stresses and the associated normal stresses for the data of Prob. 8-10. Show the results on a properly oriented element. *Ans.* 2.83 ksi, -1 ksi, $67\frac{1}{2}°$.

In the following four problems the data given follow the convention of signs for stresses established in Fig. 8-4a. In each case show the data on an infinitesimal element. Then, using the formulas developed in Arts. 8-4 and 8-5, (a) find the principal stresses and show their sense on a properly oriented element; (b) find the maximum (principal) shearing stresses with the associated normal stresses and show the results on a properly oriented element.

8-12. $\sigma_x = +20$ ksi, $\sigma_y = 0$, $\tau = -10$ ksi. *Ans.* 24.1 ksi, -4.1 ksi; 14.1 ksi.

8-13. $\sigma_x = 0$, $\sigma_y = -4$ ksi, $\tau = -6$ ksi. *Ans.* 4.33 ksi, -8.33 ksi; 6.33 ksi.

8-14. $\sigma_x = -2$ ksi, $\sigma_y = -8$ ksi, $\tau = +4$ ksi. *Ans.* 0, -10 ksi; 5 ksi.

8-15. $\sigma_x = -2,000$ psi, $\sigma_y = +4,000$ psi, $\tau = -4,000$ psi. *Ans.* 6 ksi, -4 ksi; 5 ksi.

8-16. Using Mohr's circle of stress, solve for the (a) part of Prob. 8-14.

8-17. Using Mohr's circle of stress, solve for the (a) part of Prob. 8-15.

8-18. If an element is subjected to a pure shearing stress of 8,000 psi acting opposite to the directions shown in Fig. 8-6a, using Mohr's circle of stress, find the principal stresses and show their sense on a properly oriented element. *Ans.* ± 8 ksi, $45°$.

For the data given in the following three problems in terms of the principal stresses, using Mohr's circle of stress, find the maximum (principal) shearing stresses and the associated normal stresses. Show the results, as well as the element with the initial data, on properly oriented elements.

8-19. $\sigma_x = \sigma_1 = +10$ ksi, $\sigma_y = \sigma_2 = -10$ ksi. *Ans.* 10 ksi, 0, $45°$.

8-20. $\sigma_x = \sigma_1 = +10$ ksi, $\sigma_y = \sigma_2 = +10$ ksi. *Ans.* 0, 10 ksi.

8-21. $\sigma_x = \sigma_2 = -3,000$ psi, $\sigma_y = \sigma_1 = +500$ psi. *Ans.* 1.75 ksi, -1.25 ksi.

In the following seven problems the data given follow the convention of signs for stresses established in Figs. 8-4a and 8-9a. In each case show the data on an infinitesimal element. Then, using Mohr's circle construction *and trigonometry*, (a) find the principal stresses and show their sense on a properly oriented element; (b) find the maximum (principal) shearing stresses with the associated normal stresses and show the results on a properly oriented element.

8-22. $\sigma_x = +12,000$ psi, $\sigma_y = +6,000$ psi, $\tau = 5,000$ psi. *Ans.* $+14.83$ ksi, $+3.17$ ksi, $29\frac{1}{2}°$; 5.83 ksi, 9 ksi.

8-23. Same data as Prob. 8-9. *Ans.* $\tau_{max} = 5$ ksi, $\sigma' = 5$ ksi.

8-24. Same data as Probs. 8-10 and 8-11.

8-25. $\sigma_x = -6$ ksi, $\sigma_y = -8$ ksi, $\tau = +6$ ksi. *Ans.* -0.9 ksi, -13.1 ksi, $40\frac{1}{4}°$; 6.1 ksi, -7 ksi.

8-26. $\sigma_x = -3$ ksi, $\sigma_y = +7$ ksi, $\tau = 12$ ksi. *Ans.* 15 ksi, -11 ksi, $56.3°$; 13 ksi, $+2$ ksi.

8-27. $\sigma_x = +20$ ksi, $\sigma_y = 0$, $\tau = -10$ ksi. *Ans.* see Prob. 8-12.

8-28. $\sigma_x = 0$, $\sigma_y = -4$ ksi, $\tau = -6$ ksi. *Ans.* see Prob. 8-13.

8-29. Rework Example 8-4 using Eqs. 8-1b and 8-2a.

8-30. For the data of Prob. 8-21, using Mohr's circle of stress, find the stresses acting on a plane defined by $\theta = +20°$.

8-31. If $\sigma_x = \sigma_1 = 0$ and $\sigma_y = \sigma_2 = -4,000$ psi, using Mohr's circle of stress, find the stresses acting on a plane defined by $\theta = +30°$. *Ans.* -1 ksi, 1.73 ksi.

8-32. For the data of Prob. 8-19, using Mohr's circle of stress, find the stresses acting on a plane defined by $\theta = +30°$.

8-33.* Using Mohr's circle of stress, rework Prob. 8-2.

8-34. Rederive Eq. 8-12 by assuming that the shearing deformation occurs first, then the deformation in the y-direction, and finally the deformation in the x-direction.

8-35. With the aid of Fig. 8-16, show that $\beta = (\epsilon_x - \epsilon_y) \sin \theta \cos \theta - \gamma \cos^2 \theta$.

8-36. If the unit strains are $\epsilon_x = -0.00012$, $\epsilon_y = +0.00112$, and $\gamma = -0.00020$, what are the principal strains and in which directions do they occur? Use Eqs. 8-14 and 8-15 or Mohr's circle of strain, as directed. *Ans.* $+0.00113$, -0.00013, $4°35'$.

8-37. If the unit strains are $\epsilon_x = -0.00080$, $\epsilon_y = -0.00020$, and $\gamma = +0.00080$, what are the principal strains and in which directions do they occur? Use Eqs. 8-14 and 8-15 or Mohr's circle, as directed. *Ans.* 0, -0.00100.

8-38. If the strain measurements given in the above problem were made on a steel member ($E = 29.5 \times 10^6$ psi and $\mu = 0.3$), what are the principal stresses and in which direction do they act? .

8-39. The data for a rectangular rosette, attached to a stressed steel member, are $\epsilon_{0°} = -0.00022$, $\epsilon_{45°} = +0.00012$, and $\epsilon_{90°} = +0.00022$. What are the principal stresses and in which directions do they act? $E = 30 \times 10^6$ psi and $\mu = 0.3$. *Ans.* ± 5.76 ksi, $14°18'$.

8-40. The data for an equiangular rosette, attached to a stressed aluminum alloy member, are $\epsilon_{0°} = +0.00040$, $\epsilon_{60°} = +0.00040$, and $\epsilon_{120°} = -0.00060$. What are the principal stresses and in which directions do they act? $E = 10^7$ psi and $\mu = \frac{1}{4}$. *Ans.* $+6.22$ ksi, -4.44 ksi, $30°$.

8-41. The data for a strain rosette with four gage lines attached to a stressed aluminum alloy member are $\epsilon_{0°} = -0.00012$, $\epsilon_{45°} = +0.00040$, $\epsilon_{90°} = +0.00112$, and $\epsilon_{135°} = +0.00060$. Check the consistency of the data. Then determine the principal stresses and the directions in which they act. Use the values of E and μ given in Prob 8-40. *Ans.* $+11.7$ ksi, 1.6 ksi, $4°35'$.

Chapter Nine

COMBINED STRESSES—PRESSURE VESSELS—FAILURE THEORIES

9-1. Introduction. As should have become apparent from the preceding chapters, a description of the state of stress at a point of a stressed member may be found by using the conventional formulas and may involve normal *and* shearing stresses. Formal methods for an alternate description of the state of stress at the same point in terms of principal stresses, or the principal shearing stresses and the associated normal stresses, were treated in the preceding chapter. In this chapter, mainly the method of redescribing the state of stress in terms of the principal stresses will be applied to some particular cases of stressed members. As examples, the principal stresses occurring in a circular shaft and a beam when they are subjected to some familiar loading conditions will be examined. For these, the existence at many points of biaxial principal stresses, i.e., both principal stresses different from zero, will be shown. Moreover, since the earlier treatment of allowable stresses was based on the uniaxial principal stress determined from simple tension or compression tests, the resistance of materials to a biaxial stress will be discussed under the caption of strength or failure theories of materials. For the development of this topic, the stress formulas for thin-walled pressure vessels will be established, as experiments on pressure vessels provide information on the behavior of materials under biaxial stress. Early in this chapter, the stresses on inclined planes of a straight rod subjected to an axial force will also be determined.

9-2. Investigation of Stresses at a Point. To find the principal stresses or the stresses on any inclined plane at a point of a loaded member, the same basic procedure that was repeatedly used earlier must be employed (Art. 1-10). In statically determinate problems, the reactions are found first. Then a segment of the body is isolated by passing a section perpendicular to its axis *through the point* to be investigated, and the system of forces necessary to maintain the equilibrium of the segment is determined. The magnitudes of the stresses are determined next by the conventional formulas. Then on an element isolated from the member, the computed stresses are indicated. The sense of the computed stresses is noted on this element by arrows agreeing with the sense of the internal forces at the cut. Two sides of this element are parallel and two sides are perpendicular to the axis of the member being investigated. *The definite relation of the sides of this element to the actual member must be clearly understood by the analyst.* After the sketch of an element is prepared and stresses of the same kind are compounded, the stresses may be determined on planes with any orientation through the same point. For this purpose, either analytical formulas or Mohr's circle of stress, discussed in the preceding chapter, is used. The principal stresses, or the maximum shearing stress, are usually the quantities sought.

In the following three examples, an axially loaded rod, a circular shaft in torsion, and a rectangular beam with transversely applied force will be examined for principal stresses or stresses acting on inclined planes.

Example 9-1. Find the stresses acting on an arbitrarily inclined plane in an axially loaded rod of constant cross-sectional area.

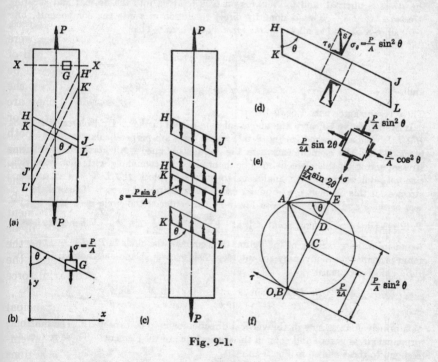

Fig. 9-1.

SOLUTION: Consider the prismatic bar subjected to axial tension shown in Fig. 9-1a. By passing a section X-X perpendicular to the axis of the rod through a general point G and applying Eq. 1-1, the stress $\sigma = P/A$, where A is the cross-sectional area of the rod. Moreover, since this stress is the *only* stress acting on the element, Fig. 9-1b, it is the principal stress. Designating this stress as σ_y, and noting that $\sigma_x = 0$ and $\tau = 0$, the normal and the shearing stresses acting on any inclined plane defined by the angle θ by Eqs. 8-1 and 8-2 are

$$\left.\begin{aligned}
\sigma_\theta &= \sigma \sin^2 \theta = \frac{\sigma}{2} - \frac{\sigma}{2} \cos 2\theta \\
\tau_\theta &= +\frac{\sigma}{2} \sin 2\theta
\end{aligned}\right\} \tag{9-1}$$

where the signs follow the conventions adopted in Fig. 8-4b. From Eq. 9-1 it is seen that the maximum or the principal stress occurs when $\theta = 90°$. These equations emphasize the fact that the state of stress at a point may be described in an infinite number of ways.

ALTERNATE SOLUTION: Instead of solving this problem by the formulas already developed, it is instructive to rework it from basic principles. Thus, consider the same bar, Fig. 9-1a, and pass through it two parallel planes HJ and KL inclined at an angle θ with the vertical. *Every* vertical fiber in the block $HJLK$, shown isolated in Fig. 9-1c, elongates the same amount. All of these fibers are subjected to the same intensity of force. Hence, although this has not been done before in this text, the stress s acting in a *vertical* direction *on an inclined plane* may be said to be $s = \dfrac{P}{A/\sin \theta}$, since $A/\sin \theta$ is the *inclined cross-sectional area of the bar*. This manner of expressing the stress is unusual, and for this reason it is resolved into the normal and shearing stresses (Art. 1-3). This is done by direct resolution of s into the components, Fig. 9-1d, since s, σ_θ, and τ_θ all act *on the same unit of area*. Thus

$$\sigma_\theta = s \sin \theta = \frac{P}{A} \sin^2 \theta$$

and

$$\tau_\theta = s \cos \theta = \frac{F}{A} \sin \theta \cos \theta = \frac{P}{2A} \sin 2\theta$$

These results agree with Eqs. 9-1.

It is instructive to carry the above solution a step further. By isolating the block $H'J'L'K'$ (shown dashed in Fig. 9-1a), whose sides are perpendicular to those of the block $HJLK$, the element shown in Fig. 9-1e is obtained. All normal and shearing stresses acting on this element may be determined by combining with the above solution an additional solution analogous to it for the block $H'J'L'K'$. The principal stresses for this element are obtained using Mohr's circle of stress. Thus on the system of the σ and τ axes shown in Fig. 9-1f, the center of the circle is at $\frac{1}{2}(\sigma_x + \sigma_x) = P/(2A)$ and the governing point A is at $[+\dfrac{P}{A} \sin^2 \theta, \ +\dfrac{P}{2A} \sin 2\theta]$. Whence, as may be found from the geometry of the figure, the radius of the circle is $P/(2A)$. The maximum principal stress given by the intercept E is $\sigma_1 = P/A$ and acts normal to the line AE. Moreover, since

$$\frac{AD}{DE} = \frac{(P/2A) \sin 2\theta}{(P/A) - (P/A) \sin^2 \theta} = \frac{(1/2) \sin 2\theta}{\cos^2 \theta} = \frac{\sin \theta}{\cos \theta} = \tan \theta$$

this principal stress acts in the vertical direction as is to be expected! The minimum principal stress is zero and acts on the vertical side of the element. These results correspond to those shown in Fig. 9-1b.

The above discussion also applies to stable compression members. In either tension or compression, in a state of pure uniaxial stress, *there are shearing stresses acting on some planes*. These shearing stresses reach their maximum value of $\sigma/2$ when $\theta = \pm 45°$, as may be seen from Eq. 9-1. For materials which are strong in tension or compression but *weak in* *shearing strength,* failures may be expected along the 45° planes. This is found to be so for several materials. Concrete and duralumin are notable examples.*

Example 9-2. Determine the largest principal stresses occurring in a solid circular shaft subjected to a torque T, Fig. 9-2.

SOLUTION: In a circular shaft, the maximum shearing stress occurs in the outermost thin lamina (*at* but not *on* the outer surface) and, by Eq. 3-3, is $\tau_{max} = Tc/J$, where c is the radius of the shaft and J is its polar moment of inertia. This state of pure shearing stress is shown acting on an element in Fig. 9-2. However, according to Art. 8-6, a state of pure shearing stress transforms into tensile and compressive principal stresses, which are equal in magnitude to the shearing stress and act

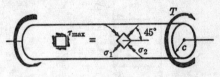

Fig. 9-2.

along the respective shear diagonals. Therefore the principal stresses are $\sigma_1 = +Tc/J$ and $\sigma_2 = -Tc/J$, acting in the direction shown in the figure.

The above solution enables one to predict the type of failure that will take place in materials *weak in tension.* Such materials fail by tearing in a line perpendicular to the direction of σ_1. For example, cast-iron shafts fail in this manner.† The failure of these shafts takes place along a helix as shown in the figure by the dashed lines. Shafts made from materials weak in shearing strength, such as mild steel, break squarely across.

Example 9-3. For a weightless rectangular beam which spans 40 in. and is loaded with a vertical downward force $P = 18.44$ kips at mid-span, Fig. 9-3a, find the principal stresses at the points A, B, C, B' and A', and the stresses acting on an inclined plane of $\theta = +30°$ for the element B'.

SOLUTION: At section AA' a shear of 9.22 kips and a bending moment of 92.2 kip-in. are necessary to maintain the equilibrium of the segment of the beam. These quantities with their proper sense are shown in Fig. 9-3c.

The principal stress at points A and A' follows directly by applying the flexure formula, Eq. 5-1. Since the shearing stresses are distributed parabolically across the cross-section of a rectangular beam, *no* shearing stresses act on these elements, Figs. 9-3d and h. The other principal stresses acting on these elements perpendicular to the boundary of the beam are zero.‡

$$\sigma_{A\ or\ A'} = \frac{Mc}{I} = \frac{M}{Z} = \frac{6M}{bh^2} = \frac{6(92.2)}{1.535(12)^2} = \pm 2.50 \text{ ksi}$$

The normal stresses acting on the elements B and B' shown in the first sketches of Figs. 9-3e and g are obtained by direct proportion from the normal stresses acting on

* Failures do not take place precisely on the 45° planes since the normal stress existing simultaneously with the shearing stress also influences the breakdown of the material.

† Ordinary chalk behaves similarly. The same type of fracture may be demonstrated in a classroom by twisting a piece of chalk to failure.

‡ This statement is applicable everywhere except at the applied force and the reactions. In the neighborhood of a concentrated force the elementary solution fails. See Fig. 2-16 and the accompanying text for a discussion of local stresses near a concentrated force.

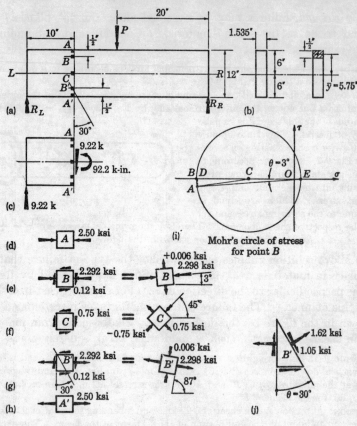

Fig. 9-3.

the elements A and A' (or Eq. 5-1a could be used). The shearing stresses acting on both of these elements are alike. Their sense *on the right-hand face* of the elements agrees with the sense of the shear at the section AA' shown in Fig. 9-3c. The magnitude of these shearing stresses is obtained by applying Eq. 6-3, $\tau = VA_{fghj}\bar{y}/(It)$. For use in this equation, the area A_{fghj}, with the corresponding $\bar{y}$, is shown shaded in Fig. 9-3b.

$$\sigma_{B \text{ or } B'} = \frac{5.5}{6}\,\sigma_A = \pm 2.292 \text{ ksi}$$

$$\tau_{B \text{ or } B'} = \frac{VA_{fghj}\bar{y}}{It} = \frac{(9.22)(1.535)(0.5)(5.75)}{(1/12)(1.535)(12)^3(1.535)} = 0.12 \text{ ksi}$$

To obtain the principal stresses at B, Mohr's circle of stress is used. Its construction is indicated in Fig. 9-3i, and the results obtained are shown in the second sketch of Fig. 9-3e. Note the invariance of the sum of the normal stresses, i.e., $\sigma_x + \sigma_y = \sigma_1 + \sigma_2$, or $-2.292 + 0 = -2.298 + 0.006$. A similar solution for the principal stresses at point B' yields the results indicated in the second sketch of Fig. 9-3g.

Point C lies on the neutral axis of the beam, hence no flexural stress acts on the corresponding element shown in the first sketch of Fig. 9-3f. The shearing stress on the right-hand face of the element at C acts in the same direction as the internal shear at the section AA'. Its magnitude may be obtained by applying Eq. 6-3, or directly by using Eq. 6-4, i.e.,

$$\tau_{\text{max}} = \frac{3}{2}\frac{V}{A} = \frac{1.5(9.22)}{1.535(12)} = 0.75 \text{ ksi}$$

The *pure* shearing stress transformed into the principal stresses according to Art. 8-6 is shown in the second sketch of Fig. 9-3f.

It is significant to further examine qualitatively the results obtained. For this purpose the computed principal stresses *acting on the corresponding planes* are shown in Figs. 9-4a and b. By examining Fig. 9-4a, the characteristic behavior of the algebraically larger (tensile) principal stress at a section of a rectangular beam may be seen. This stress progressively diminishes in its magnitude from a maximum value at A' to zero at A. At the same time the corresponding directions of σ_1 gradually turn through

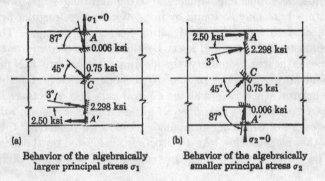

(a)   (b)

Behavior of the algebraically   Behavior of the algebraically
larger principal stress σ_1 smaller principal stress σ_2

Fig. 9-4.

90°. A similar observation may be made regarding the algebraically smaller (compressive) principal stress σ_2 shown in Fig. 9-4b.

To find the stresses acting on a plane of $\theta = +30°$ through point B', a direct application of Eqs. 8-1 and 8-2, *using the stresses shown in the first sketch of Fig. 9-3g and $2\theta = 60°$*, is made.

$$\sigma_\theta = \frac{+2.292}{2} + \frac{+2.292}{2}\cos 60° + (-0.12)\sin 60° = +1.62 \text{ ksi}$$

$$\tau_\theta = \frac{-2.292}{2}\sin 60° + (-0.12)\cos 60° = -1.05 \text{ ksi}$$

These results are shown in Fig. 9-3j. The sense of the shearing stress τ_θ is opposite to that shown in Fig. 8-4b, since the computed quantity is negative. The "wedge technique" explained in Example 8-1 or the method of Art. 8-10 can be used to obtain the same results.

*9-3. Members in a State of Two-Dimensional Stress. Within the scope of the formulas developed in this text, bodies in a state of two-dimensional stress may be studied as was done in the preceding example. A great many points in a stressed body may be investigated for the magnitude and direction of the principal stresses. Then, to study the general behavior of the stresses, selected points may be interconnected to give a visual interpretation of the various aspects of the computed data. For example, the points of algebraically equal principal stresses, regardless of their sense, when connected, provide a "map" of **stress contours.** Any point lying on a stress contour has a principal stress of the same algebraic magnitude.

Similarly, the points at which the directions of the minimum principal stresses form a *constant angle* with the x-axis may be connected.* Moreover, since the principal stresses are mutually perpendicular, the direction of the maximum principal stresses through the same points also forms a constant angle with the x-axis. The line so connected is a locus of points along which the principal stresses have *parallel directions.* This line is called an **isoclinic line.** The adjective isoclinic is derived from two Greek words, *isos* meaning equal and *klino* meaning slope or incline. Three isoclinic lines may be found by inspection in a rectangular prismatic beam subjected to transverse load acting normal to its axis. The lines corresponding to the upper and lower boundaries of a beam form two isoclinic lines, as at the boundary the flexural stresses are the principal stresses, and all of them act parallel to the boundaries.† On the other hand, the flexural stress is zero at the neutral axis, and only there do pure shearing stresses exist. These pure shearing stresses transform into principal stresses, all of which act at an angle of 45° with the axis of the beam. Hence another isoclinic line (the 45° isoclinic) is located on the axis of the beam. The other isoclinic lines are curved and are more difficult to determine.

Another set of curves may be drawn for a stressed body for which the magnitude and the sense of the principal stresses are known at a great many points. A curve whose tangent is changing in direction to conform with the direction of the principal stresses is called a **principal stress trajectory** or *isostatic line.* Like the isoclinic lines, the principal stress trajectories *do not* connect the points of equal stresses, but rather indicate the directions of the principal stresses. Since the principal stresses at any point are mutually perpendicular, the principal stress trajectories for the two principal stresses form a family of orthogonal (mutually perpendicular) curves.‡ An example of stress trajectories for a rectangular beam loaded with a concentrated force at the mid-span is shown in Fig. 9-5. The principal stress trajectories corresponding to the tensile stresses

---

* These angles are usually measured in a counterclockwise direction from the x-axis to the nearest line of action of the minimum principal stress. These angles vary from 0° to 90°. An alternative method, amounting to the same thing, consists of measuring angles counterclockwise from a vertical line to the line of action of the algebraically larger principal stress.

† If the bending moments are positive, the line corresponding to the upper boundary of a beam forms a 0° isoclinic line, while the lower boundary corresponds to a 90° isoclinic.

‡ A somewhat analogous situation is found in Fluid Mechanics where in "two-dimensional" fluid flow problems the *streamlines* and the *equipotential lines* form an orthogonal system of curves—the *flow net.*

are shown in the figure by solid lines; those for the compressive stresses are shown dashed.

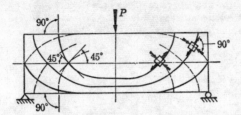

Fig. 9-5.   Principal stress trajectories for a rectangular beam.

*9-4. The Photoelastic Method of Stress Analysis. The state of stress in any two-dimensional stress problem may be expressed in terms of the stress contours, the isoclinic lines, and the principal stress trajectories discussed in the preceding article. Moreover, it is significant that the application of the same forces in the same manner to any two geometrically similar bodies made from *different elastic materials* causes the same stress distribution. The stress distribution is unaffected* by the elastic constants of a material. Therefore, to determine stresses experimentally, instead of finding the stresses in an actual member, the test specimen is prepared from any material suitable for the type of test to be performed. Glass, celluloid, and particularly certain grades of *bakelite* have the required optical properties for photoelastic work. In a stressed specimen made from one of these materials, the principal stresses *temporarily change the optical properties* of the material. This change in the optical properties may be detected and related to the principal stresses which cause them. The experimental and analytical technique necessary for the analysis of problems in this manner is known as *the photoelastic method of stress analysis.* Only a brief outline† of this method will be given here, commencing with some remarks on light.

Light travels through any given medium in a straight line at a constant velocity. For the purposes at hand, the behavior of light may be explained by considering its single ray as a series of chaotic waves which travel in a number of planes containing the ray. By restricting the vibration of the waves to a single plane, a *plane polarized light* is obtained. This is done by passing the light through a *polarizer*, which may be a suitable pile of plates, a Nicol prism, or a commercially manufactured "Polaroid" element. The plane of the polarizer through which the transverse vibrations of the light are allowed to pass is called the *plane of polarization.* A schematic diagram of the foregoing definitions is shown in Fig. 9-6a, where a second polarizer, called the *analyzer*, is also shown. Note that if the planes of polarization of the two polarizers are at right angles to each other, *no light* gets through the analyzer. This arrangement of the analyzer with respect to the polarizer is termed *crossed.*

If the light source‡ used is *monochromatic*, i.e., of one color, the transverse vibrations of the plane polarized light are regular, as the wave length in a given medium for any one color is constant. When propagating through the same medium, these transverse vibrations are described by a sinusoidal wave of constant amplitude and frequency.

---

* For this to be true, strictly speaking, the bodies must be simply connected, i.e., without interior holes.

† For more details see Frocht, M. M., *Photoelasticity*, vols. I and II. New York: Wiley, 1941 and 1948.

‡ Mercury-vapor lamps are commonly used for this purpose.

By inserting an annealed specimen made from a suitable transparent material between the polarizer and the analyzer in the arrangement shown in Fig. 9-6a, no new phenomenon is observed. However, by stressing the specimen, the optical properties of the material change, and two phenomena take place: *

1. At each point of the stressed body the polarized light wave is *resolved* into two mutually perpendicular components lying in the planes of the principal stresses occurring at that point.

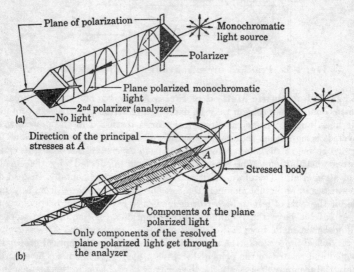

(a)

(b)

Plane of polarization — Monochromatic light source — Polarizer — Plane polarized monochromatic light — 2nd polarizer (analyzer) — No light — Direction of the principal stresses at A — Stressed body — Components of the plane polarized light — Only components of the resolved plane polarized light get through the analyzer

Fig. 9-6. The photoelastic method of stress analysis.

2. The linear velocity of each of the components of the light wave is *retarded* through the stressed specimen in direct proportion to the related principal stress.

These facts are the basis of the photoelastic method of stress analysis. A schematic representation of the behavior of a monochromatic plane polarized wave as it passes through a stressed body and an analyzer is shown in Fig. 9-6b. In the stressed specimen, a plane polarized wave is resolved into two components whose planes coincide with the planes of the principal stresses, as at point A. These components of the sinusoidal vibration leave the specimen with the same frequency but are *out of phase*. The latter effect is caused by the different amount of retardation of the light in the two principal planes of stress. Finally, the light waves emerging from the analyzer are again brought into the same plane, since only certain components of the components of the polarized light may go through the analyzer. The two monochromatic light waves which leave the analyzer vibrate out of phase in the same plane with the same frequency. Their *phase difference*, which is directly proportional to the difference in the principal stresses at a point such as A of the stressed body, provides several possibilities which may be observed on a screen placed after the analyzer. If the two waves are out of phase by a full wave length of the light used, they reinforce each other

* The first phenomenon stated was discovered by Sir David Brewster in 1816. The quantitative relation was established by G. Wertheim in 1854. The modern development of photoelasticity and its engineering applications probably owes most to the two English professors, E. G. Coker and L. N. G. Filon, whose treatise on this subject was first published in 1930.

and the brightest light is seen on the screen.   For other conditions, some interference takes place between the two light waves.   *A complete elimination of the light occurs if the amplitudes of the two light waves are equal and are out of phase by one-half wave length or its odd integer multiple.*   Therefore, since an infinite number of points in the stressed body affect the plane polarized light in a manner analogous to the point *A*, alternate bright and dark bands become apparent on a screen.   The dark bands are called *fringes.*

The greater the difference in the principal stresses, the greater the phase difference between the two light waves emerging from the analyzer.   Hence, if forces are *gradually* applied to a specimen until the principal stresses differ sufficiently to cause a phase difference of one-half wave length between the two light waves at some points, the first fringe appears on the screen.   Then as the magnitude of the applied forces is increased, the first fringe shifts to a new position and another *"higher order"* fringe makes its appearance on the screen.   The second fringe corresponds to the principal stresses which cause a phase difference of $1\frac{1}{2}$ wave lengths.   This process may be continued as long as the specimen behaves elastically, and more and more fringes appear on the screen.   A photograph with several fringes for a rectangular beam loaded at mid-span

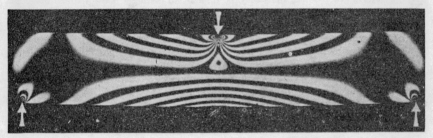

Fig. 9-7.   Fringe photograph of a rectangular beam.

is shown in Fig. 9-7.   Fringes may be calibrated in a separate experiment with a bar in tension or a beam in pure flexure.   The stresses for these simple members may be accurately computed.   It is necessary to make the calibration specimens from the same material as the specimen to be investigated.   With the calibration data, complex members subjected to complicated loading may be investigated.   For each fringe order the difference of the principal stresses, $\sigma_1 - \sigma_2$, is known from calibration, hence fringes represent a "map" of the difference in the principal stresses.   Moreover, since according to Eq. 8-8 the difference of the principal stresses divided by two is equal to the maximum shearing stress, the fringes also represent the loci of the principal shearing stresses.

A fringe photograph of a stressed body and calibration data are sufficient for determining the magnitude of the maximum or principal shearing stresses.   The principal stress at any point of the *unloaded* boundary may also be obtained.   At a free boundary, one of the principal stresses which acts normal to the boundary must be zero, and the fringe order is directly related to the other principal stress.   Additional experimental work must be performed to determine normal stresses away from the boundaries.

One method of completing the problem consists of obtaining some *very accurate measurements of the change in thickness of the stressed specimen* at a number of points. These measurements, which may be designated by Δt, where t is the thickness of the specimen, are related to the principal stresses, i.e., from the generalized Hooke's law, Eq. 2-6,* and Eq. 2-7,

* In Eq. 2-6 the stress is zero in the direction perpendicular to the plane of the specimen, hence $\sigma_x = 0$, $\sigma_y = \sigma_1$, and $\sigma_z = \sigma_2$.

$$\Delta t = -\mu \left(\frac{\sigma_1 + \sigma_2}{E} \right) t \quad \text{or} \quad \sigma_1 + \sigma_2 = -\frac{E}{\mu t} \Delta t$$

Then from an additional experiment on the same material in simple tension where $\sigma_1 \neq 0$ and $\sigma_2 = 0$, a new calibration chart may be prepared which gives the sum of the principal stresses versus Δt. From the information obtained from these two experiments, a "map" of the *sum* of the principal stresses for the specimen investigated may be prepared. By superposing this "map" with the "map" of the *differences* of the principal stresses obtained from the fringe photograph, the magnitudes of the principal stresses at any point of the stressed specimen may be determined.

Additional information must be found in the picture of fringes to determine the *direction* of the principal stresses. This information is given by the isoclinic line. This is a black line corresponding to the locus of the points where the direction of one of the principal stresses in the stressed body coincides with the plane of the polarized light leaving the polarizer. Rays passing through these points in the stressed specimen are not resolved and are blacked out by the analyzer. By rotating the polarizer into several known positions and maintaining the analyzer crossed, the isoclinic lines may be determined. These lines may be difficult to distinguish from the fringes, as both simultaneously appear on the screen. One method of differentiating the isoclinic lines from the fringes uses white instead of monochromatic light. Using white light, isoclinics appear black, while the fringes are colored and contain all the visible spectral colors of the white light. On the other hand, to eliminate the isoclinic lines which are undesirable for fringe photographs, two quarter-wave plates* may be inserted into the optical system. One of these plates is placed between the polarizer and the specimen and the other between the specimen and the analyzer. The fringe photograph shown in Fig. 9-7 was obtained by using this method.

With the aid of analytical methods, a sequence of isoclinic lines and fringe photographs are sufficient to solve the photoelastic problem without finding the sum of the principal stresses experimentally. These procedures are very detailed and laborious, and the reader is referred to books on photoelasticity for further information.

The photoelastic method of stress analysis is very versatile and has been used to solve numerous problems. Nearly all solutions for the stress-concentration factors have been established by photoelasticity. The inaccuracy of the elementary formulas of Mechanics of Materials at concentrated forces is clearly brought out by the fringe photographs. For example, in Fig. 9-7, according to the elementary formulas, the fringes in the upper half of the beam should be like those in the lower half. Also note the local disturbance of the stresses at the supports in the same photograph.

The photoelastic method is best adapted to two-dimensional stress problems. Three-dimensional problems have also been analyzed by specialized techniques. The extension of the method to inelastic or plastic problems remains for the present unsolved.

9-5. Thin-Walled Pressure Vessels.
The above investigations for the principal stresses in several stressed members illustrated numerous instances where biaxial stresses occur. On the other hand, all of the preceding philosophy of allowable stresses was based on the simple tension or torsion test. Therefore, before the study of the design of members is undertaken, it is important to reach some conclusions regarding the effect of biaxial stresses on the resistance to failure of various materials. Since the answer to this question is found from experiments on thin-walled

---

* Quarter-wave plates resolve the plane polarized light into two mutually perpendicular components; one of these is a quarter wave out of phase with the other. Combination of these components results in a "circularly polarized light."

pressure vessels, a method for analyzing them must be developed first. Attention will be confined to two types of these vessels, the cylindrical pressure vessel and the spherical. Fortunately both of these types of pressure vessels are exceedingly important in industry, hence this topic is also of great practical importance.

The walls of an ideal thin-walled pressure vessel act as a membrane, i.e., no bending of the walls takes place. A sphere is an ideal shape for a closed pressure vessel if the contents are of negligible weight. A cylindrical vessel is also good with the exception of the junctures with the ends, a matter to be commented on in more detail later.

The analysis of pressure vessels will be begun by considering a cylindrical pressure vessel such as a boiler, as shown in Fig. 9-8a. A segment is isolated from this vessel by passing two planes perpendicular to the axis of the cylinder and one additional longitudinal plane *through* the same axis, shown in Fig. 9-8b. The conditions of symmetry exclude the exist-

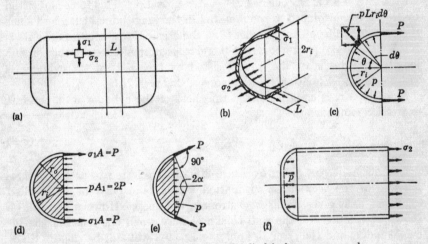

Fig. 9-8. Diagrams for analysis of cylindrical pressure vessels.

ence of any shearing stresses in the planes of the sections, as shearing stresses would cause an incompatible distortion of the tube. Therefore, the stresses which may exist on the sections of the cylinder can only be the normal stresses σ_1 and σ_2 shown in Fig. 9-8b. These stresses are the *principal stresses*. These stresses, multiplied by the respective areas on which they act, maintain the element of the cylinder in equilibrium against the internal pressure.

Let the internal pressure in excess of the external pressure be p psi (gage pressure), and let the internal radius of the cylinder be r_i. Then the *force* on an infinitesimal area $L r_i\, d\theta$ (where $d\theta$ is an infinitesimal angle) of the cylinder caused by the internal pressure acting *normal* thereto is

$pLr_i\, d\theta$, Fig. 9-8c. The component of this force acting in the horizontal direction is $(pLr_i\, d\theta) \cos \theta$, hence the total resisting force of $2P$ acting on the cylindrical segment is

$$2P = 2 \int_0^{\pi/2} pLr_i \cos \theta \, d\theta = 2pr_iL$$

Again from symmetry, half of this total force is resisted at the top cut through the cylinder and the other half is resisted at the bottom. The normal stresses σ_2 acting in a direction parallel to the axis of the cylinder do not enter into the above integration.

Instead of obtaining the force $2P$ caused by the internal pressure by integration, as above, a simpler equivalent procedure is available. From an alternate point of view, the two forces P resist the force developed by the internal pressure p which acts perpendicular to the *projected area* A_1 of the cylindrical segment onto the diametral plane, Fig. 9-8d. This area in Fig. 9-8b is $2r_iL$, hence $2P = A_1p = 2r_iLp$. This force is resisted by the forces developed in the material in the longitudinal cuts, and since the outside radius of the cylinder is r_o, the area of *both* longitudinal cuts is $2A = 2L(r_o - r_i)$. Moreover, if the *average* normal stress acting on the longitudinal cut is σ_1, the force resisted by the walls of the cylinder is $2L(r_o - r_i)\sigma_1$. Equating the two forces, $2r_iLp = 2L(r_o - r_i)\sigma_1$.

Since $r_o - r_i$ is equal to t, the thickness of the cylinder wall, the last expression simplifies to

$$\sigma_1 = \frac{pr_i}{t} \tag{9-2}$$

The normal stress given by Eq. 9-2 is often referred to as the *circumferential* or the *hoop stress*. Equation 9-2 is valid only for thin-walled cylinders, as it gives the *average* stress in the hoop. However, as will be shown in Chapter 16, the wall thickness may reach one-tenth of the internal radius and the error in applying Eq. 9-2 will still be small. Since Eq. 9-2 is used primarily for *thin*-walled vessels where $r_i \doteq r_o$, the subscript for the radius is usually omitted.

Equation 9-2 may also be derived by passing two longitudinal sections as shown in Fig. 9-8e. In this treatment, the forces P in the hoop must be considered acting tangentially to the cylinder. The horizontal components of the forces P maintain the horizontal component of the internal pressure in a state of static equilibrium.

The other normal stress σ_2 acting in a cylindrical pressure vessel acts *longitudinally*, Fig. 9-8b, and it is determined by solving a simple axial force problem. By passing a section through the vessel perpendicular to its axis, a free body as shown in Fig. 9-8f is obtained. The force developed by the internal pressure is $p\pi r_i^2$, and the force developed by the longitudinal stress σ_2 in the walls is $\sigma_2(\pi r_o^2 - \pi r_i^2)$. Equating these two forces and solving for σ_2,

$$p\pi r_i^2 = \sigma_2(\pi r_o^2 - \pi r_i^2)$$

$$\sigma_2 = \frac{pr_i^2}{r_o^2 - r_i^2} = \frac{pr_o^2}{(r_o + r_i)(r_o - r_i)}$$

However, $r_o - r_i = t$, the thickness of the cylindrical wall, and since this development is restricted to *thin*-walled vessels, $r_o \doteq r_i \doteq r$, hence

$$\sigma_2 = \frac{pr}{2t} \tag{9-3}$$

Note that for *cylindrical* pressure vessels $\sigma_2 \doteq \sigma_1/2$.

An analogous method of analysis may be used to derive an expression for *thin*-walled spherical pressure vessels. By passing a section through the center of the sphere of Fig. 9-9a, a hemisphere, shown in Fig. 9-9b,

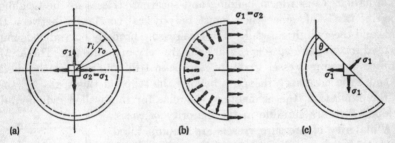

Fig. 9-9. Spherical pressure vessel.

is isolated. By using the same notations as above, an equation identical to Eq. 9-3 may be derived. However, for a sphere, *any section which passes through the center of the sphere yields the same result. Equal* principal stresses act on the elements of the sphere whatever the inclination of the element's side, Fig. 9-9c. Hence for thin-walled spherical pressure vessels,

$$\sigma_1 = \sigma_2 = \frac{pr}{2t} \tag{9-3a}$$

9-6. Remarks on Thin-Walled Pressure Vessels. The state of stress for an element of a thin-walled pressure vessel as given by Eqs. 9-2, 9-3, and 9-3a is considered biaxial, although the internal pressure acting on the wall causes a local compressive stress equal to this pressure. Actually a state of triaxial stress exists on the inside elements of the vessel, Fig. 9-10. However, for thin-walled pressure vessels this latter stress is much smaller than σ_1 and σ_2 and for this reason is generally ignored. The significant stresses acting on the properly oriented elements for cylindrical and spherical pressure vessels are shown in Figs. 9-8a and 9-9a, respectively.

For the same internal pressure, diameter, and wall-thickness, the maximum stress in a spherical vessel is approximately one-half the maximum stress occurring in a cylindrical vessel.   Also note that Mohr's circle of stress for the main stresses in a *spherical* vessel degenerates to a point.   This means that regardless of the inclination of the plane in the element investigated, the normal stress remains constant and no shearing stresses exist.*   The same conclusion is reached by passing an arbitrary cutting plane through the sphere's center, as was done in Fig. 9-9c.

Fig. 9-10.
An element of a thin - walled pressure vessel considered to be in a state of bi-axial stress.

A discontinuity of the membrane action occurs at the juncture of the cylindrical portion of a pressure vessel with the ends.   Under the action of the internal pressure, the cylinder tends to expand as shown by the dashed lines in Fig. 9-11, while the ends tend to expand a different amount, owing to differences in stress.   This incompatibility of deformations causes local bending and shearing stresses in the neighborhood of the joint, since there must be physical continuity between the ends and the cylindrical wall.   For this reason, properly curved ends must be used for pressure vessels.   Flat ends are very undesirable.   The ASME Unfired Pressure Vessel Code gives practical information on the design of ends; the necessary theory is beyond the scope of this text.   In spite of this limitation, the elementary formulas for thin-walled cylinders developed here are suitable in the majority of cases.

A majority of pressure vessels are manufactured from separate curved sheets which are joined.   A common method of accomplishing this is to arc-weld the abutting material as shown in Fig. 9-12.   Grooves into which the welding metal is deposited are prepared in a number of ways, depending on the thickness of the plates.   The so-called single-V butt joint is shown in Fig. 9-12.   Other types of butt welds are also used.   Their nomenclature depends on the preparation of the groove.   For example, if V-grooves are made from both sides, as is done for thicker plates,

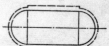

Fig. 9-11. Dashed lines showing the tendency (exaggerated), for the cylinder and the ends to expand a different amount under the action of internal pressure.

the weld is called a double-V butt joint.   Other terms are single-bevel butt joint, double-bevel butt joint, single-U butt joint, etc.   The calculations for the welds are made by assigning an allowable tensile stress to the weld, which is assumed to be of the *same depth as the thickness of the plate*.   The allowable stresses are usually expressed as a certain percentage of the strength of the original solid plate of the parent material.   This percentage factor varies greatly, depending on the workmanship.   For

* By looking on an infinitesimal element *from the top edge*, a new orientation of the element is obtained.   For this new orientation, a maximum shearing stress of $\sigma_1/2$ may be seen to exist in the material.

ordinary work, a 20% reduction in the allowable stress for the weld compared to the solid plate may be used. This factor amounts to an over-all reduction of the actual working stresses in the solid plate by 80%. This percentage factor is called the *efficiency of the joint* (see Art. 14-3). On the highest grade work, some of the newest specifications allow as much as 100% efficiency for the welded joint. For other types of welded joints, as well as a discussion on riveted joints for pressure vessels, see Chapter 14.

Fig. 9-12. Single-*V* butt joint.

In conclusion it must be emphasized that the formulas derived for thin-walled pressure vessels in the preceding article should be used only for cases of *internal pressure*. If a vessel is to be designed for external pressure, as a vacuum tank or a submarine, *instability* (buckling) of the walls may occur, and stress calculations based on the above formulas are meaningless.

The application of Eqs. 9-2, 9-3, and 9-3a is so direct that no illustrative examples are solved. However, a similar method of analysis is applicable to an important related problem which will now be analyzed.

Example 9-4. Determine the pressure p that may be carried by the wooden stave pipe shown in Fig. 9-13. Assume that the wooden staves are of adequate size to span between $\frac{1}{2}$ in. round steel hoops with upset ends* spaced 4 in. apart. Assume the allowable stress in the steel hoops at 24,000 psi, and ignore the effect of crushing of the wood by the hoops.

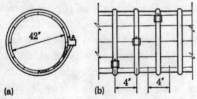

(a)   (b)

Fig. 9-13.

SOLUTION: This problem may be analyzed in the same manner as that of the cylindrical pressure vessel. Since the hoops are 4 in. apart, each hoop resists the force developed by the pressure along four lineal inches of the pipe, Fig. 9-13b. Then, considering a segment of the pipe 4 in. long similar to the one shown in Fig. 9-8b, the internal force tending to burst the pipe in this distance is $2r_iLp = (42)4p = 168p$ lb. This force is resisted by *two* cross-sectional areas of the hoop. The area of each $\frac{1}{2}$ in. diameter hoop from Table 9 in the Appendix is 0.196 in.². Hence it is good for $0.196(24,000) = 4,710$ lb. By equating the bursting force to the two resisting forces in the hoop, the allowable pressure in the pipe is found, i.e., $168p = 2(4,710)$, and $p = 56$ psi.

9-7. Failure Theories. Most of the information on yielding and fracture of materials under the action of biaxial stresses comes from experiments on thin-walled cylinders. A typical arrangement for such experiments is shown in Fig. 9-14. The ends of a thin-walled cylinder of the material being investigated are closed by substantial caps. This forms the hollow interior of a cylindrical pressure vessel. By pressurizing the available space until yielding or bursting point, the elements of the wall

---

* The diameter of the rod at the ends is enlarged by forging, i.e., "upset," in order to maintain the nominal rod diameter at the root of the threads.

are subjected to biaxial stresses of a constant ratio $\sigma_1/\sigma_2 = 2$. By applying an additional tensile force P to the caps, the σ_2 stress is increased to any predetermined amount $\sigma_2 + \sigma''$. By applying a compressive force, the σ_2 stress may be minimized or eliminated. Actual compressive stress in the longitudinal direction is undesirable, as the tube may buckle. By maintaining a fixed ratio between the principal stresses until the failure point is reached, the desired data on a material are obtained. An interpretation of these data, together with all other related experimental evidence, including the simple tension tests, permits a formulation of theories of failure for various materials subjected to combined stresses.

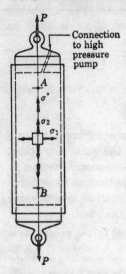

Fig. 9-14. Arrangement for obtaining controlled ratios of the principal stresses.

Unfortunately, at this date the mechanics of failure of materials is not well understood, hence no perfect answer can be given by any one theory. For this reason, there are *several* failure or strength theories, *each one of which is applicable only to a particular group of materials.*

The Maximum Stress Theory.* This theory simply asserts that the breakdown of the material depends *only* on the numerical *magnitude* of the maximum principal (normal) *stress*. Stresses in the other directions are disregarded. Only the numerically maximum principal stress must be determined to apply this criterion. Experiments show that this theory applies reasonably well to cast irons. The failure of cast-iron shafts in torsion, Example 9-2, is in accord with this theory. It overestimates the strength of steels in torsion, where $\sigma_1 = |\tau_{max}|$, and so should not be used for steel.

The Maximum Strain Theory.† This theory asserts that the breakdown of the material does not directly depend on the stresses, but upon the amount of *deformation per unit of length* that a material can withstand. For example, if the strain at which yielding begins is known for a tension specimen, the same amount of strain may take place under a compound or combined stress. To apply this theory, the principal stresses must be determined, and the elastic constants of the material must be known. Then the strain caused by these stresses, as given by Eq. 2-6, must not exceed the strain at yield point in simple tension. This theory overestimates the strength of materials under like kinds of principal stresses (both positive or both negative), and has now been virtually abandoned.

---

* This theory is generally credited to W. J. M. Rankine, an eminent English educator (1820-1872).

† Due to the great French elastician, B. de Saint Venant (1797-1886).

*The Maximum Shear Theory.** This theory asserts that the breakdown of the material depends only on the *maximum shearing stress* that is attained in an element. To apply it, the principal stresses are first determined, then, according to Eq. 8-8, $\tau_{max} = \frac{1}{2}(\sigma_1 - \sigma_2)$. This theory is in good agreement with tests on steels. It is widely used in the design of machine parts and is simple to apply.

The Maximum Energy Theory.† This theory assumes that the breakdown of the material depends on the amount of energy which the material can absorb. Thus, the same amount of energy that a material in simple tension can absorb before yielding takes place can be absorbed by it in a state of combined stress before yielding. The energy concept will be discussed in Chapter 15. After study of that chapter, these statements should become clear. This theory has been abandoned, but it served as an important step in the development of the next theory.

The Maximum Shearing Distortion Theory, or the Huber-Hencky-von Mises Theory.‡ With the exception of the unusually brittle materials, this is the most accurate failure theory for materials that is available. In this theory it is assumed that only the energy which causes the shearing deformations is responsible for the breakdown of material. After several transformations, which are beyond the scope of this text, it may be stated mathematically for a triaxial state of stress as

$$(\sigma_1 - \sigma_2)^2 + (\sigma_2 - \sigma_3)^2 + (\sigma_3 - \sigma_1)^2 = 2\sigma_{yp}^2$$

where $\sigma_1 > \sigma_2 > \sigma_3$ are the principal stresses and σ_{yp} is the yield-point stress in simple tension. For a biaxial state of stress, $\sigma_3 = 0$. Of the preceding mathematically simpler theories of failure, the maximum shear theory is in best agreement with this theory.

From the above description of the failure or strength theories, it is seen that *all of them are in agreement for uniaxial stress.* The simple tension test remains to be the standard of comparison. When one of the principal stresses at a point is large in comparison with the other, all failure theories give practically the same criterion for failure. The discrepancy between the theories is greatest when both principal stresses are numerically equal. *All failure theories are devised on the basis of a parameter, such as the maximum normal stress, the maximum shearing stress, etc., which is thought to be most significant in causing the breakdown of the material.* Experiments must be used to justify the assumption made. Much remains to be done to make these theories universally applicable. For this reason,

---

* This theory was originally proposed by Coulomb in 1773. However, it gained recognition and became widely adopted only after the early tests by J. J. Guest of England in 1900.

† First proposed by Beltrami of Italy in 1885.

‡ This theory was proposed by M. T. Huber of Poland in 1904 and was further developed and explained by R. von Mises (1913) and H. Hencky (1925), both of Germany and the United States.

in the next chapter on the design of members, departures will be made from strict adherence to the failure theories, although unquestionably failure theories provide a background of information for rational design.

Problems for Solution

9-1. A 2 in. square steel bar is subjected to an axial tensile force. If the maximum shearing stress caused by this force is 10,000 psi, what is the magnitude of the applied force? *Ans.* 80 kips.

9-2. A concrete cylinder tested in a vertical position failed at a compressive stress of 4,000 psi. The failure occurred on a plane of 30° with the vertical. On a clear sketch show the normal and the shearing stresses which acted on the plane of failure. *Ans.* $\sigma = -1$ ksi, $\tau = 1.73$ ksi.

9-3. A full-sized 2 in. by 4 in. wooden post has the grain of the wood running at an angle of 25° with its axis. If for this wood the allowable shearing stress in the direction parallel to the grain is 80 psi, what is the allowable axial force for this post controlled by the shearing stress?

9-4. A simple beam 2 in. wide by 6 in. high spans 60 in. and supports a uniformly distributed load of 500 lb/in. including its own weight. Determine the principal stresses and their directions at points A, B, C, D, and E at the section shown in the figure. *Ans.* At B, 0^+, -16.3 ksi; at C, ± 625 psi; at D, 8.37 ksi, $--0.03$ ksi; at E, 16.7 ksi, 0.

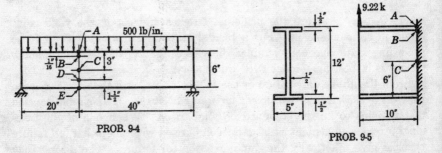

PROB. 9-4   PROB. 9-5

9-5. A very short I-beam cantilever is loaded as shown in the figure. Find the principal stresses and their direction at points A, B, and C. Point B is in the *web* at the juncture with the flange. Neglect the weight of the beam and ignore the effect of stress concentrations. I around the neutral axis for the whole section is 221 in.[4] Use the accurate formula to determine the shearing stresses. *Ans.* At A, -2.50 ksi, 0; at B, $+0.51$ ksi, -2.81 ksi, 23° 20′; at C, ± 1.84 ksi, 45°.

9-6. A cast iron beam is loaded as shown in the figure. Determine the principal stresses at the three points A, B, and C caused by the applied force. The moment of inertia of the cross-sectional area around the neutral axis is 316.2 in.[4] *Ans.* At A, 0, $-2,220$ psi; at B, $+37$ psi, $-1,117$ psi; at C, $+1,960$, 0.

9-7. A 4 in. by 18 in. rectangular timber beam supports an 8.1 kip load as shown in the figure. At a certain point A the grain of the wood makes an angle of 20° with the axis of the beam. Neglecting the weight of the beam, it is found that the bending stress acting on point A is 200 psi, and the shearing stress is 100 psi. Check these

stresses and determine the magnitude of the shearing stress in the beam acting parallel
to the grain of the wood at this point.   *Ans.* 140.6 psi.·

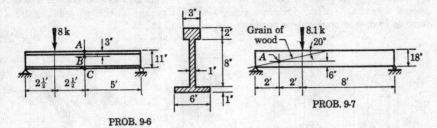

PROB. 9-6

PROB. 9-7

9-8. At a certain point in a masonry structure, the state of stress caused by the
applied forces will be as shown in the sketch.   The stone of which the structure is made
is stratified and is weak in shear along planes parallel with the plane *A-A*.   Is this
state of stress permissible?   Assume that the allowable stresses in the stone in any
direction are 225 psi in tension and 2,000 psi in compression and that the allowable
shearing stress parallel with the *A-A* plane is 325 psi.   *Ans.* Shear governs, 352 psi.

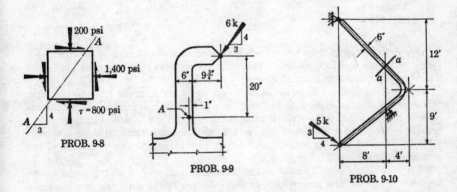

PROB. 9-8

PROB. 9-9

PROB. 9-10

9-9. For the machine bracket shown in the figure find the principal stresses at
point *A* due to the applied force of 6 kips.   Show the results on a properly oriented
element.   The applied force causes no torsional stresses.   At the section considered,
the member is rectangular and is 2 in. by 6 in.   *Ans.* 369 psi, −169 psi, 34.1°.

9-10. A 6 in. square bent bar is loaded as shown in the figure.   Determine the state
of stress at a point lying on the axis of this bar at section *a-a* caused by the applied
inclined force.   Show the results on an infinitesimal element.   Principal stresses are
not required.   *Ans.* −750 psi, 216 psi.

9-11. A special hoist is loaded with a 15 kip load suspended by a cable as shown in
the figure.   Determine the state of stress at point *A* caused by this load.   Show the
results on an element with horizontal and vertical faces.   *I* of the cross-sectional area
around the neutral axis is 165 in.[4]   *Ans.* −4.66 ksi, 1.17 ksi.

9-12. A vertical *T*-beam is loaded as shown in the figure.   Compute the normal
and shearing stresses acting on an element at point *A* caused by the applied loading.
Make a sketch of the element and indicate on it the directions of the computed stresses.
The cross-sectional area of the beam is 10 in.[2], and *I* around the neutral axis is 20.8 in.[4]
Ans. −3,150 psi, 115 psi.

9-13.* A hoisting frame, consisting of two pin-ended members, is attached to a short 14 in.-87 lb wide flange cantilever beam as shown in the figure. Set up an infinitesimal element for point A, showing the stresses which act on this element due to the applied force of 30 kips. Principal stresses are not required. Use an approximate formula to determine the shearing stress. *Ans.* +2.35 ksi, 10.2 ksi

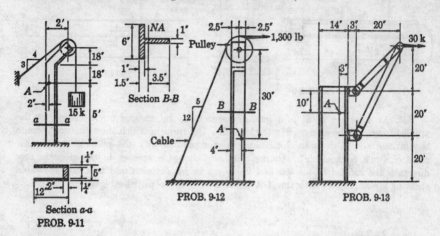

PROB. 9-11   PROB. 9-12   PROB. 9-13

9-14. A short rod of 2 in. diameter is subjected to an axial force of 6π kips and a torque of 2π kip-in. Determine the maximum (principal) shearing stresses, and show the results on a properly oriented element. *Ans.* 5 ksi, $18\frac{1}{2}°$.

9-15. A shaft of 2 in. diameter is subjected to an axial tensile force of 12π kips. What torque may be applied to this shaft in addition to this axial force without exceeding the maximum (principal) shearing stress of 10,000 psi? *Ans.* 4π kip-in.

9-16. A section of a 2 in. diameter shaft is simultaneously transmitting a torque of 3,140 in.-lb and a bending moment of 3,140 in.-lb. Determine the magnitude of the principal shearing stress.

9-17.* A shaft of 2 in. diameter is simultaneously subjected to a torque and a pure bending moment. It is known that at every section of the shaft the largest tensile principal stress caused by the applied loading is 24,000 psi, and that at the same point the largest tensile stress caused by bending, which is 18,000 psi, occurs. Determine the applied bending moment and the applied torque. *Ans.* $M = 4.5\pi$ kip-in., $T = 6\pi$ kip-in.

9-18. A solid circular shaft is loaded as shown in the figure. At section ABCD the stresses due to the 2,000 lb force, and the weight of the shaft and round drum are found to be as follows: max bending stress is 6,000 psi, max torsional stress is 4,000 psi, and max shearing stress due to V is 1,000 psi. (a) Set up elements at points A, B, C, and D and indicate the magnitudes and directions of the stresses acting on them. In each case state from which direction the element is observed. (b) Using Mohr's circle, find directions and magnitudes of the principal stresses and of the maximum shearing stress at point A. *Ans.* (b) 8 ksi, −2 ksi; 5 ksi.

9-19. A circular bar of 2 in. diameter with a rectangular block attached at its free end is suspended as shown in the figure. Also a horizontal force is applied eccentrically to the block as shown. Analysis of the stresses at section ABCD gives the following results: max bending stress is 1,000 psi, max torsional stress is 300 psi, max shearing stress due to V is 400 psi, and direct axial stress is 200 psi. (a) Set up an element at point A and indicate the magnitudes and directions of the stresses acting on it (the top edge of the element to coincide with section $ABCD$).   (b) Using Mohr's circle, find the direction and the magnitude of the maximum (principal) shearing stresses and the associated normal stresses at point A. $Ans.$ 141 psi, +100 psi, $22\frac{1}{2}°$.

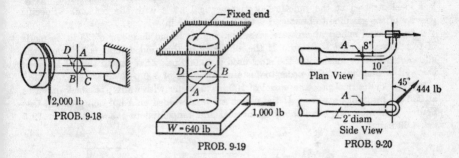

PROB. 9-18

$W = 640$ lb

PROB. 9-19

Plan View

Side View

PROB. 9-20

9-20. A machine bracket is loaded with an inclined force of 444 lb as shown in the figure.   Find the principal stresses at point A.   Show the results on a properly oriented element.   Neglect the weight of the member. $Ans.$ +570 psi, −4,470 psi, 19° 40'.

9-21. A solid triangular sign is rigidly attached to a 4 in. standard-weight steel pipe as shown in the figure.   What principal stresses occur at point A if a wind having an intensity of 30 lb/ft² is blowing on the sign from the reader's side?   Neglect the weight of the pipe and sign and the effect of the wind on the pipe itself.   Disregard wind suction on the leeward side. $Ans.$ +20.4 ksi, −0.2 ksi.

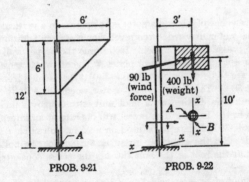

PROB. 9-21   PROB. 9-22

9-22. A 400 lb sign is supported by a $2\frac{1}{2}$ in. standard-weight steel pipe as shown in the figure.   The maximum wind force acting against this sign is estimated to be 90 lb. Determine the state of stress caused by this loading at points A and B at the built-in end.   Principal stresses are not required.   Indicate results on sketches of elements cut out from the pipe at these points.   These elements are to be viewed from outside the pipe. $Ans.$ For A: 13,350 psi, 1,422 psi; for B: 9,945 psi, 1,523 psi.

9-23. Approximately what is the bursting pressure for a cold drawn seamless steel tubing of $2\frac{1}{4}$ in. outside diameter with $\frac{1}{16}$ in. wall-thickness?   The ultimate strength of steel is 55 ksi. $Ans.$ 3,230 psi.

9-24. A "penstock," i.e., a pipe for conveying water to a hydroelectric turbine, operates at a head of 300 ft.   If the diameter of the penstock is 30 in. and the allowable stress is 8,000 psi, what wall-thickness is required?   (The allowable stress is set low to provide for corrosion and inefficiency of welded joints.)

9-25. A tank of butt-welded construction for the storage of gasoline is to be 40 ft in diameter and 16 ft high. Select the plate thickness for the bottom row of plates Allow 20 ksi for steel in tension and assume the efficiency of welds at 80%. Add approximately ⅛ in. to the computed wall thickness to compensate for corrosion. Neglect local stresses at the juncture of the vertical walls with the bottom. (Specific gravity of the gasoline to be stored is 0.721.) *Ans.* ¼ in.

9-26. A steel spherical pressure vessel having an inside diameter of 25 in. is made of two halves welded together. If the efficiency of the welded joint is 75% and the allowable stress in tension for the steel used is 10,000 psi, what should the thickness of the wall of this vessel be in order to sustain a pressure of 300 psi? *Ans.* ¼ in.

9-27. A cylindrical pressure vessel of 100 in. diameter with walls ½ in. thick operates at 200 psi internal pressure. If the plates are butt-welded on a 30° helical spiral (see figure), determine the stresses acting normal and tangential to the weld. *Ans.* 12.5 ksi, 4.33 ksi.

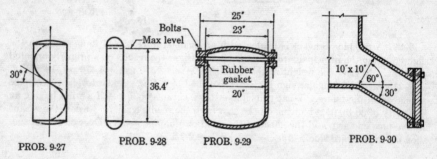

PROB. 9-27　　PROB. 9-28　　PROB. 9-29　　PROB. 9-30

9-28. A pressure vessel of 50 in. diameter is to operate in a vertical position as shown in the figure. The water may reach the level shown and, in addition, the space above the water may be pressurized to 35 psi. Determine the proper wall thickness for this pressure vessel for a welded assembly of plates. The allowable tensile stress is 10,000 psi. Since welds are to be of the open-square-butt type, welded from one side, assume their efficiency at 50%. Also assume that water weighs 62.4 lb/ft³. *Ans.* 0.25 in.

9-29. For an industrial laboratory a pilot unit is to employ a pressure vessel of the dimensions shown in the figure. The vessel will operate at an internal pressure of 100 psi. If for this unit 20 bolts are to be used on a 25 in. bolt circle diameter, what size bolts are required? Set the allowable stress in tension for the bolts at 18 ksi; however, assume that at the root of the bolt threads the stress concentration factor is 2½. *Ans.* ¾ in.

9-30. An inspection door is attached to a pressure vessel by means of twelve ¾ in. diameter bolts as shown in the cross-sectional view. The clear opening is 10 in. by 10 in. When the vessel is pressurized to 260 psi, what will the maximum stress in the bolts be? Assume a stress concentration factor of 2½ at the root of the threads. *Ans.* 20.7 ksi.

9-31. A water tank made of wood staves is 16 ft in diameter and 12 ft high. Specify the spacing of 1¼ in. by ¼ in. steel hoops if the allowable tensile stress for steel is set at 12,000 psi. Adopt uniform spacing for the hoops in the lower and upper halves of the tank.

9-32. A piece of 10 in. diameter tubing of 0.1 in. wall thickness was closed off at the ends as shown in Fig. 9-14. Then this assembly was put into a testing machine and subjected simultaneously to an axial pull P and an internal pressure of 240 psi. What was the magnitude of the applied force P if the gage points A and B, initially precisely 8 in. apart, were found to be 8.0016 in. apart after all of the forces were applied? $E = 30 \times 10^6$ psi and $\mu = 0.25$. *Ans.* 9.43 kips.

9-33. A cylindrical compressed air tank made of steel is 4 ft in diameter inside and 24 ft long. The walls are $\frac{1}{4}$ in. thick. What will the pressure gage reading be when the length of the tank increases a total of 0.025 in. in a distance of 13 ft. $E = 30 \times 10^6$ psi, $\mu = \frac{1}{4}$. *Ans.* 200 psi.

9-34. A cylindrical pressure vessel of 40 in. diameter is to be designed for 428 psi internal pressure. What must the wall thickness of the cylinder be if, as the basis for design, the maximum strain is limited to 5×10^{-4} in/in.? $E = 30 \times 10^6$ psi and $\mu = \frac{1}{4}$. (This design assumption implies the maximum strain theory of failure.) *Ans.* $\frac{1}{2}$ in.

9-35. A cylindrical pressure vessel of 120 in. diameter *outside*, used for processing rubber, is 36 ft long. If the cylindrical portion of the vessel is made from 1 in. thick steel plate and the vessel operates at 120 psi internal pressure, determine the total elongation of the circumference and the increase in the diameter's dimension caused by the operating pressure. $E = 29 \times 10^6$ psi and $\mu = 0.3$ *Ans.* 0.0778 in., 0.0247 in.

9-36. A boiler made of $\frac{1}{2}$ in. steel plate is 40 in. in diameter and 8 ft long. It is subjected to an internal pressure of 500 psi. How much will the thickness of the plate change due to this pressure? $E = 30 \times 10^6$ psi and $\mu = 0.25$. *Ans.* -0.000125 in.

9-37. A compressed air tank is hoisted off the ground by a crane as shown in the figure. The tank is 10 ft long and 2 ft in diameter and has a wall thickness of $\frac{1}{4}$ in. The pressure in the tank is 50 psi. Assume the tank and its contents weigh 65 lb per lineal foot. Determine the principal stresses at points A and B, and show the results on infinitesimal elements. *Ans.* At A: 2,400 psi, 1,045 psi; at B, 2,400 psi, 1,165 psi.

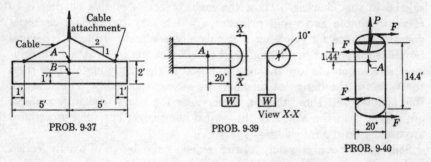

PROB. 9-37   PROB. 9-39   View X-X   PROB. 9-40

9-38. In a certain research investigation on the creep of lead, it was necessary to control the state of stress for the element of a tube. In one such case, a long cylindrical tube with closed ends was pressurized and simultaneously subjected to a torque. The tube was 4 in. in outside diameter with $\frac{1}{4}$ in. walls. What were the principal stresses at the outside surface of the wall of the cylinder if the chamber was pressurized to 200 psi and the externally applied torque was 2,000 in.-lb? *Ans.* $+1,563$ psi, $+489$ psi.

9-39. A steel pressure vessel 20 in. in diameter and of 0.25 in. wall-thickness acts also as an eccentrically loaded cantilever as shown in the figure. If the internal pressure is 250 psi and the applied weight $W = 31.4$ kips, determine the state of stress at point A. Show the results on an infinitesimal element. Principal stresses are not required. Neglect the weight of the vessel. *Ans.* $\sigma_x = 5$ ksi, $\sigma_y = 10$ ksi, $\tau = 6$ ksi.

9-40. A tank open at the top and closed at the bottom has a diameter of 20 in., a wall-thickness of 0.425 in., and is 14.4 ft long as shown in the figure. This tank is filled to the top with liquid mercury which weighs 850 lb/ft³. If this tank is lifted off the ground by means of a cable and is simultaneously subjected to equal and opposite torques of 81,000 in.-lb at the top and bottom, what is the magnitude and direction of the principal stresses at point A, which is 1.44 ft from the top of the tank? Neglect the weight of the tank. Approximately, $I = 1,350$ in.⁴ and $J = 2,700$ in.⁴ *Ans.* $+1,100$ psi, $+100$ psi, 18° 26.5'.

Chapter Ten

DESIGN OF MEMBERS BY STRENGTH CRITERIA

10-1. Introduction. The selection or design of a member depends on one of the following characteristics: its strength, its stiffness (deflection), or its stability. Any one of these criteria may govern the size of a member. However, only the *strength* requirement of statically determinate members, based on the assumption of elastic behavior of the materials, will be considered in this chapter. Thus, the main objective of this chapter is to establish simple and rapid procedures which may be used in practical design problems for selecting a member of adequate strength. Several formulas developed in the earlier chapters and the information on principal stresses and failure theories discussed in the preceding chapter form the basis for the design of members by strength criteria. The study of this chapter will show that in some cases the usual design procedures are cruder than the available theoretical knowledge, but such procedures are usually on the safe side.

This chapter contains only a brief review of the design of axially loaded and torsion members, as this subject was discussed earlier. However, a few additional comments are necessary at this time, since the preceding study of stress transformation at a point gives a more complete picture of the internal stresses. This will be followed by a detailed development of rapid design criteria for beams.

10-2. Design of Axially Loaded Members. Axially loaded tensile members and short* compression members are designed by using Eq. 1-1a, i.e., $A = P/\sigma_{\text{allow}}$. The *critical* section for an axially loaded member occurs at a section of minimum cross-sectional area, where the stress is a maximum. If an abrupt discontinuity in the cross-sectional area is imposed by the design requirements, the use of Eq. 2-11, $\sigma_{\text{max}} = KP/A$, is appropriate. The use of the latter formula is necessary in the design of machine parts to compensate for the local stress concentrations where fatigue failure may occur.

Besides the normal stresses, given by the above equations, shearing

---

* Slender compression members are discussed in Chapter 13.

stresses act on inclined planes, even in a state of uniaxial stress. Hence, if a material is weak in shearing strength in comparison to its strength in tension or compression, it will fail along planes approximating the planes of the maximum shearing stress. For example, concrete or cast-iron members in uniaxial compression and duralumin members in uniaxial tension fail on planes inclined to the direction of the load. Nevertheless, regardless of the type of failure that may actually take place, the allowable stress for design of axially loaded members is customarily based on the *normal* stress. This design procedure is consistent. The maximum normal stress which a material can withstand at the failure point is directly related to the *ultimate* strength of the material. Hence, although the actual break may occur on an inclined plane, the maximum normal stress may be considered as the ultimate normal stress.

10-3. Design of Torsion Members. The pertinent formulas for the design of torsion members were established in Chapter 3. For circular shafts, the solution of Eq. 3-5, $J/c = T/\tau_{max}$, at a critical section gives the required parameter, J/c, to provide a member of adequate strength As shafts are mainly used as parts of machines, Eq. 3-3b, $\tau_{max} = KTc/J$, should be used in most cases. Equation 3-3b, with the stress-concentration factor K, takes care of the high local shearing stress at the changes of the cross-sectional area.

Most torsion members are designed by selecting an *allowable shearing stress*, which is substituted for τ_{max} in Eqs. 3-5 or 3-3b. This amounts to a direct use of the maximum shear theory of failure. However, it is well to bear in mind that a state of pure shearing stress, which occurs in torsion, may be transformed into the principal stresses.* In some materials, failure may be caused by one of these principal stresses. For example, a member made from cast iron, a material strong in compression but weaker in tension than in shear, fails in tension.

10-4. Design Criteria for Prismatic Beams. If a beam is subjected to *pure bending*, its fibers are in a state of uniaxial stress. If, further, a beam is prismatic, i.e., of a constant cross-sectional area and shape, the critical section occurs at the section of the greatest bending moment. By assigning an allowable stress, the section modulus of such a beam may be determined using Eq. 5-5, $Z = M/\sigma_{max}$. If the required section modulus is known, a beam of correct proportions, to be of adequate strength, may be selected. However, if a beam resists shear in addition to bending, its design becomes more involved.

Consider the prismatic rectangular beam of Example 9-3 at a section 10 in. from the left support, where the beam transmits a bending moment *and* a shear, Fig. 10-1a. The principal stresses at points A, B, C, B', and A' at this section were found before and are reproduced in Fig. 10-1b. *If*

---

* By rotating an element through 45°, tension-compression stresses are found which are numerically equal to the shearing stresses. Art. 8-6

this section were the critical section, it is seen that the design of this beam would be governed by the stresses *at the extreme fibers,* as no other stresses exceed these stresses.   However, for a prismatic beam, these stresses depend only on the magnitude of the bending moment and are largest at a section where the maximum bending moment occurs.   Moreover, it is

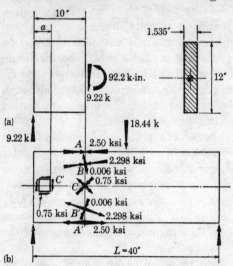

not necessary to perform the combined stress analysis for interior points, as no greater stresses exist.   In the example considered, the maximum bending moment is at the middle of the span.   The foregoing may be generalized into a basic rule for the design of beams: *A critical section for a prismatic beam carrying transverse forces acting normal to its axis occurs where the bending moment reaches its absolute maximum* value.*

Fig. 10-1.

The above criterion for the design of prismatic beams is incomplete, as attention was specifically directed to the stresses caused by the moment.   In some cases, the shearing stresses caused by the shear at a section may control the design.   In the example considered, Fig. 10-1a and b, the magnitude of the shear remains constant at every section through the beam.   At a small distance *a* from the right support, the maximum shear is still 9.22 kips, while the bending moment, 9.22*a* kip-in., is small.   The maximum shearing stress at the neutral axis corresponding to $V = 9.22$ kips is the same at point C' as it is at point C.†   Therefore, since in a general problem the bending stresses may be small, they may not control the selection of a beam, and *another critical section for any prismatic beam occurs where the shear is a maximum.*   In applying this criterion it is customary to work directly with the maximum shearing stress that may be obtained from Eq. 6-3, $\tau = VQ/(It)$, and not transform τ_{max} so found into the principal stresses.   For rectangular and *I*-beams, the

---

* For nonsymmetric cross-sections, such as *T*-beams, made from material which has different properties in tension than in compression, the *largest* moments of *both senses* (positive or negative) must be examined.   Under some circumstances, a smaller bending moment of one sense may cause a more critical stress than a larger moment of another sense.   The section at which the extreme fiber stress of either sign in relation to the respective allowable stress is highest is the critical section.

† At point C, the maximum shearing stresses are shown transformed into the principal stresses.

maximum shearing stress given by Eq. 6-3 reduces to Eqs. 6-4 and 6-5, $\tau_{max} = (3/2)(V/A)$ and $(\tau_{max})_{approx} = V/A_{web}$, respectively.

Whether the section where the bending moment is a maximum or the section where the shear is a maximum governs the selection of a prismatic beam depends on the loading and the material used. For most materials, the allowable shearing stress is less than the allowable bending stress. For example, for steel the ratio between these allowable stresses is approximately 0.6, while for some woods it may be as low as 1/15.* Regardless of these ratios of stresses, *the bending stresses usually control the selection of a beam.* Only in beams spanning a short distance does shear control the design. For small lengths of beams, the applied forces and reactions have small moment arms, and the required resisting bending moments are small. On the other hand, the shearing forces may be large if the applied forces are large.

The two criteria for the design of beams are accurate if the two critical sections are in different locations. However, in some instances the maximum bending moment and the maximum shear occur at the *same* section through the beam. In such situations, sometimes higher combined stresses than σ_{max} and τ_{max}, as given by Eqs. 5-5 and 6-3, may exist at the interior points. For example, consider an *I*-beam of negligible weight which carries a force P at the middle of the span, Fig. 10-2a. The maximum bending moment occurs at the mid-span. Except for sign, the shear is the same on either side of the applied force. At a section just to the right or just to the left of the applied force, the maximum moment *and* the maximum shear occur simultaneously. A section just to the left of P, with the corresponding system of forces acting on it, is shown in Fig. 10-2b. For this section, it can be shown that the stresses at the extreme fibers are 2.50 ksi, while the principal stresses at the juncture of the web with the flanges, neglecting stress concentrations, are ±2.81 ksi and ±0.51 ksi, acting as shown in Figs.

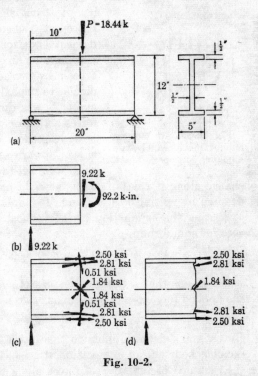

Fig. 10-2.

10-2c and d. As usual, local disturbance of stresses in the neighborhood of the applied force P is neglected. From this example it is seen that the maximum normal stress does not always occur at the extreme fibers. Nevertheless, only the extreme fiber stresses and the shearing stresses at the neutral axis are investigated in ordinary design.

* Wood is very weak in shearing strength *parallel* to its grain.

In the design codes, the allowable stresses are presumably set low enough so that an adequate factor of safety remains, even if the higher combined stresses are disregarded. Also note that, for the same applied force, by increasing the span, the flexural stresses rapidly increase, while the shearing stresses remain constant. In most cases, the flexural stresses are dominant, and the extreme fiber stress is the maximum normal stress. Only for very short beams and unusual arrangements need the combined stress analysis be performed.

From the above discussion it is seen that, for the design of prismatic beams, the critical sections must be determined in every problem, as the design is entirely based on the stresses developed at these sections. The critical sections are best located with the aid of shear and bending-moment diagrams. The required values of M_{max} and V_{max} may be easily determined from such diagrams. The construction of these diagrams has been already treated in Chapter 4. However, the importance of these diagrams is so great that an alternative procedure for rapidly constructing them will be discussed next. The procedure to be developed is self-checking.

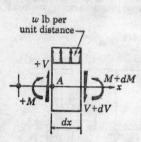

10-5. Shear Diagrams by Summation. To construct shear diagrams by an alternate procedure, the summation method, certain fundamental relations must be established. To that end, consider an element, Fig. 10-3, isolated from a beam by two adjoining sections taken perpendicular to the axis of the beam, a distance of dx apart, as was done in Art. 6-2. As before, all forces acting on this element are shown with a positive sense. The positive distributed load w acts upward and causes an increment in the shear from left to right. The shear and moment change along the beam, so on the right-hand face of the element this is denoted by writing $V + dV$ and $M + dM$.

Fig. 10-3. An element cut out from a beam by two adjoining sections dx apart.

Writing the summation of the vertical forces and setting it equal to zero for equilibrium,

$$V + w\,dx - (V + dV) = 0 \qquad \text{or} \qquad \frac{dV}{dx} = w \qquad (10\text{-}1)$$

which means that the rate of change of shear along the beam is equal to the applied force in a unit distance. Transposing and integrating gives

$$V = \int w\,dx \qquad (10\text{-}2)$$

By assigning definite limits to this integral, it is seen that, except for a possible constant of integration, the shear at a section is an integral (i.e., a sum) of the vertical forces along the beam from one end of the beam *to the section in question*. Likewise, between any two definite sections on a beam, the shear changes by the amount of the vertical force

---

* A variation of this load within an infinitesimal distance is permissible The proof of this is analogous to that given in a footnote to Art. 6-2.

included *between* these sections. If no force occurs between any two sections, no change in shear takes place. If a concentrated force comes into the summation, a discontinuity or a "jump" in the value of the shear occurs. The continuous summation process nevertheless remains valid, as a concentrated force may be thought of as being a distributed force extending for an infinitesimal distance along the beam. Using the sign convention adopted for shear in Chapter 4, Fig. 4-15, any *upward* force and *upward* vertical reaction component add the *positive* contribution of their magnitude to the shear, or vice versa.

On the basis of the above reasoning, a shear diagram may be established by the summation process. For this purpose, *the reactions must always be determined first.* Then the vertical components of forces and **reactions** are successively summed *from the left end* of the beam to preserve the mathematical sign convention. The shear at a section is equal to the sum of *all* vertical forces up to that section.

When the shear diagram is constructed from the loading diagram by the summation process, the analyst should pose two questions. First, is the change in shear positive or negative in the particular segment of the beam considered? This depends entirely on whether the forces act up or down. If they act up, the change is positive. Then, second, at what rate does the change in shear take place? This question again is answered by the loading diagram, and it dictates the shape of the shear curve in the segment of the beam under consideration. For this purpose, the value of $w\,dx$ along the segment of the beam must be examined. For example, in Fig. 10-4a, $w\,dx = dV$ is constant everywhere along the segment and is negative. Therefore, the shear curve for this segment is a *straight line of negative slope.* In Fig. 10-4b the variable load acts *up*, hence the change

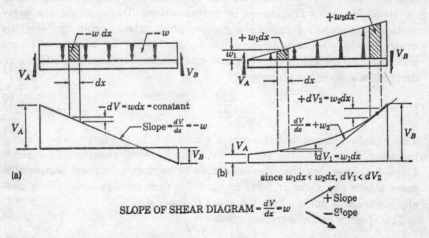

SLOPE OF SHEAR DIAGRAM $= \dfrac{dV}{dx} = w$

Fig. 10-4.   The relation between the loading and the shear diagrams.

in shear from left to right is positive. Then, examining a length dx at each end of the segment, it is seen that $w_1\,dx < w_2\,dx$, that is, $dV_1 < dV_2$. Hence, the *only possible curve* that will fit these conditions is the one in which the *slope is increasing positively*, i.e., the curve is concave upwards. Other types of loading may be analyzed in a similar fashion. Note that the derived curve in the summation process is always one degree higher than the original curve, e.g., a linearly changing loading gives a second-degree parabolic shear diagram.

A very convenient self-explanatory method for determining slopes of shear diagrams using the basic relation, Eq. 10-1, is also shown in Fig. 10-4.

Do not fail to note that *a mere systematic consecutive summation of the vertical components of the forces is all that is necessary to obtain the shear diagram.* When the consecutive summation process is used, the diagram must close at the right-hand end of the beam, as just beyond the last vertical force or reaction no shear acts through the beam. *The fact that the diagram closes offers an important check on the arithmetical calculations.* This check should never be ignored. It permits one to obtain solutions independently with almost complete assurance of being correct. The semigraphical procedure of integration outlined above is very convenient in practical problems. It is the basis for sketching qualitative shear diagrams rapidly.

Physically, the shear sign convention is not completely consistent. Whenever beams are analyzed, a shear diagram drawn from one side of the beam is opposite in sign to a diagram constructed by looking at the same beam from the other side. The reader should verify this statement on some simple cases, such as a cantilever with a concentrated force at the end and a simply supported beam with a concentrated force in the middle. For design purposes the sign of the shear is usually unimportant.

*10-6. Moment Diagrams by Summation. To formulate the summation procedure for establishing moment diagrams, again the element shown in Fig. 10-3 must be considered. By taking the moment of forces around A and setting it equal to zero for equilibrium, an expression formerly derived in Art. 6-2 is obtained.

$$\frac{dM}{dx} = V \qquad (6-1)$$

This equation states that the rate of change of the bending moment along the beam is equal to the shear. By a fundamental theorem of calculus, Eq. 6-1 also implies that the *maximum or minimum moment occurs at a point where the shear is zero,* as then the derivative is zero. This usually occurs at a point where the shear changes sign.

Transposing and integrating gives

$$M = \int V\,dx \qquad (10-3)$$

which is analogous to Eq. 10-2 developed for the construction of shear diagrams. The meaning of the term $V\,dx$ is shown graphically by the shaded areas of the shear diagrams in Fig. 10-5. The summation of these areas between definite sections through a beam corresponds to an evaluation of the above definite integral. If the ends of a beam are on rollers,

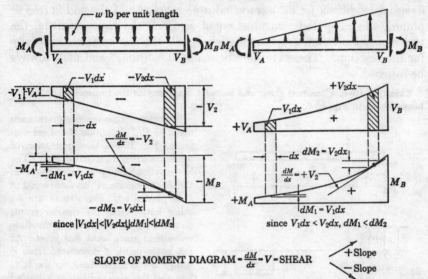

$$\text{SLOPE OF MOMENT DIAGRAM} = \frac{dM}{dx} = V = \text{SHEAR}$$

Fig. 10-5. The relation between the shear and the bending-moment diagrams.

pin-ended or free, the starting and the terminal moments are zero. If the end is built-in (fixed against rotation), in statically determinate beams the end moment is known from the reaction calculations. If the fixed end of a beam is on the left, this moment with the proper* sign is the *initial constant of integration.*

By proceeding *continuously along the beam from the left-hand end* and summing up the particular areas of the shear diagram with due regard to the sign of the shear, the moment diagram is obtained. This process of deriving the moment diagram from the shear diagram by summation is exactly the same as that employed earlier to go from loading to shear diagrams. ***The change in moment in a given segment of a beam is equal to the area of the corresponding shear diagram.*** The nature of the change (the shape of the bending-moment curve) is conveniently determined by examining a length dx at each end of the segment to determine $V\,dx = dM$. Examples are shown in Fig. 10-5. According to these principles, variable shears cause nonlinear variation of the moment. A constant shear produces a uniform change in the bending moment, resulting in a straight

---

* Bending moments carry signs according to the convention adopted in Fig. 4-16. Moments which cause *compression* in the top fibers of the beam are positive.

line in the moment diagram. If no shear occurs along a certain portion of a beam, *no change in moment* takes place; the preceding magnitude and sign of the moment continues throughout that section of the beam.

In a bending-moment diagram obtained by summation, *at the right-hand end* of the beam, an invaluable check on the work is available again. *The terminal conditions for the moment must be satisfied.* If the end is free or pinned, the computed sum must equal zero. If the end is built-in, the end moment computed by summation equals the one calculated initially for the reaction. These are the "boundary conditions" and must always be satisfied.

Example 10-1. Construct shear and moment diagrams for the symmetrically loaded beam shown in Fig. 10-6a.

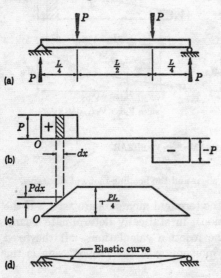

(a)

(b)

(c)

(d)

Elastic curve

Fig. 10-6.

SOLUTION: The reactions are each equal to P. To obtain the shear diagram, Fig. 10-6b, the summation of forces is started from the left end. The left reaction acts *up* so an ordinate on the shear diagram at this force equal to P is plotted *up*. Since there are no other forces until the quarter point, *no change in the magnitude of the shear ordinate is made until that point.* At the latter point, a downward force P brings the ordinate back to the base line, and this zero ordinate is indicated until the next downward force P, where the shear changes to $-P$. At the right-hand end the upward reaction closes the diagram and provides a check on the work. This shear diagram is *antisymmetrical.*

The moment diagram, Fig. 10-6c, is obtained by summing up the area of the shear diagram. As the beam is simply supported, the moment at the left end is zero. The sum of the positive portion of the shear diagram *increases at a constant rate* along the beam until the quarter point, where the moment reaches a magnitude of $+\dfrac{PL}{4}$. This moment remains constant in the middle half of the beam. *No change in the moment can be made in this zone,* as there is no corresponding shear area.

Beyond the second force, the moment decreases by $-P\,dx$ in *every dx*. Hence the shear diagram in this zone has a constant, negative slope. Since the positive and the negative areas of the shear diagram are equal, at the right end the moment is zero. This is as it should be, as the end is on a roller. Thus a check on the work is obtained. This moment diagram is *symmetrical.*

Example 10-2. Construct shear and bending-moment diagrams for the beam loaded as shown in Fig. 10-7a.

SOLUTION: Reactions must be calculated first, and, before proceeding further, the inclined force is resolved into its horizontal and vertical components. The horizontal reaction at A is 30 kips and acts to the right. From $\Sigma M_A = 0$, the vertical reaction at B is found to be 37.5 kips (check this). Similarly, the reaction at A is 27.5 kips. The sum of the vertical reaction components is 65 kips and equals the sum of the vertical forces.

With reactions known, the summation of forces is begun from the left end of the beam to obtain the shear diagram, Fig. 10-7b. At first, the downward distributed load accumulates at a rapid rate. Then, as the load intensity decreases, for an equal increment of distance along the beam a smaller change in shear occurs. Hence the shear diagram in the zone CA is a curved line, which is concave up. The total downward force from C to A is 15 kips, and this is the negative ordinate of the shear diagram,

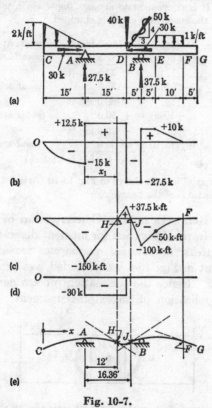

Fig. 10-7.

just to the left of the support A. At A, the *upward* reaction of 27.5 kips moves the ordinate of the shear diagram to $+12.5$ kips. This value of the shear applies to a section through the beam *just to the right* of the support A. The abrupt *change* in the shear at A is equal to the reaction, but this total does not represent the shear through the beam.

No forces are applied to the beam between A and D, hence there is no change in the value of the shear found above. At D, the 40 kip downward component of the concentrated force drops the value of the shear to -27.5 kips. Similarly, the value of the shear is raised to $+10$ kips at B. Since between E and F the uniformly distributed load acts downward, a decrease in shear takes place at a constant rate of one kip per foot. Thus at F the shear is zero, which serves as the final check.

To construct the moment diagram shown in Fig. 10-7c by the summation method, areas of the shear diagram in Fig. 10-7b must be continuously summed from the left end. In the segment CA, at first less area is contributed to the sum in a distance dx than a little further along, so a line that is concave down appears in the moment diagram. The moment at A is equal to the area of the shear diagram in the segment CA. This area is enclosed by a curved line, and it may be determined by integration, [*] since the shear along this segment may be expressed analytically. This procedure often is tedious, and instead of using it, the bending moment at A may be obtained from the fundamental definition of a moment at a section. By passing a section through A and isolating the segment CA, the moment at A is found. The other areas of the shear diagram in this example are easily determined. Due attention must be paid to the signs of these areas. It is convenient to arrange the work in tabular form. At the right end of the beam, the customary check is obtained.

$$
\begin{array}{lll}
M_A\ldots\ldots & -\tfrac{1}{2}(15)2(10) = -150.0 \text{ kip-ft} & \text{(moment around } A) \\
 & +12.5(15) = +187.5 & \text{(shear area } A \text{ to } D) \\
M_D\ldots\ldots\ldots\ldots\ldots & +\ 37.5 \text{ kip-ft} & \\
 & -27.5(5) = -137.5 & \text{(shear area } D \text{ to } B) \\
M_B\ldots\ldots\ldots\ldots\ldots & -100.0 \text{ kip-ft} & \\
 & +10(5) = +\ 50.0 & \text{(shear area } B \text{ to } E) \\
M_E\ldots\ldots\ldots\ldots\ldots & -\ 50.0 \text{ kip-ft} & \\
 & +\tfrac{1}{2}(10)10 = +\ 50.0 & \text{(shear area } E \text{ to } F) \\
M_F\ldots\ldots\ldots\ldots\ldots & 0.0 \text{ kip-ft} & \text{(check)}
\end{array}
$$

The diagram for the axial force is shown in Fig. 10-7d (Art. 4-8). This compressive force acts in the segment AD of the beam.

*10-7. Further Remarks on the Construction of Shear and Moment Diagrams. In the derivation for moment diagrams by summation of shear-diagram areas, no *external concentrated moment* acting on the infinitesimal element in Fig. 10-3 was included, yet such a moment may actually be applied. Hence the summation process derived applies only to the point of application of an external moment. *At a section just*

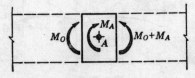

Fig. 10-8. An external concentrated moment acting on an element of a beam.

beyond an externally applied moment, a different bending moment is required to maintain the segment of a beam in equilibrium. For example, in Fig. 10-8 an external clockwise moment M_A is acting on the element of the beam at A. Then, if the internal clockwise moment on the left is M_o, for equilibrium of the element the resisting counterclockwise moment on the right is $M_o + M_A$. Situations with other sense of moments may be

---

[*] In this case, the shear curve is a second-degree parabola with vertex on a vertical line through A. For areas enclosed by various curves see Table 2 in the Appendix.

similarly analyzed. At the point of the externally applied moment, a discontinuity or a "jump" equal to the concentrated moment appears in the moment diagram. Hence, in applying the summation process, due regard must be given the concentrated moments, as their effect is not included in the shear-diagram area summation process. The summation process may be applied up to the point of application of a concentrated moment. At this point a vertical "jump" equal to the external moment must be made in the diagram. The direction of this vertical "jump" in the diagram depends upon the sense of the concentrated moment and is best determined with the aid of a sketch analogous to Fig. 10-8. After the discontinuity in the moment diagram is passed, the summation process of the shear-diagram areas may be continued over the remainder of the beam.

Example 10-3. Construct the bending-moment diagram for the horizontal beam loaded as shown in Fig. 10-9a.

SOLUTION: By taking moments about either end of the beam, the vertical reactions are found to be $P/6$. At A the reaction acts down, at C it acts up. From $\Sigma F_x = 0$ it is known that at A a horizontal reaction equal to P acts to the left. The shear diagram

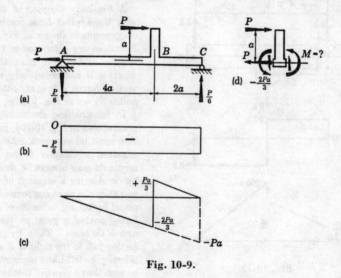

Fig. 10-9.

is drawn next, Fig. 10-9b. It has a constant negative ordinate for the *whole* length of the beam. After this, by using the summation process, the moment diagram shown in Fig. 10-9c is constructed. The moment at the left end of the beam is zero, since the support is pinned. The total change in moment from A to B is given by the area of the shear diagram between these sections and equals $-2Pa/3$. The moment diagram in the zone AB has a constant negative slope. For further analysis, an element is isolated from the beam as shown in Fig. 10-9d. The moment on the left-hand side of this element is *known to be* $-2Pa/3$, and the concentrated moment caused by the applied force P about the neutral axis of the beam is Pa, hence for equilibrium, on the right-hand side of the element the moment must be $+Pa/3$. At B an upward "jump" of $+Pa$ is made in the moment diagram, and just to the right of B the ordinate is $+Pa/3$. Beyond point B, the summation of the shear diagram area is continued. This area between B and C is equal to $-Pa/3$. This value *closes* the moment diagram at the right end of the beam, and thus the boundary conditions are satisfied. Note that the inclined lines in the moment diagrams are parallel, for if the summation of the shear-diagram area were continued uninterrupted by the concentrated moment, the ordinate on the right would be $-Pa$. Of course, the latter ordinate does not satisfy the boundary condition of this problem.

Example 10-4. Construct shear and moment diagrams for the member shown in Fig. 10-10a. Neglect the weight of the beam.

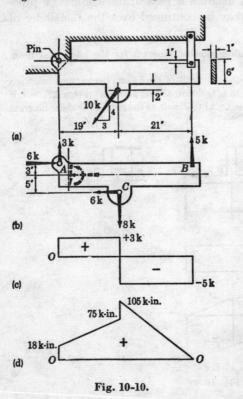

Fig. 10-10.

SOLUTION: In this case, unlike all cases considered so far, definite dimensions are assigned for the *depth* of the beam. The beam, for simplicity, is assumed to be rectangular in its cross-sectional area, consequently the *neutral axis* lies 3 in. below the top of the beam. Note carefully that this beam is not supported at the neutral axis.

A free-body diagram of the beam with the applied force resolved into components is shown in Fig. 10-10b. Reactions are computed in the usual manner. Moreover, since the shear diagram is concerned only with the vertical forces, it is easily constructed and is shown in Fig. 10-10c.

In constructing the moment diagram shown in Fig. 10-10d, particular care must be exercised. As was emphasized in Chapter 4, the bending moments may always be determined by considering a segment of a beam, and they are most conveniently computed by taking moments of external forces *around a point on the neutral axis of the beam.* Thus, by passing a section just to the right of A and considering the left-hand segment, it may be seen that a positive moment of 18 kip-in. is resisted by the beam at this end. Hence the plot of the moment diagram must *start* with an ordinate of $+18$ kip-in. The other point on the beam where a concentrated moment occurs is at C. Here the horizontal component of the applied force induces a clockwise moment of $6(5) = 30$ kip-in. around the neutral axis. Just to the right of C this moment must be resisted by an additional positive moment. This causes a discontinuity in the moment diagram. The summation process of the shear-diagram areas applies for the segments of the beam where no external moments are applied. The necessary calculations are carried out below in tabular form.

M_A..................... $+6(3) = + 18$ kip-in.

$+3(19) = + 57$ (shear area A to C)

Moment just to left of C........ $= + 75$ kip-in.

$+6(5) = + 30$ (external moment at C)

Moment just to right of C....... $= +105$ kip-in.

$-5(21) = -105$ (shear area C to B)

M_B........................... $=\quad\;\; 0$ (*check*)

Note that in solving this problem the forces were considered *wherever they actually act on the beam*. The investigation for shear and moments at a section of a beam determines what the beam is actually experiencing. At times this differs from the procedure of determining reactions where the actual framing or configuration of a member is not important.

Occasionally *hinges* or *pinned joints* are introduced into beams. A hinge is capable of transmitting only horizontal and vertical forces. *No moment can be transmitted at a hinged joint.* Therefore the point where a hinge occurs is a particularly convenient location for "separation" of the structure into parts for purposes of computing the reactions. This process is illustrated in Fig. 10-11. Each part of the beam so separated is treated independently. Each hinge provides an extra axis around which moments may be taken to determine reactions. The introduction of a hinge or hinges into a continuous beam in many cases makes the system statically determinate. The introduction of a hinge into a determinate beam results in a beam which is not stable. Note that the reaction at the hinge for one beam acts in an *opposite direction* on the other beam.

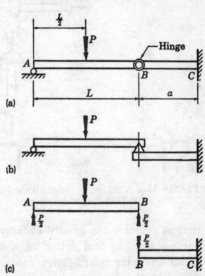

Fig. 10-11. Structures "separated" at hinges to determine the reactions by statics.

In engineering practice it is also common to find several members *rigidly joined* to form a structure. Such a structure may be treated by the methods already discussed, if it can be separated into statically determinate individual beams. To illustrate, consider the structure shown in Fig. 10-12a. Beginning at a point A, the portions of the structure AB, BC, and CD may be successively isolated as free bodies, and the system of forces at each of the cut sections may be determined. The reader should verify these forces shown in Fig. 10-12b. Thence, shear and moment diagrams may be constructed for each part, although the sign convention adopted in this text becomes ambiguous for vertical and inclined members.

However, if the direction of these quantities is understood by the analyst in a physical sense, no particular difficulty should be encountered in stress analysis or design.

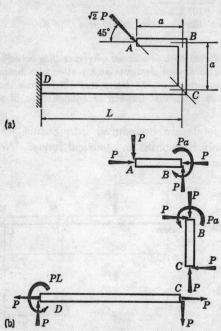

(a)

(b)

Fig. 10-12. A statically determinate frame separated into individual beams.

Finally, it must be emphasized that if a moment or a shear is needed at a *particular* section through any member, *the basic method of sections may always be used.* For inclined members, the shear acts *normal to the axis of the beam.*

*10-8. Moment Diagram and the Elastic Curve. It was stated in Art. 4-9 that a positive moment causes a beam to deform concave upwards or to "retain water," and vice versa, hence the shape of the deflected axis of a beam may be *definitely* established from the *sign* of the moment diagram. The trace of this axis of a loaded beam in a deflected position is known as the **elastic curve.** It is customary to show the elastic curve on a sketch where the actual small deflections tolerated in practice are greatly **exaggerated.** A sketch of the elastic curve clarifies the physical action of a beam. Moreover, it forms the most useful basis for quantitative calculations of beam deflections to be discussed in the next chapter. Some of the preceding examples for which bending-moment diagrams were constructed will be used to illustrate the foregoing concept.

An inspection of Fig. 10-6c shows that the bending moment throughout the length of the beam is *positive.* Accordingly, the elastic curve shown in Fig. 10-6d is *concave up at every point.* In future work, definiteness regarding the direction of curvature will be essential. The ends of the beam are assumed to rest on immovable supports.

In a more general moment diagram, Fig. 10-7c, zones of positive and negative moment occur. Corresponding to the zones of negative moment, a *definite* curvature of the elastic curve that is concave down takes place, Fig. 10-7e. On the other hand, for the zone *HJ* where the positive moment occurs, the concavity of the elastic curve is upward. Where curves join, as at *H* and *J*, there are lines which are **tangent** to the two joining curves, since the beam is physically *continuous*. Also note that the free end FG of the beam is tangent to the elastic curve at F. There is no curvature in FG, since the moment is zero in that segment of the beam.

The point of transition on the elastic curve into reverse curvature is called the ***point of inflection*** or contraflexure. At this point the moment changes its sign, and the beam is not called upon to resist any moment. This fact often makes these points a desirable place for a field connection of large members, and their location is calculated. A procedure for determining points of inflection will be illustrated in Example 10-5, which follows a summary of the above discussion.

The important process of establishing the elastic curve qualitatively may be summarized as follows:

1. Draw a bending-moment diagram.

2. Sketch the elastic curve, corresponding to the signs of moments without reference to the supports, on the moment diagram.

3. If the beam is on two supports, "bodily lift" the curve so drawn and "set it" on the supports, and, if it is a cantilever, the end of the curve is tangent to the built-in end.

Example 10-5. Find the location of the inflection points for the beam analyzed in Example 10-2, Fig. 10-7a.

Solution: From definition, an inflection point corresponds to a point on a beam where the bending moment is zero. Hence, an inflection point may be located by setting up an algebraic expression for the moment in a beam for the segment where such a point is anticipated, and solving this relation equated to zero. By measuring x from the end C of the beam, Fig. 10-7e, the bending moment for the segment AD of the beam is $M = -\frac{1}{2}(15)(2)(x - 5) + (27.5)(x - 15)$. By simplifying and setting this expression equal to zero, a solution for x is obtained.

$$M = 12.5x - 337.5 = 0 \qquad x = 27 \text{ ft}$$

Therefore, the inflection point occurring in the segment AD of the beam is $27 - 15 = 12$ ft from the support A.

Similarly, by writing an algebraic expression for the bending moment for the segment DB and setting it equal to zero, the location of the inflection point J is found.

$$M = -\frac{1}{2}(15)(2)(x - 5) + 27.5(x - 15) - 40(x - 30) = 0$$

whence $x = 31.36$ ft, hence the distance $AJ = 16.36$ ft.

Often a more convenient method for finding the inflection points consists of utilizing the known relations between the shear and moment diagrams. Thus, since the moment at A is -150 kip-ft, the point of zero moment occurs when the positive portion of the shear-diagram area from A to H equals this moment, i.e., $-150 + 12.5x_1 = 0$. Hence the distance $AH = 150/12.5 = 12$ ft as before.

Similarly, beginning with a known positive moment of $+37.5$ kip-ft at D, the second inflection point is known to occur when a portion of the negative shear-diagram area between D and J reduces this value to zero. Hence, the distance $DJ = 37.5/27.5 = 1.36$ ft, or the distance $AJ = 15 + 1.36 = 16.36$ ft, Fig. 10-7e, as before.

10-9. Design of Prismatic Beams. Besides loading conditions, the design of beams is based upon the strength properties in flexure and shear of the particular material used. Various authorities prescribe the allow-

able stresses used in design.   However, even for the same material and
the same use, the allowable stresses differ.   For example, while the New
York Building Code specifies a maximum value of 12,000 psi for shearing
stress in beams, the AISC Code specifies 13,000 psi.   In most cases the
designer must follow codes depending on the location of the installation.
As was noted in Art. 10-4, the allowable stresses in bending and shear are
different.   The allowable shearing stresses are lower than bending stresses,
as such is the physical property of materials.

The design of a prismatic member is controlled by the maximum stresses
developed at the *critical sections*.   One critical section occurs where the
bending moment is a maximum, the other where the shear is a maximum.
To determine the location of these critical sections, shear and moment
diagrams are very useful.*   The values of maximum moment and shear
may be easily found from these diagrams.   *The absolute† maximum value
of the moment is used in design*, i.e., whether positive or negative.   Likewise, the absolute maximum shear ordinate is the significant ordinate.
For example, consider a simple beam with a concentrated load, as shown
in Fig. 10-13.   The shear diagram, neglecting the weight of the beam, is

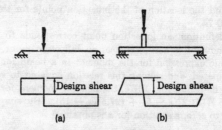

(a)   (b)

Fig. 10-13.   Determination of a design ordinate from the shear diagram.

shown in Fig. 10-13a as it is ordinarily constructed by assuming the applied
force concentrated at a point.   The shear diagram as it more nearly exists
is shown in Fig. 10-13b.   Here an allowance is made for the width of the
applied force and reactions, assuming them to be uniformly distributed.
The assumption of concentrated forces merely straightens the oblique
shear lines.   In either case, the design shear value is the greater of the
positive or negative ordinates and is not the full value of the applied
force.

After the critical values of moment and shear are determined, and the
allowable stresses are selected, the beam is usually first designed to resist a

* Construction of complete diagrams may be abandoned with experience.   After
reactions are computed, and a section where $V = 0$ or changes sign is determined, the
maximum moment corresponding to this section may be found by using the method of
sections.   For simple loadings, various handbooks give formulas for the maximum
shear and moment.

† This is not always true for materials which have different properties in tension and
compression.   See footnote, p. 238.

given moment using Eqs. 5-5 or 5-1 ($\sigma_{max} = M/Z$ or $\sigma_{max} = Mc/I$). Then the beam is *checked* for shearing stress. As most beams are governed by flexural stresses, this procedure is convenient. However, in some cases, particularly in timber (and concrete) design, the shearing stress frequently controls the dimensions of the cross-section.

The method used in computing the shearing stress depends on the type of beam cross-section. For rectangular sections, the maximum shearing stress is 1.5 times the average stress, Eq. 6-4. For wide flange and *I*-beams, the total allowable vertical shear is taken as the area of the *web* multiplied by an allowable shearing stress, Eq. 6-5. For other cases, Eq. 6-3, $\tau = VQ/(It)$, is used.

Usually there are several types or sizes of commercially available members that may be used for a given beam. Unless specific size limitations are placed on the beam, the lightest member is used for economy. The procedure of selecting a member is a trial-and-error process.

It should also be noted that some beams must be selected on the basis of allowable deflections. This topic will be treated in the next chapter.

Example 10-6. Select a Douglas fir beam of rectangular cross-section to carry two concentrated forces as shown in Fig. 10-14a. The allowable stress in bending is 1,200 psi, in shear 100 psi, and in bearing perpendicular to the grain of the wood 200 psi.

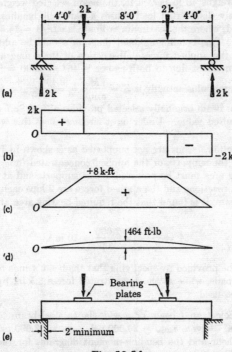

Fig. 10-14.

SOLUTION: Shear and moment diagrams for the applied forces are prepared first and are shown respectively in Figs. 10-14b and c. From Fig. 10-14c it is seen that M_{max} = 8 kip-ft.

From Eq. 5-5, $Z = \dfrac{M}{\sigma_{allow}} = \dfrac{8,000(12)}{1,200} = 80$ in.³

By *arbitrarily assuming* that the depth h of the beam is to be two times greater than its width b, from Eq. 5-6,

$$Z = \frac{bh^2}{6} = \frac{h^3}{12} = 80, \text{ hence } h = 9.86 \text{ in. and } b = 4.93 \text{ in.}$$

From Table 10 in the Appendix, a *surfaced* 6 in. by 10 in. beam is seen to fulfil this requirement. The actual size of this beam is 5½ in. by 9½ in., and its section modulus is $Z = 82.7$ in.³ For this beam, from Eq. 6-4,

$$\tau_{max} = \frac{3V}{2A} = \frac{3(2,000)}{2(5.5)(9.5)} = 57.3 \text{ psi}$$

This stress is within the allowable limit. Hence the beam is satisfactory.

Note that other proportions of the beam can be used, and a more direct method of design is to find a beam of size corresponding to the wanted section modulus directly from Table 10.

The above analysis was made without regard for the beam's own weight, which initially was unknown. (Experienced designers usually make an allowance for the weight of the beam at the outset.) However, this may be accounted for now. Assuming that wood weighs 40 lb per cu ft, the beam selected weighs 14.5 lb per lineal foot. This uniformly distributed load causes a parabolic bending-moment diagram, shown in Fig. 10-14d, where the maximum ordinate is $wL^2/8 = 14.5(16)^2/8 = 464$ ft-lb (see Example 4-6). This bending-moment diagram should be added to the moment diagram caused by the applied forces. Inspection of these diagrams shows that the maximum bending moment due to both causes is $464 + 8,000 = 8,464$ ft-lb. Hence the required section modulus actually is $Z = \dfrac{M}{\sigma_{allow}} = \dfrac{8,464(12)}{1,200} = 84.64$ in.³ The surfaced 6 in. by 10 in. beam originally selected provides a Z of 82.7 in.³, which is about 2½% below the required value. Under most circumstances this would be considered satisfactory.

In actual construction, beams are not supported as is shown in Fig. 10-14a. Wood may be crushed by the supports or the applied concentrated forces. For this reason an adequate bearing area must be provided at the supports and at the applied forces. Assuming that both reactions and the applied forces are 2 kips each, i.e., by neglecting the weight of the beam, it is found that the required bearing area at each concentrated force, by Eq. 1-1, is

$$A = \frac{P}{\sigma_{allow}} = \frac{2,000}{200} = 10 \text{ in.}^2$$

These areas may be provided by specifying that the beam's ends rest on at least 2 in. by 5.5 in. (11 in.²) pads, while at the concentrated forces 3.5 in. by 3.5 in. (12.2 in.²) steel washers can be used.

Example 10-7. Select an I-beam or a wide-flange steel beam to support the load shown in Fig. 10-15a. Given, $\sigma_{allow} = 20,000$ psi, $\tau_{allow} = 13,000$ psi.

SOLUTION: The shear and the bending-moment diagrams for the loaded beam are shown in Figs. 10-15b and c, respectively. The maximum moment is 23.4 kip-ft.

From Eq. 5-5, $Z = \dfrac{(23.4)12}{20} = 13.9$ in.^{3}

Examination of Tables 3 and 4 in the Appendix shows that this requirement for the section modulus is met by an 8 in. *I*-beam weighing 18.4 lb per ft ($Z = 14.2$ in.^{3}), and by an 8 in. wide-flange section weighing 17 lb per ft ($Z = 14.1$ in.^{3}). For economy the lighter 8 WF 17 section will be used. The weight of this beam is very small in comparison with the applied load and so is neglected.

From Fig. 10-15b, $V_{max} = 8.84$ kips. Hence,

From Eq. 6-5, $(\tau_{max})_{approx} = \dfrac{V}{A_{web}} = \dfrac{8,840}{(0.23)8}$
$$= 4,800 \text{ psi.}$$

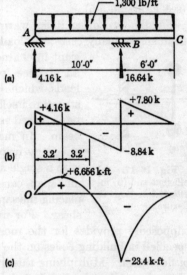

Fig. 10-15.

This stress is within the allowable value, and the beam selected is satisfactory.

At the supports or concentrated loads, *I*- and wide-flange beams should be checked for crippling of the webs. This phenomenon is illustrated at the bottom of Fig. 10-16a. Crippling of the webs is more critical for members with thin webs than direct bearing of the flanges, which may be investigated as in the preceding problem. To preclude crippling, a design rule is specified by the AISC. It states that the direct stress on area, $(a + k)t$ at the ends or $(a_1 + 2k)t$ at the interior points, must not exceed 24 ksi. In these expressions, a and a_1 are the respective lengths of bearing of the applied forces at exterior or interior portions of a beam, Fig. 10-16b, t is the thickness of the web, and k is the distance from the outer face of the flange to the toe of the web fillet. The values of k and t are tabulated in manufacturers' catalogues.

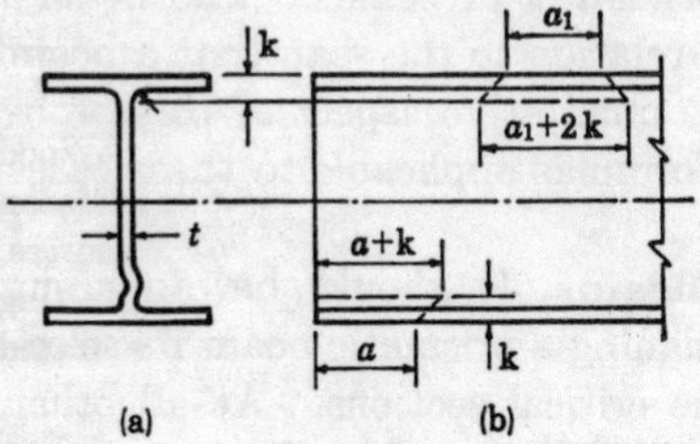

For the above problem the *minimum* widths of the supports, according to the above rule, are as follows:

At support A: $24(a + k)t = 4.16$ or
$24(a + \tfrac{5}{8})(0.23) = 4.16$ $a = 0.13$ in.

At support B: $24(a_1 + 2k)t = 16.64$ or
$24(a_1 + \tfrac{5}{4})(0.23) = 16.64$ $a_1 = 1.76$ in.

Fig. 10-16.

In Chapter 14, another type of connection for beams to other members by small auxiliary angles is fully treated.

The preceding two examples illustrate the design of beams whose cross-sections have two axes of symmetry. In both cases the bending moments controlled the design, and, since this is usually true, it is significant to note which members are efficient in flexure. A concentration of as much material as possible away from the neutral axis results in the best sections for resisting flexure, Fig. 10-17a. Material concentrated near the outside fibers works at a high stress. For this reason, I-type sections, which approximate this requirement, are widely used in practice.

The above statements apply for materials which have nearly equal properties in tension and compression. If this is not the case, a deliberate shift of the neutral axis from the mid-height position is desirable. This accounts for the wide use of T and channel sections for cast-iron beams (see Example 5-5).

Finally, two other items warrant particular attention in the design of beams. In many cases, the loads for which a beam is designed are transient in character. They may be placed on the beam all at once, piecemeal, or in *different locations*. The loads, which are not a part of the "dead weight" of the structure itself, are called **live loads**. Live loads must be so placed as to cause the highest possible stresses in a beam. In many cases the placement may be determined by inspection. For example, in a simple beam with a single moving load, the placement of the load at mid-span causes the largest bending moment, while placing the same load at the support causes the greatest shear. For most building work, the live load, which supposedly provides for the most severe expected loading condition, is specified in building codes on the basis of so many pounds per square foot of floor area. Multiplying this live load by the spacing of parallel beams gives the **uniformly distributed live load** per unit length of the beam. For design purposes, this load is added to the dead weight of construction. Situations where the applied force is delivered to a beam with a shock or impacts are discussed in Chapter 15.

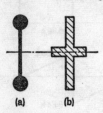

(a)　　(b)

Fig. 10-17. (a) efficient and (b) inefficient sections in flexure.

The second item pertains to *lateral instability* of beams. The beam's flanges, if not held, may be so narrow in relation to the span that a beam may buckle sideways and collapse. The qualitative aspect of this problem was discussed in Art. 5-2. Special formulas applicable to these cases are given in Art. 13-11.

*10-10. Design of Nonprismatic Beams. It should be apparent from the preceding discussion that in designing a prismatic beam its selection is based only on the stresses at the critical sections. At all other sections through the beam the stresses will be below the allowable level. Therefore the potential capacity of a given material is not fully utilized. This situation may be improved by designing a beam of variable cross-section, i.e., by making the beam nonprismatic. Since flexural stresses control the design of most beams, as has been shown, the cross-sections may everywhere be made just strong enough to resist the corresponding moment. Such beams are called *beams of constant strength*. Shear governs the design at sections through these beams where the bending moment is small.

Example 10-8. Design a cantilever of constant strength for resisting a concentrated force applied at the end. Neglect the beam's own weight.

SOLUTION: A cantilever with a concentrated force applied at the end is shown in Fig. 10-18a; the corresponding moment diagram is plotted in Fig. 10-18b. Basing the design on the bending moment, the required section modulus at an arbitrary section is given by Eq. 5-5:

$$Z = \frac{M}{\sigma_{\text{allow}}} = \frac{Px}{\sigma_{\text{allow}}}$$

A great many cross-sectional areas satisfy this requirement; so first, it will be assumed that the beam will be of rectangular cross-section and of *constant height h*. The section modulus for this beam is given by Eq. 5-6 as $bh^2/6 = Z$, hence

$$\frac{bh^2}{6} = \frac{Px}{\sigma_{\text{allow}}} \quad \text{or}$$

$$b = \left[\frac{6P}{h^2\sigma_{\text{allow}}}\right] x = \frac{b_0}{L} x$$

where the bracketed expression is a constant and is set equal to b_0/L, so that when $x = L$ the width is b_0. A beam of constant strength with a constant depth in a plan view looks like the wedge* shown in Fig. 10-18c. Near the free end this wedge must be modified to be of adequate strength to resist the shearing force $V = P$.

If the width or breadth b of the beam is constant,

$$\frac{bh^2}{6} = \frac{Px}{\sigma_{\text{allow}}} \quad \text{or} \quad h = \sqrt{\frac{6Px}{b\sigma_{\text{allow}}}} = h_0\sqrt{\frac{x}{L}}$$

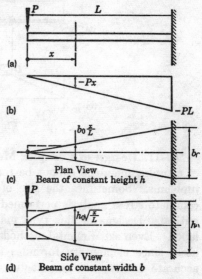

(a)

(b)

(c) Plan View
Beam of constant height h

(d) Side View
Beam of constant width b

Fig. 10-18.

This expression indicates that a cantilever of constant width loaded at the end is also of constant strength, if its height varies parabolically from the free end, Fig. 10-18d.

Beams of constant strength are used in leaf springs and in many machine parts which are cast or forged. In structural work an approximation to a beam of constant strength is frequently made. For example, the moment diagram for the beam loaded as shown in Fig. 10-19a is given by the lines AB and BC in Fig. 10-19b. By selecting a beam of flexural capacity equal only to M_1, the middle portion of the beam is overstressed. However, cover plates may be provided near the middle of the beam to boost the flexural capacity of the composite beam to the required value of the maximum moment. For the case shown, the cover plates must extend

---

* Since this beam is not of constant cross-sectional area, the use of the elementary flexure formula is not entirely correct. When the angle included by the sides of the wedge is small, little error is involved. As this angle becomes large, the error may be considerable. An exact solution shows that when the total included angle is 40° the solution is in error by nearly 10%.

at least over the length DE of the beam, and in practice they are made somewhat longer.

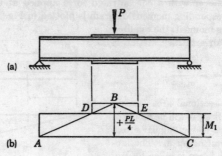

Fig. 10-19.

*10-11. Design of Complex Members. In many instances the design of complex members cannot be routinized as was done in the preceding problems. Sometimes the size of a member must be *assumed* and a complete stress analysis performed at sections where the stresses appear critical. Designs of this type may require several revisions and much labor. Even experimental methods of stress analysis must be occasionally used, since elementary formulas may not be sufficiently accurate. In accurate analyses of manufactured machine parts, the failure theories discussed in Chapter 9 are frequently used.

As a last example in this chapter, a transmission shaft problem will be analyzed. A direct analytical procedure is possible in this problem, which is of great importance in the design of power equipment.

Example 10-9. Select the size of a solid steel shaft to drive the two sprockets shown in Fig. 10-20a. These sprockets drive $1\frac{1}{4}$ in. pitch roller chains[*] as shown in Figs. 10-20b and c. Pitch diameters of the sprockets shown in the figures are from a manufacturer's catalogue. A 20 Hp speed-reducer unit is coupled directly to the shaft and drives it at 63 rpm. At each sprocket 10 Hp is taken off. Assume the maximum shear theory of failure, and let $\tau_{allow} = 6{,}000$ psi.

SOLUTION: According to Eq. 3-6 the torque delivered to the shaft segment CD is

$$T = 63{,}000 \frac{\text{Hp}}{N} = \frac{(63{,}000)20}{63} = 20{,}000 \text{ in.-lb.}$$ Hence the torques T_1 and T_2 delivered

to the sprockets are $T/2 = 10{,}000$ in.-lb *each*. Since the chains are arranged as shown in Figs. 10-20b and c, the pull in the chain at sprocket B is $P_1 = \dfrac{T_1}{D_1/2} = \dfrac{10{,}000}{10.632/2} =$

1,880 lb. Similarly, $P_2 = \dfrac{10{,}000}{7.313/2} = 2{,}730$ lb. The pull P_1 on the chain *is equivalent* to a torque T_1 and a vertical force at B as shown in Fig. 10-20d. At C the force P_2 acts horizontally and exerts a torque T_2. A complete free-body diagram for the shaft AD is shown in Fig. 10-20d.

It is seen from the free-body diagram of the shaft that this shaft is simultaneously subjected to bending and torque. These effects on the member are best studied with the aid of appropriate diagrams, which are shown in Figs. 10-20e, f, and g. Next,

[*] Similar sprockets and roller chains are commonly used on bicycles.

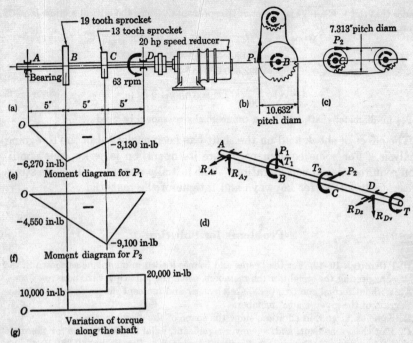

Fig. 10-20.

note that although bending takes place in two planes, a *vectorial resultant of the moments* may be used in the flexure formula, since the beam has a circular cross-section.

Bearing the last statement in mind, it will be seen that the general Eq. 8-6, which gives the principal shearing stress, at the surface of the shaft, reduces in this problem of bending and torsion to

$$\tau_{max} = \sqrt{\left(\frac{\sigma_{bending}}{2}\right)^2 + \tau_{torsion}^2}$$

or

$$\tau_{max} = \sqrt{\left(\frac{Mc}{2I}\right)^2 + \left(\frac{Tc}{J}\right)^2}$$

However, since for a circular cross-section, $J = 2I$ (Eq. 5-4), $J = \frac{\pi d^4}{32}$ (Eq. 3-2), and $c = d/2$, the last expression simplifies to

$$\tau_{max} = \frac{16}{\pi d^3} \sqrt{M^2 + T^2}$$

Whence, by assigning the allowable shearing stress to τ_{max}, a design formula, based on the maximum shear theory* of failure, for a shaft subjected to bending and torsion is

$$d = \sqrt[3]{\frac{16}{\pi \tau_{allow}} \sqrt{M^2 + T^2}} \qquad (10\text{-}4)$$

This formula may be used to select the diameter of a shaft simultaneously subjected to bending and torque. In the problem investigated, a few trials should convince the

---

* See Problem 10-80 for the formula based on the maximum stress theory of failure.

reader that the $\sqrt{M^2 + T^2}$ is largest at the sprocket C, hence the critical section is at C. Thus,

$$M^2 + T^2 = (M_{vert})^2 + (M_{horiz})^2 + T^2$$
$$= (3,130)^2 + (9,100)^2 + (20,000)^2$$
$$= 492,600,000 \text{ in.}^2\text{-lb}^2$$

$$d = \sqrt[3]{\frac{16}{6,000\pi} \sqrt{492,600,000}} = 2.68 \text{ in.}$$

A $2\frac{11}{16}$ in. diameter shaft, which is a commercial size, should be used.

The effect of shock load on the shaft has been neglected in the foregoing analysis. For some equipment, where its operation is jerky, this condition requires special consideration. The initially assumed allowable stress presumably allows for keyways and fatigue of the material.

Problems for Solution

10-1 through 10-49. For the beams and frames loaded in one plane as shown in the figures, neglecting the weight of the members, solve the following variations:

A. Without formal computations, sketch shear and moment diagrams directly below a diagram of the given loaded member.

B. Same as **A**, and, in addition, show the shape of the elastic curve.

C. Plot shear, moment, and, wherever significant, axial force diagrams for the main horizontal members. Determine all critical ordinates. For Probs. 10-36, 10-47, 10-48, and 10-49 these diagrams must be made for the entire structure.

D. Same as **C**, and, in addition, determine the points of inflection and show the shape of the elastic curve.

E. Same as **C**, and, in addition, select the proper size beams of constant cross-sectional dimensions. The type of beam to be selected is identified in the upper left-hand corner of each figure as:

$\textcircled{W}$ for wooden beams, for which the allowable bending (or normal) and shearing stresses are 1,200 psi and 100 psi, respectively;

$\textcircled{I}$ for steel I-beams, and $\textcircled{WF}$ for steel wide-flange beams, for both of which the allowable bending and shearing stresses are 20,000 psi and 13,000 psi, respectively;

$\textcircled{\diagup}$ for solid round shafts, for which the allowable bending and shearing stresses are 12,500 psi and 8,000 psi, respectively.

Assume all beams are laterally braced. Neglect stress-concentrations and the effect of small holes on strength. *Ans.* All shear and moment diagrams must close. The largest moment is given in parentheses by the figures in the units of the problem.

10-50.* Plot shear, moment, and axial force diagrams for one stairway beam of Prob. 7-13. Then, assuming that the maximum bending moment controls the design (does it exactly?), select the required size of channel. Allow 16 ksi in flexure, and 12 ksi in shear. *Ans.* 4,900 ft-lb, 6 ⌐ 8.2.

10-51. Plot shear, moment, and axial force diagrams for the jib-crane loaded as shown in the figure. Neglect the weight of the beam. *Ans.* 128.6 k-in.

10-52. Select the size of channels, separated by spacers, required for the arrangement shown in the figure. Allow 18 ksi for normal stress, and 10 ksi for shearing stress.

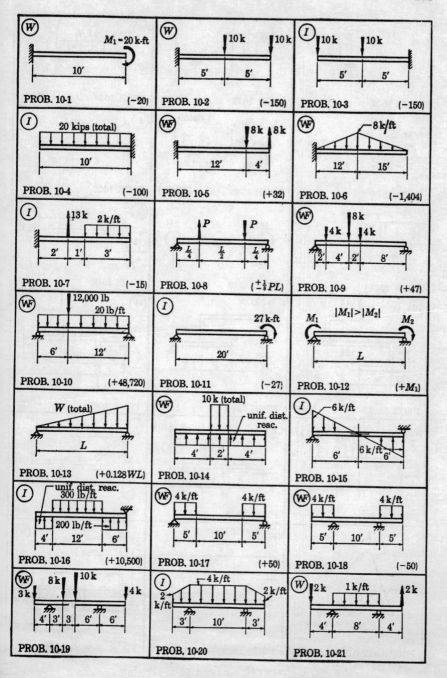

PROB. 10-1   (−20)

PROB. 10-2   (−150)

PROB. 10-3   (−150)

PROB. 10-4   (−100)

PROB. 10-5   (+32)

PROB. 10-6   (−1,404)

PROB. 10-7   (−15)

PROB. 10-8 $\left(\pm\tfrac{1}{8}PL\right)$

PROB. 10-9   (+47)

PROB. 10-10   (+48,720)

PROB. 10-11   (−27)

PROB. 10-12   (+M_1)

PROB. 10-13   (+0.128WL)

PROB. 10-14

PROB. 10-15

PROB. 10-16   (+10,500)

PROB. 10-17   (+50)

PROB. 10-18   (−50)

PROB. 10-19

PROB. 10-20

PROB. 10-21

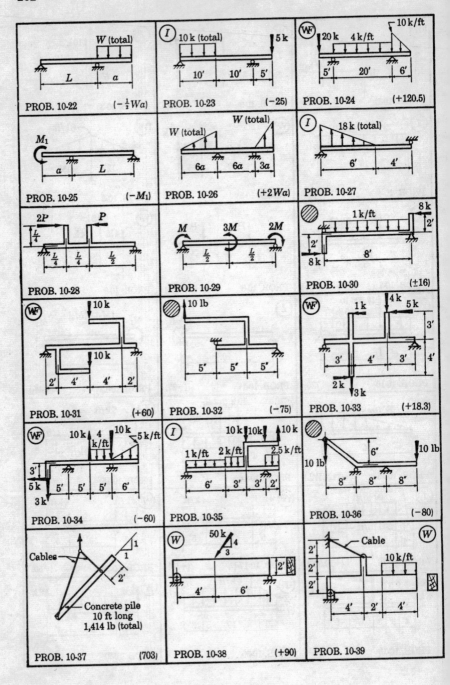

PROB. 10-22 $(-\frac{1}{2}Wa)$

PROB. 10-23 (-25)

PROB. 10-24 $(+120.5)$

PROB. 10-25 $(-M_1)$

PROB. 10-26 $(+2Wa)$

PROB. 10-27

PROB. 10-28

PROB. 10-29

PROB. 10-30 (±16)

PROB. 10-31 $(+60)$

PROB. 10-32 (-75)

PROB. 10-33 $(+18.3)$

PROB. 10-34 (-60)

PROB. 10-35

PROB. 10-36 (-80)

PROB. 10-37 (703)

PROB. 10-38 $(+90)$

PROB. 10-39

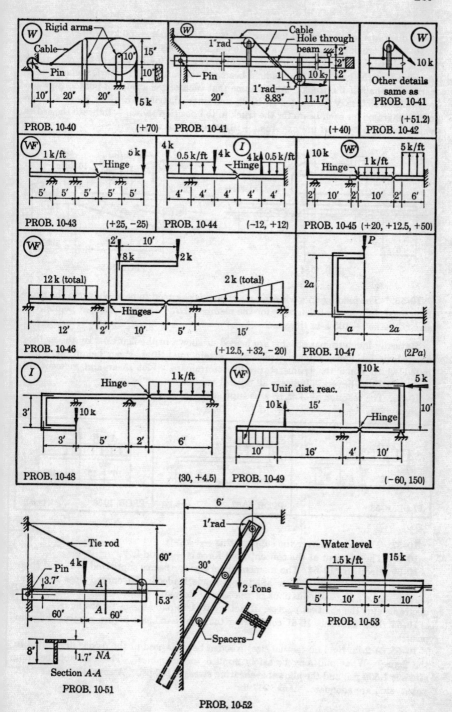

PROB. 10-40 (+70)

PROB. 10-41 (+40)

PROB. 10-42 (+51.2)

PROB. 10-43 (+25, −25)

PROB. 10-44 (−12, +12)

PROB. 10-45 (+20, +12.5, +50)

PROB. 10-46 (+12.5, +32, −20)

PROB. 10-47 (2Pa)

PROB. 10-48 (30, +4.5)

PROB. 10-49 (−60, 150)

PROB. 10-51

Section A-A

PROB. 10-52

PROB. 10-53

10-53. A small narrow barge is loaded as shown in the figure. Plot shear and moment diagrams for the applied loading. *Ans.* -10^k (max), $+ 50$ k-ft (max).

10-54. A truck is standing on a raft; it weighs $7\frac{1}{2}$ tons loaded. Assume that 0.1 of the total load is carried by each of the front wheels, and 0.4 by each of the rear wheels. Assume that the two main longitudinal beams of the raft are 6 ft apart, i.e., each beam carries one-half of the truck. Also assume that each of the groups of pontoons provide reactions which may be treated as being uniformly distributed. Plot shear and moment diagrams for each beam for the truck in the position shown. Indicate the critical values using foot-pound units. *Ans.* $+18,000$ ft-lb (max).

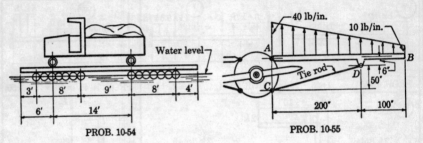

PROB. 10-54   PROB. 10-55

10-55. * The loading on a wing of an airplane is assumed to be as shown in the figure. Plot shear and moment diagrams for the member AB. Assume hinges at points A, C, and D. *Ans.* -165 k-in (max).

Statically indeterminate beams are loaded as shown in the figures. By the methods of analysis for indeterminate structures, certain quantities, given below, were computed which make the beams statically determinate. Plot shear and moment diagrams for these beams. Indicate all critical values.

10-56. The reaction at A is 13 kips (upward).

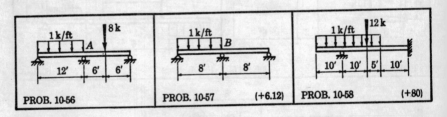

PROB. 10-56   PROB. 10-57   (+6.12)   PROB. 10-58   (+80)

10-57. The moment over the support B is -4 kip-ft.

10-58. The moment at the concentrated force is $+80$ kip-ft.

10-59 through *10-64. The moment diagrams for beams supported at A and B are as shown in the figures. How are these beams loaded? All curved lines represent parabolas, i.e., plots of equations of the second degree. (*Hint:* construction of shear diagrams aids the solution.) *Ans.* Reaction at A in parentheses by the figure.

10-65. Rework Prob. 10-61 considering the right-hand side of the moment diagram positive.

10-66. A 2 in. by 4 in. (actual size) wooden beam is used in the device illustrated in the figure. What pull may be safely applied to the cables? The allowable bending stress is 1,500 psi, and the allowable shearing stress is 100 psi. Assume that the cables, yokes, etc., are adequate. *Ans.* 267 lb.

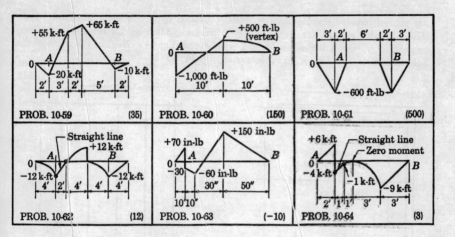

PROB. 10-59   (35)   PROB. 10-60   (150)   PROB. 10-61   (500)

PROB. 10-62   (12)   PROB. 10-63   (−10)   PROB. 10-64   (3)

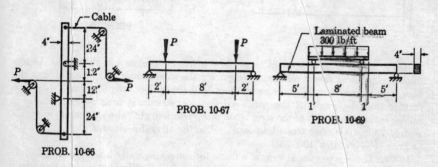

PROB. 10-66

PROB. 10-67

PROB. 10-69

10-67. A 10 in. by 12 in. (actual size) wooden beam is loaded as shown in the figure. Neglecting the weight of the beam, determine the magnitude of the allowable forces P if $\sigma_{allow} = 1,500$ psi and $\tau_{allow} = 120$ psi. *Ans.* 9.6 kips.

10-68. A full-sized 4 in. by 6 in. wooden beam (6 in. high) acts as a simple beam. What may the span L be, and what uniformly distributed load w (including the beam's own weight) may this beam support if the allowable stresses of $\sigma = 1,200$ psi and $\tau = 75$ psi are to be reached simultaneously? *Ans.* 8 ft, 300 lb/ft.

10-69. Laminated beams made up from full-sized 1 in. by 4 in. boards are to be loaded as shown in the figure. If the allowable bending stress in the wood is 1,800 psi, and the shearing strength at the glued joints is 50 psi, determine: (a) the number of laminates required to carry the bending moment; (b) the number of laminates required to carry the shear force. The number of laminates selected in each case must be a multiple of two. Neglect the weight of the beam. *Ans.* (a) 10 boards, (b) 12 boards.

10-70. A portion of the floor framing plan for an office building is shown in the figure. Wooden joists spanning 12 ft are spaced 16 in. apart and support a wooden floor above and a plastered ceiling below. Assume that the floor may be loaded by the occupants everywhere by as much as 75 lb/ft² of floor area (live load). Assume further that floor, joists, and ceiling weigh 25 lb/ft² of the floor area (dead load). (a) Determine the depth required for standard commercial joists *nominally* 2 in. thick. For wood the allowable bending stress is 1,200 psi and the shearing stress is 100 psi. (b) Select the size required for the steel beam "A." Since the joists delivering the load to this beam are spaced closely, assume that the beam is loaded by a uniformly distributed load. The allowable stresses for steel are 20,000 psi and 13,000 psi for bending and shear, respectively. Use a WF or an *I*-beam, whichever is lighter. Neglect the width of the column. *Ans.* (a) 2 in. × 10 in. (nominal), (b) 14 WF 30.

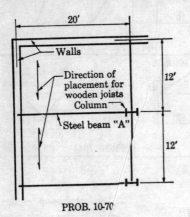

PROB. 10-70

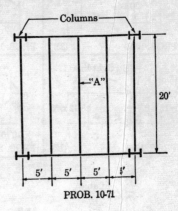

PROB. 10-71

10-71. A bay of an apartment house floor is framed as shown in the figure. Determine the required size of minimum weight for the steel beam "A". Assume that the floor may be loaded everywhere as much as 75 lb/ft² of floor area (live load). Assume further that the weight of the hardwood flooring, structural concrete slab, plastered ceiling below, the weight of the steel beam being selected, etc., also amounts to approximately 75 lb/ft² of floor area (dead load). Use the allowable stresses given in part (b) of Prob. 10-70. *Ans.* 10 *I* 25.4.

10-72. The cross-sectional view of a flume for conveying water is shown in the figure. The vertical members "B" are in pairs and are spaced longitudinally along the flume 4 ft apart. The side planking "A" therefore spans this distance. The wood used is Douglas fir, which has an allowable stress in bending of 1,600 psi and in shear parallel to the grain of 100 psi. (a) Determine the thickness required for the planking "A" (assume planking to be the same thickness throughout). (b) Determine the required dimensions for vertical member "B." Assume pin connected ends top and bottom, and neglect the effect of the axial force. *Ans.* (a) 2.05 in., (b) 8 in. × 14 in. nominal

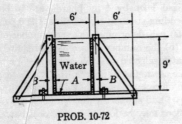

PROB. 10-72

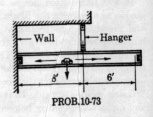

PROB. 10-73

10-73. Determine the size required for an *I*-beam rail of an overhead traveling crane of 4 ton capacity. The *I*-beam is to be attached to the wall at one end and hung from a bracket as shown in the figure. Assume pinned connection at the wall, and in computations neglect the weight of the beam. Let the allowable bending stress be 12 ksi and the allowable shearing stress be 7 ksi. *Ans.* 15 *I* 42.9.

10-74. What is the largest allowable load which may be placed at the center of a $4\frac{1}{2}$ ft simple span beam made of a 10 WF 49 section if the allowable bending stress is 24 ksi and the allowable shearing stress is 14 ksi? *Ans.* 95.2 kips.

10-75. A four-wheel car running on rails is to be used in light industrial service. When loaded this car will weigh a total of 4 tons. If the bearings are located with respect to the rails as shown in the figure, what size round axle should be used? Assume the allowable bending stress at 10 ksi, and the allowable shearing stress at 6 ksi.

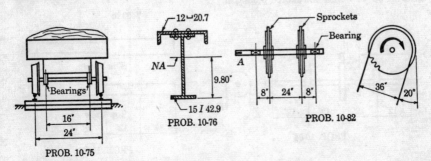

PROB. 10-75   PROB. 10-76   PROB. 10-82

10-76. A beam having the cross-sectional dimensions shown in the figure spans 40 ft. If the allowable bending stress is 11,111 psi in compression and 18,000 psi in tension, what concentrated downward force may be placed at the center of a 40 ft span? Consider the weight of the beam. $I_{NA} = 649.7$ in.[4] *Ans.* 8,650 lb.

10-77. Design a cantilever beam of constant strength for resisting a uniformly distributed load. Assume that the width of the beam is constant.

10-78. A 10 in.-25.4 lb I-beam is coverplated with two $\frac{1}{2}$ in. by 6 in. plates as shown in Fig. 10-19a (I of the composite section is 287.1 in.[4]), and it spans 20 ft. (a) What concentrated force may be applied at the center of the span if the allowable stress in bending is 16,000 psi? (b) For the above load, where are the theoretical points beyond which the cover plates need not extend? Neglect the weight of the beam, and assume that the beam is braced laterally. *Ans.* (a) 13.9 kips. (b) 4.67 ft from ends.

10-79. The middle half of a simple beam of total length of 10 ft is 6 in. wide by 12 in. deep; the end quarters are 6 in. wide by 8 in. deep. Determine the safe, uniformly distributed load this beam may carry if the allowable bending stress is 1,500 psi and the allowable shearing stress is 150 psi. Neglect stress concentrations at the change in cross-section.

10-80. (a) Show that the larger principal stress for a circular shaft simultaneously subjected to a torque and a bending moment is $\sigma_1 = \frac{c}{J}(M + \sqrt{M^2 + T^2})$.

(b) Show that the design formula for shafts, on the basis of the maximum stress theory, is $d = \sqrt[3]{\dfrac{16}{\pi\sigma_{allow}}(M + \sqrt{M^2 + T^2})}$.

10-81. At a critical section a solid circular shaft transmits a torque of 300 kip-in. and a bending moment of 80 kip-in. Determine the size of shaft required so that the maximum (principal) shearing stress would not exceed 6,000 psi.

10-82. The head shaft of an inclined bucket elevator is arranged as shown in the figure. It is driven at A at 11 rpm and requires 60 Hp for steady operation. Assuming that one-half of the delivered horsepower is used at each sprocket, determine the size of shaft required so that the maximum (principal) shearing stress would not exceed 6,000 psi. The assigned stress allows for keyways.

10-83. Rework Example 10-9 by assuming that the unit driven by sprocket B is displaced to the right (Fig. 10-20b) so that the pull P_1 makes an angle of 30° with the vertical.

10-84. A shaft is fitted with pulleys as shown in the figure. The end bearings are self-aligning, i.e., they do not introduce moment into the shaft at the supports. Pulley B is the driving pulley. Pulleys A and C are the driven pulleys and take off 9,000 in.-lb and 3,000 in.-lb of torque, respectively. The resultant of the pulls at each pulley is 400 lb acting downward. Determine the size of shaft required so that the principal shearing stress would not exceed 6,000 psi.

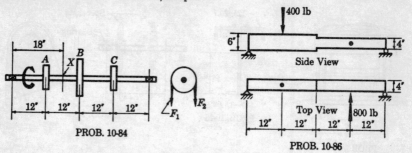

PROB. 10-84

Side View

Top View

PROB. 10-86

10-85. If the shaft in Prob. 10-84 is 2 in. in diameter, what is the magnitude and direction of the principal stresses at X? *Ans.* −13,200 psi, 2,500 psi, 23.5°.

10-86. Neglecting the weight of the beam and stress concentrations at the change in cross-section, find the largest bending stress for the beam loaded as shown in the figure.

10-87. A 10 in.-15.3 lb channel acts as a simply supported roof purlin on a span of 18 ft. Its web is inclined, as shown in the figure, since the top chord of the truss slopes. What uniformly distributed gravity load may be applied to this member if the allowable bending stress is 18,000 psi? Bending may take place around both principal axes of the cross-section; however, assume that the applied load causes no torsional stresses.

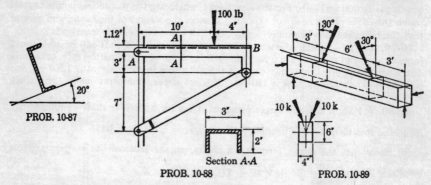

PROB. 10-87

Section A-A

PROB. 10-88

PROB. 10-89

10-88. Find the maximum stress in the machine part AB loaded as shown in the figure. The part AB is made from ⅛ in. hot-rolled steel plate. Assume that the joints are properly designed. Neglect the weight of the parts. The I at section AA around the neutral axis is 0.355 in.[4] *Ans.* 2,260 psi.

10-89. A 12 ft long beam is loaded as shown in the figure. The two applied forces act perpendicular to the long axis of the beam and are inclined 30° with the vertical. If these forces act through the centroid of the cross-sectional area, find the location and magnitude of the maximum bending stress. Neglect the weight of the beam. *Ans.* ±18,625 psi.

Chapter Eleven

DEFLECTION OF BEAMS

11-1. Introduction. Elastic deflection due to bending of statically determinate beams, neglecting shear deformation, will be discussed in this chapter. This will complete the investigation of statically determinate members for their *stiffness* characteristics.

Under the action of applied forces, the axis of a stable beam moves or deflects from its initial position. Accurate values of beam deflections are sought in many practical cases. For example, to avoid cracks in a plastered ceiling, the supporting beams cannot deflect excessively. In industry, some important machinery, as in a glass factory, must be supported on a floor system which is sufficiently rigid to prevent misalignment of different units. Likewise, deformation analysis of members is necessary in the study of vibrations of structures and machines. To solve statically indeterminate beam problems in the next chapter of this text, knowledge of the deflection of statically determinate beams will be needed.

After some basic equations are developed, two methods for obtaining deflections of straight beams will be discussed. The first method is useful if complete information on the deflection curve of a loaded beam is wanted. The second method is particularly convenient for applications where the deflection of a few points on a beam is sought. Only deflections caused by forces acting perpendicular to the axis of a beam are considered in this chapter.

11-2. Relations between Stress, Curvature, and Bending Moment. To develop the theory of deflection of beams, the geometry of the deformation of a beam's segment must be investigated. For this purpose, a segment of an initially straight beam deformed by positive bending moments is shown in Fig. 11-1a. For clarity, the deformation is *greatly exaggerated*. The smallness of the deflections considered may be judged from a rule used for many years in ordinary building construction. This rule limits the maximum deflection of any major beam to 1/360 of the span length. For the present, the segment's cross-section is assumed to have a vertical axis of symmetry, with bending taking place around a horizontal axis.

The initially straight axis becomes slightly curved in a bent beam. In a side view, this axis coincides with the neutral surface and is shown in

Fig. 11-1a by the line HJ and its extension. This line, extending over the whole length of a loaded beam, is called the **elastic curve**. This curve is always *continuous*. From the physical nature of the problem, no breaks or abrupt changes in the directions of the tangents to this curve are possible.

Next, it is recalled that according to the fundamental assumption used in establishing the flexure formula, plane sections initially perpendicular to the axis of the beam remain plane in a bent beam. Therefore, if lines AB and CD in Fig. 11-1a represent a side view of two adjoining planes in an unloaded beam, the inclined lines $A'B'$ and $C'D'$ correspond respectively to the same planes in a loaded beam.* The extensions of these lines inter-

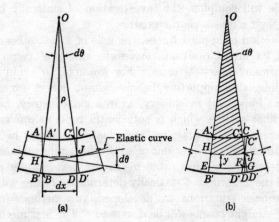

Fig. 11-1. Deformation of a segment of a beam in bending.

sect at a point O which is the center for the *radius of curvature* ρ for the infinitesimal arc HJ. The angle included between the lines $B'O$ and $D'O$, as well as *the angle between the tangents to the elastic curve* at points H and J, is $d\theta$, since these tangents are perpendicular to HO and JO, respectively.

To proceed further, Fig. 11-1a is redrawn in Fig. 11-1b. Here a line $C''D''$ is drawn parallel to the line $A'B'$ of the former figure. The *initial* lengths of all fibers parallel to HJ may now be measured between the lines $A'B'$ and $C''D''$, and they are all equal to the length of the unstressed fiber HJ. The deformations of the various fibers may be measured between the lines $C'D'$ and $C''D''$, since $D''D$ is equal to $B'B$ and CC'' to AA'. Thus the elongation of a fiber EF at a distance† y from the neutral axis is given by the distance FG, while its *strain* is $FG/EF = FG/HJ$,

---

* The very small movement of point J toward H caused by the difference in length of the arc HJ and the chord HJ is neglected.

† Radial and vertical distances are assumed to be the same for small deformations.

since $HJ = EF$. However, from the geometry of the figure, the sectors JFG and OHJ are similar, hence,

$$\frac{FG}{HJ} = \frac{JF}{OH}, \quad \text{or strain in } EF = \frac{y}{\rho}$$

since $JF = y$, and $OH = \rho$

Using Hooke's law, the strain of the fiber EF may be expressed as σ/E, where σ is the bending stress in the same fiber; thus

$$\frac{\sigma}{E} = \frac{y}{\rho} \quad \text{or} \quad \sigma = \frac{Ey}{\rho} \tag{11-1}$$

Equation 11-1 expresses the bending stress in a beam in terms of the radius of curvature ρ, location of the fiber from the neutral axis given by y, and the elastic modulus of the material E. The maximum stress occurs at the most extreme fiber, when $y = c$, i.e., $\sigma_{max} = Ec/\rho$.

Substituting into Eq. 11-1 the flexure formula, $\sigma = My/I$, for σ and simplifying, gives

$$\frac{1}{\rho} = \frac{M}{EI} \tag{11-2}$$

This equation relates the bending moment M at a given section of an *elastic beam* having a moment of inertia I around the neutral axis to the *curvature* $1/\rho$ of the elastic curve.

Note particularly that Hooke's law was used in establishing Eqs. 11-1 and 11-2. Therefore these equations are applicable only to situations where the material behaves elastically.* Likewise note that only the *deformations of a beam due to bending* were used in the derivation. Deformations due to shearing forces, which may exist at sections through a beam, were not considered. The latter deformations are usually very small (see Ex. 15-6). *These limitations of the theory will be implied in the remainder of this chapter.*

Example 11-1. A band saw for cutting metal, $\frac{1}{2}$ in. wide and 0.025 in. thick, runs over two pulleys of 16 in. diameter. What maximum bending stress is developed in the saw as it goes over a pulley? Let $E = 30 \times 10^6$ psi.

SOLUTION: As the saw goes over the pulley it conforms to the pulley's radius, i.e., $\rho \doteq 8$ in. Using Eq. 11-1 with $y = c$ gives the required solution.

$$\sigma_{max} = \frac{Ec}{\rho} = \frac{(30)10^6(0.0125)}{8} = 46,800 \text{ psi}$$

Note the high stress developed in this band saw, a fact necessitating superior materials for such applications.

11-3. Differential Equation of the Elastic Curve. In texts on analytic geometry, it is shown that the curvature of a line is defined as

* For a study of inelastic bending see Nadai, A. L., *Theory of Flow and Fracture of Solids*, vol. 1, p. 353. New York: McGraw-Hill, 1950.

$$\frac{1}{\rho} = \frac{\dfrac{d^2y}{dx^2}}{\left[1 + \left(\dfrac{dy}{dx}\right)^2\right]^{3/2}}$$

where x and y are the co-ordinates of a point on a curve. Substituting this expression for curvature into Eq. 11-2, $1/\rho = M/EI$, gives

$$\frac{\dfrac{d^2y}{dx^2}}{\left[1 + \left(\dfrac{dy}{dx}\right)^2\right]^{3/2}} = \frac{M}{EI} \qquad (11\text{-}3)$$

which is the exact differential equation of the elastic curve.

If (1) the x-axis is directed along the axis of the beam in the unloaded condition, (2) the right-hand terms of Eq. 11-3 are expressed as a function of x, and (3) the resulting equation is solved for y, then the equation of the elastic curve is obtained. Such an equation gives the deflection of a beam at any desired point. However, in general, the solutions of Eq. 11-3 are *very difficult to obtain*, and since the deflections tolerated in engineering structures are **very small,** the slope dy/dx of the elastic curve is also very small. Therefore the *square* of the slope is a negligible quantity in comparison with unity, and Eq. 11-3 simplifies to

$$\frac{d^2y}{dx^2} = \frac{M}{EI} \qquad (11\text{-}4)$$

which for the vast majority of applications is sufficiently accurate. Most of this chapter will be concerned with the methods of solution of this differential equation of the elastic curve* to obtain the deflections of beams.

In applying Eq. 11-4, beams will be considered in a horizontal position, with the x-axis directed along the axis of the unloaded beam, Fig. 11-2. Then, the deflected position of a point on the elastic curve of a beam is given by y. For a positive value of y, the deflection of a given point is up, and vice versa. At any given point, the first derivative of y with respect to x,

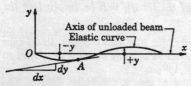

Fig. 11-2. The usual relation of the co-ordinate axes to the elastic curve.

dy/dx, is the slope θ of the elastic curve at the same point. The second derivative d^2y/dx^2 is equal to $M/(EI)$ and represents the rate of change of the slope of the elastic curve. A positive change in the slope occurs if positive bending moments act on an element of the beam to deform it

---

* The equation of the elastic curve was formulated by James Bernoulli, a Swiss mathematician, in 1694. Leonhard Euler (1707-1783) greatly extended its applications.

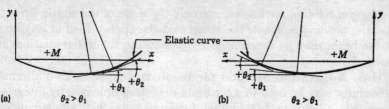

Fig. 11-3. Positive bending moments causing a positive rate of change in slope of the elastic curve, i.e., $+M$ is associated with $+d^2y/dx^2$.

concave upwards. This is true regardless of the positive direction of the x-axis, Fig. 11-3a and b. Therefore, in applying Eq. 11-4 and using the upward direction of the y-axis as positive, *the usual beam convention of signs applies to the bending moments.*

11-4. Relations between Deflection, Load, and Shear at a Section in a Beam. Before discussing the solution of Eq. 11-4, it is significant to note certain relations between the load, shear, and deflection of a beam. Thus, by differentiating Eq. 11-4 once with respect to x, assuming that EI is *constant*, and noting that by Eq. 6-1 $dM/dx = V$, the following relation is obtained,

$$\frac{d^3y}{dx^3} = \frac{d}{dx}\left(\frac{d^2y}{dx^2}\right) = \frac{d}{dx}\left(\frac{M}{EI}\right) = \frac{1}{EI}\frac{dM}{dx} = \frac{V}{EI}$$

where V is the shear at a given section.

Differentiating the above expression once more with respect to x, and observing that by Eq. 10-1 $dV/dx = w$, gives

$$\frac{d^4y}{dx^4} = \frac{d}{dx}\left(\frac{V}{EI}\right) = \frac{1}{EI}\frac{dV}{dx} = \frac{w}{EI}$$

where w is the applied load.

The above derivates, with those discussed in Art. 11-3 and the quantities which they represent, are tabulated below:

$$\left.\begin{array}{l} y = \text{deflection of the elastic curve} \\[4pt] \dfrac{dy}{dx} = \theta = \text{slope of the elastic curve} \\[6pt] \dfrac{d^2y}{dx^2} = \dfrac{d}{dx}\left(\dfrac{dy}{dx}\right) = \dfrac{M}{EI} \\[6pt] \dfrac{d^3y}{dx^3} = \dfrac{d}{dx}\left(\dfrac{d^2y}{dx^2}\right) = \dfrac{V}{EI} \\[6pt] \dfrac{d^4y}{dx^4} = \dfrac{d}{dx}\left(\dfrac{d^3y}{dx^3}\right) = \dfrac{w}{EI} \end{array}\right\} \qquad (11\text{-}5)$$

It is seen from these expressions that if the equation of the elastic curve y, and the quantity EI, representing the stiffness of a beam which is called its *flexural rigidity*, are known, not only the slope of the elastic curve, but also the bending moment, the shear, and the applied load at any section of the beam may be determined by performing the differentiations indicated above.

11-5. Integration Method for Beam Deflections. Two alternative procedures may be used to solve beam deflection problems by integration. These are so closely related that fundamentally they are not different methods. The distinction between the two is in whether one *starts* the analysis of a problem with an expression for the bending moment, *or* with the loads acting on a structure.

(A) *Double-Integration Method.* A direct solution of the differential equation Eq. 11-4, $d^2y/dx^2 = M/(EI)$, is usually possible by first formulating an *algebraic expression for the bending moment, with the usual signs, over the whole length of the beam.* This process was explained in Chapter 4 as one requiring a selection of a convenient origin of x, *passing sections through the beam*, and expressing algebraically the internal resisting moment for the isolated segment of a beam. If the flexural rigidity EI of a beam is variable, it must also be expressed as a function of the same variable x. Then, upon integrating the expression $M/(EI)$ twice, a solution for the deflection y is obtained. Since two integrations of Eq. 11-4 are performed, this procedure is called the *double-integration method*.*

Upon integrating the $M/(EI)$ function twice, *two* constants of integration appear. These are determined from the known conditions at the supports, which are termed the *boundary conditions* of the elastic curve. With the x-axis directed along the undeflected axis of a beam, the boundary conditions for the two common cases are as follows:

(a) *Roller or pinned support:* No deflection of the beam is possible, hence $y = 0$.

(b) *Fixed supports:* No deflection nor rotation of the "clamped" axis of the beam can take place, hence $y = 0$ *and* $dy/dx = 0$.

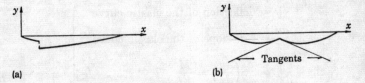

(a)   (b)

Fig. 11-4. Situations impossible in a continuous elastic curve.

Considerable latitude in the selection of the origin for x is possible. It may be chosen anywhere on the undeflected axis of a beam, and the posi-

* This term is a misnomer. In mathematics, by "double integration" is usually meant a process of obtaining areas or surfaces of bodies.

tive direction of x may be taken either to the right or to the left. In simple problems, the origin is usually taken at one of the ends. If *different* functions of $M/(EI)$ apply to different zones or segments of a beam, it may be advantageous to use a new origin of x for each zone. Additional integration constants appear in such problems, two for each zone The boundary conditions alone are insufficient to determine all of them, and the physical requirements for **continuity** of the elastic curve are used. This condition means that at the juncture of two zones the deflection and the tangent to the elastic curve is the same, regardless of the direction from which the common point is approached. The situations shown in Figs. 11-4a and b are impossible.

(B) **Method of Successive Integration.** Instead of passing sections through a beam and writing down algebraic expressions for the bending moment, the solution of a beam deflection problem may commence with the loads. Thus, as explained in the preceding chapter, by consecutive summation of the vertical forces, the shear at any section may be obtained. Then by consecutive summation of shears, bending moments may be determined. By *dividing* the values of the bending moments by the EI of the beam at the corresponding sections, an $M/(EI)$ *function* is obtained. The first integration in the double-integration method is actually an extension of the summation procedure to the $M/(EI)$ function.

Moreover, since $\dfrac{d^2y}{dx^2} = \dfrac{d}{dx}\left(\dfrac{dy}{dx}\right) = \dfrac{d\theta}{dx} = \dfrac{M}{EI}$ and $\theta = \displaystyle\int \dfrac{M}{EI}\, dx$, the new

function obtained by the summation of the $M/(EI)$ function represents the *slope* θ of the elastic curve at various points of a beam. By again applying the summation procedure to the slope function θ, the deflection y of the beam is obtained, since $dy/dx = \theta$ and $y = \int \theta\, dx$. The last step corresponds to the second integration of Eq. 11-4.

The constants of integration must be included in each step of the successive integrations described above. *Usually† such constants are the initial (boundary) values of the function at the origin* and will be identified in each case by a subscript o or a letter designating some point on a beam.

Summarizing, the four successive integrations (the last two of which correspond to the double-integration method) are

---

* This procedure, or its variation known as the conjugate beam method, is of great importance in complicated problems where approximate or graphical methods of analysis are used. For example, see Newmark, N. M., "Numerical Procedure for Computing Deflections, Moments, and Buckling Loads," *Trans. ASCE*, 1943, vol. 108, p. 1161.

† In certain cases where trigonometric functions are used, these constants have a different meaning. Basically, the *whole* function, which includes the constant of integration, must satisfy the condition at the boundary.

$$\left.\begin{aligned}
V &= \int w\,dx + V_o \\
M &= \int V\,dx + M_o \\
\theta &= \int \frac{M}{EI}\,dx + \theta_o \\
y &= \int \theta\,dx + y_o
\end{aligned}\right\} \tag{11-6}$$

Note that only statics is involved in the first two of the above equations. In the last two expressions, the property of the material E and the rigidity of the beam I are involved. The procedure expressed by Eqs. 11-6 is inverse to the one stated in Eqs. 11-5, although it is more general, since I may be variable for a beam. The constants V_o and M_o may always be determined at the boundary, as was done in Chapter 10, and θ_o and y_o, likewise, may be obtained from the known conditions at the boundaries. Diagrammatic sketches to accompany the integration process are usually very helpful.

In applying the method of successive integration, it is best to direct the x-axis toward the right to avoid ambiguity in shear signs (see last paragraph in Art. 10-5). However, Example 11-4 is solved with the x-axis directed to the left for illustration. This difficulty is not encountered in the double-integration method since expressions for moments are formulated directly and these have a more consistent sign convention.

Although the two alternate procedures discussed above are closely related, the successive integration method is most conveniently used when the *load function is continuous*, i.e., a single mathematical expression for the load applies to the whole beam. Four successive integrations of this type of function are easily made.

The application of the integration procedure for determining the deflection of beams will now be illustrated by several examples. In conformity with usual practice, the *largest* deflections, regardless of their sign, will be termed *maximum* deflections.

Example 11-2. A bending moment M_1 is applied at the free end of a cantilever of length L and of constant flexural rigidity EI, Fig. 11-5a. Find the equation of the elastic curve.

Solution: The origin of the co-ordinate system is taken at the fixed end. From Fig. 11-5b it is seen that the bending moment is constant throughout the beam and is equal to $+M_1$. Double integration of Eq. 11-4 may thus be easily performed.

$$\frac{d^2y}{dx^2} = \frac{d}{dx}\left(\frac{dy}{dx}\right) = \frac{M}{EI} = +\frac{M_1}{EI}$$

$$\theta = \frac{dy}{dx} = \int_0^x \frac{M_1}{EI}\,dx + \theta_o = \frac{M_1 x}{EI} + \theta_o$$

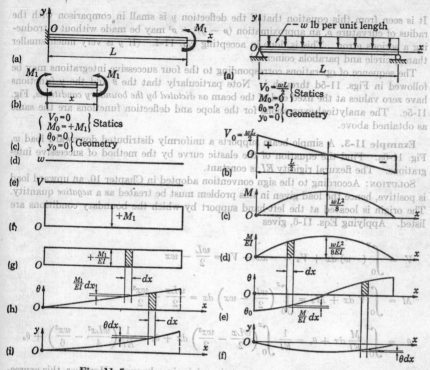

(a)

(b)

$\begin{cases} V_0 = 0 \\ M_0 = +M_1 \end{cases}$ Statics

(c) $\begin{cases} \theta_0 = 0 \\ y_0 = 0 \end{cases}$ Geometry

(d) w

(e)

(f) O $+M_1$

(g) O $+\dfrac{M_1}{EI}$ —dx

(h) θ $\dfrac{M_1}{EI}dx$| —dx

(i) O θdx| —dx

Fig. 11-5.

—w lb per unit length

O

(a) L

$V_0 = -\dfrac{wL}{2}$
$M_0 = 0$ Statics
$\theta_0 = ?$
$y_0 = 0$ Geometry

(b) $V_0 = \dfrac{wL}{2}$ + $\dfrac{L}{2}$

(c) $\dfrac{M}{O}$ $\dfrac{wL^2}{8}$

(d) $\dfrac{M}{EI}$ $\dfrac{wL^2}{8EI}$ — dx

(e) θ — dx $\dfrac{M}{EI}dx$

(f) O θdx

Fig. 11-6.

since, when $x = 0$, at the fixed support, $\dfrac{dy}{dx} = 0$ or $\left(\dfrac{dy}{dx}\right)_{x=0} = \theta_0 = 0$.

$$\frac{wL^3}{24EI}\qquad y = \int \theta\, dx + y_0 = \int_0^x \frac{M_1 x}{EI}\, dx + y_0 = \frac{M_1 x^2}{2EI} + y_0$$

since, at the fixed support, $(y)_{x=0} = y_0 = 0$. Therefore the equation of the elastic curve is

$$y = \frac{M_1 x^2}{2EI} \tag{11-7}$$

and it has a maximum value when $x = L$, i.e., $y_{max} = +M_1 L^2/(2EI)$. The positive sign indicates that the deflection due to M_1 is up. The slope of the elastic curve at the free end is $(\theta)_{x=L} = +M_1 L/(EI)$ radians.

Equation 11-7 indicates that the elastic curve is a parabola. However, every element of the beam experiences equal moments and deforms alike. Therefore the elastic curve should be a part of a circle. The inconsistency results from the use of an approximate differential equation for the elastic curve. If Eq. 11-3 were used instead of Eq. 11-4, an equation of a circle would be obtained. This solution* yields $x^2 + (y - \rho)^2 = \rho^2$, where the radius of curvature ρ is constant.

Differentiating the latter relation twice with respect to x and simplifying gives

$$\frac{d^2y}{dx^2} = \frac{\rho^2}{(\rho - y)^3}$$

* See Prob. 11-5.

It is seen from this equation that if the deflection y is small in comparison with the radius of curvature ρ, an approximation $(\rho - y)^3 \doteq \rho^3$ may be made without introducing a serious error. This is done in accepting Eq. 11-4. (If y is very much smaller than ρ, circle and parabola coincide.)

The sequence of operations corresponding to the four successive integrations may be followed in Figs. 11-5d through i. Note particularly that the θ and the y functions have zero values at the fixed end of the beam *as dictated by the boundary conditions*, Fig. 11-5c. The analytical expressions for the slope and deflection functions are the same as obtained above.

Example 11-3. A simple beam supports a uniformly distributed downward load w, Fig. 11-6a. Find the equation of the elastic curve by the method of successive integrations. The flexural rigidity EI is constant.

SOLUTION: According to the sign convention adopted in Chapter 10, an upward load is positive, hence the load given in this problem must be treated as a *negative* quantity. The origin is located at the left-hand support by which the boundary conditions are listed. Applying Eqs. 11-6, gives

$$V = \int_0^x (-w)\, dx + V_o = -wx + V_o = \frac{wL}{2} - wx$$

$$M = \int_0^x V\, dx + M_o = \int_0^x \left(\frac{wL}{2} - wx\right) dx = \frac{wLx}{2} - \frac{wx^2}{2}$$

$$\theta = \int_0^x \frac{M}{EI}\, dx + \theta_o = \frac{1}{EI}\int_0^x \left(\frac{wLx}{2} - \frac{wx^2}{2}\right) dx + \theta_o = \frac{1}{EI}\left(\frac{wLx^2}{4} - \frac{wx^3}{6}\right) + \theta_o$$

where θ_o, the slope of the elastic curve at the origin, is unknown. However, this expression may be integrated once more, and the known deflection conditions at both ends of the beam are sufficient to determine y_o and θ_o. Alternatively, since this beam is *symmetrically* loaded, the slope of the elastic curve at the middle is horizontal, i.e., $(dy/dx)_{x=L/2} = \theta_{x=L/2} = 0$. By using this condition,

$$0 = \frac{1}{EI}\left[\frac{wL}{4}\left(\frac{L}{2}\right)^2 - \frac{w}{6}\left(\frac{L}{2}\right)^3\right] + \theta_o \quad \text{or} \quad \theta_o = -\frac{wL^3}{24EI}$$

whence

$$\theta = \frac{1}{EI}\left(\frac{wLx^2}{4} - \frac{wx^3}{6} - \frac{wL^3}{24}\right)$$

and

$$y = \int_0^x \theta\, dx + y_o$$

$$= \frac{1}{EI}\int_0^x \left(\frac{wLx^2}{4} - \frac{wx^3}{6} - \frac{wL^3}{24}\right) dx + y_o$$

or

$$y = \frac{1}{EI}\left(\frac{wLx^3}{12} - \frac{wx^4}{24} - \frac{wL^3 x}{24}\right) \tag{11-8}$$

The deflection of the beam at any point may be obtained by substituting a particular value of x into Eq. 11-8. For example, at the middle of the span where $x = L/2$, from Eq. 11-8 the deflection is found to be

$$y_{max} = -\frac{5wL^4}{384\,EI} \tag{11-8a}$$

That this deflection is either a maximum or a minimum may be concluded by noting that $dy/dx = 0$ at $x = L/2$. The second derivative is positive throughout the span, which shows that this deflection is mathematically a minimum. However, numerically, this deflection is a maximum and is so designated. The negative sign of y_{max} indicates that the deflection occurs in a downward direction.

Diagrammatic constructions paralleling the above solution are shown in Figs. 11-6b through f. The solution by the double-integration method is the same as above, except that it commences with an expression for M.

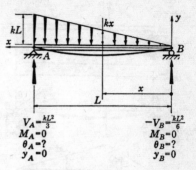

Example 11-4. A simply supported beam is subjected to a uniformly varying load as shown in Fig. 11-7. Find the equation of the elastic curve by the method of successive integrations. The flexural rigidity EI is constant.

$$V_A = \frac{kL^2}{3} \qquad -V_B = \frac{kL^2}{6}$$
$$M_A = 0 \qquad M_B = 0$$
$$\theta_A = ? \qquad \theta_B = ?$$
$$y_A = 0 \qquad y_B = 0$$

Fig. 11-7.

SOLUTION: The origin is selected at the right-hand end of the beam. Therefore the shear V_B on the right is taken as a positive quantity. This amounts to "looking at the beam from the other side." The bending moment sign in the subsequent relation is *then* consistent.

With $w = -kx$, Eqs. 11-6 are applied, giving

$$V = \int_0^x (-kx)\, dx + V_B = -\frac{kx^2}{2} + \frac{kL^2}{6}$$

$$M = \int_0^x V\, dx + M_B = \frac{k}{6}(L^2x - x^3)$$

$$\theta = \int_0^x \frac{M}{EI}\, dx + \theta_B = \frac{k}{6EI}\left(\frac{L^2x^2}{2} - \frac{x^4}{4}\right) + \theta_B$$

$$y = \int_0^x \theta\, dx + y_B = \frac{k}{6EI}\left(\frac{L^2x^3}{6} - \frac{x^5}{20}\right) + \theta_B x$$

Moreover, since the deflection is also zero at $x = L$,

$$0 = \frac{k}{6EI}\left(\frac{L^2}{6}L^3 - \frac{L^5}{20}\right) + \theta_B L, \qquad \theta_B = -\frac{k}{6EI}\frac{7L^4}{60}$$

and

$$y = \frac{k}{360EI}(-3x^5 + 10L^2x^3 - 7L^4x) \tag{11-9}$$

which is a general expression for the elastic curve. To find the location of the numerically maximum deflection, the derivative of this expression with respect to x, i.e., the expression for the slope of the elastic curve, must be set equal to zero. This yields $x = L\sqrt{1 - \sqrt{8/15}} = 0.5193L$, i.e., the maximum deflection occurs a little to the left of center.

The above solution illustrates a general procedure for solving deflection problems when the elastic curve is not symmetrical and continuous functions of its four derivatives are applicable for the whole length of the beam. Note particularly that the final integration for y is performed before θ_B is determined. There are always enough boundary conditions for a statically determinate beam to find the necessary constants of integration.

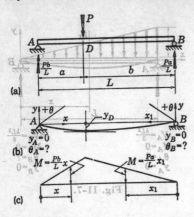

To solve the problem by the double-integration method, the function for the bending moment M must be directly formulated from a segment of a beam. The remainder of the solution is the same as above.

Example 11-5. A simply supported beam supports a concentrated downward force P at a distance a from one of the supports, Fig. 11-8a. Find the equation of the elastic curve by the double-integration method. The flexural rigidity EI is constant.

SOLUTION: Unlike the preceding examples, *different functions* for the bending moment apply to the two zones AD and DB of the beam. To simplify the work, two origins, one at each end, are selected for expressing the bending moments. This, with the known boundary conditions, is shown in Fig. 11-8b. At first the solution proceeds independently for each segment of the beam:

Fig. 11-8.

For segment AD

$$M = \frac{Pb}{L} x$$

$$\frac{d^2y}{dx^2} = \frac{M}{EI} = \frac{Pb}{EIL} x$$

$$\theta = \frac{dy}{dx} = \frac{Pb}{EIL} \frac{x^2}{2} + \theta_A$$

$$y = \frac{Pb}{EIL} \frac{x^3}{6} + \theta_A x + \cancel{y_A}$$

For segment BD

$$M = \frac{Pa}{L} x_1$$

$$\frac{d^2y}{dx_1^2} = \frac{M}{EI} = \frac{Pa}{EIL} x_1$$

$$\theta = \frac{dy}{dx_1} = \frac{Pa}{EIL} \frac{x_1^2}{2} + \theta_B$$

$$y = \frac{Pa}{EIL} \frac{x_1^3}{6} + \theta_B x_1 + \cancel{y_B}$$

where y_A and y_B are cancelled by virtue of the boundary conditions. To determine θ_A and θ_B, *continuity* conditions of the elastic curve must be used. First, the deflection y_D of the elastic curve at D, i.e., when $x = a$ and $x_1 = b$, given by the respective equations for y, must be the same. Second, the slope θ_D of the elastic curve at D, given by either one of the above expressions for θ, must be the same. However, in the second case, note from Fig. 11-8b that in the two co-ordinate systems the same slope has an opposite sign. On these bases two equations are formed:

$$y_D = \frac{Pb}{EIL} \frac{a^3}{6} + \theta_A a = \frac{Pa}{EIL} \frac{b^3}{6} + \theta_B b$$

and

$$\theta_D = \frac{Pb}{EIL} \frac{a^2}{2} + \theta_A = -\left(\frac{Pa}{EIL} \frac{b^2}{2} + \theta_B\right)$$

Solving these equations simultaneously for θ_A gives

$$\theta_A = -\frac{Pab}{6LEI} (a + 2b)$$

and the elastic curve for the left-hand segment AD of the beam reduces to

$$y = \frac{Pb}{6EIL} [x^3 + (b^2 - L^2)x]$$ (11-10)

By exchanging a for b and x_1 for x in the above equation, an expression for y of the right-hand segment of the beam may be obtained.

The maximum deflection occurs in the *longer* segment of the beam. *If $a > b$*, the point of maximum deflection is at $x = \sqrt{a(a + 2b)/3}$, which follows by setting the expression for the slope equal to zero. The maximum deflection at this point is

$$y_{max} = -\frac{Pab\,(a + 2b)\,\sqrt{3a\,(a + 2b)}}{27EI(a + b)} = -\frac{Pb(L^2 - b^2)^{3/2}}{9\sqrt{3}EIL}$$ (11-10a)

If the force P is applied at the middle of the span, i.e., $a = b = L/2$, it can be shown by direct substitution into Eq. 11-10 or 11-10a that at $x = L/2$

$$y_{max} = -\frac{PL^3}{48EI}$$ (11-11)

This problem may also be solved by using only one origin for the co-ordinate system at either end, or two origins as shown in Fig. 11-8d. For these solutions, the same continuity conditions of the elastic curve must be used at the juncture of the zones for which different expressions for $M/(EI)$ apply.

Example 11-6. A simply supported beam 10 in. long is loaded with a 10 lb downward force 8 in. from the left support, Fig. 11-9a. The beam's cross-section is such that in the segment AB the moment of inertia is $4I_1$, in the remainder of the beam it is I_1. Determine the elastic curve.

SOLUTION: A similar problem was solved in the preceding example. Here a more systematic technique will be illustrated—one that is useful in complicated problems where different $M/(EI)$ expressions are applicable to several segments of a beam. This method consists of selecting an origin at one end of a beam and completing the integrations until θ and y are obtained for the first segment adjoining the end. The values for θ and y at the *end* of the first segment become the *initial constants* for the next segment. This process is repeated until the far end of the beam is reached, where the unknown constants are determined from the boundary conditions. A new origin of x is used at every juncture of the segments. All x's are taken positive in the *same direction*.

For segment AB (Figs. 11-9c through f): $y_A = 0$ and θ_A is unknown.

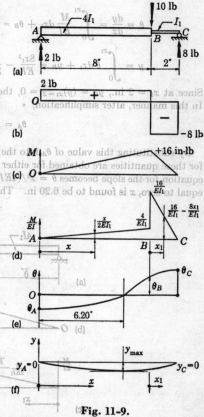

Fig. 11-9.

$$M = 2x \text{ for } 0 < x < 8$$

$$\frac{M}{EI} = \frac{2x}{4EI_1} = \frac{x}{2EI_1}$$

$$\theta = \frac{dy}{dx} = \int_0^x \frac{M}{EI}\,dx + \theta_A = \frac{x^2}{4EI_1} + \theta_A$$

$$y = \int_0^x \theta\,dx + y_A = \frac{x^3}{12EI_1} + \theta_A x + y_A$$

Therefore

$$\theta_B = (\theta)_{x=8} = \frac{8^2}{4EI_1} + \theta_A = \frac{16}{EI_1} + \theta_A$$

and

$$y_B = (y)_{x=8} = \frac{128}{3EI_1} + 8\theta_A$$

For segment BC (Figs. 11-9c through f): θ_B and y_B determined above are the initial constants.

$$M = 2(8 + x_1) - 10x_1 = 16 - 8x_1 \text{ for } 0 < x_1 < 2$$

$$\frac{M}{EI} = \frac{16 - 8x_1}{EI_1} = \frac{16}{EI_1} - \frac{8x_1}{EI_1}$$

$$\theta = \frac{dy}{dx} = \int_0^{x_1} \frac{M}{EI}\,dx_1 + \theta_B = \frac{16x_1}{EI_1} - \frac{4x_1^2}{EI_1} + \frac{16}{EI_1} + \theta_A$$

$$y = \int_0^{x_1} \theta\,dx_1 + y_B = \frac{8x_1^2}{EI_1} - \frac{4x_1^3}{3EI_1} + \frac{16x_1}{EI_1} + \theta_A x_1 + \frac{128}{3EI_1} + 8\theta_A$$

Since at $x_1 = 2$ in., $y_C = (y)_{x_1=2} = 0$, the unknown constant θ_A may be determined. In this manner, after simplification,

$$\theta_A = -\frac{48}{5EI_1}$$

By substituting this value of θ_A into the respective expressions for θ and y, equations for these quantities are obtained for either segment. For example, in segment AB, the equation for the slope becomes $\theta = x^2/(4EI_1) - 48/(5EI_1)$. Upon setting this quantity equal to zero, x is found to be 6.20 in. The maximum deflection occurs at this value of

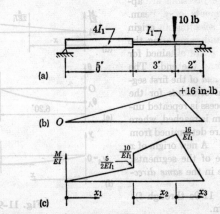

Fig. 11-10. Multiple selection of the origins of x for a discontinuous $M/(EI)$ function.

x, which is $y_{max} = -39.7/(EI_1)$. *Characteristically, the deflection at the center of the span, i.e., at $x = 5$ in., is nearly the same, being* $-37.6/(EI_1)$.

A similar procedure may be used in problems where several different functions for $M/(EI)$ are used, Fig. 11-10.

11-6. Remarks on Deflection Problems. The integration method for obtaining the elastic curve of a loaded beam is generally applicable. Numerous problems with different loadings have been solved and are readily available.* However, nearly all of such solutions are made for simple loading conditions. Deflections of beams subjected to several or complicated loading conditions are usually synthesized, using the principle of *superposition*. For example, the problem shown in Fig. 11-11

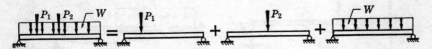

Fig. 11-11. Resolution of a complex problem into several simpler problems in computing deflections.

may be separated into three different cases as shown. The algebraic sum of the three separate deflections for the same point on this beam gives the total deflection. The same scheme may often be used to advantage in situations where actual integrations must be performed.

Beams with overhangs may also be conveniently analyzed for deflection, using the concept of superposition. For example, the beam shown in Fig. 11-12a may be reduced to that shown in Fig. 11-12b, where the effect of the overhang on the beam from A to B is included by introducing at the support B a shear P and a bending moment $-Pa$. The elastic curve for the beam AB may be determined in the usual manner, or by separately considering a uniformly loaded beam and a beam with a concentrated moment at its end and superposing the results. From the solution for the elastic curve AB,

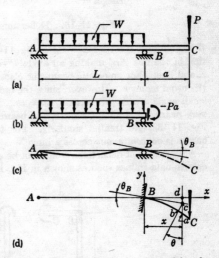

Fig. 11-12. Method of superposition for overhanging beams.

the slope θ_B, which locates the *tangent* to the continuous elastic curve ABC, may be found, Fig. 11-12c. This tangent, in general, is *not* horizontal. If the direction of this tangent is fixed at B, as shown in Fig

* See any civil or mechanical engineering handbook.

11-12d, at the angle θ_B, the deflection of the overhang is seen to consist of two parts.   One part is due to the rotation of the tangent at the support.   This causes a point at a distance x from B to deflect an amount $x \tan \theta_B \doteq x\theta_B$ for *small* θ_B measured in radians.   The second part is the same as for an ordinary cantilever, since for *small deflections and rotations* of the elastic curve, $bc = ac \cos \theta \doteq ac$.   The error caused by these approximations is negligible.

Approximations similar to the above are also made in composite structures.   In Fig. 11-13a, for example, a simple beam rests on a rigid support at one end and on a yielding support with a spring constant* k at the other end.   If R_B is the reaction at

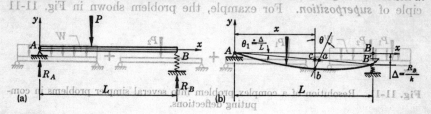

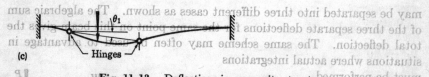

Fig. 11-13.   Deflections in composite structures.

B, the support B settles $\Delta = R_B/k$, Fig. 11-13b.   A rigid beam would assume the direction of the line AB' making an angle $\theta_1 = \tan^{-1}(\Delta/L) \doteq \Delta/L$ radians with the horizontal line.   For an elastic beam, the elastic curve between A and B' may be found in the usual manner.   However, since the ordinates such as ab, Fig. 11-13b, make a very small angle θ with the vertical, $ab \doteq cb$.   Hence the deflection of a point such as b is very nearly $\theta_1 x + cb$.   Deflections of beams in situations where hinges are introduced, Fig. 11-13c, are treated similarly.   For these, the tangent to the adjoining elastic curves is *not continuous* across a hinge.

A discussion of deflections would not be complete without some mention of statically determinate frames such as shown in Fig. 11-14a.   These problems may be treated by

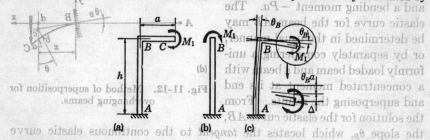

Fig. 11-14.   A method for analyzing statically determinate frames for deflection.

* See Art. 7-9, where k is defined as a force necessary to deflect a spring one inch. More generally, a beam or any other member may be considered as a "spring" and k may be defined in the same manner at the point of load application.

separating them into parts. Thus in Fig. 11-14b the vertical member alone is shown. The angular rotation at the top of this member is easily computed by the methods previously discussed. Then, by *assuming* that the joint is rigid, it follows that the tangent at B of the horizontal member also rotates through the *same* angle, Fig. 11-14c. For example, the deflection of the end C is $\theta_B a + \Delta$, where Δ is the deflection of the member BC at C from a tangent at B.

*11-7. Deflection of Beams due to Unsymmetrical Bending. In the preceding discussion, the deflection of beams was assumed to take place in one plane. More precisely, the foregoing theory applies to deflections of beams when the applied moments act around *one of the principal axes of the cross-section.* If unsymmetrical bending occurs, the deflection problem may be solved by superposition. First, the elastic curve in the plane containing one of the principal axes is determined by considering only the effect of the components of forces acting parallel to this axis. The elastic curve in the plane containing the other principal axis is found similarly. A *vectorial* addition of the deflections so found at a particular point of a beam gives the total displacement of the beam at that point. For example, if in a certain beam of rectangular cross-section subjected to unsymmetrical bending, the deflection at a particular point is y_1 in the y-direction and z_1 in the z-direction, Fig. 11-15, the total displacement is $y_1 \leftrightarrow z_1$, i.e., the distance aa'. Such deflections, without torsion, occur only if the applied forces pass through the shear center.

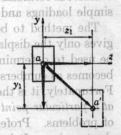

Fig. 11-15. Determination of a deflection of a beam subjected to unsymmetrical bending.

11-8. Introduction to the Moment-Area Method.* The method of obtaining beam deflections by solving the differential equation of the elastic curve $d^2y/dx^2 = M/(EI)$ is generally applicable. It is easily applicable to beams if the bending moment and the moment of inertia of the cross-section are *continuous mathematical functions along the whole length of the beam.* However, unless these conditions are fulfilled, the problem is considerably complicated. To eliminate some of the inherent difficulties of this method, a semigraphical interpretation of the mathematical operations of solving the differential equation has been developed.† Using such an interpretation, it has been found that problems with load discontinuities (concentrated loads, or start and terminus of distributed loads), moment discontinuities (concentrated moments), and arbitrary variations of the moment of inertia of the cross-sectional area of the beam cause no complications and require only a little more arithmetical work for their solution.

* In a short course, the remainder of this chapter may be omitted.
† The development of the moment-area method for finding deflections of beams is due to Charles E. Greene, of the University of Michigan, who taught it to his classes in 1873. Somewhat earlier, in 1868, Otto Mohr, of Dresden, Germany, developed a similar method which appears to have been unknown to Professor Greene.

In engineering practice, where deflections of beams must be determined, the loading is often rather complex, and frequently the cross-sectional areas of the beam vary. This is the usual situation in shafts for machines and electric motors, where gradual or stepwise variations in the shaft diameter are made to accommodate rotors, bearings, collars, retainers, etc. Likewise, haunched or tapered beams are frequently employed in structural engineering. The student's objective in studying this section of the chapter on the moment-area method is to solve such problems. Numerous formulas for deflections are available in various handbooks for simple loadings and prismatic beams.

The method to be developed has one limitation. In its usual form it gives only the displacement at a single point of a beam at a time. It can be used to determine the equation of the elastic curve, but then it often becomes as cumbersome as the direct solution of the differential equation. Fortunately, it is the deflection or the angular rotation of the elastic curve *at a particular point of a beam* that is of greatest interest in the majority of problems. Professionally, the method loses little of its value by this shortcoming. It is very useful for determining the deflection of *a point*.

The method of moment-areas is just an alternative method of solving the deflection problem. It possesses the same approximations and limitations discussed earlier in connection with the solution of the differential equation of the elastic curve. By applying it, only the deflection due to the *flexure* of the beam is determined; deflection due to shear is disregarded. As with the former method, the discussion in this chapter will be limited to statically determinate beams.

11-9. Geometry of the Elastic Curve. To develop the technique of solving the beam deflection problem by the moment-area method, the geometry of the elastic curve and the associated $M/(EI)$ *diagram* must be considered. This diagram may always be obtained by dividing the values of the ordinates of the bending-moment diagram by the corresponding rectangular moment of inertia I of the beam at the *same* section and by the elastic modulus of the material E. The ordinates of the $M/(EI)$ diagram *have the sign of the corresponding bending moments*. Corresponding to a positive $M/(EI)$ diagram, the elastic curve of the beam deflects concave up ("retains water"), since a positive bending moment compresses the top fibers of a beam. For a negative $M/(EI)$ diagram, the reverse is true. Also note particularly that regardless of the sign variation of the $M/(EI)$ diagram across the beam's length, the physical requirements of the problem prescribe complete *continuity* of the elastic curve. Tangents to the elastic curve *never* change their directions *suddenly* or abruptly (see Fig. 11-4b).

In using this method, it is absolutely imperative to make good sketches of the elastic curve, conforming in shape to the sign of the $M/(EI)$ diagram for the beam. Moreover, in any given problem, a sketch of the elastic curve must be made fulfilling the known conditions at the supports, i.e., the boundary conditions. Since no deflection is generally possible at a pinned or a roller support, the elastic curve is drawn passing *through* the supports. On the other hand, at a fixed support, neither displacement *nor rotation* of the tangent to the elastic curve is possible. Hence *at* a fixed support the elastic curve must always be drawn tangent to the direction of the unloaded axis of the beam. In preparing a sketch of the elastic curve in the above manner, it is customary to *exaggerate* the anticipated deflections, although it is fully appreciated that the actual deflections permitted for beams are very small. The purpose of the exaggeration is mainly to facilitate the application of the moment-area method of finding deflections and to clarify the action of a beam. The elastic curve so drawn is only qualitatively correct. The numerical values of rotations and deflections of the elastic curve remain to be determined with the aid of theorems to be developed.

The necessary theorems are based on the geometry of the elastic curve and the associated $M/(EI)$ diagram. Boundary conditions, or the conditions at the support of a beam, *do not enter into the derivation of the theorems.* To repeat, these theorems relate only the elastic curve to the $M/(EI)$ diagram. As will be shown later, further *geometrical* interpretations are necessary to solve a given problem.

11-10. Moment-Area Theorem 1. Consider the $M/(EI)$ diagram shown in Fig. 11-16b. Corresponding to this diagram, the elastic curve must assume the shape shown in Fig. 11-16a. The elastic curve must be

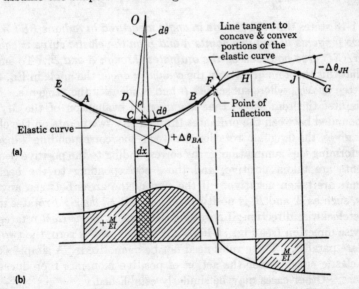

Fig. 11-16. Relationships between the angular rotations of the tangents to the elastic curve, corresponding to the $M/(EI)$ diagram.

concave upward between the points E and F, since the $M/(EI)$ diagram is positive; similarly, it must be concave down between F and G. Next, consider on this curve two neighboring points C and D and erect from them two perpendiculars to the elastic curve, which will intersect at the point O and will include an infinitesimal angle $d\theta$. As already explained in Art. 11-2, these lines within the beam's cross-section correspond to the initially vertical planes normal to the axis of the unloaded beam. The distance from O to the arc CD is ρ, which for the element CD is its radius of curvature. Hence, if the infinitesimal arc CD is denoted by ds, $ds = \rho\, d\theta$. However, since the beam deflections considered are *very* small, with sufficient accuracy ds may be replaced by its horizontal projection dx. Thus $dx \doteq \rho\, d\theta$, or $d\theta \doteq (1/\rho)\, dx$. Moreover, as by Eq. 11-2 $1/\rho = M/(EI)$,

$$d\theta = \frac{M}{EI}\, dx \tag{11-12}$$

hence the magnitude of the angle $d\theta$ is given by the cross-hatched *area* of the $M/(EI)$ diagram, Fig. 11-16b, in the interval dx. The same infinitesimal angle $d\theta$ is included *between the tangents* to the elastic curve at C and D.

By formally integrating Eq. 11-12 between any two limits, as A and B, corresponding to two points on the elastic curve, the first moment-area theorem is established,* i.e.,

$$\int_A^B d\theta = \theta_B - \theta_A = \Delta\theta_{BA} = \int_A^B \frac{M}{EI}\, dx \tag{11-13}$$

Eq. 11-13 states that *the change in angle measured in radians BETWEEN the two tangents at any two points A and B on the elastic curve is equal to the M/(EI) area bounded by the ordinates through A and B.* To emphasize that this theorem gives only the *change in angle*, the angle in Eq. 11-13 is written as $\Delta\theta_{BA}$ where subscripts B and A identify the tangents.

This first theorem shows that a numerical evaluation of the $M/(EI)$ *area* bounded between the ordinates through any two points on the elastic curve gives the angular rotation between the corresponding tangents. In performing this summation, areas corresponding to the positive bending moments are taken positive, and those corresponding to the negative moments are taken negative. If the sum of the areas between any two points, such as A and B, is positive, the tangent *on the right* rotates in the counterclockwise direction; if negative, the tangent *on the right* rotates in a clockwise direction (see Fig. 11-16a). If the net area is zero, the two tangents are parallel. These rules need not be memorized. A simple sketch of an elastic curve under the action of positive moments reproduces the first case. Other cases may be similarly established.

* The same result follows directly from the third of the Eqs. 11-6.

11-11. Moment-Area Theorem 2. The angle included between two tangents at points on the elastic curve an infinitesimal distance apart equals $(M/EI)\,dx$. Thus the magnitude of the angle $d\theta$ between the tangents at C and D in Fig. 11-17a is represented by the shaded area shown in Fig. 11-17b. If this small angle is multiplied by the horizontal distance x, a small arc uw is obtained. However, since the curvature of the elastic curve shown in Fig. 11-17a is enormously exaggerated, the quantity found is practically the same as the vertical distance zw and will be so considered. This process of multiplying the infinitesimal $M/(EI)$ areas by distances x measured from the same vertical line through B may be repeated for

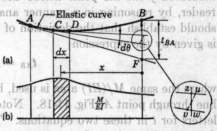

Fig. 11-17. Diagram used in deriving the second moment-area theorem.

the whole segment of a beam. If this is done for the interval from B to A and the results are summed, the vertical distance BF is obtained. Geometrically this distance represents the displacement or *deviation* of a point B from a *tangent* to the elastic curve at A. Henceforth, it will be termed the ***tangential deviation*** of a point B from a tangent at A and will be designated as t_{BA}.

The foregoing, in mathematical form, states that

$$t_{BA} = \int_B^A d\theta \; x \cong \int_B^A \frac{M}{EI} x \, dx \tag{11-14}$$

Equation 11-14 is the second moment-area theorem. It states that *the tangential deviation of a point B on the elastic curve from a tangent through another point A also on the elastic curve is equal to the statical (or first) moment of the bounded section of the $M/(EI)$ diagram around a vertical line through B.* In most cases, the tangential deviation *is not in itself the desired deflection of a beam.*

Using the definition of the center of gravity of an area, Eq. 11-14 may

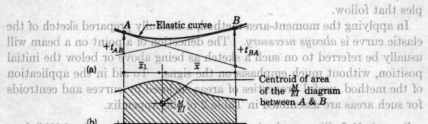

Fig. 11-18. The meaning of Eqs. 11-15 and 11-15a illustrated.

be restated for convenience in numerical applications in a simpler form as

$$t_{BA} = A\bar{x} \qquad (11\text{-}15)$$

where A is the total *area* of the $M/(EI)$ diagram between the two points considered and $\bar{x}$ is the horizontal distance to the centroid of this area *measured from the point whose deviation is sought,* Fig. 11-18. The reader, by reasoning in a manner analogous to the foregoing derivation, should establish that the deviation of a point A *from a tangent through B* is given by the expression

$$t_{AB} = A\bar{x}_1 \qquad (11\text{-}15a)$$

where the same $M/(EI)$ area is used, but $\bar{x}_1$ is measured from the vertical line through point A, Fig. 11-18. Note carefully the *order* of the subscript letters for t in these two equations. The point whose deviation is being determined is written first.

In the above equations, the distances x or $\bar{x}$ are always taken positive, and as E and I are also positive quantities, the sign of the tangential devia-

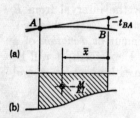

Fig. 11-19. The meaning of a negative quantity for a tangential deviation.

tion depends on the sign of the bending moments. A positive value for the tangential deviation indicates that a given point lies *above* a tangent to the elastic curve drawn through the other point. An example of this may be seen in Fig. 11-18. The reverse case, where the $M/(EI)$ diagram is negative, is shown in Fig. 11-19. Here the point B is *below* the tangent through A. Signs for a tangential deviation may always be quickly verified by sketching an elastic curve of the proper curvature.

The above two theorems are applicable between *any two points* on the elastic curve of any beam for any type of loading. They apply between and beyond the reactions for overhanging and continuous beams. However, it must be emphasized that **only relative rotation of the tangents and only tangential deviations** are obtained directly. A further consideration of the geometry of the elastic curve at the supports is necessary in every case to determine deflections. This will be illustrated in the examples that follow.

In applying the moment-area method, a carefully prepared sketch of the elastic curve is *always necessary.* The deflection of a point on a beam will usually be referred to on such a sketch as being above or below the initial position, without much emphasis on the signs. To aid in the application of the method, useful properties of areas enclosed by curves and centroids for such areas are assembled in Table 2 of the Appendix.

Example 11-7. Given an aluminum cantilever beam 16 in. long with a 1,000 lb force applied 4 in. from the free end, as shown in Fig. 11-20a. For a distance of 6 in. from the fixed end, the beam is of greater depth than beyond, having $I_1 = 5$ in.[4] For the remaining 10 in. of the beam, $I_2 = 1$ in.[4] Find the deflection and the angular rotation of the free end. Neglect the weight of the beam, and assume E for aluminum at 10^7 psi.

SOLUTION: The bending-moment diagram is shown in Fig. 11-20b. By dividing *all* ordinates of the M diagrams by $EI_1 = 5E$ in the interval from A to D, and by $EI_2 = E$ in the interval from D to C, the $M/(EI)$ diagram shown in Fig. 11-20c is obtained. Two ordinates appear at point D. One, $-1,200/E$, is applicable *just to the left* of D, the other, $-6,000/E$, applies *just to the right* of D. Since the bending moment is negative from A to C, the elastic curve *throughout* this distance is concave down, Fig. 11-20d. At the fixed support A, the elastic curve must start out tangent to the initial direction AB' of the unloaded beam. The unloaded straight segment CB of the beam is tangent to the elastic curve at C.

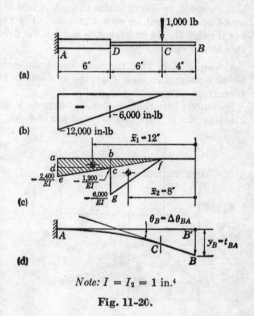

Note: $I = I_2 = 1$ in.[4]

Fig. 11-20.

After the foregoing preparatory steps, from the *geometry* of the sketch of the elastic curve it may be seen that the distance BB' represents the desired deflection of the free end. However, BB' is also the tangential deviation of the point B from the tangent at A. Therefore the second moment-area theorem may be used to obtain t_{BA}, which in this *special case* represents the deflection of the free end. Also, from the geometry of the elastic curve it is seen that the angle included between the lines BC and AB' is the angular rotation of the segment CB. This angle is the same as the one included *between the tangents* to the elastic curve at the points A and B, and the first moment-area theorem may be used to compute this quantity.

It is convenient to extend the line ec in Fig. 11-20c to the point f for computing the area of the $M/(EI)$ diagram. This gives two triangles, the areas of which are easily calculated.*

The area of triangle afe: $A_1 = -\dfrac{1}{2}(12)\dfrac{2,400}{E} = -\dfrac{14,400}{E}$

The area of triangle fcg: $A_2 = -\dfrac{1}{2}(6)\dfrac{4,800}{E} = -\dfrac{14,400}{E}$

$$\theta_B = \Delta\theta_{BA} = \int_A^B \frac{M}{EI}\,dx = A_1 + A_2 = -\frac{28,800}{10^7}$$

$$= -0.00288 \text{ radians}$$

* A little ingenuity in such cases saves arithmetical work. Of course it is perfectly correct in this example to use the two triangular areas *dce* and *bfg*, and a rectangle *abcd*.

$$y_B = t_{BA} = A\bar{x} = A_1\bar{x}_1 + A_2\bar{x}_2 = -\frac{14{,}400}{E}\,(12) - \frac{14{,}400}{E}\,(8)$$

$$= -0.0288 \text{ in.}$$

Note the numerical smallness of both of the above values. The negative sign of $\Delta\theta$ indicates clockwise rotation of the tangent at B in relation to the tangent at A. The negative sign of t_{BA} means that point B is below a tangent through A.

If a similar investigation, say for the point D, is desired, the portion of the $M/(EI)$ area bounded by the ordinates through A and D must be used. Areas $abcd$ and cde would be convenient for such a purpose. The $\bar{x}$'s would be measured from a vertical line through D. In an analogous manner, the deflection of any point on the cantilever may be determined.

Example 11-8. Find the deflection at the center of a simply supported beam due to the concentrated force P applied as shown in Fig. 11-21a. The flexural rigidity EI is constant.

SOLUTION: The bending-moment diagram is shown in Fig. 11-21b. Since EI is constant, the $M/(EI)$ diagram need not be made, as the areas of the bending-moment diagram divided by EI give the necessary quantities for use in the moment-area theorems. The elastic curve is shown in Fig. 11-21c. It is concave upwards *throughout* its length, as the bending moments are positive. This curve *must* pass through the points of the support at A and B.

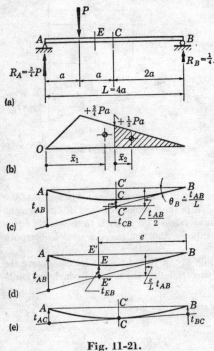

Fig. 11-21.

It is apparent from the sketch of the elastic curve that the desired quantity is represented by the distance CC'. Moreover, from purely *geometrical* considerations, it is seen that $CC' = C'C'' - C''C$, where the distance $C''C$ is measured from a *tangent* to the elastic curve passing through the point of support B. However, since the deviation of a support point from a tangent to the elastic curve at the *other support* may always be computed by the second moment-area theorem, a distance such as $C'C''$ may be found by proportions from the geometry of the figure. In this case, t_{AB} follows by taking the whole $M/(EI)$ area between A and B and multiplying it by* its $\bar{x}$ measured from a vertical through A, whence $C'C'' = t_{AB}/2$. By another application of the second theorem, t_{CB}, which is equal to $C''C$, is determined. For this case, the $M/(EI)$ area is shown shaded in Fig. 11-21b, and, for it, the $\bar{x}$ is measured from C.

* See Table 2 in the Appendix for the centroid of the whole triangular area. Alternatively, by treating the whole $M/(EI)$ area as two triangles,

$$t_{AB} = \frac{1}{EI}\left(\frac{1}{2}\,a\,\frac{3}{4}\,Pa\right)\frac{2}{3}\,a + \frac{1}{EI}\left(\frac{1}{2}\,3a\,\frac{3}{4}\,Pa\right)\left(a + \frac{1}{3}\,3a\right) = +\frac{5Pa^3}{2EI}$$

Since the right reaction is $P/4$ and the distance $CB = 2a$, the maximum ordinate for the shaded triangle is $+Pa/2$.

$$y_C = C'C'' - C''C = \frac{t_{AB}}{2} - t_{CB}$$

$$t_{AB} = A_1 \bar{x}_1 = \frac{1}{EI}\left(\frac{1}{2}\, 4a\, \frac{3}{4}\, Pa\right)\frac{1}{3}\,(a + 4a) = +\frac{5Pa^3}{2EI}$$

$$t_{CB} = A_2 \bar{x}_2 = \frac{1}{EI}\left(\frac{1}{2}\, 2a\, \frac{1}{2}\, Pa\right)\frac{1}{3}\,(2a) = +\frac{Pa^3}{3EI}$$

$$y_C = \frac{t_{AB}}{2} - t_{CB} = \frac{5Pa^3}{4EI} - \frac{Pa^3}{3EI} = \frac{11Pa^3}{12EI}$$

The positive signs of t_{AB} and t_{CB} indicate that points A and C lie above the tangent through B. As may be seen from Fig. 11-21c, the deflection at the center of the beam is in a downward direction.

The above procedure for finding the deflection of a point on the elastic curve is generally applicable. For example, if the deflection of the point E, Fig. 11-21d, at a distance e from B is wanted, the solution may be formulated as

$$y_E = E'E'' - E''E = \frac{e}{L}\, t_{AB} - t_{EB}$$

By locating the point E at a variable distance x from one of the supports, an equation of the elastic curve may be obtained.

To simplify the arithmetical work, some care in selecting the tangent at a support must be exercised. Thus while $y_C = t_{BA}/2 - t_{CA}$ (not shown in the diagram), this solution would involve the use of the unshaded portion of the bending-moment diagram to obtain t_{CA}, which is more tedious.

ALTERNATE SOLUTION: The solution of the foregoing problem may be based on a different *geometrical* concept. This is illustrated in Fig. 11-21e, where a tangent to the elastic curve is drawn at C. Then, since the distances AC and CB are equal,

$$y_C = CC' = \frac{t_{AC} + t_{BC}}{2}$$

i.e., the distance CC' is an *average* of t_{AC} and t_{BC}. The tangential deviation t_{AC} is obtained by taking the first moment of the *unshaded* $M/(EI)$ area in Fig. 11-21b about A, while t_{BC} is given by the first moment of the shaded $M/(EI)$ area about B. The numerical details of this solution are left for completion by the reader. This procedure is usually longer than the first.

Note particularly that if the elastic curve is *not* symmetrical, the tangent at the center of the beam is *not* horizontal.

Example 11-9. For a prismatic beam loaded as in the preceding example, find the *maximum* deflection caused by the applied force P, Fig. 11-22a.

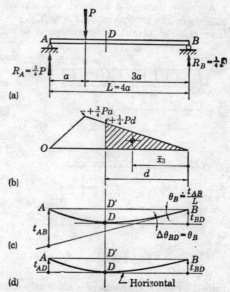

(a)

(b)

(c)

(d)

Fig. 11-22.

SOLUTION: The bending-moment diagram and the elastic curve are shown in Figs. 11-22b and c, respectively. The elastic curve is concave up throughout its length, and the maximum deflection occurs where the tangent to the elastic curve is *horizontal*. This point of tangency is designated in the figure by D and is located by the unknown horizontal distance d measured from the right support B. Then, by drawing a tangent to the elastic curve through point B at the support, it is seen that $\Delta\theta_{BD} = \theta_B$, since the line passing through the supports is horizontal. However, the slope θ_B of the elastic curve at B may be determined by obtaining t_{AB} and dividing it by the length of the span. On the other hand, by using the *first* moment-area theorem, $\Delta\theta_{BD}$ may be expressed in terms of the shaded area shown in Fig. 11-22b. Equating $\Delta\theta_{BD}$ to θ_B and solving for d locates the horizontal tangent at D. Then, again from geometrical considerations, it is seen that the maximum deflection represented by DD' is equal to the tangential deviation of B from a horizontal tangent through D, i.e., t_{BD}.

$$t_{AB} = A_1\bar{x}_1 = +\frac{5Pa^3}{2EI} \qquad \text{(see Example 11-8)}$$

$$\theta_B = \frac{t_{AB}}{L} = \frac{t_{AB}}{4a} = \frac{5Pa^2}{8EI}$$

$$\Delta\theta_{BD} = \frac{1}{EI}\left(\frac{1}{2}d\frac{1}{4}Pd\right) = \frac{Pd^2}{8EI} \qquad \text{(area between } D \text{ and } B\text{)}$$

Equating

$$\Delta\theta_{BD} = \theta_B, \qquad \frac{Pd^2}{8EI} = \frac{5Pa^2}{8EI}, \qquad \text{hence } d = \sqrt{5}\,a$$

$$y_{max} = y_D = DD' = t_{BD} = A_3\bar{x}_3$$

$$= \frac{1}{EI}\left(\frac{1}{2}d\frac{1}{4}Pd\right)\frac{2}{3}d$$

$$= \frac{5\sqrt{5}\,Pa^3}{12EI} = \frac{11.2Pa^3}{12EI}$$

After the distance d is found, the maximum deflection may also be obtained, as $y_{max} = t_{AD}$ (not shown), or $y_{max} = (d/L)t_{AB} - t_{DB}$. Also note that using the condition $t_{AD} = t_{BD}$, Fig. 11-22d, an equation may be set up for d.

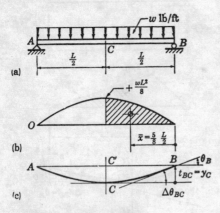

(a)

(b)

(c)

Fig. 11-23.

It should be apparent from the above solution that it is easier to calculate the deflection at the center of the beam, which was illustrated in Example 11-8, than to determine the maximum deflection. Yet, by examining the end results, it is seen that numerically the two deflections differ little: $y_{center} = 11Pa^3/(12EI)$ vs. $y_{max} = 11.2Pa^3/(12EI)$. For this reason, in many practical problems of simply supported beams where all of the applied forces act in the same direction, it is often sufficiently accurate to calculate the deflection at the center instead of attempting to obtain the true maximum.

Example 11-10. In a simply supported beam, find the maximum deflection and rotation of the elastic curve at the ends caused by the application of a uniformly distributed load of w lb per ft., Fig. 11-23a. The flexural rigidity EI is constant.

SOLUTION: The bending-moment diagram is shown in Fig. 11-23b. As established in Example 4-6, the bending-moment diagram is a second-degree parabola with a maximum value at the vertex of $wL^2/8$. The elastic curve passing through the points of the support A and B is shown in Fig. 11-23c.

In this case, the $M/(EI)$ diagram is *symmetrical* about a vertical line passing through the center. Therefore the elastic curve must be symmetrical, and the tangent to this curve at the center of the beam is horizontal. From the figure, it is seen that $\Delta\theta_{BC}$ is equal to θ_B, and the rotation of the end B is equal to *one-half* of the area* of the whole $M/(EI)$ diagram. The distance CC' is the desired deflection, and from the geometry of the figure it is seen to be equal to t_{BC} (or t_{AC}, not shown).

$$A = \frac{1}{EI}\left(\frac{2}{3}\frac{L}{2}\frac{wL^2}{8}\right) = \frac{wL^3}{24EI}$$

$$\theta_B = \Delta\theta_{BC} = A = +\frac{wL^3}{24EI}$$

$$y_C = y_{\max} = t_{BC} = A\bar{x} = \frac{wL^3}{24EI}\frac{5L}{16} = \frac{5wL^4}{384EI}$$

The value of the deflection agrees with Eq. 11-8a, which expresses the same quantity derived by the integration method. Since the point B is above the tangent through C, the sign of y_C is positive.

Example 11-11. Find the deflection caused by the applied forces of the free end A of the beam shown in Fig. 11-24a. Again, EI is constant.

SOLUTION: The bending-moment diagram for the applied forces is shown in Fig. 11-24b. The bending moment changes sign at $a/2$ from the left support. At this point an inflection in the elastic curve takes place. Corresponding to the positive moment, the curve is concave up, and vice versa. The elastic curve is so drawn and passes *over the supports* at B and C, Fig. 11-24c. First, the inclination of the tangent to the elastic curve at the support B is determined by finding t_{CB} as the statical moment of the areas with the proper *signs* of the $M/(EI)$ diagram between the verticals through C and B about C.

$$t_{CB} = A_1\bar{x}_1 + A_2\bar{x}_2 + A_3\bar{x}_2 = \frac{1}{EI}\left[\frac{1}{2}a(+Pa)\frac{2}{3}a + \frac{1}{2}\frac{a}{2}(+Pa)\right.$$
$$\left.\left(a + \frac{1}{3}\frac{a}{2}\right) + \frac{1}{2}\frac{a}{2}(-Pa)\left(\frac{3a}{2} + \frac{2}{3}\frac{a}{2}\right)\right] = +\frac{Pa^3}{6EI}$$

The *positive sign* of t_{CB} indicates that the point C must be *above* the tangent through B. Hence a corrected sketch of the elastic curve is made, Fig. 11-24d, where it is seen that the deflection sought is given by the distance AA' and is equal to $AA'' - A'A''$. Further, since the triangles $A'A''B$ and $CC'B$ are similar triangles, the distance $A'A'' = t_{CB}/2$. On the other hand, the distance AA'' is the deviation of the point A from the tangent to the elastic curve at the support B. Hence

$$y_A = AA' = AA'' - A'A'' = t_{AB} - \frac{t_{CB}}{2}$$

$$t_{AB} = \frac{1}{EI}(A_4\bar{x}_4) = \frac{1}{EI}\left[\frac{1}{2}a(-Pa)\frac{2}{3}a\right] = -\frac{Pa^3}{3EI}$$

where the negative sign means that point A is below the tangent through B. This sign is *not* used henceforth, as the geometry of the elastic curve indicates the direction of the actual displacements. Thus the deflection of point A below the line passing through the supports is

$$y_A = \frac{Pa^3}{3EI} - \frac{1}{2}\frac{Pa^3}{6EI} = \frac{Pa^3}{4EI}$$

* See Table 2 in the Appendix for a formula giving an area enclosed by a parabola, as well as for $\bar{x}$.

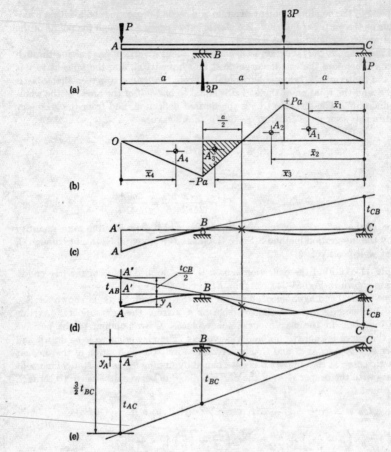

Fig. 11-24.

This example illustrates the necessity of watching the signs of the quantities computed in the applications of the moment-area method, although usually less difficulty is encountered than in the above example. For instance, if the deflection of the end A is established by first finding the rotation of the elastic curve at C, no ambiguity in the direction of tangents occurs. This scheme of analysis is shown in Fig. 11-24e, where

$$y_A = \tfrac{3}{2} t_{BC} - t_{AC}.$$

Example 11-12. A simple beam supports two equal and opposite forces P at the quarter points, Fig. 11-25a. Find the deflection of the beam at the middle of the span. The EI is constant.

SOLUTION: The bending-moment diagram and elastic curve with a tangent at C are shown in Figs. 11-25b and c, respectively. Then, since the statical moment of the positive and negative areas of the bending-moment diagram around A and B, respectively, are numerically equal, i.e., $|t_{AC}| = |t_{BC}|$, the deflection of the beam at the center of the span is *zero*. The elastic curve in this case is *anti*symmetrical. Noting this, much work may be avoided in obtaining the deflections at the *center of the span*. The deflection of any other point on the elastic curve must be found in the usual manner.

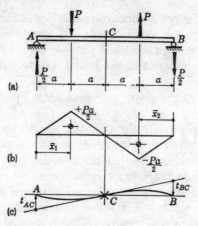

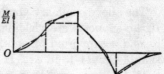

Fig. 11-25.

11-12. Step-by-Step Procedure. The foregoing examples illustrate the manner in which the moment-area method may be used to obtain the deflection of *any* statically determinate beam. No matter how complex the $M/(EI)$ diagrams may become, the above procedures are applicable, although simpler techniques can be used in certain cases to be discussed later. In practical applications, any $M/(EI)$ diagram whatsoever may be *approximated* by a number of rectangles and triangles, as is shown in Fig. 11-26. Such computations are perfectly legitimate in engineering practice. The approximation involved depends only on the diligence of the analyst. Thus, in order to clarify the fundamental moment-area procedure, it is outlined below. The sequence of the solution for obtaining the deflection of a beam by the moment-area method is definite and uniform.

Fig. 11-26. Approximation of an $M/(EI)$ diagram area in terms of triangles and rectangles. This is often used in engineering practice.

1. Make a good free-body diagram of the beam.

2. Directly below the beam, construct the bending-moment diagram. The construction of a shear diagram before the bending-moment diagram often forms a desirable auxiliary step.

3. Below the bending-moment diagram, construct the $M/(EI)$ diagram by dividing the moment ordinates by the corresponding EI of the beam at the *same* sections. This step may be omitted if the EI for a given beam is constant.

4. Below the $M/(EI)$ diagram, sketch a *definite* elastic curve which exaggerates the deflections. The curvature of the elastic curve must conform to the *sign* of the $M/(EI)$ diagram. If the $M/(EI)$ diagram is

positive, the elastic curve is concave upwards and vice versa. *No abrupt changes in the direction of the tangents to the curve are permissible.* Moreover, the elastic curve so drawn must pass *over the supports*, and, for a fixed end, it must *also* be tangent to the initial direction of the unloaded axis of the beam.

5. On the sketch of the elastic curve, indicate the desired displacement of the beam.

6. Formulate algebraically the quantity sought in (5) in terms of the geometrical conditions of the elastic curve and the tangential deviations. In a general case, this requires that the direction of a tangent to the elastic curve *at one of the supports be established.* Only at a fixed support and at the center of symmetrically loaded beams, is the direction of tangents known at the outset. For the maximum deflection of beams other than cantilevers and symmetrically loaded beams, a special treatment is required.

7. Clearly indicate the tangential deviations required in (6) on the elastic curve prepared in (4).

8. By applying the second moment-area theorem, compute the required deviations. Consider the positive areas of the $M/(EI)$ diagram positive, and the negative ones as *negative* quantities.

9. Solve the relation formulated in (6) for the required deflection.

The above summary applies to cases where the supports are unyielding. If the supports are yielding, i.e., the beam actually rests on springs, or its end is supported by another beam, the reader is referred to the discussion of Fig. 11-13 in Art. 11-6.

11-13. Superposition and the Moment-Area Method. In many instances it is desirable to express the deflection of a point on a loaded beam by an algebraic formula. Yet it frequently happens that the $M/(EI)$ diagram, even for beams of constant flexural rigidity EI, does not lend itself to ready application of the moment-area theorems because of its irregular geometric configuration. This is especially true when uniform and concentrated forces are both acting on a given beam simultaneously. In such cases it is often convenient to remove all of the given forces from the beam. Then, one at a time, the forces are applied to the beam and the corresponding moment diagram is drawn for each individual force. Each area of these bending-moment diagrams, or statical moment thereof, may then be separately determined. The combined computed deflections give the desired end result. This method is that of *superposition* and has already been recommended in Art. 11-6 for use with the integration method. It is identically equivalent to using the complete bending-moment diagram for *all* of the applied forces for determining areas or their statical moments. The separate bending-moment diagrams for a single loading at a time and the corresponding usual bending-moment diagrams for all of the applied forces are illustrated in Fig. 11-27.

Superposition of deflections applies only to beams where forces act transversely, although such forces may act in different planes (Art. 11-7). If *axial* forces are also acting on the member, the deflections are not linear functions of the applied forces and cannot be superposed (Art. 13-10).

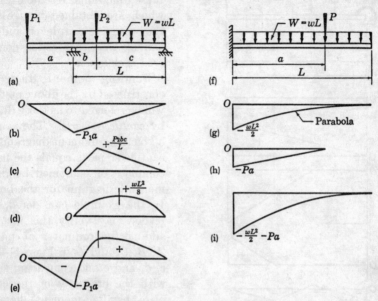

Fig. 11-27.　Separate and combined moment diagrams.

11-14. Bending-Moment Diagrams by Cantilever Parts for Use in the Moment-Area Method.

Bending-moment diagrams may be constructed for a given loading on a beam in an entirely different manner than has hitherto been described. For example, consider a loaded beam such as shown in Fig. 11-28a, for which the reactions have been determined in the usual manner. Then, by taking the origin of x at the end A, and successively passing the arbitrary sections through the beam in the intervals AB, BC, and CD, the following algebraic expressions for the bending moments result:

$$A \text{ to } B: \quad M = -1{,}000 + 200x$$

$$B \text{ to } C: \quad M = -1{,}000 + 200x - 500(x - 6)$$

$$C \text{ to } D: \quad M = -1{,}000 + 200x - 500(x - 6) + 500(x - 10)$$

It is seen from this set of expressions that the concentrated moment at the end A, $M_A = -1{,}000$ ft-lb, appears in every expression. Hence it may be plotted as a continuous function, as is done in Fig. 11-28b. Likewise, $R_A x = 200x$ ft-lb is a continuous function for the whole span and may be plotted as is shown in Fig. 11-28c. It reaches a maximum value of $+3,000$ ft-lb at D. Next, if $(x - 6)$ is treated as a new variable for P_1 and $(x - 10)$ for R_C, the bending moments caused by these forces may be represented as is shown respectively in Figs. 11-28d and e. For

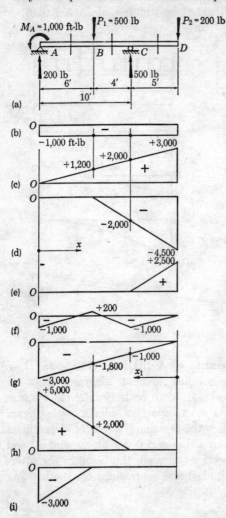

each force, including reactions, these diagrams resemble those which are obtained by treating the beam as a cantilever, and imagining that the section considered is clamped.

Bending-moment diagrams constructed by the above method will be referred to as those drawn by *cantilever parts*. The *sum of all* bending-moment diagrams by cantilever parts equals the usual complete or combined bending-moment diagram for the beam. In the example considered, the reader may verify this fact by adding the ordinates at points A, B, C, and D in Figs. 11-28b, c, d, and e and comparing them with the ordinates of the complete bending-moment diagram shown in Fig. 11-28f.

Bending-moment diagrams by cantilever parts may be drawn by considering an origin *or origins* of x at any convenient point. By measuring x_1 from the end D, the complete bending-moment diagram is a sum of those shown by parts in Figs. 11-28g, h, and i. Bending-moment diagrams by cantilever parts from A to C, Fig. 11-28b, c and d, and from D to C, Fig. 11-28g, also make up the complete bending-moment diagram.

Fig. 11-28. A method for constructing bending-moment diagrams by cantilever parts.

In some instances, the use of the bending-moment diagrams by cantilever parts leads to simpler solutions for the deflections of beams, as the resulting areas and their centroids for use in the moment-area method are easily determined

Example 11-13. Find the deflection at the center of the span due to the applied loads for the partially loaded beam shown in Fig. 11-29a. The EI is constant.

SOLUTION: The reactions are determined first and are indicated in Fig. 11-29a. The origin of x for the bending-moment diagrams by cantilever parts is taken at B. These diagrams are shown in Figs. 11-29b, c, and d. For uniform loading, the curves are second-degree parabolas. The diagram is bounded by a straight line between A

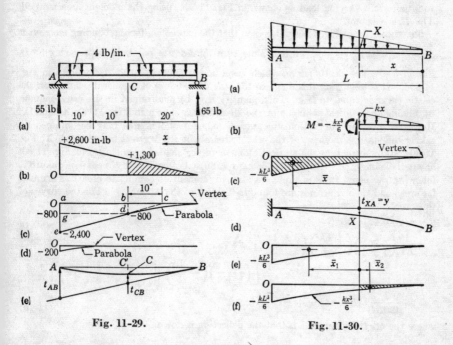

Fig. 11-29.   Fig. 11-30.

and C in Fig. 11-29c. The elastic curve is shown in Fig. 11-29e, and the deflection sought is represented by the distance $C'C$. Henceforth, the moment-area method is applied in the usual manner. See Table 2 of the Appendix for various expressions of areas and their centroids. For the second-degree parabola, $n = 2$.

$$y_C = C'C = \frac{t_{AB}}{2} - t_{CB}$$

$+\frac{1}{2}(40)2,600(\frac{1}{3})40 \quad = +693,000 \qquad$ (for triangle in Fig. 11-29b)

$-\frac{1}{3}(20)800\left(20 + \frac{20}{4}\right) = -133,000 \qquad$ (for parabola in Fig. 11-29c)

$-20(800)10 \qquad\qquad = -160,000 \qquad$ (for rectangle $abdg$)

$-\frac{1}{2}(20)1,600(\frac{2}{3})20 \quad = -107,000 \qquad$ (for triangle gde)

$-\frac{1}{3}(10)200(\frac{1}{4})10 \quad\; = -\;\;\;\; 1,670 \qquad$ (for parabola in Fig. 11-29d)

$\qquad\qquad EIt_{AB} = +291,000$

$+\frac{1}{2}(20)1,300(\frac{1}{3})20 \quad = +\;\; 86,700 \qquad$ (for the shaded triangle)

$-\frac{1}{3}(20)800(\frac{1}{4})20 \quad\; = -\;\; 26,700 \qquad$ (for parabola from C to B)

$\qquad\qquad EIt_{CB} = +\;\; 60,000$

hence
$$y_C = \frac{t_{AB}}{2} - t_{CB} = \frac{86,000}{EI}$$

Another technique of working with the $M/(EI)$ areas, which avoids the necessity of direct integration of the areas, is best illustrated by an example.

Example 11-14. Find the equation of the elastic curve for the cantilever subjected to a uniformly varying load as shown in Fig. 11-30a, using the moment-area method. The EI is constant.

SOLUTION: From Fig. 11-30b it is seen that the expression for the bending moment is $M = -\frac{1}{2}x(kx)\frac{x}{3} = -\frac{kx^3}{6}$ which plots as a *third-degree* parabola with vertex at B, Fig. 11-30c. The elastic curve, which has a horizontal tangent at A, is shown in Fig. 11-30d. It is seen from this diagram that the deflection y of a general point X on the elastic curve is equal to t_{XA}. This quantity may be determined in the usual manner by finding the statical moment of the shaded area shown in Fig. 11-30c around X. However, to avoid integration, the statical moment of this area may be obtained by taking the statical moment of the whole area about the vertical line through X, Fig. 11-30e, and subtracting the statical moment of the shaded area shown in Fig. 11-30f about the same line. For the latter case $\bar{x}_2$ must be treated as a negative quantity, following the usual rules of finding a statical moment of composite areas. Formulas for areas and their centroids are found in Table 2 of the Appendix. For the curves of this problem, $n = 3$. Hence

$$y = t_{XA} = A\bar{x} = A_1\bar{x}_1 - A_2(-\bar{x}_2)$$

$$= \frac{1}{EI}\left(\frac{L}{3+1}\right)\left(-\frac{kL^3}{6}\right)\left(\frac{3+1}{3+2}L - x\right)$$

$$\qquad\qquad - \frac{1}{EI}\left[\left(\frac{x}{3+1}\right)\left(-\frac{kx^3}{6}\right)\right]\left[-\left(x - \frac{3+1}{3+2}x\right)\right]$$

$$= -\frac{k}{120EI}(4L^5 - 5L^4x + x^5) \qquad\qquad\qquad (11\text{-}16)$$

where the negative sign means that the deflection is down.

Problems for Solution

11-1. A round aluminum bar of $\frac{1}{4}$ in. diameter is bent into a circular ring having a mean diameter of 125 in. What is the maximum stress in the bar? $E = 10^7$ psi. *Ans.* 20 ksi.

11-2. What will the radius of curvature of an 8 WF 17 beam bent around the X-X axis be if the stress in the extreme fibers is 20 ksi? $E = 29 \times 10^6$ psi.

11-3. If the equation of the elastic curve for a simply supported beam of length L having a constant EI is $y = (k/360EI)(-3x^5 + 10x^3L^2 - 7xL^4)$, how is the beam loaded?

11-4. Rework Example 11-2 by taking the origin of the coordinate system at the free end. *Ans.* $y = (M_1/2EI)(x^2 - 2Lx + L^2)$.

11-5.* Using the exact differential equation, Eq. 11-3, show that the equation of the elastic curve in Example 11-2 is $x^2 + (y - \rho)^2 = \rho^2$, where ρ is a constant. (*Hint:* let $dy/dx = \tan\theta$ and integrate.)

11-6. Rework Example 11-3 by integrating the general expression for M twice and then finding the constants of integration from the conditions at the boundaries.

11-7 through 11-15. For the beams loaded as shown in the figures, determine the equations of the elastic curves using either the double integration method or the method of successive integrations, as directed.   In all cases, EI is constant.   *Ans.* See Table 11 in the Appendix, and

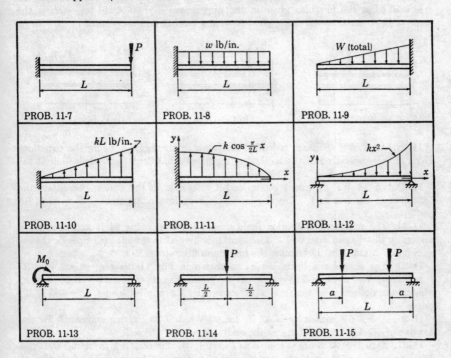

PROB. 11-7	PROB. 11-8	PROB. 11-9
PROB. 11-10	PROB. 11-11	PROB. 11-12
PROB. 11-13	PROB. 11-14	PROB. 11-15

Prob. 11-10: $EIy = \dfrac{kL^3x^2}{6} - \dfrac{kL^2x^3}{12} + \dfrac{kx^5}{120}$;

Prob. 11-11: $EIy = \dfrac{16kL^4}{\pi^4}\cos\dfrac{\pi x}{2L} - \dfrac{kLx^3}{3\pi} + \dfrac{kL^2x^2}{\pi} - \dfrac{16kL^4}{\pi^4}$;

Prob. 11-12: $EIy = \dfrac{kL^3x^3}{72} - \dfrac{kx^6}{360} = \dfrac{kL^5x}{90}$.

11-16. If a cantilever is loaded as shown in Prob. 11-7 and its width *and* flexural strength are constant (see Fig. 10-18d), what is the equation of the elastic curve?   Neglect the increase in depth at the end of the beam for the shear force.   *Ans.* $EI_o y = 2\,PL^2x - \frac{4}{5}PL^{3/2}\,x^{3/2} - \frac{2}{5}PL^3$, where I_o is the moment of inertia of the cross-section at the fixed end.

11-17. If in Prob. 11-14 the cross-sectional area of the beam is constant, and the left half of the span is made of steel ($E = 30 \times 10^6$ psi) and the right half is made of aluminum ($E = 10 \times 10^6$ psi), determine the equation of the elastic curve.

11-18. Rework Example 11-5 using the procedure of Example 11-6.

11-19. Determine the equations of the elastic curve for the beam loaded as shown in Fig. 11-10.

11-20. Compute the maximum flexural stress and the maximum deflection for a 15 I 42.9 simply supported beam spanning 20 ft loaded with a 10 kip concentrated downward force in the middle of the span and a uniformly distributed gravity load, including the weight of the beam, of 1 kip per ft. $E = 29 \times 10^6$ psi.   Use the formulas given in the Appendix and the method of superposition.   *Ans.* 20.4 ksi, 0.505 in.

11-21. A 10 WF 49 cantilever supports a concentrated force as shown in the figure. Calculate the deflections caused by the applied force (a) at the applied force, (b) at the free end. Use the formulas given in the Appendix. $E = 30 \times 10^6$ psi. (*Hint:* the slope of the beam between the applied force and the free end is constant.)

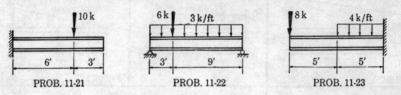

PROB. 11-21   PROB. 11-22   PROB. 11-23

11-22. An 8 WF 40 beam is loaded as shown in the figure. Using the equations given in the Appendix and the method of superposition, calculate the deflection at the center of the span. $E = 29 \times 10^6$ psi.

11-23.* A 14 WF 87 cantilever is loaded as shown in the figure. Calculate the deflection of the free end. Use the formulas given in the Appendix. $E = 30 \times 10^6$ psi.

11-24. The maximum deflection for a simple beam spanning 24 ft and carrying a uniformly distributed load of 100 kips (total) is limited to 0.5 in. (a) Specify the required WF beam. (b) Determine the maximum fiber stress.

11-25. The data for a beam loaded as shown in Fig. 11-12a are: $w = 2$ kips/ft, $P = 5$ kips, $L = 10$ ft, and $a = 4$ ft. If the beam is made from an 8 WF 20 section, what is the deflection of the free end C caused by the applied loads? $E = 30 \times 10^6$ psi.

11-26. A 3 I 5.7 cantilever is 42 in. long. What is its "spring constant" for the downward application of a force at the end? $E = 29 \times 10^6$ psi.

11-27. A 10 WF 33 beam is loaded as shown in the figure. A 1 in. round steel rod 8 ft long provides the anchorage for the right-hand end. Determine the deflection of the left end caused by the applied concentrated force. $E = 30 \times 10^6$ psi.

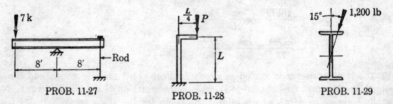

PROB. 11-27   PROB. 11-28   PROB. 11-29

11-28. A small frame is loaded as shown in the figure. The cross-sectional areas of the vertical and the horizontal parts of the frame are equal. Determine the vertical deflection of the end at the applied force. Neglect the effect of the axial force on deflection and neglect shortening of the column due to the same force. Express the result in terms of P, L, E and I. (*Hint:* synthesize the solution from the results of Example 11-2 and the appropriate formula from the Appendix.) *Ans.* 13| $PL^3/192EI$.

11-29. Determine the deflection of the end of an 8 I 18.4 cantilever $6\frac{1}{2}$ ft long due to an inclined force of 1,200 lb applied at the end as shown in the figure.

11-30. The M/EI diagram for a simple beam is as shown in the figure. Draw a qualitative elastic curve and compute t_{AB} and $\Delta\theta_{AD}$. *Ans.* $878,000/EI$ in., $6,000/EI$.

11-31. If a positive M/EI diagram for a simple beam were as shown in the figure, what would the statical moment of the shaded area around a line through X give? Illustrate on a sketch.

11-32. An aluminum bar 1.2 in. wide and 1 in. deep is supported and loaded as shown in the figure. Calculate the angles (in radians) between the tangent to the elastic curve at A and the corresponding tangents at B, C, and D caused by the applied loads. $E = 10^7$ psi. *Ans.* 0.03125, 0.0625, 0.

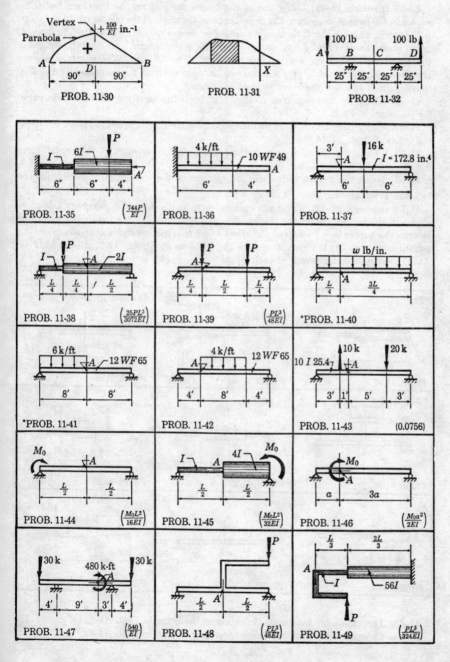

PROB. 11-30

PROB. 11-31

PROB. 11-32

PROB. 11-35 $\left(\frac{744P}{EI}\right)$

PROB. 11-36

PROB. 11-37

PROB. 11-38 $\left(\frac{25PL^3}{3072EI}\right)$

PROB. 11-39 $\left(\frac{PL^3}{48EI}\right)$

*PROB. 11-40

*PROB. 11-41

PROB. 11-42

PROB. 11-43 (0.0756)

PROB. 11-44 $\left(\frac{M_0L^2}{16EI}\right)$

PROB. 11-45 $\left(\frac{M_0L^2}{32EI}\right)$

PROB. 11-46 $\left(\frac{M_0a^2}{2EI}\right)$

PROB. 11-47 $\left(\frac{540}{EI}\right)$

PROB. 11-48 $\left(\frac{PL^3}{48EI}\right)$

PROB. 11-49 $\left(\frac{PL^3}{324EI}\right)$

11-33. If an additional downward force of 1,000 lb is applied at D to the beam of Example 11-7, what will be the deflection of the end B?   *Ans.* 0.0338 in.

11-34. Using the moment-area method, find the maximum deflection for the beam of Prob. 11-9.

11-35 through 11-49. Using the moment-area method for the members loaded as shown in the figures, determine the deflection and the slope of the elastic curve at points A. Specify whether the deflection is upward or downward. If the size of the member is not given, assume that EI is constant over the entire length. Neglect the weight of the members. Wherever needed, assume $E = 30 \times 10^6$ psi. Wherever the answer is expressed in terms of EI, no adjustment for units need be made. *Ans.* The deflection sought is noted in the lower right-hand corner.

11-50. Using the moment-area method, establish the equation of the elastic curve for the beam of Prob. 11-7.

11-51. Using the moment-area method, establish the equation of the elastic curve for the beam of Prob. 11-14.

11-52.* Using the moment-area method, establish the equation of the elastic curve for the beam of Prob. 11-40.

11-53. Using the moment-area method, determine the maximum deflection for the beam of Prob. 11-44.   *Ans.* $M_oL^2/9\sqrt{3}\,EI$.

11-54 through 11-62. Using the moment-area method for the members loaded as shown in the figures, determine the location and magnitude of the maximum deflection *between* the supports. Disregard the effect of axial forces on deflections wherever this condition occurs. Other conditions are the same as in Probs. 11-35 through 11-49. *Ans.* Lower right-hand corner of each figure.

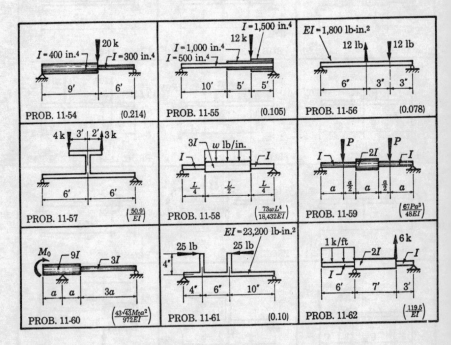

11-63. Determine the maximum deflection of the beam in Prob. 11-39.

11-64. Determine the maximum deflection of the beam in Prob. 11-42.

11-65. For the beam of Prob. 11-56, determine (a) the deflection at the center of the span and (b) the deflection at the point of inflection. *Ans.* (a) 0.075 in., (b) 0.047 in.

11-66. Rework Example 11-11 using the procedure shown in Fig. 11-24e.

11-67 through 11-72. Using the moment-area method, determine the deflection of the overhang at A for the beams loaded as shown. Other conditions are the same as in Probs. 11-54 through 11-62. *Ans.* Lower right-hand corner of each figure.

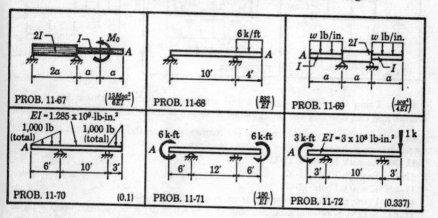

PROB. 11-67 $\left(\frac{13M_0a^2}{6EI}\right)$ PROB. 11-68 $\left(\frac{832}{EI}\right)$ PROB. 11-69 $\left(\frac{wa^4}{4EI}\right)$

PROB. 11-70 (0.1) PROB. 11-71 $\left(\frac{180}{EI}\right)$ PROB. 11-72 (0.337)

11-73. Determine the maximum *upward* deflection for the overhang of a beam loaded as shown in the figure. The E and I are constant. *Part Ans.* At 2.93 ft from right support.

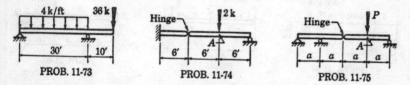

PROB. 11-73 PROB. 11-74 PROB. 11-75

11-74. A structure is formed by joining a simple beam to a cantilever beam with a hinge as shown in the figure. If a 2 kip force is applied at the center of the simple span, determine the deflection caused by this force at A. Use the moment-area method. The EI is constant over the entire structure.

11-75. Two beams, both of the same, constant, flexural rigidity EI, are connected by a hinge as shown in the figure. Find the deflection at A caused by the applied force P. Use the moment-area method. *Ans.* $Pa^3/3EI$.

PROB. 11-76

11-76. Determine the deflection at the mid-span of a simple beam, loaded as shown in the figure, by solving the two separate problems indicated and superposing the results. Use the moment-area method. The EI is constant. *Ans.* $11PL^3/768EI$.

11-77 and 11-78. Using the moment-area method, determine the deflection at the center of the span for the beams loaded as shown in the figures. In Prob. 11-78, $I_1 = 10$ in.^{4}, $I_2 = 20$ in.^{4}, and $E_{Al} = 10^7$ psi. *Ans. Prob.* 11-77: $4Pa^3/3EI$. *Prob.* 11-78: $).162$ in.

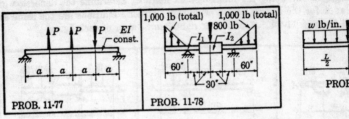

PROB. 11-77   PROB. 11-78

PROB. 11-79

11-79. Using the moment-area method and superposition, determine the end deflection and end slope for the beam loaded as shown in the figure. The EI is constant.

In the following three problems use the moment-area method and obtain the results by superposing the solutions for separate loadings.

11-80. Rework Example 11-11.

11-81. Rework Prob. 11-22.

11-82. Rework Prob. 11-23.

11-83. Using the moment-area method, rework Prob. 11-24.

11-84. A light pointer is attached only at A to a 6 in. by 6 in. (actual) wooden beam as shown in the figure. Determine the position of the end of the pointer after a concentrated force of 1,200 lb is applied. $E = 1.2 \times 10^6$ psi.

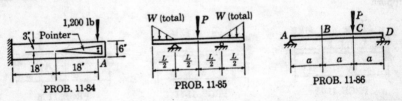

PROB. 11-84   PROB. 11-85   PROB. 11-86

11-85. What must the ratio of the loads W and P be for the beam loaded as shown in the figure so that the elastic curve shall be horizontal at the supports? The EI is constant. *Ans.* $\frac{3}{8}$.

11-86. The beam $ABCD$ is initially horizontal. A load P is then applied at C as shown in the figure. It is desired to place a vertical force at B to bring the position of the beam *at* B back to the original level $ABCD$. What force is required at B? *Ans.* $7P/8$.

11-87 through 11-89. For the beams loaded as shown in the figures, plot moment diagrams by cantilever parts.

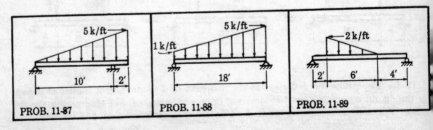

PROB. 11-87   PROB. 11-88   PROB. 11-89

Solve the following three problems by using moment diagrams constructed by cantilever parts.

11-90. Rework Prob. 11-39.

11-91. Rework Prob. 11-41.

11-92. Rework Prob. 11-44.

11-93. Using the moment-area method, establish the equation of the elastic curve for a uniformly loaded cantilever beam of constant flexural rigidity.

Chapter Twelve

STATICALLY INDETERMINATE MEMBERS

12-1. Introduction. There is a large and important class of problems in which the reactions cannot be determined from statics alone. For example, if the beam shown in Fig. 12-1a has an extra support at A as in Fig. 12-1b, four reaction components are unknown. These cannot be found directly from the equations of statics. Further examination of

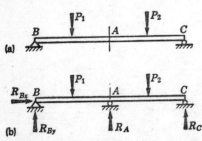

Fig. 12-1. The same beam is statically determinate in (a) and indeterminate in (b).

Fig. 12-1b shows that any one of the three vertical reactions can be removed, and the beam will remain in equilibrium. Therefore one of these reactions is *superfluous*, or *redundant*, for maintaining equilibrium. Problems where extra or redundant reactive forces and/or moments exist are known as *statically indeterminate problems*. The solution of such problems, when materials behave elastically, is the main object of this chapter. Particular attention will be directed toward the methods of finding the magnitudes of the redundant reactions. *After the redundant reactions are known, a member becomes statically determinate and may be analyzed for strength or stiffness by the methods treated earlier.*

When the number of unknown reactions exceeds that which may be determined by statics by one, the member is said to be indeterminate to the *first degree*. As the number of the unknowns increases, the degree of indeterminacy also increases. For example, by providing an additional support for the beam in Fig. 12-1b, the beam becomes indeterminate to the second degree. When the *internal* forces in a structure cannot be found from statics, it is said to be indeterminate *internally*. Such problems will also be discussed in this chapter.

The treatment of statically indeterminate beams will be limited to situations where the applied forces act perpendicularly to the axes of straight beams. Moreover, it will be *assumed that in all cases the horizontal components of the reactions are negligible*. This reduces the degree of inde-

310

terminacy by one. On the basis of this assumption, the beam shown in Fig. 12-2a with pins at both ends, which presumably cannot move toward each other, is a determinate beam. Likewise, the beams shown in Figs. 12-2b and c are indeterminate to

the first and second degree, respectively. This assumption is justified, as the exact analysis* of the problem shows that, for small deflections of beams, the horizontal force caused by the difference in lengths of the elastic curve and of the chord is small.†

12-2. The Basis of Analysis. The equations of statics *RE-MAIN VALID* in all statically indeterminate problems. They are *necessary, but not sufficient,* to solve the indeterminate problems. The supplementary conditions come from *geometrical* considerations. In statically indeterminate problems, the conditions of static equilibrium *and*

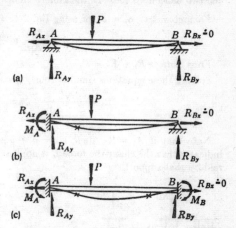

Fig. 12-2. Assuming that the horizontal components of the reactions are negligible, the beam in (a) is determinate, the beam in (b) is indeterminate to the first degree, and the beam in (c) is indeterminate to the second degree.

the prescribed geometrical conditions governing the *deformation* must be fulfilled simultaneously.

The necessary formulas and procedures for making a geometrical study of the *deformations* for statically determinate members were developed earlier in this text. More specifically, elastic deformation of axially loaded rods, elastic twist of shafts, and elastic deflection of beams were treated in detail. The same procedures can be used to formulate the deformations of any structure. Moreover, since in statically indeterminate problems, certain parts must, of physical necessity, deflect together, twist together, expand together, etc., or remain stationary, these facts furnish the additional conditions for formulating the auxiliary equations. This underlying concept is applicable whatever the structure.

Example 12-1. A stepped rod is built-in at both ends to immovable planes, Fig. 12-3a. The upper part of the rod has a cross-sectional area A_1; the area of the lower part is A_2. If an axial force P is applied at the point of discontinuity of the section, what are the reactions R_1 and R_2? The elastic modulus of the material is E.

SOLUTION: The point on the rod where the force P is applied deflects the same amount whether the upper or the lower part of the rod is considered. By separating

* See Timoshenko, S., *Theory of Plates and Shells.* New York: McGraw-Hill, 1940. The horizontal force becomes important in thin plates.

† From the practical point of view it is also known that in actual constructions it is usually very difficult to prevent inward movement of the supports.

the rod at P, the two free-body diagrams shown in Figs. 12-3b and c are obtained. The upper part of the rod is subjected throughout its length to the force R_1 and deflects an amount Δ_1. The lower part deflects Δ_2 under the action of R_2. Of physical necessity, the two deflections must be the same. Hence

From geometry: $\Delta_1 = \Delta_2$, or using Eq. 2-4, $\Delta = PL/(AE)$.

$$\frac{R_1 a}{A_1 E} = \frac{R_2 b}{A_2 E}$$

From statics: $R_1 + R_2 = P$.

Solving these equations simultaneously gives

$$R_1 = \frac{P}{1 + \dfrac{aA_2}{bA_1}} \quad \text{and} \quad R_2 = \frac{P}{1 + \dfrac{bA_1}{aA_2}}$$

Note that if $A_1 = A_2$, then, since $a + b = L$, $R_1 = Pb/L$ and $R_2 = Pa/L$. This indicates that the closer the force P is applied to a given support, the more of it is carried by that support.

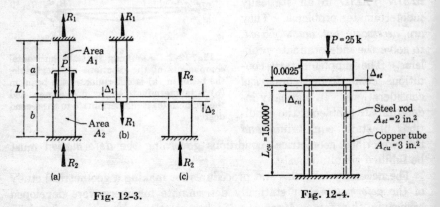

Fig. 12-3.   Fig. 12-4.

Torsional problems may also be statically indeterminate. For example, if a shaft is built-in at both ends and a torque is applied at some intermediate point, the two torques at the ends cannot be found from statics alone. However, analogous to the above example, by separating the shaft at the applied torque and equating the angular rotation of one part of the shaft to the angular rotation of the other part, an auxiliary geometrical equation may be formulated and the problem can be solved.

Example 12-2. A steel rod 2 in.² in cross-sectional area and 15.0025 in. long is loosely inserted into a copper tube as shown in Fig. 12-4. The copper tube has a cross-sectional area of 3 in.² and is 15.0000 in. long. If an axial force $P = 25$ kips is applied through a rigid cap, what stresses will exist in the two materials? Assume that the elastic moduli of steel and copper are $E_{st} = 30 \times 10^6$ psi and $E_{cu} = 17 \times 10^6$ psi, respectively.

SOLUTION: If the applied force P is sufficiently large to close the small gap, a force P_{st} will be developed in the steel rod and a force P_{cu} in the copper tube. Moreover, upon loading, the steel rod will compress axially Δ_{st}, which is as much as the axial deformation Δ_{cu} of the copper tube plus the initial gap. Hence

From geometry: $\Delta_{st} = \Delta_{cu} + 0.0025$, or using Eq. 2-4, $\Delta = PL/(AE)$,

$$\frac{P_{st}L_{st}}{A_{st}E_{st}} = \frac{P_{cu}L_{cu}}{A_{cu}E_{cu}} + 0.0025$$

or

$$\frac{15.0025}{2(30)10^6} P_{st} - \frac{15}{3(17)10^6} P_{cu} = 0.0025$$

or

$$P_{st} - 1.176P_{cu} = 10,000 \text{ lb}$$

From statics: $P_{st} + P_{cu} = 25,000$ lb.

Solving these equations simultaneously gives

$$P_{cu} = 6,900 \text{ lb} \quad \text{and} \quad P_{st} = 18,100 \text{ lb}$$

whence, dividing these forces by the respective cross-sectional areas gives

$$\sigma_{cu} = \frac{6,900}{3} = 2,300 \text{ psi} \quad \text{and} \quad \sigma_{st} = \frac{18,100}{2} = 9,050 \text{ psi}$$

If either of the above stresses were above the proportional limit of its material, or the applied force were too small to close the gap, the above solution would not be valid. Also note that since the deformations considered are small, *it is always sufficiently accurate to use* $L_{st} = L_{cu}$.

This example illustrates a case of *internal* indeterminacy.

ALTERNATE SOLUTION: The force F necessary to close the gap may be found first, using Eq. 2-4. In developing this force the rod acts as a "spring" and resists a part of the applied force. The *remaining* force P' causes equal deflections Δ_{st}' and Δ_{cu}' in the two materials.

$$F = \frac{\Delta A_{st}E_{st}}{L_{st}} = \frac{(0.0025)2(30)10^6}{15.0025} = 10,000 \text{ lb} = 10 \text{ kips}$$

$$P' = P - F = 25 - 10 = 15 \text{ kips}$$

Then if P_{st}' is the force resisted by the steel rod in *addition to the force* F, and P_{cu}' is the force carried by the copper tube,

From statics: $P_{st}' + P_{cu}' = P' = 15$

From geometry: $\Delta_{st}' = \Delta_{cu}'$ or $\dfrac{P_{st}'L_{st}}{A_{st}E_{st}} = \dfrac{P_{cu}'L_{cu}}{A_{cu}E_{cu}}$,

$$\frac{15.0025}{2(30)10^6} P_{st}' = \frac{15}{3(17)10^6} P_{cu}', \qquad P_{cu}' = \frac{17}{20} P_{st}'$$

By solving the two appropriate equations simultaneously, it is found that $P_{cu}' = 6.9$ kips and $P_{st}' = 8.1$ kips, or $P_{st} = P_{st}' + F = 18.1$ kips.

Example 12-3. Two cantilever beams AD and BE of equal flexural rigidity $EI = 9 \times 10^9$ lb-in.², shown in Fig. 12-5a, are interconnected by a taut steel rod DC ($E_{st} = 30 \times 10^6$ psi). The rod DC is 12 ft 6 in. long and has a cross-section of 0.5 in.² Find the deflection of the cantilever AD at D due to a force $P = 10$ kips applied at E.

SOLUTION: The force exerted by the rod DC on the cantilever AD must be found. This cannot be done by using statics alone. However, the solution can be found in a manner analogous to Example 12-1, except that the deformations of the structure consist of deflections of beams and the stretch of the rod. The deflection of the point D is the same whether the beam AD at D or the top of the rod DC is considered. By separating the structure at D, the two free-body diagrams shown in Figs. 12-5b and c are obtained. In both diagrams the *same unknown force* X is shown acting (a condition of statics). The deflection Δ_1 of the point D in Fig. 12-5b caused by X may be found, say, by using the moment-area method. For this purpose, the bending-moment diagram is shown in Fig. 12-5d. The deflection Δ_2 of the point D on the rod is equal to the deflection y_C of the beam BE caused by the forces P *and* X, *less the* elastic stretch of the rod DC. The deflection y_C may also be found by the moment-area method, using the bending-moment diagrams shown in Fig. 12-5e.   Hence

From statics: $X_{\text{pull on }AD} = X_{\text{pull on }DC} = X$

From geometry: $\Delta_1 = \Delta_2$ or $y_D = y_C - \Delta_{\text{rod}}$

However, $y_D = t_{DA} = \dfrac{1}{EI}\left[\dfrac{1}{2}\,60(-60X)\dfrac{2}{3}\,60\right] = -(8)10^{-6}\,X$ *down*

$\qquad y_C$ *due to* P $= t_{CB}$ *due to* P

$$= \frac{1}{EI}\left[60(-600{,}000)\frac{1}{2}\,60 + \frac{1}{2}\,60(-600{,}000)\frac{2}{3}\,60\right]$$

$$= -0.200 \text{ in. } down$$

$\qquad y_C$ *due to* X $= t_{CB}$ *due to* X $= |\,t_{DA}\,| = 8(10)^{-6}X$ *up*

$$\Delta_{\text{rod}} = \frac{XL_{CD}}{A_{CD}E} = \frac{X(12.5)12}{0.5(30)10^6} = 10(10)^{-6}X$$

whence, $(8)10^{-6}X = 0.200 - (8)10^{-6}X - (10)10^{-6}X$,

or $X = +7{,}690$ lb, and $y_D = -(8)10^6(7{,}690) = -0.0615$ in. *down.*

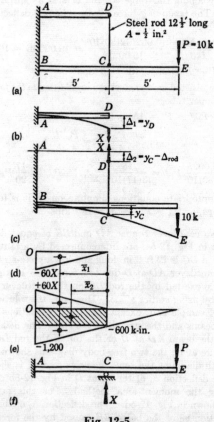

Fig. 12-5.

Note particularly that the deflection of point C is caused by the applied force P *as well as by the unknown force* X. The signs of the deflections used in the equation where the deflections are equated follow from the geometry of the deformed structure. Several equations for elastic curves for different loadings are given in Table 11 of the Appendix to facilitate computations of beam deflections.

If in the above problem the rod DC were attached to a *very* rigid beam AD, by geometry y_D would equal zero and y_C would equal Δ_{rod}. If, further, the rod AD were also made *very* rigid, the problem would become the one shown in Fig. 12-5f, where the geometrical condition is $y_C = 0$.

12-3. Stresses Caused by Temperature. Deformations of bodies caused by temperature change were disregarded in the preceding chapters of the text. It was possible to do so because a member is *free* to expand or contract in statically determinate systems. However, in statically *indeterminate* systems, expansion or contraction of a body may be *inhibited* or entirely *prevented* in certain directions. This effect may cause significant stresses in the body and must be investigated.

To determine the stresses caused by temperature, the deformations caused by a change in temperature must be known. This *linear* deformation Δ taking place in every direction due to a **change** in temperature of δT degrees is

$$\Delta = \alpha \, (\delta T) \, L \qquad (12\text{-}1)$$

where α is the coefficient of thermal expansion for a particular material and L is the length of a member in the direction of Δ. The coefficient α is experimentally determined and in the English system of units is given in inches per inch per degree Fahrenheit. For a positive change in temperature δT, materials expand, and vice versa. Linear strain ϵ follows from Eq. 12-1 by dividing it by L, i.e., $\epsilon = \alpha \, \delta T$. Typical values of α for a few materials are given in Table 1 of the Appendix.

The solution of indeterminate problems involving temperature deformations follows the concepts of statics and geometry discussed in the preceding article.

Example 12-4. A copper tube 12 in. long and having a cross-sectional area of 3 in.² is placed between two very rigid caps made of Invar,* Fig. 12-6a. Four ¾ in. steel bolts are symmetrically arranged parallel to the axis of the tube and are lightly tightened. Find the stress in the copper tube if the temperature of the assembly is raised from 60°F to 160°F. Let $E_{cu} = 17 \times 10^6$ psi, $E_{st} = 30 \times 10^6$ psi, $\alpha_{cu} = 0.0000091$ per degree Fahrenheit, and $\alpha_{st} = 0.0000065$ per degree Fahrenheit.

SOLUTION: *If* the copper tube and the steel bolts were *free* to expand, the axial thermal elongations shown in Fig. 12-6b would take place. However, since the axial deformation of the tube must be the same as that of the bolts, the copper tube will be *pushed back* and the bolts will be *pulled out*, so that the net deformations will be the same. Moreover, as may be established by considering a free body of the assembly above some arbitrary plane, as X-X in Fig. 12-6a, the *compressive force* P_{cu} in the copper tube and the *tensile force* P_{st} in the steel bolts are equal. Hence

---

* Invar is a steel alloy which at ordinary temperatures has an $\alpha \doteq 0$ and for this reason is used in the best grades of surveyor's tapes and watch springs.

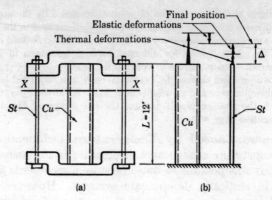

Fig. 12-6.

From statics: $P_{cu} = P_{st} = P$

From geometry: $\Delta_{cu} = \Delta_{st} = \Delta$ (in Fig. 12-6b) or from Eqs. 12-1 and 2-4,

$$\alpha_{cu}\, \delta T\, L_{cu} - \frac{P_{cu} L_{cu}}{A_{cu} E_{cu}} = \alpha_{st}\, \delta T\, L_{st} + \frac{P_{st} L_{st}}{A_{st} E_{st}}$$

or since $\delta T = 100°$, and 0.442 in.² is the cross-section of *one* bolt,

$$(0.0000091)100 - \frac{P_{cu}}{3(17)10^6} = (0.0000065)100 + \frac{P_{st}}{4(0.442)30(10)^6}$$

Solving the two equations simultaneously, $P = 6{,}750$ lb. Therefore the stress in the copper tube is $\sigma_{cu} = 6{,}750/3 = 2{,}250$ psi.

The geometrical expression used above may also be set up on the basis of the following statement: The **differential expansion** of the two materials due to the change in temperature is accommodated by or is equal to the elastic deformations which take place in the two materials.

Example 12-5. A steel bolt having a cross-sectional area $A_1 = 1$ in.² is used to grip two steel washers of total thickness L, each having the cross-sectional area $A_2 = 9$ in.², Fig. 12-7a. If the bolt in this assembly is initially so tightened that its stress is 20 ksi, what will be the final stress in this bolt after a force $P = 15$ kips is applied to the assembly?

SOLUTION: A free body of the assembly corresponding to the initial conditions is shown in Fig. 12-7b, where I_t is the initial tensile force in the bolt and I_c is the initial compressive force in the washers. From statics, $I_t = I_c$. A free body of the assembly

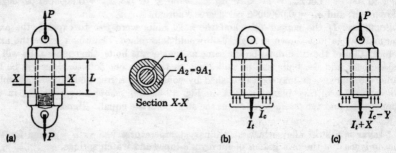

Fig. 12-7.

after the force P is applied is shown in Fig. 12-7c, where X designates the *increase* in the tensile force in the bolt, and Y is the *decrease* in the compressive force on the washers due to P. As a result of these forces, X and Y, if the adjacent parts remain in contact, the bolt elongates the same amount as the washers expand elastically. Hence for the final conditions,

From statics: $P + (I_c - Y) = (I_t + X)$, or since $\overset{*}{I}_c = I_t$,

$$X + Y = P$$

From geometry: $\Delta_{\text{bolt}} = \Delta_{\text{washers}}$, or using Eq. 2-4,

$$\frac{XL}{A_1E} = \frac{YL}{A_2E}$$

or

$$Y = \frac{A_2}{A_1} X$$

Solving the two equations simultaneously,

$$X = \frac{P}{1 + \dfrac{A_2}{A_1}} = \frac{P}{1 + 9} = 0.1P = 1{,}500 \text{ lb}$$

Therefore the *increase* of the stress in the bolt is $X/A_1 = 1{,}500$ psi, and the stress in the bolt *after* the application of the force P becomes 21,500 psi. This remarkable result indicates that most of the applied force is carried by *decreasing* the initial compressive force on the assembled washers, since $Y = 0.9P$.

The solution is not valid if one of the materials ceases to behave elastically, or if the applied force is such that the initial precompression of the assembled parts is destroyed.

Situations approximating the above idealized problem are found in many practical cases. A hot rivet used in the assembly of plates, upon cooling, develops within it enormous tensile stresses. Likewise, thoroughly tightened bolts used in the assembly of machine parts or fastening of lids of pressure vessels may initially be highly stressed. In operation, additional tensile forces may be applied to such rivets or bolts, and it is significant that only a negligible increase in their stresses occurs if the area of the initially compressed material is large.

12-4. The Method of Superposition. In analyzing statically indeterminate members, it is often expedient to *temporarily remove the redundant reactions*, which renders the structure statically determinate. Then, in this structure artificially reduced to statical determinacy, it is possible to find any desired deflection by the methods previously discussed.

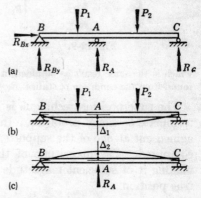

Fig. 12-8. Illustration of the superposition technique.

For example, by removing the redundant reaction* at A from the indetermi-

* In the analysis of beams, bending moments at the supports are often treated as redundant. Rotations of tangents at the supports are considered in such cases instead of deflections.

nate beam shown in Fig. 12-8a, the deflection Δ_1 at A, Fig. 12-8b, may be found. By reapplying the removed redundant reaction R_A to the *same determinate beam*, Fig. 12-8c, the deflection Δ_2, found as a function of R_A, may also be determined. Then, **superposing** (adding) the two deflections, as* $\Delta_1 + \Delta_2 = 0$, a solution for R_A follows. The effect of this superposition means that under the action of the applied forces *and* the redundant reaction, point A actually does not move.

This method of superposition for statically indeterminate members is very convenient in applications and is widely used in structural analysis. *After a redundant reaction is found, the problem becomes statically determinate, and any further analysis for stresses and deformations proceeds in the usual manner.* The method is applicable to problems of any degree of indeterminacy, and its extension to such problems will be discussed after the two examples that follow.

Example 12-6. Rework Example 12-1, using the method of superposition, Fig. 12-9a.

SOLUTION: The rod is imagined cut at the upper support (either top or bottom could

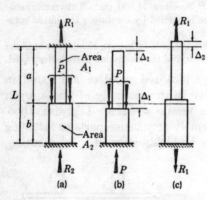

be cut). Then, in this determinate member, the top deflects an amount Δ_1 owing to the applied force P, Fig. 12-9b. Re-application of the unknown force R_1, Fig. 12-9c, causes a deflection Δ_2. Superposing these deflections in order to have no movement of the top of the rod, as required by the conditions of the problem, gives

$$\Delta_{\text{top of rod}} = \Delta_1 + \Delta_2 = 0$$

whence, using Eq. 2-4, $\Delta = PL/(AE)$, and taking downward deflections as positive,

Fig. 12-9.

$$\frac{Pb}{A_2 E} - \left(\frac{R_1 a}{A_1 E} + \frac{R_1 b}{A_2 E}\right) = 0$$

and $$R_1 = \frac{P}{1 + (aA_2/bA_1)}$$

which is the same result as obtained in Example 12-1. The bottom reaction may be found from the condition of statics: $R_1 + R_2 = P$.

The superposition technique is also very convenient in statically indeterminate torsional problems. In such cases, the torsion member is imagined cut at one of the supports, and the rotation of the released end is computed. The magnitude of the redundant torque is determined by making it of sufficient magnitude to restore the member's cut end to its true position.

Example 12-7. Plot shear and moment diagrams for a uniformly loaded beam fixed at one end and simply supported at the other, Fig. 12-10a. The EI is constant.

SOLUTION: The reactions must be determined in order to plot the shear and moment diagrams. This cannot be done by statics alone, as this beam is indeterminate to the

---

* An arbitrary algebraic convention of signs for the direction of deflections must be selected. For the case cited, it is also true *numerically* that $\Delta_1 = \Delta_2$.

first degree. However, by removing the right support, finding the deflection at B, reapplying R_B, again finding the deflection at B, etc., the reaction R_B may be found. This solution is left for completion by the reader. Instead, a solution treating the moment M_A as the redundant will be discussed. This alternative procedure will be found useful in subsequent work.

The structure reduced to determinacy by removing M_A is shown in Fig. 12-10b, and the accompanying bending-moment diagram is given in Fig. 12-10c. By using the moment-area method, the rotation θ_A' of the tangent at A is determined. Reapplying M_A, Fig. 12-10d, and using the corresponding bending-moment diagram, Fig. 12-10e, one finds the rotation θ_A'' of the same tangent due to M_A by means of the moment-area method, noting that $\theta_A'' \doteq t_{BA}/L$. By superposing the two rotations so as to preclude rotation at A, which actually must be zero, a solution for M_A is obtained.

$$\theta_A' = \Delta\theta_{AC} = \frac{1}{2}\frac{2}{3}L\frac{wL^2}{8EI} =$$

$$\frac{wL^3}{24EI} \quad (clockwise)$$

$$t_{BA} = \frac{1}{2}L\left(-\frac{M_A}{EI}\right)\frac{2}{3}L =$$

$$-\frac{M_A L^2}{3EI}$$

$$\theta_A'' = \frac{t_{BA}}{L} = -\frac{M_A L}{3EI}$$
$$(counterclockwise)$$

$$\theta_A = \theta_A' + \theta_A'' = 0$$

whence, taking clockwise rotations as positive,

$$\frac{wL^3}{24EI} - \frac{M_A L}{3EI} = 0,$$

$$\text{hence} \quad M_A = \frac{wL^2}{8}$$

The positive sign of the result indicates that a correct direction for M_A was assumed. In the beam convention of signs, M_A is a negative bending moment.

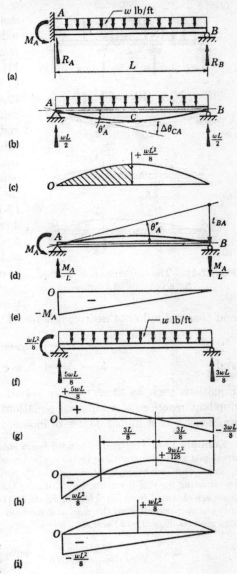

(a)

(b)

(c)

(d)

(e)

(f)

(g)

(h)

(i)

Fig. 12-10.

The remainder of the problem may be solved by using statics. Reactions, shear diagram, and moment diagram are shown in Figs. 12-10f, g, and h, respectively. The equivalent bending-moment diagram is shown in Fig. 12-10i.

The superposition method is applicable to members indeterminate to a higher degree than the first. In such cases, it is necessary to remember that *the deflection of **every** point on a member reduced to statical determinacy is effected by **each** reapplied redundant force.* For example, after the redundant reactions R_B and R_C are removed from the beam shown in Fig. 12-11a, the deflections at B and C of the *determinate* beam, Fig. 12-11b, may be computed. These deflections are designated as Δ_{BP} and Δ_{CP}, respectively, where the first subscript indicates the point considered and the second the cause of the deflection. By reapplying R_B to the same determinate beam, Fig. 12-11c, the deflections at B and C due to R_B are found to be Δ_{BB} *and* Δ_{CB}, respectively. Similarly, Δ_{BC} and Δ_{CC}, Fig. 12-11d, due to R_C, may be established. Superposing the deflections at each support and setting the sum equal to zero, since points B and C actually do not deflect, it is found that the two equations are

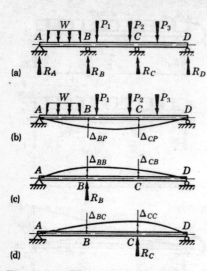

Fig. 12-11. The superposition method for a continuous beam.

$$\Delta_B = \Delta_{BP} + \Delta_{BB} + \Delta_{BC} = 0$$

and

$$\Delta_C = \Delta_{CP} + \Delta_{CB} + \Delta_{CC} = 0$$

Equations such as these may be solved simultaneously for the two redundant reactions. Additional equations of this type may be set up in problems with a higher degree of indeterminacy.

Example 12-8. For the fixed-ended beam shown in Fig. 12-12a, find the moments developed at the supports due to the applied force P. The EI is constant.

SOLUTION: This beam, indeterminate to the second degree, is reduced to determinacy by removing the end moments, Fig. 12-12b. The rotations of the tangents at the supports are obtained from Eq. 11-10 in Example 11-5. The rotations of the tangents at *each end* corresponding to the reapplied moment M_A are found by using the moment-area method, Figs. 12-12d and e. Hence

$$\theta_A{'} = \left(\frac{dy}{dx}\right)_{x=0} = -\frac{Pab}{6EIL}(a + 2b) \quad (clockwise)$$

$$\theta_B{'} = \left(\frac{dy}{dx}\right)_{x_1=0} = -\frac{Pab}{6EIL}(b + 2a) \quad (counterclockwise)$$

$$\theta_A{''} = \frac{t_{BA}}{L} = \frac{\frac{1}{2}L\left(\frac{-M_A}{EI}\right)\frac{2}{3}L}{L} = -\frac{M_A L}{3EI} \quad (counterclockwise)$$

$$\theta_B'' = \frac{t_{AB}}{L} = \frac{\frac{1}{2}L\left(\frac{-M_A}{EI}\right)\frac{1}{3}L}{L} = -\frac{M_A L}{6EI} \quad \text{(clockwise)}$$

Using Figs. 12-12f and g, one determines rotations of the ends due to M_B as above.

$$\theta_A''' = -\frac{M_B L}{6EI} \quad \text{(counterclockwise)}$$

$$\theta_B''' = -\frac{M_B L}{3EI} \quad \text{(clockwise)}$$

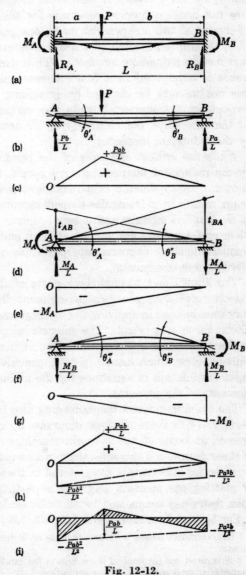

Fig. 12-12.

The sum of the angular rotations due to three separate applications of forces to the determinate beam must equal zero at each end, since no actual rotation of the tangents at the supports takes place. Whence, by taking the counterclockwise rotations positive, two equations are obtained:

$$\theta_A = \theta_A' + \theta_A'' + \theta_A''' = -\frac{Pab}{6EIL}$$

$$\times (a + 2b) + \frac{M_A L}{3EI} + \frac{M_B L}{6EI} = 0$$

$$\theta_B = \theta_B' + \theta_B'' + \theta_B''' = +\frac{Pab}{6LEI}$$

$$\times (b + 2a) - \frac{M_A L}{6EI} - \frac{M_B L}{3EI} = 0$$

Solving these equations simultaneously gives

$$M_A = \frac{Pab^2}{L^2} \quad \text{and} \quad M_B = \frac{Pa^2 b}{L^2}$$

where the positive signs of the bending moments indicate that their *assumed* directions were chosen correctly. According to the beam convention, these moments are *negative*.

After the moments at the supports are known, the alternative plots of the bending-moment diagrams shown in Figs. 12-12h and i may be prepared. Note particularly that in computing the reactions, *the moments at the supports must be included in the equations of statics.* Alternatively, the *sum* of the reactions shown in Figs. 12-12b, d, and f gives the same reactions.

This problem may also be solved by treating R_B and M_B as the redundants, as their temporary removal makes the structure determinate. This procedure is particularly convenient if one of the supports moves vertically, since then the composite deflection caused by the applied forces and the redundants is equated to the movement of the support.

12-5. Moment-Area Method for Statically Indeterminate Beams.
The application of the superposition method to indeterminate beams may be greatly accelerated, according to the following reasoning: Restrained * and continuous beams differ from simply supported beams mainly by the presence of redundant moments at the supports. Therefore the bending-moment diagrams for these beams may be considered to consist of two independent parts, one part for the moment caused by all of the applied loading on a beam assumed simply supported, the other part for the redundant moments. Thus the effect of redundant end moments is superposed to a beam assumed simply supported. Physically this notion may be clarified by imagining an indeterminate beam cut through at the supports† while the vertical reactions are maintained. At the same time, the continuity of the beam's elastic curve is preserved by the redundant moments.

While the critical ordinates of the bending-moment diagrams caused by the redundant moments are *not known*, their shape *is* definite and *is* known. An application of a redundant moment at an end of a simple beam results in a triangular-shaped moment diagram with a maximum at the applied moment and a zero ordinate at the other end. Likewise, when end moments are present at both ends of a simple beam, two triangular moment diagrams superpose into a trapezoidal-shaped diagram (verify these statements).

The known and the unknown parts of the bending-moment diagram together give a *complete* bending-moment diagram. This whole diagram may then be used in applying the moment-area theorems to the continuous elastic curve of a beam. The geometrical conditions of a problem, such as the continuity of the elastic curve at the support, or the tangents at built-in ends which cannot rotate, provide conditions which permit a rapid formulation of equations for the unknown values of the redundant moments at the supports.

The bending-moment diagrams may also be plotted by cantilever parts (Art. 11-14). Some of these diagrams by cantilever parts must be expressed in terms of the *unknown* reactions or moments. Since the sum of these diagrams is also equivalent to a *complete* bending-moment diagram, no essential difference is encountered in their applications. This method of plotting the moment diagrams is particularly advantageous for one-span restrained beams and for partially loaded beams.

For beams of variable flexural rigidity, $M/(EI)$ diagrams must be used.

---

* Indeterminate beams with one or more ends fixed or built-in are called restrained beams.

† This must not be done at the supports for cantilevers or overhanging ends. The moments at such supports are *not* redundant.

Example 12-9. Find the maximum downward deflection for the small aluminum beam shown in Fig. 12-13a due to an applied force $P = 100$ lb. The beam's constant flexural rigidity $EI = 25,000$ lb-in.²

SOLUTION: The solution of this problem consists of two parts. First, a redundant reaction must be determined to establish the numerical values for the bending-moment diagram, then the usual moment-area procedure is applied to find the deflection.

Imagining the beam released from the redundant end moment, the simple beam-moment diagram is constructed above the base line in Fig. 12-13b. The moment diagram of known shape due to the unknown redundant moment M_A is shown on the same diagram below the base line. One assumes M_A to be positive, since in this manner its correct sign according to the beam convention is automatically obtained. The composite diagram represents a *complete* bending-moment diagram.

The tangent at the built-in end remains horizontal after the application of the force P. Hence the geometrical condition is $t_{BA} = 0$. An equation formulated on this basis yields a solution for M_A.* The equations of static equilibrium are used to compute the reactions. The final bending-moment diagram, Fig. 12-13d, is obtained in the usual manner after the reactions are known.

$$t_{BA} = 0 \quad \text{or} \quad \frac{1}{EI}\left[\frac{1}{2}10(+240)\frac{1}{3}(10+4) + \frac{1}{2}10(+M_A)\frac{2}{3}10\right] = 0$$

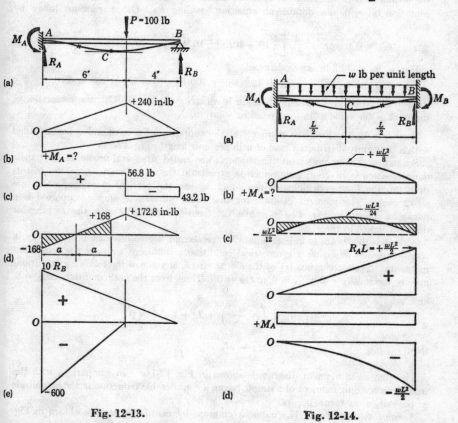

Fig. 12-13.   Fig. 12-14.

* See Table 2 of the Appendix for the centroidal distance of a whole triangle.

Hence, $M_A = -168$ in.-lb

$$\Sigma M_A = 0 \circlearrowright +, \qquad 100(6) - R_B(10) - 168 = 0, \quad R_B = 43.2 \text{ lb}$$

$$\Sigma M_B = 0 \circlearrowleft +, \qquad 100(4) + 168 - R_A(10) = 0, \quad R_A = 56.8 \text{ lb}$$

Check: $\Sigma F_y = 0 \uparrow +, \qquad 43.2 + 65.8 - 100 = 0.$

The maximum deflection occurs where the tangent to the elastic curve is horizontal, point C in Fig. 12-13a. Hence, by noting that the tangent at A is also horizontal and using the first moment-area theorem, point C is located. This occurs when the shaded areas in Fig. 12-13d having opposite signs are equal, i.e., at a distance $2a = 2(168/56.8)$ $= 5.92$ in. from A. The tangential deviation t_{AC} (or t_{CA}) gives the deflection of point C.

$$y_{max} = y_C = t_{AC}$$

$$= \frac{1}{EI} \left[\frac{1}{2} 2.96(+168)(2.96 + \frac{2}{3} 2.96) + \frac{1}{2} 2.96 (-168) \frac{1}{3} 2.96 \right]$$

$$= \frac{982}{EI} = 0.0393 \text{ in. } down$$

ALTERNATE SOLUTION: A rapid solution may also be obtained by plotting the moment diagram by cantilever parts. This is shown in Fig. 12-13e. Note that one of the ordinates is in terms of the redundant reaction R_B. Again using the geometrical condition $t_{BA} = 0$, one obtains an equation yielding R_B. Other reactions follow by statics.

$$t_{BA} = 0 \qquad \text{or} \qquad \frac{1}{EI} \left[\frac{1}{2} 10(+10R_B) \frac{2}{3} 10 + \frac{1}{2} 6(-600)(4 + \frac{2}{3} 6) \right] = 0$$

Hence, $R_B = 43.2$ lb, *up as assumed.*

$$\Sigma M_A = 0 \curvearrowright +, \qquad M_A + 43.2(10) - 100(6) = 0, \quad M_A = 168 \text{ in.-lb} \circlearrowleft$$

After the combined moment diagram is constructed Fig. 12-13d, the remainder of the work is the same as in the preceding solution.

Example 12-10. Find the moments at the supports for a fixed-ended beam loaded with a uniformly distributed load of w lb per unit length, Fig. 12-14a.

SOLUTION: The moments at the supports are called *fixed-end moments,* and their determination is of great importance in structural theory. Due to *symmetry* in this problem, the fixed-end moments are equal, as are the vertical reactions, which are $wL/2$ each. The moment diagram for this beam considered simply supported is a parabola, shown in Fig. 12-14b, while the fixed-end moments give the rectangular diagram shown in the same figure.

Although this beam is indeterminate to the second degree, because of symmetry, a single equation based on a geometrical condition is sufficient to yield the redundant moments. From the geometry of the elastic curve, any one of the following conditions may be used: $\Delta\theta_{AB} = 0,$* $t_{BA} = 0$, or $t_{AB} = 0$. Thus, from the first condition, $\Delta\theta_{AB} = 0$, or

$$\frac{1}{EI} \left[\frac{2}{3} L \left(+ \frac{wL^2}{8} \right) + L(+M_A) \right] = 0$$

then,

$$M_A = M_B = - \frac{wL^2}{12}$$

The composite moment diagram is shown in Fig. 12-14c. In comparison with the maximum bending moment of a simple beam, a considerable reduction in the magnitude of the critical moments occurs.

ALTERNATE SOLUTION: The moment diagram by cantilever parts is shown in Fig

---

* Also since the tangent at the center of the span is horizontal, $\Delta\theta_{AC} = 0$ and $\Delta\theta_{CB} = 0$.

12-14d. Noting that $R_A = R_B = wL/2$, and using the same geometrical condition as above, $\Delta\theta_{AB} = 0$, one can verify the former solution as follows:

$$\frac{1}{EI}\left[\frac{1}{2}L\left(+\frac{wL^2}{2}\right) + L(+M_A) + \frac{1}{3}L\left(-\frac{wL^2}{2}\right)\right] = 0, \quad \text{or } M_A = -\frac{wL^2}{12}$$

Example 12-11. Rework Example 12-8, using the moment-area method, Fig. 12-15a.

SOLUTION: Treating the beam AB as a simple beam, the moment diagram due to P is shown above the base line in Fig. 12-15b. The fixed-end moments are *not equal* and result in the trapezoidal diagram. Three geometrical conditions for the elastic curve are available to solve this problem indeterminate to the second degree:

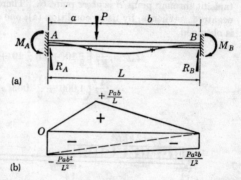

(a)

(b)

Fig. 12-15.

(a) $\Delta\theta_{AB} = 0$, since the tangents at A and B are parallel.

(b) $t_{BA} = 0$, since the support B does not deviate from a fixed tangent at A.

(c) Similarly, $t_{AB} = 0$.

Any two of the above conditions may be used; arithmetical simplicity of the resulting equations governs the choice. Thus, using condition (a), which is always the simplest, and condition (b), two equations are *

$$\Delta\theta_{AB} = \frac{1}{EI}\left(\frac{1}{2}L\frac{Pab}{L} + \frac{1}{2}LM_A + \frac{1}{2}LM_B\right) = 0$$

or

$$M_A + M_B = -\frac{Pab}{L}$$

$$t_{BA} = \frac{1}{EI}\left[\frac{1}{2}L\frac{Pab}{L}\frac{1}{3}(L+b) + \frac{1}{2}LM_A\frac{2}{3}L + \frac{1}{2}LM_B\frac{1}{3}L\right] = 0$$

or

$$2M_A + M_B = -\frac{Pab}{L^2}(L+b)$$

Solving the two reduced equations simultaneously gives

$$M_A = -\frac{Pab^2}{L^2} \quad \text{and} \quad M_B = -\frac{Pa^2b}{L^2}$$

These results agree with those found in Example 12-8, except that the signs of the moments follow the beam convention of signs. These signs resulted from initially taking M_A and M_B as positive quantities. Note the great similarity of this solution to that of Example 12-8. In effect, this solution is commenced with the moment diagram shown in Fig. 12-12h of the former case.

Example 12-12. Plot moment and shear diagrams for the continuous beam loaded as shown in Fig. 12-16a. The EI is constant for the whole beam.

SOLUTION: This beam is indeterminate to the second degree. By treating each span as a simple beam with the redundant moments, Fig. 12-16b, the moment diagram shown in Fig. 12-16c is obtained. No end moments exist at A as this end is on a roller. The clue to the solution is contained in two geometrical conditions for the elastic curve for the whole beam, Fig. 12-16d:

* See Table 2 in the Appendix for the centroidal distance of a whole triangle.

(a) $\theta_B = \theta_B'$. Since the beam is physically continuous, there is a line at the support B which is tangent to the elastic curve in *either* span.

(b) $t_{BC} = 0$, since the support B does not deviate from a fixed tangent at C.

To apply condition (a), t_{AB} and t_{CB} are determined, and, by *dividing these quantities by the respective span lengths*, the two angles θ_B and θ_B' are obtained. These angles are equal. However, although t_{CB} is algebraically expressed as a positive quantity, the tangent through point B is *above* point C. Therefore this deviation must be considered negative. Whence, by using condition (a), one equation with the redundant moments is obtained.

$$t_{AB} = \frac{1}{EI} \left[\frac{2}{3} 10(+30) \frac{1}{2} 10 + \frac{1}{2} 10(+M_B) \frac{2}{3} 10 \right]$$

$$= \frac{1}{EI} \left(1{,}000 + \frac{1}{3} 100 M_B \right)$$

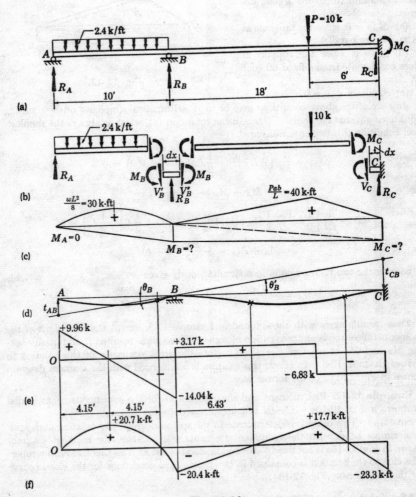

Fig. 12-16.

$$t_{CB} = \frac{1}{EI} \left[\frac{1}{2} 18(+40) \frac{1}{3} (18 + 6) + \frac{1}{2} 18(+M_B) \frac{2}{3} 18 + \frac{1}{2} 18(+M_C) \frac{1}{3} 18 \right]$$

$$= \frac{1}{EI} (2{,}880 + 108M_B + 54M_C)$$

Since $\theta_B = \theta_B'$,   or $\dfrac{t_{AB}}{L_{AB}} = -\dfrac{t_{CB}}{L_{CB}}$,

$$\frac{1}{EI} \left(\frac{1{,}000 + \frac{1}{3} 100 \, M_B}{10} \right) = -\frac{1}{EI} \left(\frac{2{,}880 + 108M_B + 54M_C}{18} \right)$$

or

$$\frac{28}{3} M_B + 3M_C = -260$$

Using condition (b) for the span BC provides another equation, $t_{BC} = 0$, or

$$\frac{1}{EI} \left[\frac{1}{2} 18(+40) \frac{1}{3} (18 + 12) + \frac{1}{2} 18(+M_B) \frac{1}{3} 18 + \frac{1}{2} 18(+M_C) \frac{2}{3} 18 \right] = 0$$

or

$$3M_B + 6M_C = -200$$

Solving the two reduced equations simultaneously,

$$M_B = -20.4 \text{ ft-lb} \quad \text{and} \quad M_C = -23.3 \text{ ft-lb}$$

where the signs agree with the convention of signs used for beams. These moments with their proper sense are shown in Fig. 12-16b.

After the redundant moments M_A and M_C are found, *no new techniques* are necessary to construct the moment and shear diagrams. *However, particular care must be exercised to include the moments at the supports while computing shears and reactions.* Usually, isolated beams as shown in Fig. 12-16b are the most convenient free bodies for determining shears. Reactions follow by adding the shears on the adjoining beams. In units of kips and feet,

For free body AB:

$$\Sigma M_B = 0 \; \curvearrowright +, \qquad 2.4(10)5 - 20.4 - 10R_A = 0, \qquad R_A = 9.96 \text{ kips} \uparrow$$
$$\Sigma M_A = 0 \; \curvearrowleft +, \qquad 2.4(10)5 + 20.4 - 10V_B' = 0, \qquad V_B' = 14.04 \text{ kips} \uparrow$$

For free body BC:

$$\Sigma M_C = 0 \; \curvearrowright +, \qquad 10(6) + 20.4 - 23.3 - 18V_B'' = 0, \qquad V_B'' = 3.17 \text{ kips} \uparrow$$
$$\Sigma M_B = 0 \; \curvearrowleft +, \qquad 10(12) - 20.4 + 23.3 - 18V_C = 0, \qquad V_C = R_C = 6.83 \text{ kips} \uparrow$$

Check: $\qquad R_A + V_B' = 24 \text{ kips} \uparrow \quad$ and $\quad V_B'' + R_C = 10 \text{ kips} \uparrow$

From above, $R_B = V_B' + V_B'' = 17.21 \text{ kips} \uparrow$.

The complete shear and moment diagrams are shown in Figs. 12-16e and f, respectively.

12-6. The Three-Moment Equation. Generalizing the procedure used in the preceding example, a recursion formula, i.e., an equation which may be repeatedly applied for *every two adjoining* spans, may be derived for continuous beams. For any n number of spans, $n - 1$ such equations may be written. This gives enough simultaneous equations for the solution of redundant moments over the supports. This recursion formula is called the *three-moment equation* because three unknown moments appear in it.

Consider a continuous beam, such as shown in Fig. 12-17a, subjected to any transverse loading. For *any* two adjoining spans, as LC and CR, the bending-moment diagram is considered to consist of two parts. The areas A_L and A_R to the left and to the right of the center support C, Fig. 12-17b, correspond to the bending-moment diagrams in the respective spans, if these spans are treated as being *simply supported*. These moment diagrams depend entirely upon the nature of the known forces applied within each span. The other part of the moment diagram of known shape is due to the unknown moments M_L at the left support, M_C at the center support, and M_R at the right support.

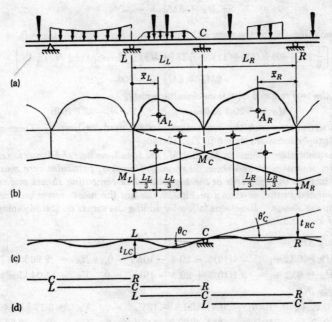

Fig. 12-17. Deriving the three-moment equation.

Next, the elastic curve shown in Fig. 12-17c must be considered. This curve is continuous for any continuous beam. Hence the angles θ_C and θ_C', which define, from the respective sides, the inclination of the same tangent to the elastic curve at C, are equal. By using the second moment-area theorem to obtain t_{LC} and t_{RC}, these angles are defined as $\theta_C = t_{LC}/L_L$ and $\theta_C' = -t_{RC}/L_R$, where L_L and L_R are span lengths on the left and on the right of C, respectively. The negative sign for the second angle is necessary, since the tangent from point C is *above* the support R, while a positive deviation of t_{RC} locates a tangent below the same support. Hence, following the steps outlined,

$$\theta_C = \theta_C' \quad \text{or} \quad \frac{t_{LC}}{L_L} = -\frac{t_{RC}}{L_R}$$

and

$$\frac{1}{L_L}\frac{1}{EI_L}\left(A_L\bar{x}_L + \frac{1}{2}L_LM_L\frac{1}{3}L_L + \frac{1}{2}L_LM_C\frac{2}{3}L_L\right)$$

$$= -\frac{1}{L_R}\frac{1}{EI_R}\left(A_R\bar{x}_R + \frac{1}{2}L_RM_R\frac{1}{3}L_R + \frac{1}{2}L_RM_C\frac{2}{3}L_R\right)$$

where I_L and I_R are the respective moments of inertia of the cross-sectional area of the beam in the left-hand and the right-hand spans. Throughout each span, I_L and I_R are assumed constant.* The term $\bar{x}_L$ is the distance *from the left support* L to the centroid of the area A_L, and $\bar{x}_R$ is a similar distance for A_R measured *from the right support* R. The terms M_L, M_C, and M_R denote the unknown moments at the supports.

Simplifying the above expression, the three-moment equation† is

$$L_LM_L + 2\left(L_L + \frac{I_L}{I_R}L_R\right)M_C + \frac{I_L}{I_R}L_RM_R$$

$$= -6A_L\frac{\bar{x}_L}{L_L} - 6A_R\frac{I_L}{I_R}\frac{\bar{x}_R}{L_R} \qquad (12\text{-}2)$$

Equation 12-2 applies to continuous beams on unyielding supports, with the beam in each span of constant I. In a particular problem, all terms, with the exception of the redundant moments at the supports, are constant. A sufficient number of simultaneous equations for the unknown moments is obtained by successively *imagining* the supports of the adjoining spans as L, C, and R as shown in Fig. 12-17d. *However, in these equations the subscripts of the M's must correspond to the actual designation of the supports,* such as A, B, C, etc. Also note that at pinned ends of beams the moments are known to be zero. Likewise, if a continuous beam has an overhang, *the moment at the first support is known from statics.* Fixed supports will be discussed in Example 12-14. For symmetrical beams symmetrically loaded, work may be minimized by noting that moments at symmetrically placed supports are equal.

In deriving the three-moment equation, the moments at the supports were assumed positive. Hence an algebraic solution of simultaneous equations automatically gives the correct sign of moments according to the convention for beams.

12-7. Special Cases. As a specific example of evaluating the constant terms on the right-hand side of the three-moment equation, consider two adjoining spans loaded with the *concentrated forces* P_L and P_R, Fig. 12-18. Considering these spans simply supported, since the maximum moment in the left-hand span is $+P_Lab/L_L$, and $\bar{x}_L = \frac{1}{3}(L_L + a)$, one writes

---

* The expressions become very involved if variation of I occurs *within* any one span.
† The three-moment equation was originally derived by E. Clapeyron, a French engineer, in 1857, and sometimes is referred to as Clapeyron's equation.

$$-6A_L \frac{\bar{x}_L}{L_L} = -6 \frac{1}{2} L_L \frac{P_L ab}{L_L} \frac{1}{3} \frac{(L_L + a)}{L_L} = -P_L ab \left(1 + \frac{a}{L_L}\right) \quad (12\text{-}3)$$

Similarly, by interchanging the role of the dimensions a and b in the right-hand span, i.e., by always measuring a's from the outside support toward the force,

$$-6A_R \frac{I_L}{I_R} \frac{\bar{x}_R}{L_R} = -P_R a'b' \left(1 + \frac{a'}{L_R}\right) \frac{I_L}{I_R} \quad (12\text{-}4)$$

If a number of concentrated forces occur within a span, the contribution of each one of them to the above constant may be treated separately.

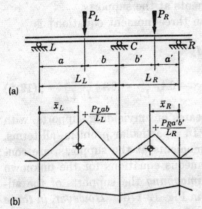

(a)

(b)

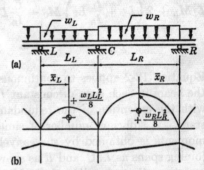

(a)

(b)

Fig. 12-18. Establishing the constants on the right hand of the three-moment equation for concentrated loads.

Fig. 12-19. Establishing the constants on the right hand of the three-moment equation for uniformly distributed loads.

Hence a constant term for the right-hand side of the three-moment equation applicable for any number of concentrated forces applied within the spans is

$$-\Sigma P_L ab \left(1 + \frac{a}{L_L}\right) - \Sigma P_R a'b' \left(1 + \frac{a'}{L_R}\right) \frac{I_L}{I_R} \quad (12\text{-}5)$$

where the summation sign designates the fact that a separate term appears for **every concentrated force** P_L in the left span, and similarly, **for every** P_R force in the right span. In both cases, a or a' is the distance from the *outside support* to the particular concentrated force, and b or b' is the distance to the force from the *center support*. If any one of these forces acts upwards, the term contributed to the constant by such a force is of opposite sign.

The constant for the right-hand side of the three-moment equation, when **uniformly distributed loads** are applied to a beam, is determined similarly. Thus, using the diagram shown in Fig. 12-19,

$$-6A_L \frac{\bar{x}_L}{L_L} = -6\frac{2}{3}L_L \frac{w_L L_L^2}{8}\frac{1}{2}\frac{L_L}{L_L} = -\frac{w_L L_L^3}{4} \qquad (12\text{-}6)$$

and similarly,

$$-6A_R \frac{I_L}{I_R}\frac{\bar{x}_R}{L_R} = -\frac{w_R L_R^3}{4}\frac{I_L}{I_R} \qquad (12\text{-}7)$$

Constants for other types of loading may be determined by using the same procedure as above.

Example 12-13. Find the moments at all supports and the reactions at C and D for the continuous beam loaded as shown in Fig. 12-20a. The flexural rigidity EI is constant.

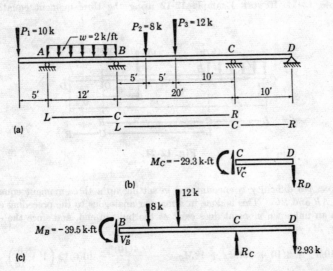

Fig. 12-20.

SOLUTION: By using Eq. 12-2 and treating the span AB as the left span and BC as the right, one equation is written. From statics, the beam convention being used for signs, $M_A = -10(5) = -50$ kip-ft. Equations 12-5 and 12-6 are used to obtain the right-hand terms. The moments of inertia I_L and I_R are equal.

$$12M_A + 2(12 + 20)M_B + 20M_C$$
$$= -\frac{2(12)^3}{4} - 8(15)5\left(1 + \frac{15}{20}\right) - 12(10)10\left(1 + \frac{10}{20}\right)$$

Substituting $M_A = -50$ kip-ft and simplifying gives

$$64M_B + 20M_C = -3{,}114$$

Next, Eq. 12-2 is again applied for the spans BC and CD. No constant terms are contributed to the right-hand side of the three-moment equation by the unloaded span CD. At the pinned end, $M_D = 0$.

$$20M_B + 2(20 + 10)M_C + 10M_D = -8(5)15\left(1 + \frac{5}{20}\right) - 12(10)10\left(1 + \frac{10}{20}\right)$$

or

$$20M_B + 60M_C = -2{,}550$$

Solving the reduced equations simultaneously gives

$$M_B = -39.5 \text{ kip-ft} \quad \text{and} \quad M_C = -29.3 \text{ kip-ft}$$

Isolating the span CD as shown in Fig. 12-20b, one obtains the reaction R_D from statics. Instead of isolating the span BC and computing $V_C{}'$ to add to $V_C{}''$ to find R_C, as was done in Example 12-12, the free body shown in Fig. 12-20c is used.

For free body CD:

$$\Sigma M_C = 0 \circlearrowright +, \quad 29.3 - 10R_D = 0, \quad R_D = 2.93 \text{ kips} \downarrow$$

For free body BD:

$$\Sigma M_B = 0, \circlearrowright +, \quad 8(5) + 12(10) - R_C(20) + 2.93(30) - 39.5 = 0$$
$$R_C = 10.42 \text{ kips} \uparrow$$

Example 12-14. Rework Example 12-12 using the three-moment equation, Fig 12-21.

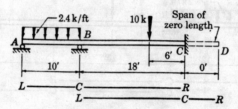

Fig. 12-21.

SOLUTION: No difficulty is encountered in setting up a three-moment equation for the spans AB and BC. This is done in a manner analogous to the preceding example. Note that an unknown moment does exist at the built-in end, and since the end A is on a roller, $M_A = 0$.

$$10M_A + 2(10 + 18)M_B + 18M_C = -\frac{2.4(10)^3}{4} - 10(6)12\left(1 + \frac{6}{18}\right)$$
$$56M_B + 18M_C = -1{,}560$$

To set up the next equation, an artifice is introduced. *An imaginary span of zero length is added at the fixed end*, and the three-moment equation is set up in the usual manner.

$$18M_B + 2(18 + 0)M_C + 0(M_D) = -10(12)6\left(1 + \frac{12}{18}\right)$$
$$18M_B + 36M_C = -1{,}200$$

Solving the reduced equations simultaneously gives

$$M_B = -20.4 \text{ kip-ft} \quad \text{and} \quad M_C = -23.3 \text{ kip-ft}$$

The remainder of the problem is the same as before.

The use of a "zero-length span" at the fixed ends of beams is justified by the moment-area procedure. This expedient is equivalent to the requirement of a zero deviation of a support nearest the fixed end from the tangent at the fixed end. For example, if the second of the above reduced equations is divided through by 6, the corresponding equation in Example 12-12 is obtained, where the latter condition was used directly.

12-8. Double-Integration Method for Indeterminate Beams.
The double-integration method may be used to determine the redundant

reactions, as well as the equations of the elastic curve, for statically inde-terminate beams. This method is best adapted to restrained beams, and the treatment of continuous beams is excluded.

When the double-integration method is applied to restrained' beams, essentially the same procedure as used for determinate beams is em-ployed. Algebraic expressions must first be established for the bending moment applicable to particular segments of the beam. However, since in statically indeterminate beams the reactions are unknown, *expressions for the bending moment contain terms with the unknown reactions.* Hence, upon integrating Eq. 11-4, $d^2y/dx^2 = M/(EI)$, twice, in addition to the constants of integration, *the unknown reactions which initially ap-pear in the expression for the bending moment must also be determined.* All of these unknown quantities are determined from the known conditions at the boundaries or supports. Thus the boundary conditions are used to determine the constants of integration and *also to obtain the redundant reactions.* For the latter purpose, in some cases, equations of static equilibrium must also be used simultaneously.

After the redundant reactions are known, all reactions may be deter-mined from statics, and the equation of the elastic curve is obtained. As was explained in Chapter 11, the double-integration method is convenient if a single expression for the bending moment applies for the whole span. The same situation is true for indeterminate beams.*

Example 12-15. Find the equation of the elastic curve for the uniformly loaded beam shown in Fig. 12-22a. The EI is constant.

SOLUTION: The origin of x is selected at A, and R_A is considered a redundant reaction. The expression for the bend-ing moment is written by referring to Fig. 12-22b. By successively integrat-ing the differential equation of the elastic curve and using the boundary conditions *three* times, the answer is obtained.

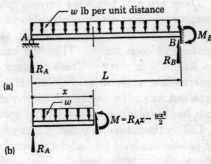

(a)

(b)

Fig. 12-22.

$$M = R_A x - \frac{wx^2}{2}$$

$$\frac{d^2y}{dx^2} = \frac{M}{EI} = \frac{1}{EI}\left(R_A x - \frac{wx^2}{2}\right)$$

$$\theta = \frac{dy}{dx} = \frac{1}{EI}\left(\frac{R_A x^2}{2} - \frac{wx^3}{6}\right) + \theta_o$$

However, $(\theta)_{x=L} = 0$, hence

$$0 = \frac{1}{EI}\left(\frac{R_A L^2}{2} - \frac{wL^3}{6}\right) + \theta_o \quad \text{or} \quad \theta_o = -\frac{1}{EI}\left(\frac{R_A L^2}{2} - \frac{wL^3}{6}\right)$$

* Much progress has been made by mathematicians to overcome this difficulty, and a mathematically inclined reader will enjoy pursuing the subject further by examining solutions based upon the use of the Laplace transforms. For example see Pipes, Louis A., *Applied Mathematics for Engineers and Physicists.* New York: McGraw-Hill, 1946.

$$\theta = \frac{dy}{dx} = \frac{1}{EI}\left(\frac{R_Ax^2}{2} - \frac{wx^3}{6} - \frac{R_AL^2}{2} + \frac{wL^3}{6}\right)$$

$$y = \frac{1}{EI}\left(\frac{R_Ax^3}{6} - \frac{wx^4}{24} - \frac{R_AL^2x}{2} + \frac{wL^3x}{6}\right) + y_o$$

since $y_o = (y)_{x=0} = 0$.   *Moreover* $(y)_{x=L} = 0$, hence

$$0 = \frac{1}{EI}\left(\frac{R_AL^3}{6} - \frac{wL^4}{24} - \frac{R_AL^3}{2} + \frac{wL^4}{6}\right) \text{ or } R_A = \frac{3}{8}wL$$

Substituting the value found for R_A into the equation for deflection and simplifying gives

$$y = -\frac{w}{48EI}(2x^4 - 3Lx^3 + L^3x) \tag{12-8}$$

If the origin of x were taken at B, the expression for the bending moment would contain two unknowns R_B and M_B. To obtain the solution, this procedure requires the use of an equation of statics, $\Sigma M_A = 0$, or $R_BL - M_B - wL^2/2 = 0$, in addition to the equation obtained by integrations.

12-9. Concluding Remarks. In practice, statically indeterminate members occur in numerous situations. Some of the methods for analyzing these members have been discussed in this chapter. Sometimes the stresses caused by indeterminacy, particularly those due to temperature, are undesirable. More often, however, members are deliberately arranged to be indeterminate, as such members are *stiffer*, which is highly desirable in many cases. Likewise a reduction in stresses may be so accomplished. For example, the maximum bending moments in indeterminate beams are often smaller than the maximum moments in similar determinate beams. This permits selection of smaller members and results in an economy of material.

There are also two very serious disadvantages to using indeterminate members. Some uncertainty always exists as to whether the supports completely fix the ends. Likewise, the supports may settle or move in relation to each other. Then the calculated stresses or deflections may be seriously in error. These matters are of little concern in a statically determinate structure. Lastly, the method of analysis becomes very involved when the degree of indeterminacy is high. However, this situation has been largely overcome by specialized methods.*

Unlike the *elastic* methods of analysis discussed in this chapter, inelastic or plastic analysis for indeterminate beams is gaining prominence in applications for *static* loads.† The perfection of this method is currently an active field of research.

---

* The most notable of these methods for beams and frames is Professor Hardy Cross's method of "moment-distribution." See Cross, Hardy, "Analysis of Continuous Frames by Distributing Fixed-End Moments," *Trans. ASCE*, vol. 96, 1932; or Grinter, L. E., *Theory of Modern Steel Structures*, vol. II. New York: Macmillan, 1949.

† See van den Broek, J. A., *Theory of Limit Design*. New York: Wiley, 1948. For a short exposition of the methods see the author's "Limit Design of Prismatic Beams," *Engineering News-Record*, May 13, 1948.

Problems for Solution

12-1. A rigid loading plate is placed horizontally on a concrete block and a steel pipe as shown in the figure. Where must a concentrated force of 190 kips be applied so that the plate would remain horizontal? If it is so placed, what is the stress in the steel pipe? $E_C = 3 \times 10^6$ psi, $E_{St} = 30 \times 10^6$ psi. *Ans.* 10 in. from A, 10 ksi.

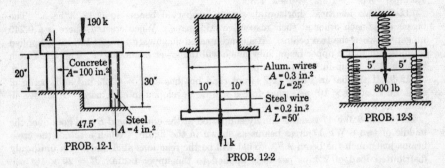

PROB. 12-1   PROB. 12-2   PROB. 12-3

12-2. If a load of 1 kip is applied to a rigid bar suspended by three wires as shown in the figure, what force will be resisted by each wire? The outside wires are aluminum ($E = 10^7$ psi). The inside wire is steel ($E = 30 \times 10^6$ psi). Initially there is no slack in the wire. *Ans.* Each wire carries $\frac{1}{3}$ kip.

12-3. A rigid horizontal bar is attached to three springs as shown in the figure. The upper spring is $4\frac{3}{4}$ in. O.D. and has 10 active coils. The lower springs are alike and are $3\frac{3}{4}$ in. O.D. with 20 active coils in each. All springs are made of $\frac{3}{4}$ in. diameter steel wire. What will be the maximum shearing stress in the upper spring caused by applying a force of 800 lb? In analyzing the deflection of springs, neglect the effect of direct shear. *Ans.* 237 lb, 7,300 psi.

12-4. A round shaft of constant cross-sectional area is subjected to a torque T as shown in the figure. If both ends of the shaft are built in, what torques are resisted at each end? *Ans.* $T_A = Ta/L$.

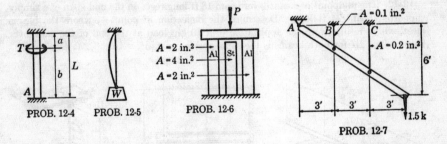

PROB. 12-4   PROB. 12-5   PROB. 12-6   PROB. 12-7

12-5. A 2 ton weight is to be lifted by means of two rods, each nearly 10 ft long as shown in the figure. One rod is made of steel ($E = 30 \times 10^6$ psi), the other of aluminum ($E = 10^7$ psi). Each rod has a cross-sectional area of 0.20 in.² Which rod must be made shorter and by how much in order to distribute the load equally between them? *Ans.* Aluminum; 0.08 in.

12-6. A rigid platform rests on two aluminum bars ($E = 10^7$ psi) each 10.000 in. long. A third bar made of steel ($E = 30 \times 10^6$ psi) standing in the middle is 9.995 in. long. (a) What will be the stress in the steel bar if a load P of 100 kips is applied on the platform? (b) How much do the aluminum bars shorten? *Ans.* (a) 15 ksi, (b) 0.01 in.

12-7.* A rigid bar is supported by a pin at A and two wires at B and C as shown in the figure. Determine the reactions at A, B, and C caused by the applied load of 1.5 kips. *Ans.* -1.2 k, $+0.9$ k, 1.8 k.

12-8. Two identical, horizontal, simply supported beams span 12 ft each. The beams cross each other at their respective mid-spans. When erected, there is a 0.249 in. gap between the two beams. If a concentrated downward force of 10 kips is applied at mid-span to the upper beam, how much will the lower beam carry? The EI of each beam is 2×10^9 lb-in.^{2} *Ans.* 1 kip.

12-9. If the bar in Prob. 12-2 is not rigid but has an $I = 0.222$ in.^{4} and, being of steel, an E of 30×10^6 psi, what forces will be developed in each wire? *Ans.* 428 lb in middle wire.

12-10. An 8 WF 17 beam is simply supported at the ends A and B and goes over the middle of two 8 WF 17 cross beams as shown in the figure. When erected, the cross beams just touch the beam AB. What will be the reactions at A and B if a uniformly distributed load of 2 kips per ft is applied to the upper beam. $E = 29 \times 10^6$ psi. *Ans.* 6.74 kips.

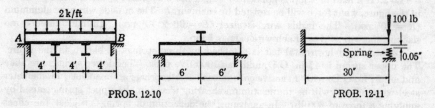

PROB. 12-10

PROB. 12-11

12-11. A 30 in. cantilever beam of constant flexural rigidity, $EI = 10^7$ lb-in.^{2}, initially has a gap of 0.05 in. between its end and the spring. The spring's constant $k = 10$ kips/in. If a force of 100 lb, shown in the figure, is applied to the end of this cantilever, how much of this force will be carried by the spring? *Ans.* 40 lb.

12-12. The midpoint of a cantilever beam 18 ft long rests on the mid-span of a simply supported beam 24 ft long. Determine the deflection of point A, where the beams meet, which results from the application of a 10 kip load at the end of the cantilever beam. The EI for both beams is the same and is constant. *Ans.* $3,290/EI$.

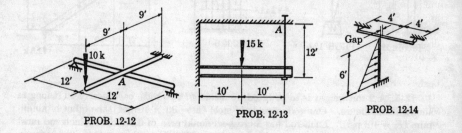

PROB. 12-12

PROB. 12-13

PROB. 12-14

12-13. One end of an 18 WF 50 beam is cast into concrete; the other is supported by a 1 in. square steel rod 12 ft long as shown in the figure. What will be the tensile force, caused by applying the load of 15 kips, in the rod if, during the application of this load, the rod slips a distance of $\frac{1}{2}$ in. at the support at A? $E = 30 \times 10^6$ psi. *Ans.* 2.03 kips.

12-14. A vertical cantilever is subjected to hydrostatic loading totaling 5,000 lb. After closing the initial gap of 0.0288 in., the end of this cantilever receives support from a horizontal beam as shown in the figure. How much of the applied load will be carried by the horizontal beam? For both beams, $EI = 1.728 \times 10^9$ lb-in.^{2} *Ans.* 522 lb.

12-15. A small beam AB in an unloaded condition just touches a spring as shown in the figure. What will be the force exerted on the spring if two 10 lb weights are applied to the beam? The flexural rigidity EI of the beam is 833,000 lb-in.^{2}, and the spring constant $k = 5,000$ lb/in. *Ans.* 7.92 lb.

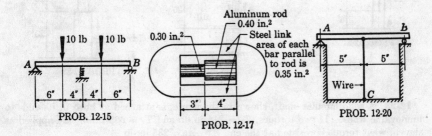

PROB. 12-15

PROB. 12-17

PROB. 12-20

12-16. If in Example 12-5, instead of a bolt, a rivet with no initial tension at 1,600° F is used in the assembly of the washers, what tensile stress will develop in the rivet when the temperature drops to 100° F? $E = 30 \times 10^6$ psi, $\sigma_{yp} = 40$ ksi, and $\alpha = 0.0000065$.

12-17. An aluminum rod 7 in. long, having two different cross-sectional areas, is inserted into a steel link as shown in the figure. If at 60° F no axial force exists in the aluminum rod, what will be the magnitude of this force when the temperature rises to 160° F? $E_{Al} = 10^7$ psi and $\alpha_{Al} = 0.0000120$ per ° F; $E_{St} = 30 \times 10^6$ psi and $\alpha_{St} = 0.0000065$. *Ans.* 1,650 lb.

12-18. A gray cast iron bolt $\frac{3}{4}$ in. in diameter passes through an aluminum tube 3.000 in. long which has an inside diameter of 1 in. and an outside diameter of 2 in. The nut on the end of the bolt is so tightened that at 60° F the stress in the tube becomes 600 psi. Compute the temperature at which the stress in the shank of the bolt will double. Let $E_{CI} = 12 \times 10^6$ psi and $\alpha_{CI} = 0.0000062$ per ° F, and $E_{Al} = 10 \times 10^6$ psi and $\alpha_{Al} = 0.0000124$ per ° F. *Ans.* 112.8° F.

12-19. Three parallel bars of metal 10 in. long are riveted together at each end with one $\frac{1}{2}$ in. diameter rivet. The outer bars are steel, the inner one is aluminum. All bars are $\frac{1}{2}$ in. by 1 in. in cross-section. The rivet's grip is $1\frac{1}{2}$ in. The distance from center to center of the rivets located in the middle of the bars is 8 in. If the temperature drops 100° F, what is the shearing stress in the rivets? $E_{St} = 30 \times 10^6$ psi, $E_{Al} = 10 \times 10^6$ psi, $\alpha_{St} = 0.0000065$ per ° F and $\alpha_{Al} = 0.0000130$ per ° F. *Ans.* 7,110 psi.

12-20. A steel piano wire 30 in. long is stretched from the middle of an aluminum beam AB to a rigid support at C as shown in the figure. What is the increase in unit stress in the wire if the temperature drops 100° F? The cross-sectional area of the wire is 0.0001 in.^{2}; $E = 30 \times 10^6$ psi. For the aluminum beam $EI = 1,040$ lb-in.^{2} Let $\alpha_{St} = 6.5 \times 10^{-6}$ per ° F, $\alpha_{Al} = 12.9 \times 10^{-6}$ per ° F. *Ans.* 6,500 psi.

12-21. Find the reactions at A and D and draw the axial force diagram for the rod shown in the figure. The surfaces at A and D are immovable and the steel rod is welded to them at both of its ends. $A_{rod} = 2$ in.^{2} *Ans.* At A, 5 kips ↑.

12-22. An assembly of steel, brass, and aluminum parts between rigid planes, A and B, is made as shown in the figure. The steel rod ($E = 30 \times 10^6$ psi) has a cross-sectional area of 4 in.²; the brass rod ($E = 15 \times 10^6$ psi) of 1 in.²; the aluminum tube ($E = 10 \times 10^6$ psi) of 1 in.² Initially there is a gap of 0.010 in. between the brass rod and the aluminum tube. If an axial force of 8 kips is applied as shown, what stress will be developed in the aluminum tube? *Ans.* 1,880 psi.

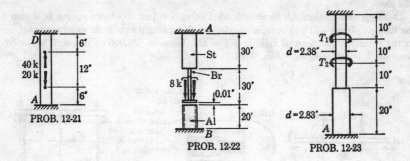

PROB. 12-21   PROB. 12-22   PROB. 12-23

12-23. A solid circular shaft, shown in the figure, is attached at both of its ends to immovable walls. If two torques, $T_1 = 314$ in.-lb and $T_2 = 628$ in.-lb, are applied as shown, what torque is resisted at the end A? *Ans.* 235 in.-lb.

12-24. Rework Example 12-7 by removing the right redundant reaction.

12-25 through 12-27. (a) For the beams loaded as shown in the figures, using the method of superposition, determine the redundant reactions. In all cases EI is constant. (b) For the same beams, plot shear and moment diagrams. *Ans.* M_A is given in parentheses by each figure.

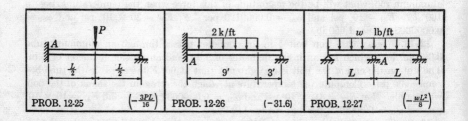

PROB. 12-25 $\left(-\dfrac{3PL}{16}\right)$ PROB. 12-26 (-31.6) PROB. 12-27 $\left(-\dfrac{wL^2}{8}\right)$

12-28. Assuming that the center support settles an amount $wL^4/48EI$, rework Prob. 12-27.

12-29. Rework Example 12-8 by treating the right-hand reaction and moment as the redundants. (*Hint:* the slope and deflection of the right end must be zero.)

12-30. Rework Example 12-11 by using a moment diagram constructed by cantilever parts.

12-31 through 12-33. For the beams loaded as shown in the figures, using the moment-area method, determine the redundant reactions and plot shear and moment diagrams. In all cases EI is constant. (*Hint for Prob. 12-33:* use superposition or moment diagrams by cantilever parts.) *Ans.* M_A is given in parentheses by the figures.

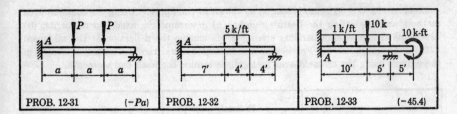

PROB. 12-31   (−Pa) | PROB. 12-32 | PROB. 12-33   (−45.4)

12-34. (a) Using the moment-area method, determine the redundant moment at the built-in end for the beam shown in the figure and plot the shear and moment diagrams for design. Neglect the weight of the beam. (b) Select the depth for a $7\frac{1}{2}$ in. wide wooden beam using an allowable bending stress of 1,200 psi and a shearing stress of 150 psi. (c) Determine the maximum deflection of the beam between the supports and the maximum deflection of the overhang. For wood, E is 1.5×10^6 psi. *Ans.* (b) $15\frac{1}{2}$ in.

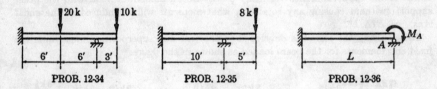

PROB. 12-34   PROB. 12-35   PROB. 12-36

12-35. (a) Using the moment-area method, determine the redundant moment at the built-in end for the beam shown in the figure, and plot the shear and moment diagrams for design. Neglect the weight of the beam. (b) Select a WF beam using an allowable bending stress of 18,000 psi and a shearing stress of 12,000 psi. (c) Determine the maximum deflection of the beam between the supports and the maximum deflection of the overhang. $E = 29 \times 10^6$ psi. *Ans.* (b) 12 WF 27.

12-36. For the beam loaded as shown in the figure, (a) determine the ratio of the moment at the built-in end to the applied moment M_A; (b) determine the rotation of the end A. The EI is constant. *Ans.* $-\frac{1}{2}$, $-M_A L/4EI$.

12-37. Assuming that the left half of the beam has a flexural rigidity of $2\,EI$, rework Prob. 12-36; the rigidity of the right half remains EI.

12-38. Using the moment-area method, show that the maximum deflection of a beam fixed at both ends and carrying a uniformly distributed load is one-fifth the maximum deflection of the same beam simply supported. The EI is constant.

12-39 and 12-40. For the beams loaded as shown in the figures, using the moment-area method, (a) determine the fixed end moments and plot shear and moment diagrams. Neglect the weight of the beams. (b) Express the maximum deflection in terms of the loads, distances, and EI. No adjustment for units need be made.

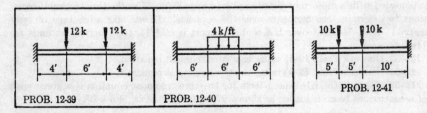

PROB. 12-39   PROB. 12-40   PROB. 12-41

12-41. A 12 WF 36 beam is loaded as shown in the figure.   Using the moment-area method, and neglecting the beam's weight, (a) determine the fixed end moments, (b) determine the maximum bending stress, (c) determine the deflection at the midspan.

12-42 through 12-44. For beams of constant flexural rigidity loaded as shown in the figures, using the moment-area method, determine the fixed end moments.

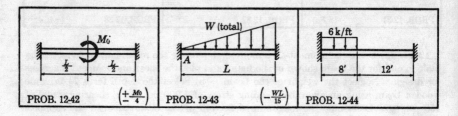

PROB. 12-42 $\left(\pm\frac{M_0}{4}\right)$ PROB. 12-43 $\left(-\frac{WL}{15}\right)$ PROB. 12-44

12-45. A beam of constant flexural rigidity EI is built in at both its ends, L ft apart. If one of the supports settles vertically downward an amount Δ relative to the other support (without causing any rotation), what moments will be induced at the ends? *Ans.* $\pm 6\,EI\Delta/L^2$.

12-46. Using the formulas developed in the text and superposition, determine the fixed end moments for the beam loaded as shown in the figure.

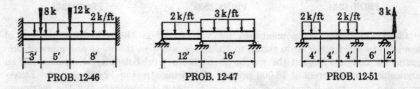

PROB. 12-46   PROB. 12-47   PROB. 12-51

12-47. For the continuous beam loaded as shown in the figure, using the moment-area method, determine the bending moment acting over the middle support, and plot shear and moment diagrams.   The I of the beam in the right-hand span is twice as large as in the left span.

12-48. Rework Prob. 12-47 after assuming that the right support is fixed. *Ans.* M at the fixed end is 73.4 k-ft.

12-49. Rework Example 12-12 after assuming that the right support C is pinned.

12-50. Rework Example 12-12 after assuming that both supports A and C are fixed.

12-51. For the continuous beam loaded as shown in the figure, using the moment-area method, determine the bending moment directly over the center support.   The EI is constant. *Ans.* -13.44 k-ft.

12-52. A beam of constant flexural rigidity EI is continuous over four spans of equal length L.   Plot shear and moment diagrams for this beam if throughout its length it is loaded with a uniformly distributed load of w lb/ft.   Use the three moment equations to determine the moments over the supports.   (*Hint:* take advantage of symmetry.)   *Ans.* Moment over the center support is $wL^2/14$, the reactions at ends are $11wL/28$ each.

12-53. Rework Prob. 12-51 using the three moment equation.

12-54. Rework Prob. 12-50 using the three moment equation.

12-55. What is the right-hand term for the three moment equation if a given span of a continuous beam is loaded as shown in the figure? *Ans.* $+6$ k-ft².

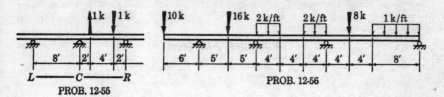

PROB. 12-55

PROB. 12-56

12-56. Using the three moment equation, determine the moments over the supports for the beam loaded as shown in the figure. The EI is constant.

12-57. Rework Prob. 12-36 using the double integration method.

Chapter Thirteen

COLUMNS

13-1. Introduction. In all cases hitherto considered, members were assumed to be in *stable equilibrium.* But not all arrangements are necessarily stable. For example, consider a stick 5 ft long of the cross-sectional area of an ordinary pencil. If this stick were stood on end, one might conclude that the stress at the base would be equal to the total weight of the stick divided by its cross-sectional area. However, the equilibrium of this stick is precarious. With the smallest imperfection in the stick or the lightest gust of wind, the stick would fall down, thus the aforementioned stress calculation is meaningless. This physically obvious example is introduced to accustom the reader to the thought that stability considerations may be primary in some problems.

There are many engineering problems where the instability of a member, or of a structure itself, is possible. For example, the thin shell of a submarine must be stiffened with rings to prevent its collapse. Likewise, the compression chords of a truss must be braced, and the compression flanges of beams must be supported at intervals. Among these problems, that of the analysis of *columns,* i.e., of compression members, *of constant cross-sectional* ai a will be the chief concern of this chapter.

In common with all instability problems, the column problem is complicated by the fact that different phenomena contribute to the capacity of a column, depending on its length. Thus if a steel rod of, say, one-quarter inch diameter were made one-eighth of an inch long to act as a "column," no question of instability would enter and a considerable force could be applied to this piece. On the other hand, if the **same** rod were made several feet long, at a *smaller* applied force than the one a short piece could carry, the rod would become laterally unstable through sidewise buckling and would collapse.

The range of column lengths at which instability occurs and formulas for the carrying capacity of slender columns will be established. Through algebraic manipulations, the expressions to be derived for the carrying capacity of columns are made to look like the usual stress formulas. This customary conversion of column formulas leads some engineers to extrapolate the usual strength formulas into the range where the instability phenomenon governs. The history of many engineering structural failures attests to this tragic blunder; bridges, buildings, machines, and airplanes turned to "spaghetti."

13-2. The Nature of Column Instability. In order to emphasize the physical nature of column instability, a qualitative description of the phenomenon is discussed. First, attention is directed to a *long, perfectly straight* (ideal) column built-in at one end and free at the other as shown in Fig. 13-1a. The subsequent reasoning applies to other long columns with other end conditions, although no quantitative meaning to the term "long" is ascribed as yet.

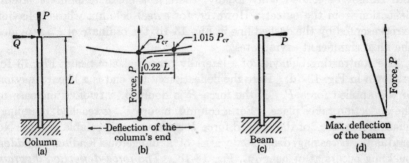

Fig. 13-1. A comparison of the deflection behavior of a column (a) and a beam (c).

If a small *axial* force P is applied to this column, the column will compress a little but will remain straight. Moreover, with this force P acting on the column, a small lateral force Q may be applied, then removed, and the column will return to its initial straight position. The same cycle may be repeated with the force P increasing in magnitude until a *critical force P*, called the *Euler load* P_{cr}, is reached, at which the column remains in a slightly deformed position after the application and removal of the lateral force Q. By applying the force Q in the opposite direction, the column may be returned to the straight position. This instantaneous condition is a state of *neutral equilibrium*.

At P_{cr}, a lateral force of negligible magnitude is sufficient to precipitate lateral buckling and thereby to destroy the precarious equilibrium of the straight position. If the force P is increased above P_{cr} even by an extremely small amount, the column, after a minute force Q is applied and removed, will not return to its initial position. By using an exact differential equation of the elastic curve, it is possible* to find the new equilibrium position corresponding to the applied force P higher than P_{cr}. Such analyses, for example, show that an increase of P_{cr} by a mere 1.5% causes a maximum sidewise deflection equal to 22% of the length of the column, provided the material remains elastic. This general behavior of a column

* See Timoshenko, S., *Theory of Elastic Stability*, p. 72. New York: McGraw-Hill, 1936.

is shown approximately in Fig. 13-1b by the solid lines. The possible deflections of a column in either direction are shown in Fig. 13-1b. It is seen from this diagram that the deflections caused by a P higher than P_{cr} are *very large* and cannot be tolerated in engineering practice, since large stresses are induced in the column by the resulting eccentricity of the applied force, and the column collapses. Therefore the determination of the critical force P_{cr} is the most important quantity in column analysis, as, practically speaking, it represents the *ultimate* capacity of an ideal column. For real columns, which unavoidably are not perfectly straight and cannot be loaded truly axially, there is a small amount of lateral deflection from the outset. However, for a real column, whose behavior is represented by the dashed line in Fig. 13-1b, the ordinate of P_{cr} provides the most significant asymptote.

The contrasting behavior of a laterally braced elastic beam, Fig. 13-1c, is shown in Fig. 13-1d. Here the deflection of the end is a linear function of the applied force P. If the force P is doubled, a twofold increase in the deflection takes place. For a column, before P_{cr} is reached, doubling, quadrupling, etc., of the applied force P causes no appreciable effect. No gradually increasing deflection warns of a dangerous loading. *Sudden* buckling occurs at or near P_{cr}, Fig. 13-1b. *The force-deflection diagram is not a linear function of the applied force.* For this reason, column failures in engineering structures are spectacular and most *dangerous*. *In the structural engineering field, the vast majority of failures have been caused by instability of members.*

13-3. The Euler Formula for a Pin-Ended Column. At the critical load, a column which is circular or tubular in its cross-sectional area may buckle sidewise in any direction. In the more usual case, a compression member does not possess equal flexural rigidity in all directions. The moment of inertia I_{zz} is a maximum around one centroidal axis of the cross-sectional area, Fig. 13-2, a minimum around the other. The significant flexural rigidity EI of a column depends on the **minimum I**, and at the critical load a column buckles either to one side or the other in the X-X plane. The use of a minimum I in the derivation which follows is understood.

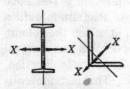

Fig. 13-2. Columns buckle in the plane of the major axis of the cross-section.

Consider a column with its ends free to rotate around frictionless pins. Such columns, having pinned supports at both ends, are called *pin-ended columns*. In Fig. 13-3a the equivalent boundary conditions are shown by means of rounded ends in frictionless supports. *The buckled shape shown is possible only at a critical or Euler load, as prior to this load the column remains straight.* The *smallest* force at which a buckled shape is possible is the critical force.

It is seen from Fig. 13-3b that the bending moment at any section is
$-Py$, which conforms to the usual sign con-
vention for beams.* With this value of the
bending moment, the differential equation for
the elastic curve, Eq. 11-4, *at* the critical load is

$$\frac{d^2y}{dx^2} = \frac{M}{EI} = -\frac{P}{EI}\, y \qquad (13\text{-}1)$$

whence by letting $k^2 = P/(EI)$, and transposing, gives

$$\frac{d^2y}{dx^2} + k^2 y = 0 \qquad (13\text{-}2)$$

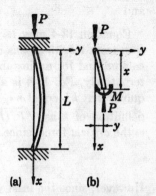

This is an equation of the same form as the one
for simple harmonic motion, and its solution is †

$$y = A \sin kx + B \cos kx \qquad (13\text{-}3)$$

(a)   (b)

Fig. 13-3. Pin- or round-
ended column used in the
derivation of the Euler load.

where A and B are arbitrary constants which must be determined from
the conditions at the boundary.   These conditions are

$$(y)_{x=0} = 0 \qquad \text{and} \qquad (y)_{x=L} = 0$$

* For the positive direction of the deflection y shown, the bending moment is negative.   (Rotate the diagram through 90° counterclockwise.)   If the column were deflected in the other direction, the moment would be positive.   However, y would be
negative.   Hence, to make Py positive, it must likewise be treated as a negative quantity.

† If the reader is not familiar with this solution, Eq. 13-3 may be obtained as follows:
Write Eq. 13-1 as

$$\frac{d\left(\dfrac{dy}{dx}\right)}{dx} = -\frac{Py}{EI} = -k^2 y.$$

Multiply both sides by $2\, dy$ and simplify to $2\dfrac{dy}{dx} d\left(\dfrac{dy}{dx}\right) = -2k^2 y\, dy.$ Each side
in this equation is an exact differential of the form $2u\, du$, hence $\left(\dfrac{dy}{dx}\right)^2 = -k^2 y^2 + c_1^2.$
The constant is written as c_1^2 since it is always positive, otherwise the slope dy/dx would
be imaginary.   Recasting the above equation into $dx = \dfrac{dy}{\sqrt{c_1^2 - k^2 y^2}}$ and integrating
yields

$$x + c_2 = \frac{1}{k}\sin^{-1}\frac{ky}{c_1}$$

or $$y = (c_1/k)\sin\,(kx + c_2 k)$$

$$= [(c_1/k)\cos\,(c_2 k)]\sin kx + [(c_1/k)\sin\,(c_2 k)]\cos kx$$

If in the last equation the first bracketed expression is denoted by a constant A and the
second by B, Eq. 13-3 is obtained.

Hence $(y)_{x=0} = 0 = A \sin 0 + B \cos 0$, or $B = 0$,

and $(y)_{x=L} = 0 = A \sin kL$ (13-4)

Equation 13-4 may be satisfied by taking $A = 0$; however, as may be seen from Eq. 13-3, this corresponds to a condition of no buckling of the column and for an instability problem represents a trivial solution. Alternatively, Eq. 13-4 is also satisfied if the sine term vanishes. This requires that kL equal $n\pi$, where n is an integer. Hence, using the earlier definition of k as $\sqrt{P/(EI)}$, and solving $\sqrt{P/(EI)}L = n\pi$ for P which is the critical force, since it makes the curved shape possible,

$$P_{cr} = \frac{n^2\pi^2 EI}{L^2}$$ (13-5)

However, since the least value of the critical or Euler load is sought, n in Eq. 13-5 must be taken as one. Therefore the *Euler load formula** for a column pin-ended at both ends* is

$$P_{cr} = \frac{\pi^2 EI}{L^2}$$ (13-6)

where I is the *least* moment of inertia of the constant cross-sectional area of a column, and L is its length. This case of a column with pinned or round ends at both ends is often referred to as the *fundamental case*.

According to Eq. 13-3, at the critical load, the equation of the elastic curve is

$$y = A \sin kx$$ (13-3a)

The coefficient A remains indeterminate, since an approximate equation of the elastic curve was used in this derivation (Eq. 11-4 rather than Eq. 11-3). For $n = 1$, the elastic curve is a half-wave sine curve, Fig. 13-4. The discarded values of n correspond to buckled shapes with additional points of inflection. These shapes are not physically significant, since the least critical load occurs at $n = 1$.

13-4. Euler Formulas for Columns with Different End Conditions. The critical loads for columns with end conditions other than pinned at both ends may be derived in a manner analogous to that used in the preceding article. A critical load for the column built-in at one end and free at the other, Fig. 13-5a, may be deduced from the fundamental case by using Eq. 13-6. The solid line in the figure shows this column in a slightly deflected position. By constructing the dashed curve, which is a mirror image of the solid line, this composite case reverts to the fundamental case, except that $L = 2L_1$. Hence the critical load for this column is

$$P_{cr} = \frac{\pi^2 EI}{4L_1^2}$$ (13-6a)

* This formula was derived by the great mathematician Leonhard Euler in 1757.

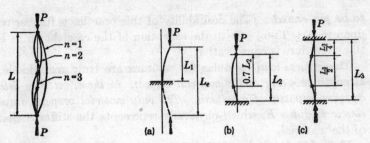

Fig. 13-4. Different values of the integer n correspond to different modes of buckling.

Fig. 13-5. Columns with different end conditions.

For a column fixed at one end and pinned at the other, Fig. 13-5b, it can be shown that the critical load is*

$$P_{cr} = \frac{2.05\pi^2 EI}{L_2^2} \tag{13-6b}$$

For this case, the point of inflection of the elastic curve is approximately $0.7L_2$ from the pinned end.

For a prismatic column fixed at both ends, the tangents to the elastic curve do not rotate at the ends and at the center. The inflection points occur at quarter points, Fig. 13-5c, and the critical load is

$$P_{cr} = \frac{4\pi^2 EI}{L_3^2} \tag{13-6c}$$

In all of these formulas, I is the *minimum* moment of inertia of the cross-sectional area, and all of these formulas may be made to look like Eq. 13-6 if *effective column lengths* are used. The effective column length L_e for the fundamental case is L, while for the above cases it is $2L_1$, $0.7L_2$, and $0.5L_3$, respectively. For a general case, $L_e = cL_n$, where c is a constant dependent on the end restraints.

The concept of effective length is useful in practical applications, since actual compression members are seldom truly pinned or completely fixed against rotation at the ends, as was assumed in the foregoing idealized cases. In many cases, the effective length is estimated or based on the results of tests. For example, columns with flat ends, called "square-ended" columns, are extensively employed. For these columns, points of inflection at the critical load occur somewhere between the two limiting cases shown in Figs. 13-3 and 13-5c. In building and bridge practice, the coefficient c is sometimes taken equal to $\frac{3}{4}$ for columns whose ends are riveted to other members and at $\frac{7}{8}$ for pinned ends, as the pins are known to develop some moment resistance by friction. *However, because of the uncertainty regarding fixity of the ends, columns are most often assumed*

* Timoshenko, *op. cit.*, p. 89.

to be pin-ended. (The desirability of this practice is further commented upon in Art. 13-6.) With the exception of the case shown in Fig. 13-5a, this procedure is conservative.

The critical-load formulas for columns are truly remarkable, since *no strength property of the material appears in them, yet they determine the carrying capacity of a column. The only material property involved is the elastic modulus E,* which physically represents the stiffness characteristic of the material.

13-5. Limitations of the Euler Formulas. The elastic modulus E was used in the derivation of the Euler formulas for columns. Therefore all the reasoning presented earlier is applicable *while the material behaves elastically.* To bring out this significant limitation, Eq. 13-6 of Art. 13-3 will be written in a different form. By definition, $I = Ar^2$, where A is the cross-sectional area and r is its *radius of gyration.* Substitution of this relation into Eq. 13-6 gives

$$P_{cr} = \frac{\pi^2 EI}{L^2} = \frac{\pi^2 EAr^2}{L^2}$$

or
$$\sigma_{cr} = \frac{P_{cr}}{A} = \frac{\pi^2 E}{(L/r)^2} \tag{13-7}$$

where the *critical stress* σ_{cr} for a column is defined as P_{cr}/A, i.e., as an *average* stress over the cross-sectional area A of a column at the critical load P_{cr}. The length* of the column is L, and r is the *least* radius of gyration of the cross-sectional area, since the original Euler formula is in terms of the minimum I. The ratio L/r of the column length to the *least* radius of gyration is called the column **slenderness ratio.** *No factor of safety is included in the above equation.*

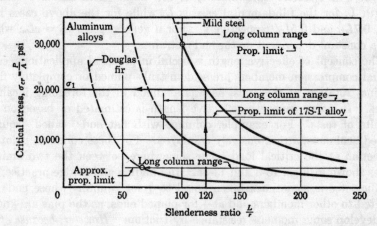

Fig. 13-6. Variation of the critical column stress with the slenderness ratio for three different materials.

* By using the effective length, the expression becomes general.

A graphical interpretation of Eq. 13-7 is shown in Fig. 13-6, where the critical column stress is plotted versus the slenderness ratio for three different materials. For each material E is constant, and the resulting curve is a hyperbola. However, since Eq. 13-7 is based on the elastic behavior of a material, σ_{cr} determined by this equation cannot exceed the proportional limit of a material. Therefore the hyperbolas shown in Fig. 13-6 are drawn dashed beyond the individual material's proportional limit, and these portions of the curves *cannot be used*.

The useful portions of the hyperbolas do not represent the behavior of one column, but rather the behavior of an infinite number of ideal columns. For example, a particular steel column, say with an $L/r = 120$, may at the most carry a load of $\sigma_1 A$. Also note that σ_{cr} *always decreases with increasing ratios of* L/r. Moreover, note that, with the aid of these diagrams, a precise definition of a *long* column is now possible. Thus, a column is said to be long if the *elastic* Euler formula applies. The beginning of the long-column range is shown for some particular materials in Fig. 13-6.

13-6. The Generalized Euler or the Tangent Modulus Formula.

A column with an L/r less than the smallest L/r of the long-column range remains stable after the proportional limit has been exceeded. On a compression stress-strain diagram, Fig. 13-7, this means that the stress level in the column has passed point A and has reached perhaps some point B. At this higher stress level, it may be said that, in effect, a column of *different material* has been created, since the stiffness of the material is no longer represented by the elastic modulus. At this point, the material's stiffness is instantaneously given by the tangent to the stress-strain curve, i.e., by the *tangent modulus* E_t. The column remains stable if its new flexural rigidity $E_t I$ at B is sufficiently great, and it can carry a higher load. As the load is increased, the stress level rises, and the tangent modulus decreases. A column of ever "less stiff material" is acting under an increasing load. Substitution of the tangent modulus E_t for the elastic modulus E is then the only modification necessary to make the elastic Euler formula applicable in the inelastic range. Hence the *generalized Euler formula*,[*] or the *tangent modulus formula*,[†] for the fundamental case becomes

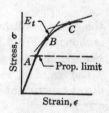

Fig. 13-7. A compression stress-strain diagram.

---

[*] Although this formula has been known for some time, its final clarification is very recent. See Shanley, F. R., "Inelastic Column Theory," *Journal of Aeronautical Sciences*, vol. 14, no. 5, May, 1947.

[†] The tangent modulus formula gives the carrying capacity of a column defined at the instant it tends to buckle. A further increase in the load in effect creates a column of still "another material." If a column deforms to the left, Fig. 13-Aa, the inner fibers at A are subjected to additional compression. These fibers, if the general stress level is at σ_1 as shown in Fig. 13-Ab, exhibit a tangent modulus E_t. On the other hand, as the column bends, the fibers at B are relieved of some stress and these fibers, as is

$$\sigma_{cr} = \frac{\pi^2 E_t}{(L/r)^2} \tag{13-7a}$$

In this equation, E_t is a variable quantity to which a certain stress level σ_{cr} corresponds. These quantities, which apply simultaneously to a material, may be determined from its stress-strain diagram. Then, since σ_{cr} and E_t, are known, Eq. 13-7a may be solved for the L/r ratio at which

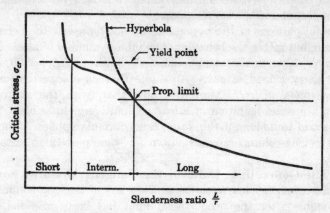

Fig. 13-8. Variation of the critical column stress over the entire range of slenderness ratios.

the column will buckle at this stress. A plot representing this behavior is shown in Fig. 13-8. Tests on individual columns verify this curve with remarkable accuracy.*

Curves of σ_{cr} vs. L/r based on the tangent modulus theory, as well as direct experiments, usually turn up at the low L/r ratios. Physically this

---

known from the property of materials, behave with the *original elastic modulus E.* These facts led to the establishment of the so-called *double-modulus theory* of load-carrying capacity of columns. The end results as obtained by this theory do not differ greatly from those obtained by the tangent modulus theory.

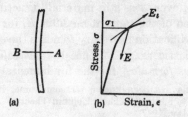

Fig. 13-A.

For further details see Timoshenko, S., *Theory of Elastic Stability.* New York: McGraw-Hill, 1936.

* See Van den Broek, J. A., "Column Formula for Materials of Variable Modulus," *The Engineering Journal* (Canada), December, 1945.

represents the transition from the instability type of failure to that of the direct compression type. At low L/r ratios, because of the "squashing out" effect observed in many materials, very large loads may be carried. For mild steels in this range, the ultimate capacity of a member is usually taken at the yield point. If a material does not possess a clearly defined yield point, one is arbitrarily selected on the basis of the allowable deformations by the offset method (Art. 2-5).

The generalized Euler theory permits a definite classification of columns. Columns that are more like blocks to which a strength criterion is applied are termed *short columns*. Columns for which the variable tangent modulus applies are referred to as those of *intermediate* length. Beyond the latter zone the columns are *long*. These zones are shown in Fig. 13-8. The extent of these zones varies for each material. Strictly speaking, if the generalized Euler theory is used, no distinction between intermediate and long columns needs to be made, but this is customarily done.

In the above discussion attention was focused on the fundamental case, i.e., on columns with pinned ends. It is worth while to compare the behavior of columns with different end conditions, particularly in the intermediate and short range. A comparison of critical stresses for a fixed-ended column with those of a pin-ended column is shown in Fig. 13-9.

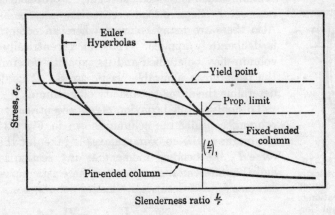

Fig. 13-9. Comparison of the behavior of pin-ended and fixed-ended columns.

As the material of the columns is the same, the same proportional limit cuts off the Euler hyperbolas in both cases. The carrying capacity of columns for $(L/r)_1$ and greater is in a ratio of 4 to 1. *As the L/r ratio decreases, less and less benefit is derived by fixing the ends.* At low L/r ratios the curves merge, since it makes little difference whether the "blocks" are pinned or fixed at the ends. The analysis of columns based on the tangent modulus theory smoothly closes the "gap" between the short and the long column range.

Example 13-1. Find the shortest length L for a pin-ended steel column having a cross-sectional area of 2 in. by 3 in. for which the elastic Euler formula applies. Let $E = 30 \times 10^6$ psi and assume the proportional limit at 36 ksi.

SOLUTION: The *minimum* moment of inertia of the cross-sectional area $I_{min} = 3(2)^3/12 = 2$ in.[4] Hence

$$r = r_{min} = \sqrt{\frac{I_{min}}{A}} = \sqrt{\frac{2}{2(3)}} = \frac{1}{\sqrt{3}} \text{ in.}$$

Then using Eq. 13-7, $\sigma_{cr} = \pi^2 E/(L/r)^2$, and solving it for the L/r ratio at the proportional limit, gives

$$\left(\frac{L}{r}\right)^2 = \frac{\pi^2 E}{\sigma_{cr}} = \frac{\pi^2 (30) 10^6}{(36) 10^3} = 8{,}220$$

or $$\frac{L}{r} = 90.7 \quad \text{and} \quad L = \frac{90.7}{\sqrt{3}} = 52.3 \text{ in.}$$

For 2 in. by 3 in. rectangular columns of this material longer than 52.3 in., the elastic Euler formula applies; for shorter columns, the tangent modulus formula must be used.

13-7. The Secant Formula.

A different method of analysis may be used to determine the capacity of a column than was discussed above. Since no columns are perfectly straight nor the applied forces perfectly concentric, the behavior of real columns may be studied on a statistical

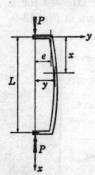

Fig. 13-10. An eccentrically loaded column for derivation of the secant formula.

or probability basis. Then, for the design of an actual column, which is termed "straight," a probable crookedness or an effective load eccentricity may be assigned. Also there are many columns where an eccentric load is deliberately applied. Thus, an eccentrically loaded column may be studied and its capacity determined on the basis of an allowable elastic stress. This does not determine the ultimate capacity of a column.

To analyze the behavior of an eccentrically loaded column, consider the column shown in Fig. 13-10. If the origin of the co-ordinate axes is taken at the upper force P, the bending moment at any section is $-Py$, and the differential equation for the elastic curve is the same as for a concentrically loaded column, i.e.,

$$\frac{d^2y}{dx^2} = \frac{M}{EI} = -\frac{P}{EI} y \qquad (13\text{-}1)$$

whence by again letting $k = \sqrt{P/(EI)}$, the general solution is as before,

$$y = A \sin kx + B \cos kx \qquad (13\text{-}3)$$

However, the remainder of the problem is not the same, since *the boundary conditions are now different*. At the upper end, y is equal to the eccentricity of the applied load, i.e., $(y)_{x=0} = e$. Hence $B = e$, and Eq. 13-3 becomes

$$y = A \sin kx + e \cos kx \tag{13-8}$$

Next, noting that, by virtue of symmetry, the elastic curve has a vertical tangent at the mid-height of the column,

$$\left(\frac{dy}{dx}\right)_{x=L/2} = 0$$

Therefore, by setting the derivative of Eq. 13-8 equal to zero at $x = L/2$, it is found that

$$A = e \frac{\sin kL/2}{\cos kL/2}$$

Hence the equation for the elastic curve is

$$y = e\left(\frac{\sin kL/2}{\cos kL/2}\sin kx + \cos kx\right) \tag{13-9}$$

No indeterminacy of any constants appears in this equation, and the maximum deflection y_{max} may be found from it. This maximum deflection occurs at $L/2$, since at this point the derivative of Eq. 13-9 is equal to zero. Hence

$$(y)_{x=L/2} = y_{max} = e\left(\frac{\sin^2 kL/2}{\cos kL/2} + \cos \frac{kL}{2}\right) = e \sec \frac{kL}{2}$$

In the column shown in Fig. 13-10, the largest bending moment M is developed at the point of maximum deflection and numerically is equal to Py_{max}. Therefore, since the direct force and the largest bending moment are now known, the *maximum* compressive stress occurring in the column (contrast this with the *average* stress P/A acting on the column) may be computed by the usual formula, as

$$\sigma_{max} = \frac{P}{A} + \frac{Mc}{I} = \frac{P}{A} + \frac{Py_{max}c}{Ar^2} = \frac{P}{A}\left(1 + \frac{ec}{r^2}\sec\frac{kL}{2}\right)$$

But $k = \sqrt{P/(EI)} = \sqrt{P/(EAr^2)}$, hence

$$\sigma_{max} = \frac{P}{A}\left(1 + \frac{ec}{r^2}\sec\frac{L}{r}\sqrt{\frac{P}{4EA}}\right) \tag{13-10}$$

This equation, since it contains a secant term, is known as *the secant formula for columns*, and it applies for all cases provided the maximum stress remains within the elastic limit. A condition of equal eccentricities of the applied forces in the same direction causes the largest deflection.

Note that in Eq. 13-10 r *may not be minimum*, since it is obtained from the value of I associated with the axis around which bending occurs. In some cases a more critical condition for buckling may exist in the direction of no definite eccentricity. Also note that in Eq. 13-10 *the relation between σ_{max} and P is not linear; σ_{max} increases faster than P. Therefore the solutions for maximum stresses in columns caused by different axial forces cannot be superposed;* instead the forces must be superposed first, and then the stresses can be calculated.

For an allowable force P_a on a column, nP_a, where n is the factor of safety, must be substituted for P in Eq. 13-10, while σ_{max} must be set at the yield point* of a material, i.e.,

$$\sigma_{max} = \sigma_{yp} = \frac{nP_a}{A}\left(1 + \frac{ec}{r^2}\sec\frac{L}{r}\sqrt{\frac{nP_a}{4EA}}\right) \qquad (13\text{-}11)$$

This procedure assures a correct factor oi safety for the applied force, since such a force may be increased n times before a critical stress is reached. Note the term nP_a appearing under the radical.

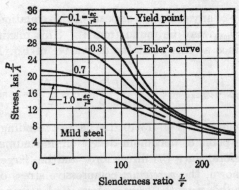

Fig. 13-11. Results of analysis for different columns by the secant formula.

Equations 13-10 and 13-11 having been established, mathematically the problem is solved. However, the application of these equations to design is very cumbersome.† They may be solved by trial-and-error procedures, or they may be studied graphically. Such a study is shown in Fig. 13-11.‡ In this plot, note the large effect which the load eccentricity has on short columns and the negligible one on very slender columns. Graphs of this kind form a suitable aid in practical design. The secant equation covers the whole range of column lengths. The greatest handicap in using this formula is that some eccentricity e must be assumed even for supposedly straight columns, and this is a difficult task.§

* If the stress-strain diagram is roughly a straight line up to the ultimate strength, σ_{ult} may be used.

† Try it sometime and see how long it takes.

‡ This figure is taken from a paper by Young, D. H., on "Rational Design of Steel Columns," *Trans.*, ASCE, 1936, vol. 101, p. 431.

§ Moreover, there is some question as to the philosophical correctness of the secant formula. The fact that the stress reaches a certain value does not mean that the column buckles, i.e. stress is not a measure of buckling load in every case.

The secant formula for *short* columns reverts to a familiar expression when L/r approaches zero. For this case, the value of the secant approaches unity, hence, in the limit, Eq. 13-10 becomes

$$\sigma_{max} = \frac{P}{A} + \frac{Pec}{Ar^2} = \frac{P}{A} + \frac{Mc}{I}$$

a relation normally used for short blocks.

13-8. Design of Columns. For economy, the cross-sectional areas of columns, other than short blocks, should possess the largest possible least radius of gyration. This gives a smaller L/r ratio, which permits the use

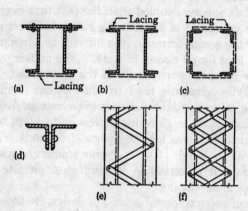

Fig. 13-12. Typical built-up cross-sections of columns.

of a higher axial stress. Tubes form excellent columns, although, unless welding is used, connections are difficult to make. Wide-flange sections (which are also sometimes called *H*-sections) are superior to *I*-sections.

In columns built-up from rolled shapes, the individual pieces are spread out to obtain the desired effect. Cross-sections for typical bridge compression members are shown in Figs. 13-12a and b, for a boom in Fig. 13-12c, and for an ordinary truss in Fig. 13-12d. The angles in Fig. 13-12d are separated by spacers. The main shapes in Figs. 13-12a, b, and c are *laced* or latticed together by light bars, as

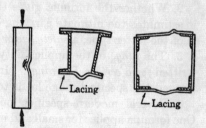

Fig. 13-13. Examples of local instability in columns.

shown in Figs. 13-12e and f. Sometimes less efficient members, as single angles and plain rectangular bars, are used because of some other design requirements.

Obtaining a large r by placing a given amount of material away from the centroid of an area, illustrated above, soon reaches a limit. The material becomes so thin that it crumples locally.   This behavior is termed *local instability*.   When failure caused by local instability takes place in the flanges or the component plates of a member, the column becomes unservicable.   An illustration of local buckling is shown in Fig. 13-13. It is usually characterized by a change in the shape of a cross-section. The equations derived earlier are for the instability of a column as a whole, or for *primary instability*.

The column formulas discussed earlier were derived theoretically, hence they are termed *rational*.   As yet, in engineering practice rational formulas are not always used.   The relative recency of a clear understanding of the generalized Euler's theory, coupled with the fact that every material has its own peculiar variation* of E_t with the stress, hampers progress in this field.   Also, for the secant formula, it is difficult to agree on the probable eccentricities of load for all classes of work.   The matter of local buckling further obscures research, particularly in the intermediate column range. In traditional civil-engineering (and to some extent in mechanical-engineering) practice, *columns of intermediate length occur most frequently*.   These facts and tradition led the engineering profession to adopt several modified or simply empirical formulas for the design of columns.   These formulas were developed as the result of an *enormous* amount of research.   As the number of structural materials is increasing, a definite trend toward rational formulas is developing.

Several types of column formulas used in design are listed below.   This listing is not exhaustive but primarily illustrates the usual types.   The reader will note the over-all similarity of practical formulas to the rational ones previously discussed.   In using these formulas the designer must note particularly the following items:

1. The material for which the formula is written.

2. Whether the formula gives the working load (or stress) or whether it estimates the ultimate carrying capacity of a member.   If the formula is of the latter type, a *safety factor must be introduced*.

3. The *range* of the applicability of the formula.   Usually formulas are written *for a certain L/r range*.   In some cases, an empirical formula used beyond the specified range leads to unsafe design.

4. Several modern specifications stipulate column formulas in pairs. One formula applies for small and intermediate values of L/r, which roughly corresponds to the short and the intermediate column lengths.   The other formula is specified for longer columns, and this second formula is frequently an Euler formula with an appropriate factor of safety.   The equations for these formulas represent curves which have *a common tangent* at one point for a particular value of L/r.   In several specifications for short columns, no formula is used; the stress is set at some constant value.

---

* The aircraft industry has solved the problem by publishing graphs for each material used in design.

In all of these formulas, r represents the *least* radius of gyration of the cross-sectional area.

13-9. Formulas for Nominally Concentric Loading of Columns. *The Parabolic Formula.* The secant formula, Eq. 13-10, is unwieldy to use. It simplifies considerably if a constant "eccentricity ratio" $ec/r^2 = 0.25$ is *assumed* for nominally concentrically loaded straight columns. Over a limited range, the results of this analysis and research may be well approximated by a parabolic equation. The American Institute of Steel Construction Specifications (AISC 1948) provide a working stress formula of this type for structural steel, which for an *average* axial stress permitted on a column reads

$$\frac{P}{A} = 17{,}000 - 0.485 \left(\frac{L}{r}\right)^2 \qquad\qquad \text{[psi] (13-12)}$$

This formula is applicable *only* in the L/r range between zero and 120. The formula for larger values of L/r is cited later, Eq. 13-14. Equation 13-12, or ones of similar type, are widely used in building work. A plot of Eq. 13-12 is shown in Fig. 13-14.

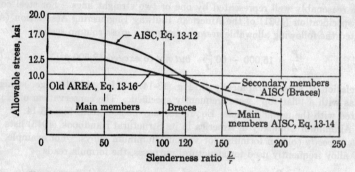

Fig. 13-14. Allowable axial stresses versus slenderness ratios.

The Rankine-Gordon Formula. If an *assumption* is made that the maximum deflection or crookedness of a column varies as L^2/c, i.e., $y_{max} = \phi L^2/c$, where ϕ is a constant of proportionality, the *maximum* stress in a column is

$$\sigma_{max} = \frac{P}{A} + \frac{Mc}{I} = \frac{P}{A} + \frac{P y_{max} c}{A r^2} = \frac{P}{A}\left[1 + \phi \left(\frac{L}{r}\right)^2\right]$$

hence the formula for an *average* axial stress for a column is

$$\frac{P}{A} = \frac{\sigma_{max}}{1 + \phi(L/r)^2} \tag{13-13}$$

This formula, perfected by Rankine in the 1860's, is still widely used. If proper constants are selected, experiments provide a reasonable justification for it over a considerable L/r range.

The AISC Specifications (1948) assign 18,000 for σ_{max}, and also for $1/\phi$, in Eq. 13-13 to obtain a working stress formula for structural steel for *bracing and other secondary members*. It is used only for L/r ratios between 120 and 200. In the above range, the equation is modified for *main members* (all members except braces) by multiplying it by a reduction factor to read

$$\frac{P}{A} = \frac{18{,}000}{1 + \dfrac{L^2}{18{,}000 r^2}}\left[1.6 - \frac{(L/r)}{200}\right] \qquad\qquad \text{[psi] (13-14)}$$

Under no circumstances can a member more slender than one having an $L/r = 200$ be used for any compression member according to this specification. A plot of allowable stresses according to AISC specifications is shown in Fig. 13-14.

In machine design, a modified Rankine-Gordon formula is sometimes used, bearing the name *Ritter's semirational formula*. First, the numerator in Eq. 13-13 is set equal to the elastic limit σ_e of a given material. Then Eq. 13-13 is equated to the Euler formula, whence in the limit for *large values of L/r*, the constant ϕ is approximately equal to $\sigma_e/\pi^2 E$. Whereupon the *working stress formula* for an *average* axial stress becomes

$$\frac{P}{A} = \frac{\sigma_c}{1 + \frac{\sigma_e}{\pi^2 E} \left(\frac{L_e}{r}\right)^2} \qquad (13\text{-}15)$$

In this expression, σ_c is the allowable stress in compression on a short block, and L_e is the effective column length. This formula possesses the advantage that it can be used for any material. Its rationality for intermediate columns is dubious.

The Straight-Line Formula. For columns in the low L/r range, the results of tests may be reasonably well represented by one or two straight lines. For steel columns, an old specification (1931) of the American Railway Engineering Association (AREA) stipulated the following allowable *average* stress on a gross column section

$$\frac{P}{A} = 15{,}000 - 50 \frac{L}{r}, \quad \text{but not to exceed 12,500 psi} \qquad (13\text{-}16)$$

This relation is shown graphically in Fig. 13-14. A few decades ago, straight-line formulas with a "flat top" were frequently specified. The conservatism of Eq. 13-16 compared with the newer formula, Eq. 13-12, may be seen from Fig. 13-14.

The Aluminum Company of America in its Structural Handbook (1945) lists twenty *ultimate capacity* column formulas for various aluminum alloys. For example, for the 24 S-T alloy frequently used for structural purposes, the formula reads

$$\sigma_{\text{cr}} = \frac{P_{\text{cr}}}{A} = 56{,}600 - 510 \frac{L_e}{r}, \text{ but not to exceed 46,000 psi} \qquad (13\text{-}17)$$

where L_e is the effective column length. This formula is applicable for L_e/r ratio up to 73. For more slender columns, Euler's formula is specified.

The Forest Products Laboratory Formula. The Forest Products Laboratory, as a result of a large number of tests, recommends, as a working load formula for solid wood rectangular columns,

$$\frac{P}{A} = C \left[1 - \frac{1}{3} \left(\frac{L}{Kd}\right)^4\right] \qquad (13\text{-}18)$$

in which C is the allowable unit stress in compression parallel to the grain on short blocks; $K = 0.702\sqrt{E/C}$, where E is the elastic modulus; and d is the dimension of the *least* side of a column. Equation 13-18 is used in the range: $11 < L/d < K$. For $L/d \leq 11$, the value of C may be used directly. A strength reduction factor should be used* if columns are not made from solid wood.

The Euler Formula. In some situations, very slender columns are employed, although in building and bridge work columns with L/r ratios higher than 200 are generally prohibited. For very slender columns, Euler's formula is generally used. For example, The Aluminum Company of America (1945) specifies an *ultimate strength* formula for long columns as

$$\sigma_{\text{cr}} = \frac{P_{\text{cr}}}{A} = \frac{102{,}000{,}000}{(L_e/r)^2} \qquad (13\text{-}19)$$

---

* Forest Products Laboratory, *Wood Handbook*, U. S. Dept. of Agri.

This formula is used for all aluminum alloys, as E is nearly the same for them all. Its range of applicability depends on the proportional limit of the individual alloy. For example, for 24 S-T it applies above an L_e/r ratio of 73, for 4 S-$\frac{1}{4}$H above 112, etc.

The Forest Products Laboratory recommends a working stress formula for solid wood rectangular long columns as

$$\frac{P}{A} = \frac{0.329E}{(L/d)^2} \qquad\qquad (13\text{-}20)$$

In this formula, as in Eq. 13-18, d is the dimension of the least side of a column. This formula should be used when L/d is greater than K, defined previously, and L/d should not exceed 50.

Example 13-2. Compare the allowable axial compressive loads for a 3 in. by 2 in. by $\frac{1}{4}$ in. 17 S-T aluminum-alloy angle 43 in. long, (a) if it acts as a pin-ended column, and (b) if it is so restrained that its effective length is $0.9\,L$. Assume a factor of safety of 2.5.

SOLUTION: The proportions of aluminum-alloy angles are the same as those of steel. Hence for this size of angle from Table 7 of the Appendix, the *least* radius of gyration $r = 0.43$ in., while its area $A = 1.19$ in.^{2} The solution follows by applying Eq. 13-19 and using the specified factor of safety.

Case (a): $L_e = L = 43$ in., $L_e/r = 43/(0.43) = 100$.

$$\frac{P_{cr}}{A} = \frac{102,000,000}{(L_e/r)^2} = 10,200 \text{ psi}$$

$$P_{cr} = A\sigma_{cr} = (1.19)10,200 = 12,100 \text{ lb}$$

$$P_{allow} = \frac{P_{cr}}{\text{F.S.}} = \frac{12,100}{2.5} = 4,830 \text{ lb}$$

Case (b): $L_e = 0.9L = 38.7$ in., $L_e/r = (38.7)/(0.43) = 90$.

$$P_{cr} = A\sigma_{cr} = (1.19)12,590 = 15,000 \text{ lb}$$

$$P_{allow} = \frac{P_{cr}}{\text{F.S.}} = \frac{15,000}{2.5} = 6,000 \text{ lb}$$

Example 13-3. By AISC specifications select a "square-ended" column 15 ft long to carry a concentric load of 120 kips.

SOLUTION: The AISC specifications do not differentiate between pin- and square-ended columns, therefore Eqs. 13-12 and 13-14 apply directly. Since no information on the size of the column is available, a trial-and-error procedure must be used.* By *guessing* at an allowable stress, the cross-sectional area of a column is estimated. With this information, a particular column is selected for which the *least* radius of gyration becomes known. Then the assumed stress is compared with the allowable stress, which now is based on the L/r ratio of the selected column.

First try: Let $P/A = 17$ ksi, then $A = 120/17 = 7.06$ in.^{2} This requires an 8 WF 24 section, whose $r_{min} = 1.61$ in. Hence $L/r = 15(12)/(1.61) = 112$, and the allowable stress is

$$\frac{P}{A} = 17,000 - 0.485\left(\frac{L}{r}\right)^2 = 10,920 \text{ psi}$$

Second try: Let $P/A = 10.92$ ksi, then $A = 120/(10.92) = 11.0$ in.^{2} This requires an 8 WF 40 section, whose $r_{min} = 2.04$ in. Hence $L/r = 15(12)/2.04 = 88.3$ and

$$\frac{P}{A} = 17,000 - 0.485(88.3)^2 = 13,230 \text{ psi}$$

* The allowable load by these formulas on columns of various sizes are actually available in the AISC Steel Construction Manual.

Since the area of 8 WF 40 sections is 11.76 in.², this column 15 ft long is good for 11.76(13.23) = 155 kips, which is excessive. An additional try shows that 8 WF 31 section is adequate. By using some ingenuity, the above trial-and-error process may be shortened. For example, the stress assumed in the first try is known to be too high, as it applies only to short blocks (see Fig. 13-14).

13-10. Formulas for Eccentric Loading of Columns. *The Secant Formula.* Formulas of the secant type are occasionally employed for columns with known eccentricity of loading. The AREA specifications (1935) provide the following allowable stress formula for an *average* axial stress of this type for all slenderness ratios:

$$\frac{P}{A} = \frac{\dfrac{y}{n}}{1 + \left(\dfrac{ec}{r^2} + 0.001\dfrac{L}{r}\right) \sec\left[\dfrac{L_e}{2r}\sqrt{\dfrac{nP}{AE}}\right]} \tag{13-21}$$

where the yield point in tension y is 33,000 psi for structural steel, 45,000 psi for silicon steel, 50,000 psi for nickel steel. The factor of safety n is 1.76 for structural steel, 1.80 for silicon steel, 1.78 for nickel steel. The term e is the known eccentricity of the applied load; c is the distance from the neutral axis to the extreme fiber; r is the *least* radius of gyration of the member; L is the length of the member; L_e is equal to $\frac{3}{4}L$ for riveted ends and to $\frac{7}{8}L$ for pin ends; E is the modulus of elasticity, which is 29,400,000 psi.

Equation 13-21 is an adaptation of Eq. 13-11, derived formerly. The term $0.001L/r$ provides for a probable imperfection in a column. Equation 13-21 appears to be unduly conservative if the known eccentricity occurs in the major plane of the cross-sectional area, since *only the least radius of gyration* appears in the formula.

The "Conservative" Method. The *maximum compressive stress* in an eccentrically loaded column may be approximately computed as is done for short blocks, i.e.,

$$\sigma_{max} = \frac{P}{A} + \frac{Mc}{I} = \frac{P}{A} + \frac{Pec}{I} \tag{13-22}$$

where Pe is the bending moment caused by the applied force. Then if the allowable *maximum stress* is set at the *average allowable stress* given by any one of the column formulas for axially loaded columns, a rather conservative design procedure results.

Application of this procedure, for example, using Eq. 13-16, requires the satisfaction of the following inequality

$$12,500 \geq 15,000 - 50\frac{L}{r} \geq \frac{P}{A} + \frac{Pec}{I}$$

This method is applicable for wood and steel columns selected on the basis of the usual specifications *where L/r is limited*, since the elastic deflections, such as Δ in Fig. 13-15, are very small. However, if a member is slender, and transverse loads occur in addition to the axial load, the deflection of the elastic curve may become very important. These situations occur in aircraft work, and such members are termed *beam-columns*. The analysis of beam-columns involves simultaneous considerations of bending moments caused by the transverse loads *and the moment caused by* *the axial force multiplied by the deflection.* Akin to the column problem, this leads to nonlinear relations between loads and deflections. For these problems, the ordinary method of superposition does not apply. This topic is beyond the scope of this text.*

The AISC Method. In an eccentrically loaded column, much of the total stress may result from the applied moment. However, *the allowable stress in flexure is usually higher than the allowable axial stress.* Hence for a particular column, it is desirable to accomplish some balance between the two stresses, depending on the relative magnitudes of the bending moment and the axial force. Thus, since in bending $\sigma = Mc/I = Mc/Ar_1^2$, where r_1 is the radius of gyration *in the plane of bending,* in effect the area A_b required by the bending moment M is

Fig. 13-15
An eccentrically
loaded column.

$$A_b = \frac{Mc}{\sigma_{ab}r_1^2}$$

where σ_{ab} is the allowable *maximum stress in bending.* (Also see Art. 13-11.) Similarly, the area A_a required for the axial force P is

$$A_a = \frac{P}{\sigma_{aa}}$$

where σ_{aa} is the *allowable axial average stress for the member acting as a column,* and which depends on its L/r ratio. Therefore the *total* area A required for a column subjected to an axial force and a bending moment is

$$A = A_a + A_b = \frac{P}{\sigma_{aa}} + \frac{Mc}{\sigma_{ab}r_1^2} \tag{13-23}$$

whence, dividing by A,

$$\frac{\dfrac{P}{A}}{\sigma_{aa}} + \frac{\dfrac{Mc}{Ar_1^2}}{\sigma_{ab}} = 1 \qquad \text{or} \qquad \frac{\sigma_a}{\sigma_{aa}} + \frac{\sigma_b}{\sigma_{ab}} = 1 \tag{13-24}$$

where σ_a is the axial stress caused by the applied vertical loads, and σ_b is the bending stress caused by the applied moment. This formula shows that if the column is carrying only an axial force and the bending moment is zero, the column is designed for the stress σ_{aa}. If the "column" carries no compressive force, the allowable stress becomes the flexural stress σ_{ab}. Between these two extreme cases, Eq. 13-24 "weighs in" the relative importance of the two kinds of action. This is the formula specified by the AISC Manual, where it is stated that the sum of the two ratios *must*

---

* See Niles, A. S.. and Newell, J. S., *Airplane Structures,* vol. II. New York: Wiley, 1943

*not exceed unity.** Equation 13-24 is sometimes referred to as the *inter-action formula.*

The philosophy implied in Eq. 13-24 has found favor in applications other than those pertaining to structural steel. The Aluminum Company of America (1945) suggests a similar relation. The Forest Products Laboratory developed a series of formulas to serve the same purpose.

Another Empirical Method. In the Rankine-Gordon formula, Eq. 13-13, the *maximum* stress in a concentric column is assumed to be $\sigma_{max} = (P/A)[1 + \phi(L/r)^2]$. However, in a column with an eccentric load, an additional bending stress σ_b exists, which is $\sigma_b = Mc/I = Pec/(Ar_1{}^2)$, where r_1 is the radius of gyration associated with the particular bending plane. By combining these stresses and equating them to an *allowable* stress, a design formula is obtained,

$$\sigma_{allow} = \frac{P}{A}\left[1 + \phi\left(\frac{L}{r}\right)^2 + \frac{ec}{r_1{}^2}\right] \tag{13-25}$$

An allowance for eccentricity and the instability phenomena of columns is supposedly made in this formula.

Example 13-4. Select a column for the loading shown in Fig. 13-16 by the "conservative" method, using the allowable stress given by the old AREA specification, Eq. 13-16.

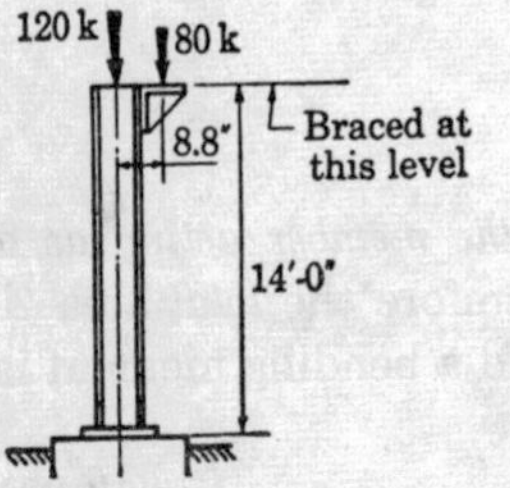

120 k   80 k

8.8"   └ Braced at this level

14'-0"

Fig. 13-16.

SOLUTION: In this problem the following relation must be satisfied:

$$12{,}500 \text{ psi} \ge 15{,}000 - 50\frac{L}{r} \ge$$

$$\frac{120{,}000 + 80{,}000}{A} + \frac{80{,}000(8.8)}{Z}$$

where r, A, and Z depend on the column selected. A trial-and-error procedure is used to solve the problem.

First try:[†] 8 WF 58 section for which $A = 17.06$ in.^{2}, $r_{min} = 2.10$ in., and $Z = 52.0$ in.^{3} (see Table 4 of the Appendix). Hence $L/r = 14(12)/(2.10) = 80$ and

$$\frac{P}{A} = 15{,}000 - 50(80) = 11{,}000 \text{ psi}$$

while the stresses caused by the applied loads are

$$\frac{200{,}000}{17.06} + \frac{80{,}000(8.8)}{52.0} = 25{,}200 \text{ psi.}$$

These stresses greatly disagree, hence a much larger section must be tried.

Second try: 10 WF 112 section for which $A = 32.92$ in.^{2}, $r_{min} = 2.67$ in., and $Z = 126.3$ in.^{3} Hence $L/r = 14(12)/(2.67) = 63$ and

$$\frac{P}{A} = 15{,}000 - 50(63) = 11{,}850 \text{ psi}$$

$$\sigma_{due\ to\ loads} = \frac{200{,}000}{32.92} + \frac{704{,}000}{126.3} = 11{,}650 \text{ psi}$$

Therefore the 10 WF 112 section is satisfactory.

* If the column is bent about both principal axes of the cross-section, Eq. 13-24 must be modified. For details see the AISC Manual.

† This poor guess may be arrived at by neglecting bending, thus $A = 200/12.5 = 16$ in.^{2}

Example 13-5. Select a column by the AISC specifications for the loading of the preceding example, assuming that the allowable bending stress is 20,000 psi.

SOLUTION: The solution may be obtained by the trial-and-error process, using Eq. 13-23 for the total required area A. Hence

$$A \geq \frac{P}{\sigma_{aa}} + \frac{Mc}{\sigma_{ab}r_1{}^2} = \frac{200,000}{\sigma_{aa}} + \frac{80,000(8.8)c}{\sigma_{ab}r_1{}^2}$$

After a few trials, it is found that a 10 WF 77 section satisfies this relation. For this section, $A = 22.67$ in.^{2}, $r_{min} = 2.60$ in., $r_1 = 4.49$ in., and $c = 5.31$ in. Therefore $L/r = 14(12)/(2.60) = 64.7$, and, from Eq. 13-12,

$$\frac{P}{A} = \sigma_{aa} = 17,000 - 0.485 \left(\frac{L}{r}\right)^2 = 14,970 \text{ psi}$$

As given $\sigma_{ab} = 20,000$ psi (also see Art. 13-11). Then*

$$\frac{c}{r_1{}^2} = \frac{5.31}{(4.49)^2} = 0.263$$

and

$$A = 22.67 > \frac{200}{14.97} + \frac{704(0.263)}{20} = 22.62$$

13-11. Beams without Lateral Supports. The strength and deflection theory of beams developed in this text applies only if such beams are in *stable equilibrium*. Narrow beams which do not have occasional lateral supports may buckle sidewise and thus become unstable. A physical illustration of this situation was cited in Art. 5-2 with reference to a sheet of paper on edge acting as a beam. Actual beams may collapse similarly. The tendency for lateral buckling is developed in the *compression zone* of a beam, which, in a sense, is a continuous column loaded longitudinally by the bending stresses. The theoretical analysis of this problem is beyond the scope of this text. The results of these analyses are, however, very important, and for steel I and WF beams have been so simplified,† that they are easily applicable.

According to the AISC specifications (1948), steel I and WF beams whose compression flanges are not laterally braced must be designed by means of the usual flexure formula with a **reduced stress** in the extreme fibers. The formula for the reduced bending stress, in *pounds per square inch*, is

$$\sigma_{\text{allow}} = \frac{12,000,000}{\dfrac{Ld}{bt}} \tag{13-26}$$

where L is the laterally unsupported length of a beam, d is its depth, b is the breadth or width of the flange, and t is the thickness of the flange. (For cantilevers L is twice the actual length.) All dimensions are in inches. This formula is to be used *if Ld/bt exceeds* 600, otherwise the basic flexural stress of 20,000 psi applies.

* The quantities $c/r_1{}^2$ and c/r^2 are tabulated in the AISC Manual, where they are termed bending factors and denoted by B_x and B_y, respectively.

† See de Vries, Karl, "Strength of Beams as Determined by Lateral Buckling," *Trans. ASCE*, 1947, vol. 112, p. 1245.

Equation 13-26 is somewhat analogous to the AISC parabolic formula, Eq. 13-12, since it also attempts by a simple expression to approximate the results of rational analyses. Similar formulas are in use for other materials.

Problems for Solution

13-1. (a) If a pin-ended solid circular shaft is 50 in. long and its diameter is 2 in., what is the shaft's slenderness ratio? (b) If the same amount of material as above is reshaped into a square bar of the same length, what is the slenderness ratio of the bar? *Ans.* 100, 97.7.

13-2. The cross-section of a compression member for a small bridge is made as shown in Fig. 13-12a. The top cover plate is $\frac{1}{2}$ in. by 18 in. and the two 12 ⌴ 20.7 are placed 10 in. from back to back. If this member is 20 ft long, what is its slenderness ratio? (Check L/r in two directions.) *Ans.* 51.5.

13-3. If the capacity of the jib-crane, the dimensions of which are shown in the figure, is to be 2 tons, what size standard steel pipe AB should be used? Use the Euler formula with a factor of safety of 3.5. $E = 30 \times 10^6$ psi. Neglect the weight of construction. *Ans.* $2\frac{1}{2}$ in.

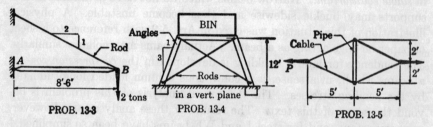

PROB. 13-3   PROB. 13-4   PROB. 13-5

13-4. A rectangular bin for clinker storage is supported by four inclined columns. Each column is a 5 in. by 5 in. by $\frac{3}{8}$ in. steel angle. If the empty bin weighs 4,000 lb, what additional weight may be safely stored in the bin? Assume that the columns are adequately braced at the ends and are pin-ended. Use the Euler formula and a factor of safety of 3. $E = 30 \times 10^6$ psi. Justify the use of the Euler formula on the basis of the slenderness ratio and the proportional limit for steel. *Ans.* 53.2 kips.

13-5. A 1 in. standard steel pipe 4 ft long acts as a spreader bar in the arrangement shown in the figure. If cables and connections are properly designed, what pull P may

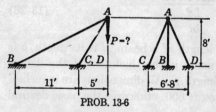

PROB. 13-6

be applied to the assembly? Use Euler's formula and assume a factor of safety of 3. *Ans.* 9.35 kips.

13-6. A tripod made up from 2 in. standard steel pipes is to be used for lifting loads vertically with a pulley at A as shown in the figure. What load rating may be assigned to this structure? Use the Euler formula and a factor of safety of 3. All joints may be considered pinned, and assume that the connection details, anchorages, and the tension leg AB are adequate. *Ans.* 5 kips.

13-7. A tripod is made from three 3 in. by 3 in. by $\frac{1}{4}$ in. steel angles each 10 ft long. In a plan view these angles are placed 120° apart, and the tripod is 8 ft high. Assuming that the ends of these angles are pin-ended, what is the magnitude of the allowable vertical downward force P that may be applied to the tripod? Use the Euler formula with a factor of safety equal to three. Neglect the weight of the angles. $E = 30 \times 10^6$ psi. *Ans.* 8.25 kips.

13-8. If the proportional limit of steel is 36,000 psi and $E = 30 \times 10^6$ psi, in what range of slenderness ratios is the use of the Euler formula for fixed end columns not permissible?

13-9. What value of E is assumed in Eq. 13-19?

13-10. What factor of safety is used in Eq. 13-20? *Ans.* $2\frac{1}{2}$.

13-11. What size WF column is required to carry a concentric load of 220 kips if it is 12 ft long? Use the AISC formulas.

13-12. Same as Prob. 13-11 for a load of 2,000 lb.

13-13. Same as Prob. 13-11 for a load of 90 kips.

13-14. Rework Prob. 13-11 using Eq. 13-16.

13-15. Two 10 in.-15.3 lb channels form a 24 ft long square compression member; the flanges are turned in, and the channels thoroughly laced together. What is the allowable axial force on this member according to Eq. 13-16? (Check L/r in both directions.)

13-16. A compression member made of two 8 ⊔ 11.5 is arranged as shown in Fig. 13-12b. (a) Determine the distance back to back of the channels so that the moments of inertia about the two principal axes are equal. (b) If the member is 32 ft long, what axial load may be applied according to the AISC code? Assume that lacing is adequate.

13-17. A boom for an excavating machine is made of four $2\frac{1}{2}$ in. by $2\frac{1}{2}$ in. by $\frac{1}{4}$ in. steel angles arranged as shown in Fig. 13-12c. Out to out dimensions of the square column (exclusive of the dimensions of the lacing bars) are 14 in. What axial load may be applied to this member if it is 52 ft long? Use the Euler formula for pinned columns and a factor of safety of 5.

13-18. A compression chord of a small truss consists cf two 4 in. by 4 in. by $\frac{3}{8}$ in. steel angles arranged as shown in Fig. 13-12d. The vertical legs of the angles are separated $\frac{1}{2}$ in. apart by spacers. If the length of this member between braced points is 8 ft, what axial load may be applied according to the AISC code?

13-19. A 14 WF 320 core section has two 24 in. by 3 in. cover plates as shown in the figure. If this member is 20 ft long, what axial compressive force may be applied according to the AISC code?

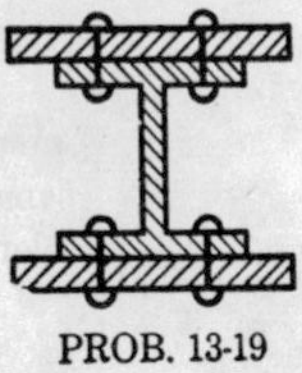

PROB. 13-19

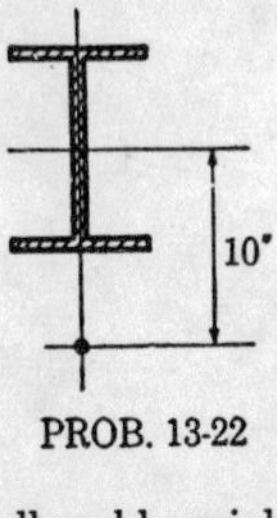

PROB. 13-22

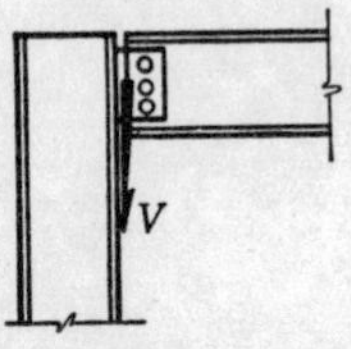

PROB. 13-23

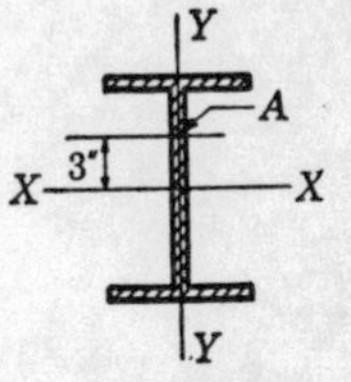

PROB. 13-24

13-20. Determine the allowable axial loads for 4 in. by 4 in. (nominal) Douglas Fir posts 8 ft and 14 ft long. $C = 1{,}200$ psi and $E = 1.6 \times 10^6$ psi.

13-21. A round platform 6 ft in diameter, to be used by a "flag-pole sitter," is attached to a standard 6 in. pipe 20 ft long. If the "sitter" weighs 150 lb, what weight of equipment for his comfort may be allowed on the platform? Locate the weights in the most critical position, i.e., at 3 ft from the vertical centerline of the pipe. The answer is to be based on a conservative criterion: $P/A + Mc/I \leq$ allow stress for columns by Euler formula with FS = 3. (*Hint:* see Fig. 13-5a.) *Ans.* 340 lb.

13-22. A 12 WF 85 column 20 ft long is subjected to an eccentric load of 180 kips located as shown in the figure. Using the AISC interaction formula, determine whether this column is overstressed. The allowable bending stress is 20 ksi. *Ans.* Overstressed.

13-23. What may be the magnitude of the maximum beam reaction that may be carried by a 14 WF 34 column 12 ft 2 in. long, according to the AISC code? Assume that the beam delivers the reaction at the outside flange of the column concentrically with respect to the minor axis as shown in the figure. The top and bottom of the column are held laterally. Neglect the weight of the column.

13-24. An 8 WF 24 section is used as a 20 ft long column. Using the AISC formulas, determine the magnitude of an eccentric load that may be applied to the column at A, as shown in the figure, in addition to a concentric load of 10 kips. The column is braced at top and bottom. The allowable bending stress is given by Eq. 13-26.

13-25. * Using the AISC code, select a WF column to carry a concentric load of 60 kips and an eccentric load of 25 kips applied on the Y-Y axis at a distance of 6 in. from the X-X axis. The column is braced top and bottom, and is 14 ft long. The allowable bending stress is 20 ksi.

13-26. A 24 WF 100 simple beam 24 ft long is laterally unsupported. What uniformly distributed load, including the weight of the beam, may be applied according to the AISC specifications?

13-27. An 8 WF 17 section is used as a laterally unsupported cantilever 10 ft long. According to the AISC code, what concentrated force P may be applied at the end? Neglect the weight of the beam. (*Hint:* the effective length for buckling is 20 ft.) *Ans.* 1.19 kips.

Chapter Fourteen

CONNECTIONS

14-1. Introduction. The design of various members based on strength, stiffness, and stability considerations was discussed in the preceding chapters. In this chapter, the methods of analysis and design of connections for these members are treated. The analysis of connections cannot be made on as rigorous a basis as was laid down in much of the preceding work. In fabricated connections or joints, shop practices and uncertainties in workmanship influence the methods of analysis. For this reason, two different methods of design of riveted connections are discussed, each applicable to a particular class of work.

The major part of this chapter will be concerned with riveted and bolted connections, which, in spite of welding, are indispensable in engineering construction. Methods will be discussed for the selection of the proper number and size of rivets to transmit a given force through a joint. The remainder of the chapter will be devoted to welded connections.

14-2. Riveted Connections. Most members are made up of platelike parts, as actual plates, webs, and flanges of I-beams, legs of angles, etc. The design of a riveted connection is mainly concerned with the transfer of forces through these plates. For a riveted assembly of ordinary parts, matching holes are punched in the plates for the insertion of hot rivets.* For more accurate work, as well as for the larger size of rivets (1 in. to $1\frac{1}{4}$ in. diameter), the holes are drilled,† or first punched, and then reamed (enlarged) to size. One end of a rivet has a head, while the other head is formed from the shank by a pneumatic hammer as a back-up tool is held against the prefabricated head, Fig. 14-1. It is desirable to have the clearance of the rivet in a prepared hole as small as possible. For rivets of $\frac{1}{2}$ in. diameter and larger, an increase of $\frac{1}{32}$ to $\frac{1}{16}$ in. in the diameter of the hole over the nominal rivet diameter is customarily made. On proper

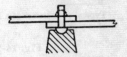

Fig. 14-1. One of the rivet heads formed from the original shank.

---

* Ordinary steel rivets are driven at a temperature between 1000°F (blood red) and 1950°F (light yellow). Small steel rivets and some aluminum rivets are driven without preheating, although hot (1040°F ±) and cold (32°F) rivets are frequently employed in aluminum work. Several patented rivet types are available for nonferrous metals.

† For excerpts from structural steel specifications see footnote in Art. 14-6.

driving, a hot rivet expands in the prepared hole, and, while hot, it presses the surrounding material outward. Upon cooling, the rivet diameter diminishes somewhat, but the elastic return of the surrounding material helps to reduce this tendency for undesirable looseness. Moreover, *a rivet also shrinks lengthwise upon cooling.* This effect causes a permanent tensile stress in the shank of a rivet and a compression stress in the assembled plates (see Example 12-5). The compressive force so set up between the plates may be rather large, and this force is capable of developing a large frictional resistance normal to the axis of the rivet. This action may be sufficient to carry the applied working load. However, in determining the required number of rivets, it is customary to *disregard* the frictional resistance of the joint. The capacity of a joint is thought of in terms of its ultimate capacity after the frictional resistance between the plates is "broken."

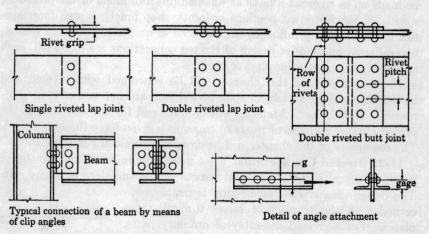

Fig. 14-2. Typical arrangements of riveted connections.

Ingenuity must be exercised in arranging the rivets at a joint. Accessibility for riveting and proper tool clearances are important considerations. Several typical arrangements of rivets, with self-explanatory titles, are shown in Fig. 14-2. Riveted joints are normally designed to transmit shear rather than tension through the rivets. The design of a connection is more involved than a check of stresses in an existing joint.

14-3. Methods of Failure of a Riveted Joint. Riveted or bolted joints may fail in a number of different ways (also see Arts. 1-5 and 1-6). These are as follows:

Failure in Tension. A riveted joint transmitting a tensile force may fail in a plate weakened by the rivet holes. For example, in a single-riveted lap joint, Fig. 14-3a, the *net* area in either plate across the section *A-A* in Fig. 14-3b is the least area, and a tear would occur there. At working loads, before failure occurs, large stress concentrations exist at the rivet holes in a plate, Fig. 14-3c, since the holes interrupt the continuity of the plate. However, as the applied force is increased, a nearly uniform stress distribution will prevail at the yield point for ductile materials (Art. 2-11). Since riveting is employed only for ductile materials, it is customary to base the capacity of a joint in tension on the assumption of a *uniform stress distribution across the net section* of a plate. Because of the fatigue properties of materials, this assumption should not be used for riveted joints subjected to severe fluctuating loadings, since stress concentrations are important for such cases. Usually no deduction for the rivet holes in a compression joint is made.

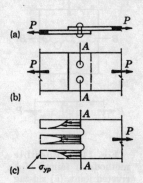

Fig. 14-3. Tensile stresses in a plate of a riveted joint.

Failure in Shear. In a riveted joint, the rivets themselves may fail in shear. This type of failure is shown in Figs. 14-4a and b. In analyzing this possible manner of failure, one must always note whether a rivet acts in single or double shear. In the latter case, *two* cross-sectional areas of the same rivet resist the applied force. In practical calculations, the shearing stress is assumed to be *uniformly distributed over the cross-section of a rivet.* This assumption is justified for ductile materials after the elastic limit has been exceeded.

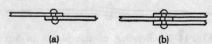

(a)   (b)

Fig. 14-4. (a) Single and (b) double shear of a rivet.

Failure in Bearing. A riveted joint may fail if a rivet crushes the material of the plate against which it bears, Figs. 14-5a and b, or if the rivet itself is deformed by the plate acting on it. The stress distribution is very complicated in this type of failure and is somewhat like that shown in Fig. 14-5c. In practice, this stress distribution is approximated on the basis of an *average bearing stress acting over the projected area of the rivet's shank onto a plate*, i.e., on area td in Fig. 14-5d. It is difficult to justify this procedure theoretically. However, the allowable

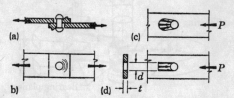

Fig. 14-5. A bearing failure of a riveted joint and bearing stress distributions, (c) probable, (d) assumed.

bearing stress is determined from experiments and is interpreted on the basis of this *average stress* acting on the projected area of a rivet. Therefore the inverse process used in design is satisfactory. Tests show that plates *confined* between other plates, as the middle plate in Fig. 14-4b, can withstand a greater average bearing pressure than unconfined plates, as in Fig. 14-5a or the outer plates in Fig. 14-4b. For this reason, several specifications allow a greater bearing stress for rivets in double shear acting on *inside* plates than for rivets in single shear acting on outside plates.

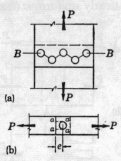

(a)

(b)

Fig. 14-6. Possible methods of failure of a riveted joint, (a) zig-zag tear, and (b) "tear out" due to insufficient edge (end) distance.

Other Methods of Failure. In a multiple-riveted joint with several rows of rivets, the net area to be used in calculations is sometimes difficult to determine. For example, if, as in Fig. 14-6a, the rivet rows are very close together, a zig-zag tear is more likely to occur than a tear across the normal section *B-B*. However, the standard specifications for shop practice are so written that this type of failure is not common. Therefore the possibility of a zig-zag tear will not be considered here, as it will be assumed that in all cases the rows of rivets are sufficiently far apart.* It will also be assumed that the *edge distance e* is large enough to prevent failure in shear across the *a-a* planes in Fig. 14-6b. Likewise, in conformity with usual practice, local bending of plates in lap joints, Fig. 14-7, will be neglected.

Although there is general agreement on the methods of failure of riveted joints as enumerated above, two methods for their analysis are in common use. One is called the

Fig. 14-7. Bending of the plates in lap joints, commonly neglected.

structural and the other the *boiler* method of rivet analysis. In this text, for either method, the capacity of a riveted joint will be based only on the probable tear, shear, and bearing capacities. This assumed action of a riveted joint is illustrated in Fig. 14-8.† The frictional resistance between the plates is neglected. The *smallest* of the three resistances is the strength of a joint. The ratio of this strength divided by the strength of a solid plate or member, expressed in percent, is called the *efficiency of a joint*, i.e.,

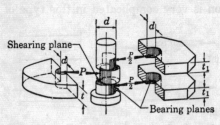

Fig. 14-8. The assumed action of a riveted joint.

$$efficiency = \frac{\textit{strength of the joint}}{\textit{strength of the solid member}} \times 100 \qquad (14\text{-}1)$$

* For details see AISC Manual.

† From Dreyer, G., *Festigkeitslehre und Elastizitätslehre*, p. 34. Leipzig: Jänecke, 1938.

14-4. Structural Method of Analysis. The structural method of analysis for riveted joints is more widely used than the boiler method. Its use developed along with the field erection of structures, where good alignment of rivet holes is difficult to obtain. In this method of analysis, the effective shear area of a rivet is based on the *nominal rivet diameter*, although it is known that well-driven rivets expand to the size of the holes. The rivet bearing area is likewise computed on the basis of the *nominal rivet diameter* multiplied by the thickness of the plate. In this work, the rivet holes are usually *punched* $\frac{1}{16}$ in. larger in diameter than the rivet. This operation damages some of the material surrounding a rivet hole. Therefore in computing the net area at a section, it is usual practice to assume that an additional $\frac{1}{16}$ in. of the material beyond the hole diameter is ineffective for resisting tension. For calculation purposes, this assumption means that the *nominal rivet diameter plus $\frac{1}{8}$ in.* is the *width* of the strength-destroying hole.*

The above assumptions are sufficient for the analysis of single lap and single butt joints. Another assumption is introduced for multiple-riveted joints: *The total force acting concentrically on a joint is equally distributed between rivets of equal size.* In many cases, this assumption is not con-

sistent elastically. For example, consider two plates of equal size connected by five rivets as shown in Fig. 14-9.† On the basis of this assumption, one-fifth of the applied force P is transferred from one plate to the other at each rivet, and the forces in the plates between the adjoining rivets are as shown

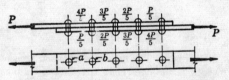

Fig. 14-9. Distribution of forces in the lap-riveted plates based on the assumption used in the structural method of analysis.

on the diagram. These forces are not equal in the upper and lower plates. For example, between the rivets a and b, the force in the upper plate is seen to be four times larger than that in the lower plate. Therefore the *elastic* deformations of the plates are not compatible. An accurate elastic analysis shows that initially the outer rivets resist the largest force, while the middle rivet is a "dud." This condition does not last as the force P is increased. The ductile deformation of the rivets permits an equal redistribution of the force P between all rivets before the capacity of the connection is reached. This redistribution is possible as the rivets continue to carry a full load during yielding. Therefore the

---

* In structural work, some codes allow the use of the actual hole diameter for calculations of the net tension area for drilled holes.

† This figure is reproduced from Van den Broek, J. A., "Theory of Limit Design," *Trans. ASCE*, 1940, vol. 105, p. 658.

usual practice of assigning equal forces to the rivets of a concentrically loaded joint is not far from being correct.*

The same assumptions are commonly used in the analysis of bolted joints. Turned bolts in reamed holes made $\frac{1}{32}$ in. over the bolt diameter are usually specified for load-carrying connections. The allowable shear and bearing stresses are considerably reduced for unfinished bolts.

Example 14-1. Find the capacity of the tension member *AB* of the Fink truss shown in Fig. 14-10a if it is made from two 3 in. by 2 in. by $\frac{5}{16}$ in. angles attached to a $\frac{3}{8}$ in. thick gusset plate by four $\frac{3}{4}$ in. rivets in $1\frac{3}{8}$ in. diameter holes. The allowable stresses (AISC) are 20,000 psi in tension, 15,000 psi in shear, and 32,000 psi or 40,000 psi in bearing for single and double shear, respectively.

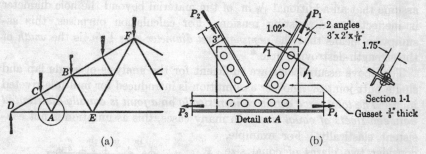

(a)   (b)

Fig. 14-10.

SOLUTION: The net cross-sectional area of the angles is obtained by deducting the width of the rivet holes (rivet diameter plus $\frac{1}{8}$ in.) multiplied by the thickness of the angle from the gross area of the angles (Appendix, Table 7). The net area multiplied by the allowable tensile stress gives the allowable force controlled by tensile stresses. Similar calculations are made for the other methods of failure, based on the following observations: There are *eight* bearing surfaces with single shear between the rivets and the angles, four rivets provide *eight* shearing surfaces, and *four* bearing surfaces with double shear are provided for the rivets by the gusset plate. In following through the solution of this problem, the reader is urged to note the sequence of load transfer, from angles to rivets, and from rivets to the gusset plate.

Tear at Section 1-1:

$$A_{net} = 2[1.47 - \tfrac{5}{16}(\tfrac{3}{4} + \tfrac{1}{8})] = 2.40 \text{ in.}^2$$
$$P_{allow} = A_{net}\sigma = 2.40(20) = 48 \text{ kips}$$

Bearing on angles:

$$A = 8td = 8\,(\tfrac{5}{16})(\tfrac{3}{4}) = 1\tfrac{5}{8} \text{ in.}^2$$
$$P_{allow} = A\sigma_b = 1\tfrac{5}{8}\,(32) = 60 \text{ kips}$$

Shear of rivets:

$$A_{one\ rivet} = \tfrac{1}{4}\pi\left(\frac{3}{4}\right)^2 = 0.4418 \text{ in.}^2$$
$$P_{allow} = 8(0.4418)15 = 53 \text{ kips}$$

---

* A conclusive experimental verification of this assumption may be found in the paper by Davis, R. E., Woodruff, G. B., and Davis, H. E., "Tension Tests of Large Riveted Joints," *Trans. ASCE*, 1940, vol. 105, p. 1193.

Bearing on gusset:

$$A = 4t_1 d = 4 \left(\tfrac{3}{8}\right) \tfrac{3}{4} = \tfrac{9}{8} \text{ in.}^2$$
$$P_{\text{allow}} = A\sigma_b = \tfrac{9}{8}(40) = 45 \text{ kips}$$

The bearing stress on the gusset plate governs the capacity of the connection. If the gusset plate were made a little thicker, the tensile stress at Section 1-1 would govern.

Note that standard gage lines are generally used for the rivet lines (see AISC Manual), and the rivets are usually spaced 3 in. apart. The standard gage line for the angles of this example is 1.75 in. On the other hand, the centroid of the cross-sectional area for the same angle is 1.02 in. from the corner (Appendix, Table 7). Hence there is an eccentricity of $1.75 - 1.02 = 0.73$ in. of the applied force with respect to the rivet line. For small trusses, it is customary to neglect the effect of this eccentricity, as presumably the allowable stresses are set low enough to provide for this contingency. No less than two rivets are used at all main connections. An excessively large number of rivets in one line is avoided.

The compression members of small trusses are often connected to a gusset plate in the same manner as shown for the tension member. The compression members of a truss are designed as columns. Effective column lengths are determined from a center-line diagram such as shown in Fig. 14-10a and a study of bracing in the direction perpendicular to the plane of the truss. The *gross areas* of columns are used to determine their load-carrying capacities, while the connection is governed either by bearing or shearing stresses. In some cases, members of a truss may act in tension, then, under a different loading condition, in compression. Such members must be designed accordingly.

Example 14-2. Find the capacity of the standard AISC connection for the 12 WF 36 beam shown in Fig. 14-11. The connection consists of two 4 in. by $3\tfrac{1}{2}$ in. by $\tfrac{3}{8}$ in. angles, each $8\tfrac{1}{2}$ in. long, and $\tfrac{7}{8}$ in. rivets spaced 3 in. apart are used in $\tfrac{15}{16}$ in. holes. Use the AISC allowable stresses given in Example 14-1.

SOLUTION: A tension tear cannot occur in this connection, so only shearing and bearing capacities need be investigated.

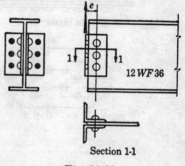

Section 1-1

Fig. 14-11.

Bearing on the web of 12 WF 36 beam: Thickness of the web is found from Appendix, Table 4. Bearing stress in double shear is 40 ksi.

$$P_b = 3(0.305) \tfrac{7}{8}(40) = 32 \text{ kips}$$

Shear of rivets: There are 6 cross-sectional areas.

$$A_{\text{one rivet}} = 0.601 \text{ in.}^2$$
$$P_s = 6(0.601)15 = 54.1 \text{ kips}$$

Bearing of rivets on angles: Bearing stress in single shear is 32 ksi.

$$P_b = 6(\tfrac{7}{8})\tfrac{3}{8}(32) = 63.0 \text{ kips}$$

Hence the capacity of this connection is 32 kips.

The legs of the angles perpendicular to the web of the beam are called the *outstanding legs*. They are used to attach the connection to a column or a plate. Adequate shear resistance across the additional rivets and bearing in the outstanding legs is always available. However, the thickness of the plate to which the connection is made must be investigated. If this plate is thin, the capacity of the joint may be lower than computed above. Note that the effect of eccentricity e, as well as bending and shear in the connection angles, is usually not investigated. The capacities of standard connections are tabulated in the AISC Manual.

Example 14-3. Find the allowable tensile force which the multiple-riveted structural joint shown in Figs. 14-12a and b can transmit. Also find the efficiency of this joint. All rivets are nominally $\frac{7}{8}$ in. in $1\frac{3}{16}$ in. diameter holes. Use the AISC allowable stresses given in Example 14-1.

SOLUTION: The analysis of a multiple-riveted structural joint is based on the assumption that the *concentrically applied force is distributed equally between rivets of equal size*. Therefore the free body for one of the main plates is as shown in Fig. 14-12c, while that for the *two* cover plates is as shown in Fig. 14-12f. Tensile stresses must be investi-

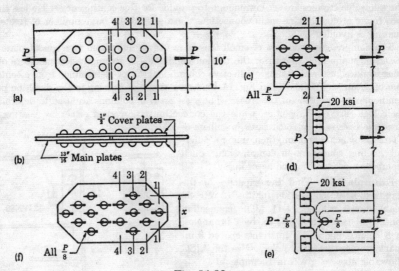

Fig. 14-12.

gated at several sections. This is done by considering the free bodies as shown in Figs. 14-12d and e and assuming uniform stress distribution in the plates. Nominal rivet diameter is used for shear and bearing calculations.

Capacity P_s of the joint in shear: 16 cross-sectional areas of rivets are available. $\tau = 15$ ksi.

$$A_{\text{one rivet}} = \tfrac{1}{4}\pi \left(\frac{7}{8}\right)^2 = 0.601 \text{ in.}^2$$

$$P_s = 16(0.601)15 = 144 \text{ kips}$$

Capacity P_B of the joint in bearing on the main plate: 8 bearing surfaces in double shear are available. $\sigma_B = 40$ ksi.

$$P_B = 8 \left(\tfrac{7}{8}\right)\left(\tfrac{13}{16}\right)(40) = 227 \text{ kips}$$

Capacity P_b of the joint in bearing on the cover plates: 16 bearing surfaces in single shear. $\sigma_b = 32$ ksi.

$$P_b = 16 \left(\tfrac{7}{8}\right)\tfrac{1}{2}(32) = 224 \text{ kips}$$

Capacity of the main plate in tension: $\sigma = 20$ ksi.

Without holes: $P_t = \tfrac{13}{16}(10)20 = 162.5$ kips.

Section 1-1, free body, Fig. 14-12d: $P_{1-1} = \tfrac{13}{16}[10 - (\tfrac{7}{8} + \tfrac{1}{8})]20 = 146$ kips.

Section 2-2, free body, Fig. 14-12e:

$$P_{2-2} = \tfrac{1}{8} P_{2-2} + \tfrac{13}{16} [10 - 2 (\tfrac{7}{8} + \tfrac{1}{8})] 20 \qquad \text{or} \qquad \tfrac{7}{8} P_{2-2} = 130 \text{ kips}$$

hence $P_{2-2} = 149$ kips

This result means that, if a tensile force $P_{2-2} = 149$ kips were applied to the joint, only seven-eights of this force need be resisted by the Section 2-2 at a 20 ksi stress, since one-eighth of this force is resisted by the *outer rivet*.   Similarly,

$$\tfrac{5}{8} P_{3-3} = \tfrac{13}{16} (10 - 3)20 \qquad \text{or} \qquad P_{3-3} = 182 \text{ kips}$$

and

$$\tfrac{2}{8} P_{4-4} = \tfrac{13}{16} (10 - 2)20 \qquad \text{or} \qquad P_{4-4} = 520 \text{ kips}$$

Capacity of the two cover plates in tension: $\sigma = 20$ ksi.   *Across Section 4-4,* Fig. 14-12f, the *whole* force P is transmitted, hence,

$$P_{4-4} = 2(\tfrac{1}{2}) [10 - 2(\tfrac{7}{8} + \tfrac{1}{8})] 20 = 160 \text{ kips}$$

Then, by considering free-body diagrams of the cover plates to one side of a section, as was done for the main plate,

$$\tfrac{6}{8} P_{3-3} = 1(10 - 3)20 \qquad \text{or} \qquad P_{3-3} = 187 \text{ kips}$$

and

$$\tfrac{3}{8} P_{2-2} = 1(10 - 2)20 \qquad \text{or} \qquad P_{2-2} = 427 \text{ kips}$$

Similarly, Section 1-1 is not critical.   Therefore the width of the *cover plates* at Section 1-1 may be reduced to a width x to provide, at an allowable stress, a net area for only one-eighth of the applied force.

The capacity of this joint is limited by the allowable shearing stress in the rivets. Hence the capacity of this joint is 144 kips.   The efficiency of this joint is $(144/162.5)100 = 88.6\%$, which is very good.*

The same calculation procedure would be used for a compression splice if the ends of the main plates were not machined.   However, if the ends are milled, the transfer of a compression force is direct.   Nevertheless, even in such cases, it is customary to provide a riveted connection calculated at a certain fraction, say 50%, of the total actual force.

14-5. Boiler Method of Analysis.†

Welding is more widely used than riveting in fabricating pressure vessels and boilers.   This was considered in Art. 9-6.   The design of riveted joints for pressure vessels, in conformity with the ASME Boiler Construction Code, will be discussed here.

In boiler practice, two kinds of joints are analyzed, longitudinal and circumferential (or girth) joints.   The meaning of these terms may be clarified by reference to Fig. 14-13.   In boiler work,

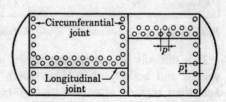

Fig. 14-13. A riveted pressure vessel.

certain rivet patterns repeat along the joint, and calculations are made for a typical strip or hoop, which embraces a *repeating pattern* of rivets; see dimension p in Fig. 14-13.   Several standardized rivet patterns are

---

* It is not desirable to depend on an actual efficiency of more than about 80% in any riveted joint in tension, since tests indicate that efficiencies higher than this are rarely obtained in practice.

† The remainder of the chapter may be omitted.

in common use. Lap joints are permitted by the codes for smaller boilers only. Multiple-riveted butt joints are preferred and are used for the larger pressure vessels.

According to the ASME Code,* the analysis of riveted joints should be made by first computing the capacity of the separate items which make up a joint. Thus the capacity of the plates to resist tearing at different sections and the capacity of the rivets in shear and in bearing are found. A realistic combination of these items, which conceptually permits *an actual separation of the joint,* is studied. The combination sought is the one which gives the least value of force required to separate the joint. The ultimate strengths of various plates and rivets, to be assumed in the analysis according to the ASME Boiler Code (1946), are tabulated below. A uniform factor of safety of 5 is recommended in conjunction with the stresses listed. A somewhat lower safety factor is occasionally specified by other codes for first-class work

Minimum Strengths of Plates and Rivets †

Plates	Spec. no.	Crushing, psi	Tensile, psi
Carbon steel (or unknown steel)....	SA-70	95,000	55,000
Chrome-manganese-silicon steel....	SA-202	120,000	75,000 (A)
			85,000 (B)
Carbon-silicon steel.............	SA-201	95,000	55,000 (A)
			60,000 (B)
Low-carbon nickel steel..........	SA-203	105,000	65,000 (A)
			70,000 (B)

Rivets	Spec. no.	Shear, psi
Steel........................	SA-31	44,000 (A)
		52,000 (B)
Alloy steel....................	SA-202	60,000 (A)

Note: Letters in ( ) refer to the grade of steel, thus (A) means grade A steel.

It is difficult to match prepunched holes on curved surfaces of pressure vessels and boilers. For this reason, rivet holes are punched undersize and then reamed after the plates are securely held together. In other cases, the holes are simply drilled through the plates to be riveted. As a result of these procedures, the holes prepared for riveting are true, clean, and concentric. Moreover, riveting is generally done in a shop. These

---

* Consult the ASME Code for actual design of a boiler. Many specific items regarding openings, ends, and attachments may be found there.

† The stresses given apply only in the range of temperatures from −20°F to +650°F. Considerably reduced stresses must be used for service at higher temperature. For example, for carbon steel with a safety factor of 5, the allowable tensile stress is 11,000 psi up to 650°F, 8,000 psi at 800°F, and 1,350 psi at 1,000°F. Moreover, carbon steel may not be used beyond the temperature of 1,000°F.

practices are reflected in the computation details generally used for the analysis of boiler joints. The *expanded rivet diameter*, i.e., the diameter of the actual hole, is used to determine the shearing capacity of a rivet. For bearing stress calculations, the *expanded rivet diameter* times plate thickness is used. Likewise, it is assumed that the drilling or reaming operation does not damage the surrounding material, so to determine the net tension area, the *actual rivet hole diameter* is deducted from the gross width of the plate. Initial clearances of rivets in holes are the same as in structural work, although for rivets up to $\frac{7}{8}$ in. in diameter, $\frac{1}{32}$ in. clearance is preferred.

Occasionally existing boiler joints are analyzed by the structural method, although the expanded rivet diameter is used.

Example 14-4.* Find the allowable force on a repeating section of the butt and double-strap double-riveted joint shown in Fig. 14-14 by the ASME Code. Assume carbon-steel plates and steel rivets of A grade complying with SA-31 specifications. Assume that the *prepared rivet holes* are 1 in. in diameter, i.e., the expanded rivet area is 0.785 in.²

SOLUTION: The rivet pattern repeats every $4\frac{7}{8}$ in. (= 4.875 in.). The actual capacities or "worth" of the various components of the joint are computed first, *without regard to the joint action as was done in the structural method.*

Solid plate in tension: $\frac{3}{8}$ (4.875)55 = 100.5 kips.

Main plate in tension at Section 1-1: $\frac{3}{8}$ (4.875 − 1)55 = 80.0 kips.

Main plate in tension at Section 2-2: $\frac{3}{8}$ (4.875 − 2)55 = 59.3 kips.

Two straps in tension† at Section 2-2: $2(\frac{5}{16})(4.875 − 2)55 = 98.8$ kips.

One rivet in single shear: (0.785)44 = 34.5 kips.

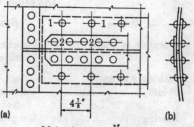

(a)   (b)

Main plates are $\frac{3}{8}''$ thick
Straps are both $\frac{5}{16}''$ thick

Fig. 14-14.

One rivet in double shear: 34.5(2) = 69.0 kips.

Bearing of one rivet on one strap: $1(\frac{5}{16})95 = 29.7$ kips.

Bearing of one rivet on main plate: $1(\frac{3}{8})95 = 35.6$ kips.

With these quantities computed, the possibilities for actual separation (failure) of the joint as a whole may be studied. Thus:

(A) The joint may fail in tension across Section 1-1 of the main plate. To produce this failure, 80 kips are required.

(B) All of the rivets may shear off. For this to happen, two rivets must fail in double shear and one in single shear, i.e., 2(69) + 34.5 = 172.5 kips. A comparison of bearing and shear values per rivet suggests that this failure is not as likely to occur as a bearing failure throughout. It takes 2(35.6) + 29.7 = 100.9 kips to produce a bearing failure.

(C) The main plate may tear across Section 2-2, but at the same time an outer rivet must either shear off or crush the *strap*, whichever is weaker. To produce this failure, 59.3 + 29.7 = 89.0 kips are required.

* Modified example from ASME Boiler Code (1946). See Section on Power Boilers, p. 184. Fig. 14-14a is reproduced from this source.

† If the ASME Boiler Code is followed, the straps are always sufficiently thick.

The joint under consideration would fail as noted above in (A).   No other combination is as critical.   Therefore *the allowable force for a 4⅝ in. width of plate in this connection with a safety factor of 5 is 80/5 = 16 kips*.   The efficiency of the joint is $(80/100.5)100 = 79.6\%$.

14-6. Résumé of the Two Methods of Rivet Analysis. To aid in the application of the foregoing methods of rivet analysis, the basic concepts and procedures are outlined tersely below.

Common to Both Methods

(A) Riveted joints may fail in one of the following ways:
  (1) Tension on the *net* area;
  (2) Shear across rivets;
  (3) Bearing or crushing of the plates by the rivet or vice versa.

Edge (end) failure and the zig-zag type of tension failure between rows of rivets need not be considered, since in this text it is assumed that rivets are spaced in accordance with some code requirement.

(B) Holes for rivets of the sizes normally used, say ⅝ in. diameter and up, are usually made $\frac{1}{16}$ in. larger than the nominal size of the rivet.

Different in Both Methods

Details	Structural Method	Boiler Method
Preparation of holes:	Punched; in special cases, drilled*	Drilled
To calculate areas:		
Shear................	Use nominal rivet diameter	Use diameter of the drilled hole
Bearing..............	Use projected area of the nominal rivet	Use projected area of the drilled hole
Net tension...........	From gross width subtract (nominal rivet diameter $+\frac{1}{8}$ in.)†	From gross width subtract the diameter of the hole

* In the fabrication of structural steel for buildings, holes for rivets are usually punched $\frac{1}{16}$ in. larger than the nominal rivet diameter.   According to the AISC specifications (1951), if the thickness of the material exceeds the diameter of the rivet plus ⅛ in., the holes must be sub-punched $\frac{3}{16}$ in. smaller than the nominal rivet diameter and then reamed to size.   The requirements for fabrication of structural steel for bridges are more exacting.   The Standard Specification for Highway Bridges of the AASHO (American Association of State Highway Officials, 1949) requires sub-punching and reaming to size in the following instances: (a) when the thickness of any layer of main material exceeds ¾ in., (b) when more than five layers of material are being riveted together, (c) for all field connections and splices.   In the latter case, the work must be preassembled in the shop and reamed after correct alignment is obtained.   Similar but slightly more rigid restrictions are given in the Specifications for Steel Railway Bridges of the AREA (American Railway Engineering Association): *in all cases*, the size of the hole used in calculation of the net section is ⅛ in. larger than the nominal rivet diameter.

† For drilled holes in structural work some codes allow the use of the actual hole diameter for calculations of the net tension area.

Main assumption:	Each rivet carries an equal share of the load (per unit shear area)	Joint examined by making up possible combinations for failure after the "worth" of each element is known

In either method do not fail to check at least:

1. Shear on all rivets.
2. Bearing of all rivets.
3. Tension in the main plate at the outer row.   (If second row contains more rivets than outer row, check second row also.)
4. Tension in the splice plate at the inner row.

14-7. Eccentric Riveted Connections. The foregoing discussion of riveted connections applies to situations where the line of action of the applied force passes through the centroid of a rivet group.   More precisely, it is assumed that each rivet possesses a certain allowable shear or bearing resistance in *every* direction.   Thus each rivet in a group of rivets has a certain resistance, say in the horizontal direction, indicated by F_1, $F_2 \ldots F_5$ in Fig. 14-15.   The best place to apply horizontal force to this group of rivets is in the direction of E_1, which is an equilibrant of the allowable rivet forces. A force applied along this line of action distributes itself among the various rivets without any tendency to twist the attached plate. By similar reasoning, the line of action of E_2 may be established in the vertical direction. Then, if the point of intersection of E_1 and E_2 is denoted by B, it is seen that an inclined force E_3 must pass through B to cause no twisting of the plate, since E_3 may be resolved into horizontal and vertical components.   Point B is synonymous with the *centroid of rivet areas*, since in most practical cases the resistance of a

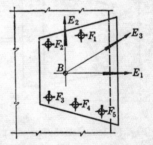

Fig. 14-15.   The applied force must act through the centroid of rivet areas to prevent twisting of a connection.

rivet depends on its cross-sectional area.   A force acting in any direction, but passing through the centroid of rivet areas, is the former problem of a concentrically loaded connection.   However, since forces are not always applied through this point, eccentrically loaded connections result.

Consider a joint such as shown in Fig. 14-16a with a force P applied eccentrically with respect to the centroid B of the rivet areas.   This problem is not changed by introducing at B two equal and opposite forces P parallel to the applied force P.   The new problem may be conveniently resolved into the two problems shown in Figs. 14-16b and c.   The first problem, Fig. 14-16b, was discussed earlier, and, using the assumptions of the *structural* method of rivet analysis, the average *direct* shearing stress in *all* rivets is

$$\tau_d = \frac{P}{\Sigma A} \tag{14-2}$$

where ΣA is the sum of all the cross-sectional areas of the rivets. If all n rivets are of equal size, $\Sigma A = nA$, where A is the cross-sectional area of one rivet, and

$$\tau_d = \frac{P}{nA} \qquad \text{or} \qquad F_1 = A\tau_d = \frac{P}{n} \tag{14-2a}$$

where F_d is the direct force in each rivet. For equilibrium, τ_d and F_d act in a direction opposite to the force P applied at B.

The second problem, Fig. 14-16c, is a problem in torsion, in which the applied torque T is equal to Pe. In this problem, if it is assumed that the plate is *rigid* and that it twists around the point B, the shearing strains in rivets vary linearly from B. Further, if the rivets are assumed to be elastic, the average shearing stress in each rivet also varies linearly from

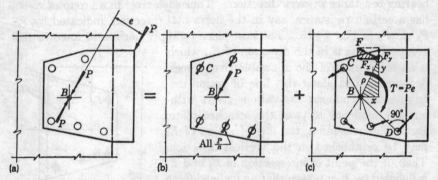

(a)   (b)   (c)

Fig. 14-16. Resolution of a problem of an eccentrically loaded riveted connection into two problems.

B. Therefore this problem resembles the torsion problem of a circular shaft (or a bolted coupling, Art. 3-12), and the torsion formula $\tau = T\rho/J$ may be adapted for its solution. By means of this formula, if each rivet is assumed to be concentrated at a point, the distance ρ (c to the farthermost rivet) from the *centers* of the various rivets to B may be easily determined, and only the quantity J needs further comment. Thus, since by definition $J = \int \rho^2 \, dA$, and the "area of the torsion member" in this case is a discrete number of rivet areas, with sufficient accuracy,

$$J \doteq \Sigma \rho^2 A$$

where the summation includes the product of the cross-sectional area A of *every* rivet by the square of *its* distance ρ from the centroid of all rivet areas. Moreover, since from Fig. 14-16c, each $\rho^2 = x^2 + y^2$, where x and y are the co-ordinates of a particular rivet's center from the centroid of all rivet areas, $J \doteq \Sigma(x^2 + y^2)A$.

By using the approximation for J established above, the *torsional* shearing stress on any one rivet at a distance ρ from the centroid of all rivet areas becomes

$$\tau_t = \frac{T\rho}{J} \doteq \frac{T\rho}{\Sigma\rho^2 A} = \frac{T\rho}{\Sigma(x^2 + y^2)A} \tag{14-3}$$

whereas, if all rivets are of equal size,

$$\tau_t = \frac{T\rho}{A\Sigma(x^2 + y^2)} \quad \text{or} \quad F_t = A\tau_t = \frac{T\rho}{\Sigma(x^2 + y^2)} \tag{14-3a}$$

where F_t is a force due to a torque T acting on a rivet at a distance ρ from the centroid of all rivet areas. *Either τ_t or F_t acts perpendicular to the direction of ρ.* Further, by noting the similarity of the triangle with sides x, y, and ρ to the triangle of force at a rivet and its components, shown shaded in Fig. 14-16c, it follows that the **components** of the torsional stresses in the x- and y-directions, respectively, are

$$(\tau_t)_x = \frac{Ty}{\Sigma(x^2 + y^2)A} \quad \text{and} \quad (\tau_t)_y = \frac{Tx}{\Sigma(x^2 + y^2)A} \tag{14-3b}$$

A *vectorial superposition* of the direct and torsional shearing stresses (or forces) given by the above equations gives the *total* shearing stress (or force) acting on any one rivet. The highest stressed rivet may usually be found by inspection. For example, in Fig. 14-16 the rivet C does not appear to be highly stressed, since the force P/n and the force at C due to torque act approximately in the opposite directions. On the other hand, the corresponding forces at the rivet D are nearly collinear and of the same sense.

Note that the solution for an eccentrically loaded connection is based on the superposition of two entirely different solutions. The first, for the direct stresses, is based on a nonelastic hypothesis; the second, for the torsional stresses, is based on the elastic concepts. The superposition of these two solutions is not completely consistent. The potential capacity of the joint in torsion is not accurately appraised, since rivets situated close to the centroid of the whole rivet group can resist higher forces at ultimate loads. The solution obtained is, however, "conservative" and hence its use in practice is justified.*

Example 14-5. Find the maximum shearing stress caused by an inclined force $P = 12$ kips in the rivets of the connection shown in Fig. 14-17a. The rivets are of 1 in. diameter ($A = 0.785$ in.²).

SOLUTION: The applied force is first resolved into the horizontal and vertical components, which simplifies the determination of the components of the direct shearing stress, as well as the torque T. The centroid of all rivet areas is between the top and bottom rivets at B. Inspection of Fig. 14-17b, where the anticipated direct and torsional stresses are shown acting simultaneously, shows that the top rivet is the highest

* Also see the last paragraph in Art. 3-12.

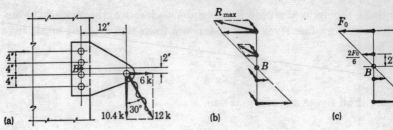

Fig. 14-17.

stressed rivet. This rivet is $c = 6$ in. from B. Note that the rivet pattern is symmetrical, and that the x's in the $\Sigma(x^2 + y^2)$ term are zero.

$$P_x = 12 \sin 30° = 6 \text{ kips} \rightarrow, \quad P_y = 12 \cos 60° = 10.4 \text{ kips} \downarrow$$

$$T = 10.4(12) - 6(2) = 113 \text{ kip-in.} \circlearrowright$$

$$(\tau_d)_y = \frac{P_y}{nA} = \frac{10.4}{4(0.785)} = 3.31 \text{ ksi, resisting} \uparrow$$

$$(\tau_d)_x = \frac{P_x}{nA} = \frac{6}{4(0.785)} = 1.91 \text{ ksi, resisting} \leftarrow$$

$$\tau_t = \frac{Tc}{A\Sigma(x^2 + y^2)} = \frac{113(6)}{0.785(6^2 + 2^2)2} = 10.8 \text{ ksi} \leftarrow$$

$$\tau_{max} = \sqrt{(1.91 + 10.8)^2 + 3.31^2} = 13.1 \text{ ksi}$$

The torsional part of an eccentrically loaded connection problem may always be solved from the first principles without the use of the torsion formula. Thus, assuming, as before, that the plate is *rigid*, also assuming a linear variation of strain in the rivets from the center of twist, and using Hooke's law, it is found that the stresses in the rivets vary linearly from the center of twist. Hence, for the above problem with equal cross-sectional areas of all rivets, in terms of the force F_o at the outer rivets, from Fig. 14-17c,

$$F_o(12) + \tfrac{2}{6} F_o(4) = T = 113 \quad \text{and} \quad F_o = 8.48 \text{ kips}$$

whence, as above, $\tau_t = 8.48/0.785 = 10.8$ ksi. This procedure amounts to a rederivation of the torsion formula.

14-8. Welded Connections. The connection of members by means of welding is widely used in industry and is gradually becoming an accepted procedure in building and bridge work. *Butt welds* have already been discussed in Art. 9-6 for use in the manufacture of pressure vessels. The strength of these welds is simply found by multiplying the cross-sectional area of the thinnest plate being connected by the allowable tensile or compressive stress for a weld. The American Welding Society

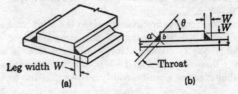

Fig. 14-18. An example of a fillet weld.

(AWS) specifications (1946) allow a 20,000 psi tensile stress for butt welds subjected to static loads in steel buildings.

Another common type of weld, which is designed on an empirical basis, is the so-called *fillet weld* shown in Fig. 14-18. These welds are designated by the size of the legs, Fig. 14-18b, which are usually made of equal width W. The smallest dimension across a weld is called its *throat*. For example, a standard $\frac{1}{2}$ in. weld has both legs $\frac{1}{2}$ in. wide and a throat equal to $(0.5)\sin\theta = (0.5)\sin 45° = 0.707(0.5)$ in. The strength of a fillet weld, *regardless of the direction of the applied force,** is based on the cross-sectional area at the *throat* multiplied by the allowable *shearing stress* for the weld metal. If these bases and the AWS allowable shearing stress of 13,600 psi for weld metal on structural steel for buildings are used, the allowable force q *per inch of weld* is

$$q = 13,600(0.707)W \doteq 9,600\,W \tag{14-4}$$

where W is the width of the legs. Equation 14-4 reduces to some simple values for the usual sizes of welds. For example, for a $\frac{1}{4}$ in. fillet weld, $q = 2,400$ lb per in.; for a $\frac{3}{8}$ in. fillet weld, $q = 3,600$ lb per in., etc.

Example 14-6. Determine the proper lengths of welds for the connection of a 3 in. by 2 in. by $\frac{7}{16}$ in. steel angle to a steel plate, Fig. 14-19. The connection is to develop the full strength of the angle uniformly stressed to 20 ksi. Use $\frac{3}{8}$ in. fillet welds, whose strength per AWS specification is 3.6 kips per linear inch.

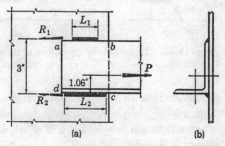

Fig. 14-19.

SOLUTION: Many arrangements of welds are possible. If two welds of length L_1 and L_2 are to be used, their strength must be such as to maintain the applied force P in equilibrium without any tendency to twist the connection. This requires the resultant of the forces R_1 and R_2 developed by the welds to be equal and opposite to P. For the optimum performance of the angle, the force P must act through the centroid of the cross-sectional area (Appendix, Table 7). For the purposes of computation, the welds are assumed to have only linear dimensions.

$$A_{\text{angle}} = 2.00 \text{ in.}^2, \qquad \sigma_{\text{allow}} = 20 \text{ ksi}$$
$$P = A\,\sigma_{\text{allow}} = 2(20) = 40 \text{ kips}$$
$$\Sigma M_d = 0 \,\circlearrowleft+, \qquad R_1(3) - 40(1.06) = 0, \qquad R_1 = 14.1 \text{ kips}$$
$$\Sigma M_a = 0 \,\circlearrowleft+, \qquad R_2(3) - 40(3 - 1.06) = 0, \quad R_2 = 25.9 \text{ kips}$$

Check: $\qquad\qquad R_1 + R_2 = 14.1 + 25.9 = 40 \text{ kips} = P$

Hence, using the specified value for the strength of the $\frac{3}{8}$ in. weld, note that $L_1 = 14.1/3.6 = 3.91$ in. and $L_2 = 25.9/3.6 = 7.19$ in. The actual length of welds is usually increased a small amount over the lengths computed to account for craters at the

---

* This is a considerable simplification of the real problem.

beginning and end of the welds. The eccentricity of the force P with respect to the plane of the welds is neglected.

To minimize the length of the connection, end fillet welds are often used. Thus, in the above example, a weld along the line ad could be added. The centroid of the re- sistance for this weld is midway between a and d. For this arrangement, the lengths L_1 and L_2 are so reduced that the resultant force for all three welds coincides with the resultant of R_1 and R_2 of the former case. To accomplish the same purpose, slots and notches in the attached member are also used.

14-9. Eccentric Welded Connections. A fillet weld, for purposes of calculation, is concentrated into a line and is assumed to resist an equal force per lineal inch in any direction. Therefore the most advantageous line of action for a force applied to a welded connection passes through the *centroid of weld lines*. If this does not occur, an eccentrically loaded connection results. The analysis of these connections is analogous to that of the eccentrically loaded riveted connections. The problem is

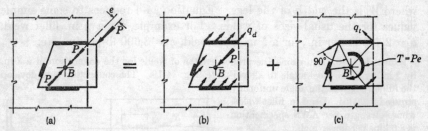

Fig. 14-20. Resolution of a problem of an eccentrically loaded welded connection into two separate problems.

resolved into two problems as shown in Fig. 14-20. The first problem, Fig. 14-20b, is a concentrically loaded connection where the applied force P acts through the centroid B of all welds. For this case, the *direct* force q_d per inch length of weld acting in the direction opposite to P is

$$q_d = \frac{P}{\Sigma L} \qquad \left[\frac{\text{lb}}{\text{in.}}\right] \quad (14\text{-}5)$$

where ΣL is the *total length* of all welds. If the force P is resolved into the horizontal and vertical components P_x and P_y, respectively, the com- ponents of the direct force per inch of weld are

$$(q_d)_x = \frac{P_x}{\Sigma L} \quad \text{and} \quad (q_d)_y = \frac{P_y}{\Sigma L} \qquad (14\text{-}5a)$$

The second problem, Fig. 14-20c, is analogous to the torsion problem, if the plate is assumed to be *rigid* and to twist around the point B. Then, by further assuming elastic action of the welds, the torsion formula, with a modified value of J, may be applied. A particular value of J for a group of *straight* welds may be found as outlined below.

The polar moment of inertia J is equal to the sum of two rectangular moments of inertia with respect to any two mutually perpendicular axes, i.e., $J = I_{xx} + I_{yy}$. Likewise, bearing in mind the parallel axis theorem, Eq. 5-2, the contribution to J with respect to the center of twist B of *any individual straight weld* such as ab in Fig. 14-21 is*

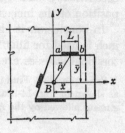

Fig. 14-21.

$$I_{xx} + I_{yy} = 0 + L\bar{y}^2 + \tfrac{1}{12}L^3 + L\bar{x}^2 \qquad [\text{in.}^3]$$

where L is the length of a weld, and $\bar{x}$ and $\bar{y}$ are the respective co-ordinate distances from the centroid B of all welds *to the center of the weld considered*. This expression remains the same for any position or inclination of a straight weld, since $\bar{x}^2 + \bar{y}^2 = \bar{\rho}^2 = \bar{x}_1^2 + \bar{y}_2^2$. Therefore the total equivalent J for several straight welds is

$$J = \Sigma\left(\frac{L^3}{12} + L\bar{x}^2 + L\bar{y}^2\right)$$

where the expression in parentheses is computed for *every* weld in the connection whose individual length is L, and the results are added.

Using the above equivalent value of J in the torsion formula, the *torsional* force q_t per inch of weld is

$$q_t = \frac{T\rho}{\Sigma\left(\dfrac{L^3}{12} + L\bar{x}^2 + L\bar{y}^2\right)} \qquad \left[\frac{\text{lb}}{\text{in.}}\right] \qquad \textbf{(14-6)}$$

where ρ is the distance from the centroid of all welds to *a particular point on any weld*. The torsional force q_t acts perpendicular to the radius vector ρ. The horizontal and vertical *components* of q_t, in a manner analogous to that employed in the analysis of riveted connections, may be shown to be, respectively,

$$(q_t)_x = \frac{Ty}{\Sigma\left(\dfrac{L^3}{12} + L\bar{x}^2 + L\bar{y}^2\right)}$$

$$\textbf{(14-6a)}$$

and

$$(q_t)_y = \frac{Tx}{\Sigma\left(\dfrac{L^3}{12} + L\bar{x}^2 + L\bar{y}^2\right)}$$

where as above, T is the **total torque** Pe on the connection, and x and y are the co-ordinate distances to a selected point on the weld.

The vectorial superposition of the direct and torsional forces per inch of weld gives the *intensity of the total force per inch of weld*. Inspection of the diagram for the joint on which the anticipated q_d and q_t are esti-

* Note that I of a line around itself equals zero.

mated generally reveals the highest stressed point on the welds. Usually the size of all welds is based on the highest stressed point. Like the eccentrically loaded riveted connection, this solution is obtained by super-position of the inelastic and elastic solutions.

In conclusion it should be noted that vector summation of forces per inch is used for fillet welds only. In the case of butt welds the direct and torsional stresses are combined by using Mohr's circle.

Example 14-7. Find the size of the two welds required to attach a plate to a machine as shown in Fig. 14-22a if the plate carries an inclined force $P = 10$ kips. Use the stresses allowed by the AWS.

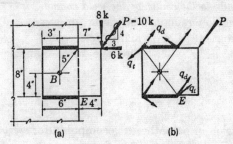

(a)   (b)

Fig. 14-22.

SOLUTION: The applied force is resolved into horizontal and vertical components. The centroid of the two welds is seen to be at B. In computing J, symmetry and the fact that $\bar{x}$'s are zero are noted. Inspection of the anticipated direct and torsional forces on the welds in Fig. 14-22b shows that point E has the highest stress. Application of Eqs. 14-5a and 14-6a yields the components of q_d and q_t, which are then used to find q_{max}.

$$P_x = \tfrac{3}{5}(10) = 6 \text{ kips} \qquad P_y = \tfrac{4}{5}(10) = 8 \text{ kips}$$
$$T = 8(7) - 6(4) = 32 \text{ kip-in.}$$

$$J = 2\left(\frac{L^3}{12} + L\bar{y}^2\right) = 2\left[\frac{6^3}{12} + 6(4)^2\right] = 228 \text{ in.}^3$$

$$(q_d)_x = \frac{P_x}{\Sigma L} = \frac{6,000}{6+6} = 500 \frac{\text{lb}}{\text{in.}} \rightarrow; \qquad (q_d)_y = \frac{P_y}{\Sigma L} = \frac{8,000}{12} = 667 \frac{\text{lb}}{\text{in.}} \uparrow$$

$$(q_t)_x = \frac{Ty}{J} = \frac{32,000(4)}{228} = 562 \frac{\text{lb}}{\text{in.}} \rightarrow; \qquad (q_t)_y = \frac{Tx}{J} = \frac{32,000(3)}{228} = 421 \frac{\text{lb}}{\text{in.}} \uparrow$$

$$q_{max} = q_E = \sqrt{(500 + 562)^2 + (667 + 421)^2} = 1,520 \text{ lb per in.}$$

Finally, since by Eq. 14-4 the allowable force per inch of weld, regardless of the direction of the applied force, is $9,600\,W$, where W is the width of the leg,

$$q = 9,600W = 1,520 \text{ lb per in.} \qquad \text{or} \qquad W = 0.158 \text{ in.}$$

Hence a uniform size of $\tfrac{3}{16}$ in. fillet weld should be used throughout.

Problems for Solution

14-1. A member of a truss to be made of two 4 in. by 4 in. by $\tfrac{1}{2}$ in. angles must transmit an axial force of 70 kips to a $\tfrac{1}{2}$ in. gusset plate. The angles are to be arranged as shown in Fig. 14-10. How many $\frac{7}{8}$ in. rivets are required? How many rivets should be used to develop the full tensile capacity of the angles? Use the allowable stresses given in Example 14-1. *Ans.* 4, 8.

14-2. A standard AISC "Series B" connection for a 20 *I* 65.4 beam consists of two 4 in. by $3\frac{1}{2}$ in. by $\frac{7}{8}$ in. angles with five $\frac{3}{4}$ in. rivets through the web and ten rivets in the outstanding legs. Determine the capacity of the connection. Use the allowable stresses given in Example 14-1. *Ans.* 66.3 kips.

14-3. An 18 WF 50 beam is attached to two 12 WF 65 columns by means of connections, each of which consists of two 4 in. by $3\frac{1}{2}$ in. by $\frac{3}{8}$ in. angles. Four $\frac{3}{4}$ in. rivets go through the web of the beam and eight $\frac{3}{4}$ in. rivets are used at each column. What force *P*, governed by allowable bearing and shear on rivets, may be applied to the beam as shown in the figure? Use the AASHO (American Association of State Highway Officials) stresses: shear, 13.5 ksi; single *or* double bearing, 27 ksi. *Ans.* 58 kips.

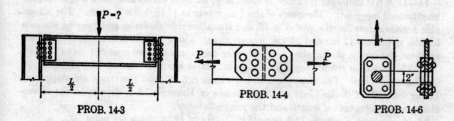

PROB. 14-3   PROB. 14-4   PROB. 14-6

14-4. What direct tensile force may be applied to the multiple-riveted, structural butt joint shown in the figure? What is the efficiency of the joint? The main plates are $\frac{1}{2}$ in. thick by 9 in. wide; the *two* cover plates are each $\frac{3}{8}$ in. thick. The rivets are $\frac{7}{8}$ in. in diameter. Use the allowable stresses given in Example 14-1. *Ans.* 70 kips.

14-5. A multiple-riveted, structural butt joint has the same arrangement of rivets as the joint of the preceding problem. The main plates are $\frac{3}{8}$ in. thick by 8 in. wide; the *two* cover plates are each $\frac{1}{4}$ in. thick by 8 in. wide. One inch rivets are used in $1\frac{1}{16}$ in. diameter holes. If the joint transmits a force of 30 kips: (a) what is the tensile stress in the cover plates at the inner row of rivets; (b) what is the tensile stress in the main plate at the inner and outer rows of rivets? *Ans.* (a) 13 ksi, (b) 10.4 ksi, 13.9 ksi.

14-6. A $\frac{1}{2}$ in. by 8 in. plate transmitting a pull of 52 kips is reinforced with two side plates at a 2.00 in. diameter pin for bearing requirements as shown in the figure. (a) Determine the required thickness of the side plates if the allowable bearing stress in single or double shear is 27 ksi. State the answer to the nearest $\frac{1}{16}$th of an inch. (b) Determine the required number of $\frac{5}{8}$ in. rivets for attaching the side plates to the main plate if the allowable shearing stress is 13.5 ksi. *Ans.* (a) $\frac{1}{4}$ in., (b) 4.

14-7. Two $\frac{1}{2}$ in. by 12 in. plates are lapped and riveted with 1 in. rivets as shown in the figure. Determine the allowable load and efficiency of the joint. The allowable stresses are 18 ksi, 15 ksi, and 32 ksi in tension, shear, and bearing, respectively. *Ans* 97.8 kips, 90.5%.

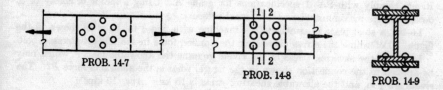

PROB. 14-7   PROB. 14-8   PROB. 14-9

14-8. A structural, multiple-riveted lap joint, such as is shown in the figure, is designed for a 42 kip load. The plates are $\frac{3}{8}$ in. thick by 10 in. wide. The rivets are $\frac{3}{4}$ in. (a) What is the shearing stress in the middle rivet? (b) What are the tensile stresses in the *upper* plate in row 1-1 and row 2-2? *Ans.* (a) 13.6 ksi, (b) 6.5 ksi, 7.02 ksi.

14-9. A 20 I 85.0 beam has two 1 in. by 10 in. cover plates as shown in the figure. This composite beam carries a total vertical shear of 150 kips at a particular section. Using the stresses allowed by the AISC code (Example 14-1), specify the required spacing of $\frac{3}{4}$ in. rivets between the beam and the cover plates.

14-10. Two $\frac{1}{2}$ in. by 6 in. low-carbon nickel steel plates (Grade A) are lap-joined by means of two $\frac{7}{8}$ in. alloy-steel rivets driven into $\frac{15}{16}$ in. diameter holes. What is the capacity and efficiency of this joint in direct tension? Use a factor of safety of 5 and the stresses specified by the ASME Boiler Code. *Ans.* 16.6 kips, 42.6%

14-11. A 5 ft diameter penstock is made of $\frac{5}{16}$ in. steel plates and has a single riveted longitudinal lap-joint. The pitch of the $\frac{3}{4}$ in. rivets in $\frac{13}{16}$ in. holes is $2\frac{1}{2}$ in. The allowable tensile stress for the plates is 16 ksi; the allowable shearing and bearing stresses for the rivets are 12 ksi and 25 ksi, respectively. Using the ASME method for boiler analysis, determine under what head of water the penstock may operate. *Ans.* 191 ft.

14-12. A double riveted lap joint for $\frac{5}{16}$ in. plates has two rows of $\frac{3}{4}$ in. rivets in $\frac{13}{16}$ in. diameter holes. The rivet pitch in both rows is 3 in., and the rivets are staggered. Using the ASME Boiler Code and the stresses of Example 14-4, determine the allowable load on a repeating length and the joint efficiency.

14-13. Rework Example 14-4 using $\frac{7}{8}$ in. rivets in $\frac{15}{16}$ in. diameter holes.

14-14. * A triple-riveted and double-strap boiler joint, recommended by the ASME Boiler Code for large boilers, is illustrated in the figure. The thickness of the plates is $\frac{3}{4}$ in.; the thickness of the splice plates is $\frac{5}{16}$ in.; the long pitch p is $6\frac{1}{2}$ in.; the diameter of the rivet holes is $\frac{13}{16}$ in. Determine the efficiency of the joint. Assume plate steel of unknown composition and steel rivets of grade A complying with Spec. No. SA-31.

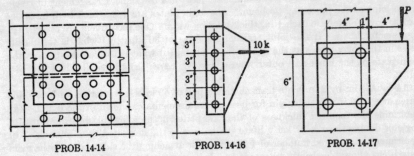

PROB. 14-14   PROB. 14-16   PROB. 14-17

14-15. * A carbon-steel cylindrical pressure vessel 36 in. in diameter and $\frac{5}{16}$ in. thick has dished ends of the same thickness that are joined to the cylinder by single-riveted circumferential lap joints using $\frac{3}{4}$ in. rivets at $3\frac{1}{2}$ in. spacing. The longitudinal joint of the cylinder is a double-riveted butt joint of the type shown in Example 14-4 with $\frac{3}{4}$ in. rivets. The splice plates are $\frac{5}{16}$ in. thick and the pitch of the outer rivets is 5 in. Rivets comply with SA-31 specifications for grade A. Using a factor of safety of 5, determine the maximum allowable internal pressure.

14-16. A steel plate is attached to a machine with five $\frac{3}{4}$ in. bolts as shown in the figure. Determine the stress caused by the applied force in the highest stressed bolt.

14-17. If the shearing stress in the rivets governs the allowable load P which may be applied to the connection shown in the figure, what is the allowable force P? The rivets are $\frac{3}{4}$ in. and the allowable shearing stress is 15 ksi. *Ans.* 10 kips

14-18. For the riveted connection shown in the figure, and used in an aeroplane, (a) determine the maximum stress on the highest stressed rivet. All rivets are $\frac{1}{8}$ in. in diameter. (b) If rivet A were knocked out, what would be the stress on the highest stressed rivet? *Ans.* (a) 1,920 psi, (b) 1,680 psi.

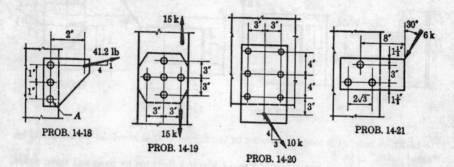

PROB. 14-18   PROB. 14-19   PROB. 14-20   PROB. 14-21

14-19. Calculate the maximum shearing stress in the rivet group shown in the figure if all rivets are $\frac{3}{4}$ in. The plates form a lap joint. *Ans.* 15.3 ksi.

14-20. Calculate the shearing stress caused by the applied force in each of the 1 in. diameter rivets for the connection shown in the figure.

14-21. Determine the maximum shearing stress in the rivets in the bracket loaded as shown in the figure. All rivets are 1 in. in diameter. *Ans.* 9,140 psi.

14-22. In order to obtain a wood beam of sufficient length, two short pieces of 2 in. by 10 in. timbers were spliced to the end of a 4 in. by 10 in. timber by six $\frac{3}{4}$ in. bolts as shown in the figure. If the working load of a $\frac{3}{4}$ in. bolt in double shear in any direction is limited to 1,000 lb, what is the maximum load P that the beam can support? Neglect the weight of the beam. *Ans.* 1,210 lb.

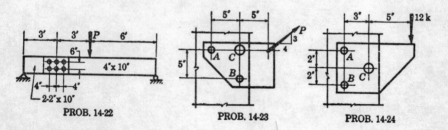

PROB. 14-22   PROB. 14-23   PROB. 14-24

14-23. Determine the allowable load P that may be applied to a riveted connection having the dimensions shown in the figure. Rivets A and B are 0.2 in.², and rivet C is 0.6 in.² in cross-sectional area. The allowable shearing stress in the rivets is 20 ksi. *Ans.* 8.37 kips.

14-24. Calculate the maximum shearing stress in the rivets for the connection shown in the figure. Rivets A and B have cross-sections of 1 in.² each, and rivet C has a cross-section of 2 in.² *Ans.* 10 ksi (max).

14-25. Rework Example 14-6 for an 8 in. by 6 in. by $\frac{3}{4}$ in. angle using $\frac{1}{2}$ in. fillet welds.

14-26. Determine the proper lengths of welds L_1 and L_2 in Example 14-6 if, to minimize the length of connection, a weld is made along ad.

14-27. A 12 WF 65 beam is attached to a column by means of two angles as shown in the figure. If a moment of +480 kip-in. is transmitted to the connection, what lengths of ½ in. fillet welds are required to join the beam to the angles? *Ans.* 8.25 in.

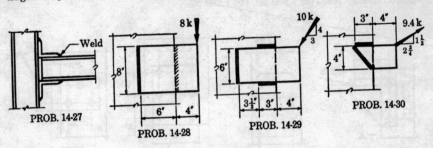

PROB. 14-27   PROB. 14-28   PROB. 14-29   PROB. 14-30

14-28. A bracket is loaded as shown in the figure. What size fillet welds should be used? *Ans.* ³⁄₁₆ in.

14-29. A bracket is to be attached to a body of a machine by means of three welds as shown in the figure. If the applied inclined force is 10 kips, what size fillet welds are required? *Ans.* ¼ in.

14-30.* Determine the required size of fillet welds for the connection loaded as shown in the figure. *Ans.* ⅜ in.

14-31. If in Prob. 14-9 the cover plates are to be attached to the *I*-beam by means of welds, specify the size of fillet welds required. (*Hint:* determine shear flow per foot of beam's length, then decide on the size and length of the weld needed in such a distance. Intermittent welds are permitted.)

Chapter Fifteen

THE ENERGY METHODS

15-1. Introduction. In the preceding chapters of the text, static equilibrium equations were always employed to solve the basic problems in Mechanics of Materials. An equally fundamental concept for the solution of these problems is based on the principle of conservation of energy. Methods of problem analysis which are generally applicable result by using this concept, and the study of these methods will be the object of this chapter.

In mechanics, energy is defined as the capacity to do work, while work is the product of a force by the distance in the direction the force moves. In solid deformable bodies, stresses multiplied by their respective areas are forces, and deformations are distances. The product of these two quantities is the *internal work* done in a body by externally applied forces. This internal work is stored in a body as the *internal elastic energy of deformation,* or *the elastic strain energy.* Methods of computing this internal energy will be discussed first. Then, by using the principle of the conservation of energy, and equating the internal work to·the analytically expressed *external work,* one can obtain deflections of axially loaded members, torsional members, and beams. This procedure will permit the investigation of stresses and deflections of members subjected not only to steadily applied forces, as has been the case hitherto, but also of members subjected to *energy or impact loads.*

The direct solution of problems by equating the external to the internal work will be limited to cases where only one force is applied to a member. Then a generalized procedure will be treated under the caption of *virtual work.* This method will be used in discussing deflection problems of a very general nature, such as those caused by any loading of trusses and curved bars. In all cases, the members will be assumed to be in equilibrium, as the solution of instability problems by the energy methods are beyond the scope of this text.

15-2. Elastic Strain Energy for Uniaxial Stress. Consider an infinitesimal element, such as shown in Fig. 15-1a, for which the elastic energy is wanted when it is subjected to a normal stress σ. The force acting on the right or the left face of this element is $\sigma\, dx\, dz$, where $dx\, dz$ is an infinitesimal area of the element. Owing to this force, the element elongates an amount $\epsilon\,dy$, where ϵ is strain in the y-direction.   If the element considered is *elastic*, stress is proportional to strain, Fig. 15-1b.   Therefore,

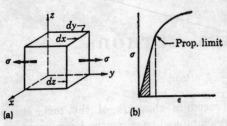

if the element is *initially free* of stress, the force which finally acts on the element increases *linearly* from zero until it attains its full value.   The *average* force acting on the element while deformation occurs is $\frac{1}{2}\sigma\,dx\,dz$.   This average force multiplied by the distance through which it acts is the work done on the element.

Fig. 15-1.   (a) An element in tension, and (b) a stress-strain diagram.

However, since in a perfectly *elastic* body no energy is dissipated, the work done on the element is stored as *recoverable* internal strain energy.   Hence, the internal elastic strain energy U_i for an infinitesimal element subjected to uniaxial stress is

$$dU_i = \underbrace{\tfrac{1}{2}\sigma\,dx\,dz}_{\text{average force}} \times \underbrace{\epsilon\,dy}_{\text{distance}} = \tfrac{1}{2}\sigma\epsilon\,dV \qquad (15\text{-}1)$$

$$\underbrace{\phantom{\tfrac{1}{2}\sigma\,dx\,dz \times \epsilon\,dy}}_{\text{work}}$$

where dV is an infinitesimal volume of the element.

By recasting Eq. 15-1, the energy stored in an elastic body *per unit volume* of the material at a constant stress is obtained, thus:

$$\frac{dU_i}{dV} = \frac{1}{2}\,\sigma\epsilon \qquad (15\text{-}1a)$$

This expression may be graphically interpreted as an area under the stress-strain diagram, Fig. 15-1b.   From this figure, it is seen that Eqs. 15-1 and 15-1a are valid only up to the proportional limit of the material. Moreover, since in the elastic range Hooke's law, $\sigma = E\epsilon$, applies, Eq. 15-1a may be written as

$$\frac{dU_i}{dV} = \frac{E\epsilon^2}{2} = \frac{\sigma^2}{2E} \qquad (15\text{-}1b)$$

or

$$U_i = \int_{\text{vol}} \frac{\sigma^2}{2E}\,dV \qquad (15\text{-}1c)$$

These forms of the equation for the elastic strain energy are convenient in applications, although they mask the dependence of the energy expression on the force and distance.

For a particular material, substitution into Eq. 15-1b of the value of the stress at the proportional limit gives an index of the material's ability to store or absorb energy without permanent deformation.   The quantity so found is termed the **modulus of resilience** and is used to differentiate materials for applications where energy must be absorbed by members. For example, steel with a proportional limit of 30,000 psi and an E of 30×10^6 psi has a modulus of resilience of $\sigma^2/(2E) = (30,000)^2/2(30)10^6 = 15$ in.-lb per cu in., whereas a good grade of Douglas fir, having a proportional limit of 6,450 psi and an E of 1,920,000 psi. has a modulus of resilience of $(6,450)^2/2(1,920,000) = 10.8$ in.-lb per cu in.

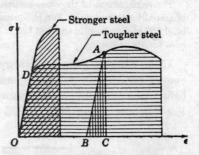

Fig. 15-2.   Definition of toughness.

By reasoning analogous to the above, the area under a complete stress-strain diagram, Fig. 15-2, gives a measure of a material's ability to resist energy load up to fracture and is called its **toughness**. The larger the total area under the stress-strain diagram, the tougher the material. In the inelastic range, only a small part of the energy absorbed by a material is recoverable. Most of the energy is *dissipated* in permanently deforming the material. The energy which may be recovered when a specimen has been stressed to some such point as A in Fig. 15-2 is represented by the triangle ABC. The line AB of this triangle is parallel to the line OD, since all materials behave elastically upon the release of stress.

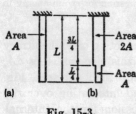

Fig. 15-3.

Example 15-1. Two elastic bars, whose proportions are shown in Fig. 15-3, are to absorb the same amount of energy delivered by axial forces. Neglecting stress concentrations, compare the stresses in the two bars.

SOLUTION: The bar shown in Fig. 15-3a is of uniform cross-sectional area, therefore the normal stress σ_1 is constant throughout. Using Eq. 15-1c and integrating over the volume V of the bar, one can write the total energy for the bar as

$$U_1 = \int_V \frac{\sigma_1^2}{2E} \, dV = \frac{\sigma_1^2}{2E} \int_V dV = \frac{\sigma_1^2}{2E}(AL)$$

where A is the cross-sectional area of the bar, and L is its length.

The bar shown in Fig. 15-3b is of variable cross-section. Therefore, if the stress σ_2 acts in the lower part of the bar, the stress in the upper part is $\frac{1}{2}\sigma_2$. Again using Eq. 15-1c and integrating over the volume of the bar, it is found that the total energy which this bar will absorb in terms of the stress σ_2 is

$$U_2 = \int_V \frac{\sigma^2}{2E} \, dV = \frac{\sigma_2^2}{2E} \int_{\substack{\text{lower} \\ \text{part}}} dV + \frac{(\sigma_2/2)^2}{2E} \int_{\substack{\text{upper} \\ \text{part}}} dV$$

$$= \frac{\sigma_2^2}{2E} \left(\frac{AL}{4}\right) + \frac{(\sigma_2/2)^2}{2E} \left(2A \, \frac{3L}{4}\right) = \frac{\sigma_2^2}{2E} \left(\frac{5}{8} AL\right)$$

If both bars are to absorb the same amount of energy, $U_1 = U_2$ and

$$\frac{\sigma_1^2}{2E}\,(AL) = \frac{\sigma_2^2}{2E}\left(\frac{5}{8}\,AL\right) \qquad \text{or} \qquad \sigma_2 = 1.265\,\sigma_1$$

The enlargement of the cross-sectional area over a part of the bar in the second case is actually detrimental. For the same energy load, the stress in the "reinforced" bar is 26.5% higher than in the first bar. This situation is not found in the design of members for static loads.

15-3. Elastic Strain Energy in Pure Bending. The elastic strain energy for an infinitesimal element in uniaxial stress having been established, one may obtain the elastic strain energy for beams in pure bending. For this special case, the normal stress is known to vary linearly from the

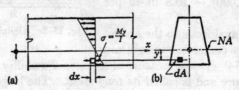

Fig. 15-4. A segment of a beam used in deriving the expression for strain energy in bending.

neutral axis as is shown in Fig. 15-4a, and the stress acting on an arbitrary element is $\sigma = My/I$, Eq. 5-1a. The volume of this element is $dx\,dA$, where dx is the element's length and dA is its cross-sectional area, Fig. 15-4b. Hence, using Eq. 15-1c and integrating over the volume V of the beam, the expression for the internal elastic strain energy for a beam is,

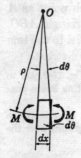

$$U_i = \int_V \frac{\sigma^2}{2E}\,dV = \int_V \frac{1}{2E}\left(\frac{My}{I}\right)^2 dx\,dA$$

Rearranging terms and remembering that M at a section of a beam is constant and that the order of performing the integration may be chosen arbitrarily, one obtains

Fig. 15 - 5. A segment of a beam used in an alternate derivation of the strain energy in bending.

$$U_i = \int_{\text{length}} \frac{M^2}{2EI^2}\,dx \int_{\text{area}} y^2\,dA = \int_0^L \frac{M^2\,dx}{2EI} \quad (15\text{-}2)$$

where the last simplification is possible since by definition $I = \int y^2\,dA$. Equation 15-2 reduces the volume integral for the elastic energy of prismatic beams in pure flexure to a single integral to be taken over the length L of a beam.

For further emphasis, Eq. 15-2 will be rederived from a different of point view, by considering an elementary segment of a beam dx long, as is shown in Fig. 15-5. Before the application of the bending moments M, the two planes perpendicular to the axis of the beam are parallel. After the application of the bending moments, extensions of the same two planes, which remain plane, intersect at O, and the angle included between these two planes is $d\theta$. Moreover, since the full value of the moment M is attained *gradually*, the *average* moment acting through an angle $d\theta$ is $\frac{1}{2}M$. Hence the external work U_e done on a segment of a beam is $dU_e = \frac{1}{2} M \, d\theta$. Further, since for small deflections $dx \doteq \rho \, d\theta$, where ρ is the radius of curvature of the elastic curve and $1/\rho = M/EI$, from the principle of conservation of energy the internal strain energy of an element of a beam is

$$dU_i = dU_e = \frac{1}{2} M \, d\theta = \frac{1}{2} M \frac{dx}{\rho} = \frac{M^2 \, dx}{2EI}$$

which has the same meaning as Eq. 15-2.

Example 15-2. Find the elastic strain energy stored in a rectangular cantilever beam subjected to a bending moment M applied at the end, Fig. 15-6.

SOLUTION: The bending moment at every section of this beam, as well as the flexural rigidity EI, is constant. By direct application of Eq. 15-2,

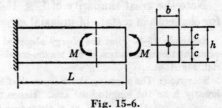

$$U_i = \int_0^L \frac{M^2 \, dx}{2EI} = \frac{M^2}{2EI} \int_0^L dx = \frac{M^2 L}{2EI}$$

Fig. 15-6.

It is instructive to write this result in another form. Thus, since $\sigma_{max} = Mc/I$, $M = \sigma_{max}I/c = 2\sigma_{max}I/h$, and $I = bh^3/12$,

$$U_i = \frac{\left(\dfrac{2\sigma_{max}I}{h}\right)^2 L}{2EI} = \frac{\sigma_{max}^2}{2E}\left(\frac{bhL}{3}\right) = \frac{\sigma_{max}^2}{2E}\left(\frac{1}{3}\text{vol}\right)$$

For a given maximum stress, the volume of the material in this beam is only a third as effective for absorbing energy as it would be in a uniformly stressed bar where $U_i = \frac{\sigma^2}{2E}$ (vol). This results from the presence of *variable* stresses in a beam. If the bending moment also varies along a prismatic beam, the volume of the material becomes even less effective.

15-4. Elastic Strain Energy for Shearing Stresses. An expression for the elastic strain energy for an infinitesimal element in *pure shear* may be established in a manner analogous to that for one in uniaxial stress.

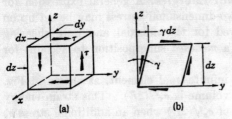

Thus consider an element in a state of pure shear as shown in Fig. 15-7a. The distorted shape of this element is shown in Fig. 15-7b, where it is assumed that the bottom plane of the element is fixed in position.* As this element is deformed, the force on the top plane reaches a final value of $\tau \, dx \, dy$. The total dis-

Fig. 15-7. An element used in deriving the expression of strain energy for shearing stresses.

* No generality is lost by this assumption.

placement of this force, if only *small elastic distortions of the element are considered*, is $\gamma\,dz$, Fig. 5-7b. Therefore, by using the principle of conservation of energy, one notes that the external work done on this element is equal to the internal recoverable elastic strain energy in pure shear, hence

$$(dU_i)_{\text{shear}} = (dU_e)_{\text{shear}} = \underbrace{\tfrac{1}{2}\tau\,dx\,dy}_{\text{av force}} \times \underbrace{\gamma\,dz}_{\text{distance}} = \tfrac{1}{2}\tau\gamma\,dV \qquad (15\text{-}3)$$

where dV is the volume of the infinitesimal element. By using Hooke's law for shearing stresses, $\tau = G\gamma$, one may transform Eq. 15-3 as follows,

$$(dU_i)_{\text{shear}} = \frac{G\gamma^2}{2}\,dV = \frac{\tau^2}{2G}\,dV \qquad (15\text{-}3a)$$

Note the great similarity of Eqs. 15-3 and 15-3a to Eqs. 15-1 and 15-1b for elements in a state of uniaxial stress.

Example 15-3. Find the energy absorbed by an elastic circular rod subjected to a constant torque in terms of the maximum shearing stress and the volume of the material, Fig. 15-8.

SOLUTION: The shearing stress in an elastic circular rod subjected to a torque varies linearly from the longitudinal axis. Hence the shearing stress acting on an element at a distance ρ from the center of the cross-section is $\tau_{\text{max}}\rho/c$. Then, using Eq. 15-3a and integrating it over the volume V of the rod L inches long, one obtains

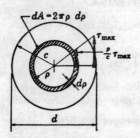

Fig. 15-8.

$$U_i = \int_V \frac{\tau^2}{2G}\,dV = \int_V \frac{\tau_{\text{max}}{}^2\rho^2}{2Gc^2}\,2\pi\rho\,d\rho\,L$$

$$= \frac{\tau_{\text{max}}{}^2}{2G}\frac{2\pi L}{c^2}\int_0^c \rho^3\,d\rho = \frac{\tau_{\text{max}}{}^2}{2G}\frac{2\pi L}{c^2}\frac{c^4}{4}$$

$$= \frac{\tau_{\text{max}}{}^2}{2G}\left(\frac{1}{2}\text{vol}\right)$$

If there were uniform shearing stress throughout the member, a more efficient arrangement for absorbing energy would be obtained. In practice this condition is nearly attained in sandwich type rubber mountings for machinery.

*15-5. Superposition of Strain Energies. A general expression for the elastic strain energy for a "two-dimensional" stress may be set up on the basis of the equations derived for the uniaxial and pure shearing stresses. This is done by using a *modified* superposition to account for the Poisson effect.

If a stress σ_x is applied to an infinitesimal element, as shown in Fig. 15-9a, the strain energy per unit volume is $\sigma_x{}^2/(2E)$. This strain energy is not increased by the full value of $\sigma_y{}^2/(2E)$ when an additional stress σ_y is added, Fig. 15-9b, since while σ_y is applied, a *transverse contraction of the element occurs*. This transverse contraction is equal to $\mu(\sigma_y/E)$, and it causes the displacement of the forces already acting in the x-direction opposite to their line of action. Therefore, as σ_y is applied to the element,

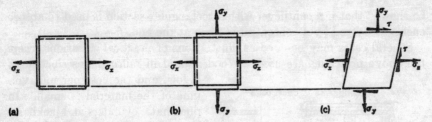

Fig. 15-9. The effect of the superposition of stresses on deformations.

the strain energy per unit volume is increased by $\sigma_y{}^2/(2E)$ and *decreased* by* $\sigma_x\mu(\sigma_y/E)$. Hence the *elastic* strain energy per unit volume for biaxial stress is

$$\frac{dU_i}{dV} = \frac{\sigma_x{}^2}{2E} + \frac{\sigma_y{}^2}{2E} - \mu\frac{\sigma_x\sigma_y}{E} \qquad (15\text{-}4)$$

This equation may be directly established by gradually applying σ_x and σ_y to an element simultaneously and using the generalized Hooke's law for linear strains (see Prob. 15-8). Such a procedure is usually followed in the Theory of Elasticity.

Strain energy due to shearing stresses may be added *directly* to Eq. 15-4. For *small* shearing deformations, as may be seen from Fig. 15-9c, no work is done by the normal forces when such deformations occur.

15-6. Design of Members for Energy Loads. Examination of the results in the examples solved shows certain common characteristics which must be considered in the design of members to resist energy loads. Thus, whether an axially loaded member, a beam, or a torsion member is considered, the maximum stress for a given energy load U absorbed by a member may be expressed as

$$\sigma_{\max} = \sqrt{\frac{2EU}{fV}} \qquad \text{or} \qquad \tau_{\max} = \sqrt{\frac{2GU}{fV}}$$

where f is a fraction by which the total volume V of the member must be multiplied, depending on the type of stress distribution.

It may be seen from these expressions that, for a given U, the smallest stresses will be obtained:

(1) By selecting a material with a low E or G;
(2) By making the total *volume* of the member large;
(3) By stressing the material uniformly.

When constant stress exists throughout a body, $f = 1$. Solid circular members in torsion, as commonly found in springs, are reasonably good, since $f = 0.5$. For the same stress, the volume of the material in a beam is at best only one-third as effective as it is in an axially loaded rod. This situation is found only in constant-strength beams. For example, it can

---

* Since σ_x acts at its full value as σ_y is applied, no factor of one-half is used.

be shown* that if a cantilever with a rectangular section is used to absorb energy delivered by a concentrated force at the end, $f = \frac{1}{9}$.

Several cases may be cited as illustrations of practical situations where the above principles are used. Wood is used in railroad ties since its E

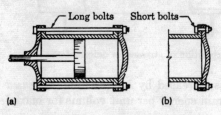

is low, and the cost per unit volume of the material is small. In pneumatic cylinders and jackhammers, Fig. 15-10, very long bolts are used to attach the ends to the tube. Long bolts provide a large volume of material, which, in operation, is uniformly stressed in tension. In the early stages of the development of this equipment, short bolts were used, and frequent failures occurred. A prac-

Fig. 15-10. (a) Good and (b) bad design of a pneumatic cylinder.

tical approximation to a constant-strength beam is found in leaf springs, Fig. 5-11b and c. The various leaves of the spring, when spread out, Fig. 15-11a, are approximately equivalent to a beam of constant strength† (see Fig. 10-18c).

15-7. Deflections by the Energy Method. As stated in the introduction, the principle of conservation of energy may be used to find the deflection of a loaded member. For this purpose, the internal strain energy U_i for a member is determined by using the equations derived above. Then, by equating this energy to the external work U_e done by an applied force, one can establish a relation from which the deflection of an applied force is found. This direct procedure will be used only in situations where one force is applied

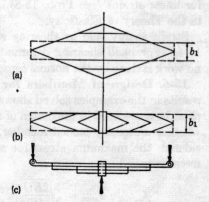

Fig. 15-11. Leaf spring. (a) composite leaves of a spring in one plane approximate a beam of constant strength.

to a member. A general method for finding the deflection of any point on a member caused by any loading will be discussed in Art. 15-9.

For the present, it will be assumed that an external force is *gradually applied* to a body. This means that, as a force or a torque is being applied, its full effect on the material is reached gradually from zero. Therefore the external work U_e is equal to one-half of the total force multiplied by the total deflection.

---

* Prob. 15-6.

† In operation, some energy is dissipated through friction between the leaves of the spring.

Note that since $U_e = U_i$, unlike the procedure used in the following examples, the strain energy may often be easily computed by using expressions for the deflection of members derived earlier in the text.

Example 15-4. Find the deflection of the free end of an elastic rod of constant cross-sectional area A and of length L due to an axial force P applied at the free end.

SOLUTION: If the force P is gradually applied to the rod, the external work $U_e = \frac{1}{2} P\Delta$, where Δ is the deflection of the end of the rod. The expression for the internal strain energy U_i of the rod was found in Example 15-1, and since $\sigma_1 = P/A$, it is

$$U_i = \frac{\sigma_1^2}{2E} AL = \frac{P^2 L}{2AE}$$

Then from $U_e = U_i$

$$\frac{P\Delta}{2} = \frac{P^2 L}{2AE} \quad \text{and} \quad \Delta = \frac{PL}{AE}$$

which is the same as Eq. 2-4.

Example 15-5. Find the rotation of the end of a circular shaft with respect to the built-in end when a torque T is applied at the free end.

SOLUTION: If the torque T is gradually applied to the shaft, the external work $U_e = \frac{1}{2} T\varphi$, where φ is the angular rotation of the free end in radians. The expression for the internal strain energy U_i for the circular shaft was found in Ex. 15-3. This relation may be written in a more convenient form by noting that $\tau_{\max} = Tc/J$, the volume of the rod is $\pi c^2 L$, and $J = \pi c^4/2$. Thus

$$U_i = \frac{\tau_{\max}^2}{2G} \left(\frac{1}{2} \text{vol} \right) = \frac{T^2 c^2}{2J^2 G} \frac{1}{2} \pi c^2 L = \frac{T^2 L}{2JG}$$

Then from $U_e = U_i$,

$$\frac{T\varphi}{2} = \frac{T^2 L}{2JG} \quad \text{and} \quad \varphi = \frac{TL}{JG}$$

which is the same as Eq. 3-9.

Example 15-6. Find the maximum deflection due to a force P applied at the end of a cantilever having a rectangular cross-section, Fig. 15-12. Consider the effect of the shearing deformations.

SOLUTION: If the force P is gradually applied to the beam, the external work $U_e = \frac{1}{2} P\Delta$, where Δ is the total deflection of the end of the beam. The internal strain energy consists of two parts. One part is due to the bending stresses, the other is caused by the shearing stresses. According to Art. 15-5, these strain energies may be directly superposed.

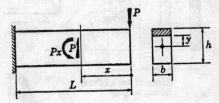

Fig. 15-12.

The strain energy in pure bending is obtained from Eq. 15-2, $U_i = \int M^2\, dx/(2EI)$, by noting that $M = -Px$. The strain energy in shear is found from Eq. 15-3a, $(dU_i)_{\text{shear}} = [\tau^2/(2G)]dV$. In this particular case, the shear at every section is equal to the applied force P, while the shearing stress τ, according to Example 6-3, is distributed parabolically, as $\tau = [P/(2I)][(h/2)^2 - y^2]$. At any one level y, this shearing stress does not vary across the breadth b and the length L of the beam. Therefore the infinitesimal volume dV in the shear energy expression is taken as $Lb\, dy$. By equating the sum of these two internal strain energies to the external work, the total deflection is obtained:

$$(U_i)_{\text{bending}} = \int_0^L \frac{M^2\,dx}{2EI} = \int_0^L \frac{(-Px)^2\,dx}{2EI} = \frac{P^2L^3}{6EI}$$

$$(U_i)_{\text{shear}} = \int_{\text{vol}} \frac{\tau^2}{2G}\,dV = \frac{1}{2G}\int_{-(h/2)}^{+(h/2)} \left\{ \frac{P}{2I}\left[\left(\frac{h}{2}\right)^2 - y^2\right]\right\}^2 Lb\,dy$$

$$= \frac{P^2Lb}{8GI^2}\frac{h^5}{30} = \frac{P^2Lbh^5}{240G}\left(\frac{12}{bh^3}\right)^2 = \frac{3P^2L}{5AG}$$

where $A = bh$ is the cross-section of the beam. Then

$$U_e = U_i = (U_i)_{\text{bending}} + (U_i)_{\text{shear}}$$

$$\frac{P\Delta}{2} = \frac{P^2L^3}{6EI} + \frac{3P^2L}{5AG} \quad \text{or} \quad \Delta = \frac{PL^3}{3EI} + \frac{6PL}{5AG}$$

The first term in this answer, $PL^3/(3EI)$, is the deflection of the beam due to the flexure. The second term is the deflection due to shear. The factor, such as $\frac{6}{5}$ in this term, varies for different shapes of the cross-section, since it depends on the nature of the shearing-stress distribution.

Usually the effect of the shearing deformations on the deflection of a beam is very small, and in Chapter 11 it was entirely neglected. If the span L of a beam is small, the deflection due to shear is important. For example, consider a beam with a rectangular cross-section of 2 in. by 6 in. deep ($I = 36$ in.[4], $E = 30 \times 10^6$ psi and $G = 12 \times 10^6$ psi). If $L = 6$ in. and $P = 3$ kips, the total deflection consists of 0.00020 in. due to flexure and 0.00015 in. due to shear. However, as the length of the span increases, the deflection due to bending soon becomes dominant, since the span length is *cubed* in the term for the flexural deflection.

15-8. Impact Loads. A freely falling weight, or a moving body, which strikes a structure delivers what is called a *dynamic* or *impact* load or force.

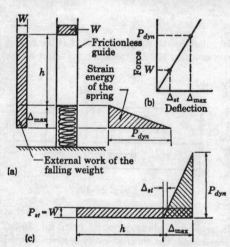

Fig. 15-13. Behavior of an elastic system under an impact force.

Problems involving such forces may be analyzed rather simply on the basis of the following idealizing assumptions:

1. Materials behave elastically, and no dissipation of energy takes place at the point of impact or at the supports owing to local inelastic deformation of materials.

2. The inertia of a system resisting an impact may be neglected.

3. The deflection of a system is directly proportional to the magnitude of the applied force whether a force is dynamically or statically applied.

Then, on the basis of the principle of conservation of energy, it may be further assumed that at the *instant* a moving body is stopped, its kinetic energy is completely transformed into the internal strain energy of the resisting system. At this instant, the maximum deflection of a resisting system occurs and vibrations commence. However, since in this text only maximum stresses and deflections are of primary interest, the latter subject will not be pursued.

As an example of a dynamic force applied to an elastic system, consider a falling weight striking a spring. This situation is illustrated in Fig. 15-13a, where a weight W falls from a height h above the free length of a spring. *This system represents a very general case, since, in a broad sense, every elastic system may be treated as an equivalent spring.* The spring constant k [lb/in.] is defined as the force required to deflect the "spring," such as a beam or an actual helical spring, one inch. In terms of the spring constant, the static deflection Δ_{st} of the spring due to the weight W is $\Delta_{st} = W/k$. Similarly, the maximum dynamic deflection Δ_{max} $= P_{dyn}/k$, where P_{dyn} is the maximum dynamic force experienced by the spring. Therefore the dynamic force in terms of the weight W and the deflections of the spring is

$$P_{dyn} = \frac{\Delta_{max}}{\Delta_{st}} W \qquad (15\text{-}5)$$

This relationship is shown in Fig. 15-13b.

At the instant the spring deflects its maximum amount, all energy of the falling weight is transformed into the strain energy of the spring. Therefore an equation representing the equality of external work to internal strain energy may be written as:

$$W(h + \Delta_{max}) = \tfrac{1}{2} P_{dyn}\Delta_{max}$$

A graphical interpretation of this equation is shown in Fig. 15-13c. Note that a factor of one-half appears in front of the strain energy expression, since the spring takes on the load *gradually*. Then, from Eq. 15-5.

$$W(h + \Delta_{max}) = \frac{1}{2} \frac{(\Delta_{max})^2}{\Delta_{st}} W$$

or $$(\Delta_{max})^2 - 2\Delta_{st}\Delta_{max} - 2h\Delta_{st} = 0$$

whence $$\Delta_{max} = \Delta_{st} + \sqrt{(\Delta_{st})^2 + 2h\Delta_{st}}$$

or $$\Delta_{max} = \Delta_{st}\left(1 + \sqrt{1 + \frac{2h}{\Delta_{st}}}\right) \qquad (15\text{-}6)$$

and again using Eq. 15-5,

$$P_{dyn} = W\left(1 + \sqrt{1 + \frac{2h}{\Delta_{st}}}\right) \qquad (15\text{-}7)$$

Equation 15-6 gives the maximum deflection occurring in a spring struck by a weight W falling from a height h, while Eq. 15-7 gives the maximum force experienced by the spring for the same condition. To apply these equations, the static deflection Δ_{st} caused by the gradually applied known weight W is computed by the formulas derived earlier in the text.

After the effective dynamic force P_{dyn} is found, it may be used in computations as a static force. The magnification effect of a static force when dynamically applied is given by the expression in parenthesis appearing in both Eqs. 15-6 and 15-7 and is termed the **impact factor**. The impact factor is surprizingly large in most cases. For example, if a force is applied to an elastic system *suddenly*, i.e., $h = 0$, it is equivalent to *twice* the same force *gradually* applied. If h is large compared to Δ_{st}, the impact factor is approximately equal to $\sqrt{2h/\Delta_{\text{st}}}$.

Similar equations may be derived for the case where a weight W is moving horizontally with a velocity v and is suddenly stopped by an elastic body. For this purpose, it is necessary to replace the external work done by the falling weight in the preceding derivation by the kinetic energy of a moving body, *using a consistent system of units*. Therefore, since the kinetic energy of a moving body is $\dfrac{Wv^2}{2g}$, where g is the acceleration of gravity, it can be shown that

$$P_{\text{dyn}} = W\sqrt{\frac{v^2}{g\Delta_{\text{st}}}} \quad \text{and} \quad \Delta_{\text{max}} = \Delta_{\text{st}}\sqrt{\frac{v^2}{g\Delta_{\text{st}}}}$$

where Δ_{st} is the static deflection caused by W assumed acting in the horizontal direction.

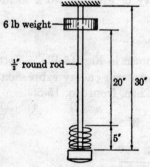

6 lb weight

$\frac{1}{2}''$ round rod

20″   30″

5″

Fig. 15-14.

Example 15-7. Find the maximum stress in the steel rod shown in Fig. 15-14 caused by a 6 lb weight falling freely through 20 in. The steel helical spring of $1\frac{1}{4}$ in. outside diameter inserted into the system is made of $\frac{1}{4}$ in. round wire and has 10 live coils.

SOLUTION: The static deflection of this system due to the 6 lb weight is computed first. It consists of two parts: the deflection of the rod given by Eq. 2-4, and the deflection of the spring given by Eq. 7-3a. For use in Eq. 7-3a, $\bar{r} = 0.5$ in. Then, from Eq. 15-7, the dynamic force experienced by the spring and the rod is found. This force is used as a static force to find the stress in the rod.

$$\Delta_{\text{st}} = \Delta_{\text{rod}} + \Delta_{\text{spr}} = \frac{PL}{AE} + \frac{64F\bar{r}^3N}{Gd^4}$$

$$= \frac{6(30)}{0.196(30)10^6} + \frac{(64)6(0.5)^3 10}{(12)10^6(0.25)^4} = 0.01027 \text{ in.}$$

$$P_{\text{dyn}} = W\left(1 + \sqrt{1 + \frac{2h}{\Delta_{\text{st}}}}\right) = 6\left(1 + \sqrt{1 + \frac{2(20)}{0.01027}}\right) = 381 \text{ lb}$$

$$\sigma_{\text{dyn}} = \frac{P_{\text{dyn}}}{A} = \frac{381}{0.196} = 1{,}940 \text{ psi}$$

Example 15-8. Find the instantaneous maximum deflections and bending stresses for the rectangular steel beam shown in Fig. 15-15 when struck by a 30 lb weight falling from a height 3 in. above the top of the beam, if (a) the beam is on rigid supports, and (b) the beam is supported at each end on springs. The constant k for each spring is 1,667 lb per in.

SOLUTION: The deflection of the system due to the 30 lb weight statically applied is computed for each case. In the first case, this deflection is that of the beam only; see Appendix, Table 11. In the second case, the static deflection of the beam is augmented by sagging of the springs subjected to a 15 lb force each. The impact factors from Eqs. 15-6 and 15-7 are then computed. Static deflections and stresses are multiplied by the impact factors to obtain the answers.

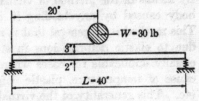

Fig. 15-15.

Case (a):

$$\Delta_{st} = \frac{PL^3}{48EI} = \frac{30(40)^3}{48(30)10^6(\frac{1}{12})2^4} = 0.001 \text{ in.}$$

$$\text{impact factor} = 1 + \sqrt{1 + \frac{2h}{\Delta_{st}}}$$

$$= 1 + \sqrt{1 + \frac{2(3)}{0.001}} = 78.5$$

Case (b):

$$\Delta_{st} = \Delta_{\text{beam}} + \Delta_{\text{spr}} = 0.001 + \frac{15}{1,667} = 0.010 \text{ in.}$$

$$\text{impact factor} = 1 + \sqrt{1 + \frac{2(3)}{0.010}} = 25.5$$

For either case, the maximum bending stress in the beam due to a static application of W is

$$(\sigma_{\text{max}})_{st} = \frac{M}{Z} = \frac{WL}{4Z} = \frac{30(40)}{4(\frac{1}{6})2^3} = 225 \text{ psi}$$

Multiplying the static deflections and stress by the respective impact factors gives the answers.

	Static		Dynamic	
	With springs	No springs	With springs	No springs
Δ_{max}, in............	0.010	0.001	0.255	0.0785
σ_{max}, psi...........	225	225	5,740	17,700

It is apparent from this table that large deflections and stresses are caused by a dynamically applied load. The stress for the condition with no springs is particularly large; however, owing to the flexibility of the beam, it is not excessive. The results for the dynamic load are probably somewhat high, since in both cases the ratio of h/Δ_{st} is large, and, in such cases, the equations used are only approximately true.

15-9. Virtual Work.* Obtaining deflections by directly equating external to internal work, as discussed in Art. 15-7, has the disadvantage that usually only the deflection caused by one force can be found. There are two alternative methods based on the energy concept which overcome

* The remainder of this chapter may be omitted.

this difficulty.   The one selected in this text* is called the method of *virtual work*, since a fictitious or imaginary force is used in the analysis. By means of the method of virtual work, the deflection of *any point* on a body caused by any loading in *any desired direction* may be obtained. This method is so general that it not only applies in finding the deflection due to elastic deformations in statically determinate structures, but is equally applicable for cases where the dimensions of a body change because of temperature, plastic deformations, movement of the supports, etc.   This generality of the virtual-work method makes it a very valuable tool of analysis.

To develop the virtual-work method, consider the body shown in Fig. 15-16a.   The deflection of some point A in the direction A-B caused by deformation of the body is sought.   For this, the following sequence of reasoning is employed:

FIRST, apply to the **unloaded** body an *imaginary* or *virtual unit force* acting in the direction A-B.   This applied force will cause reactions and will set up internal forces throughout the body.   These *internal forces*

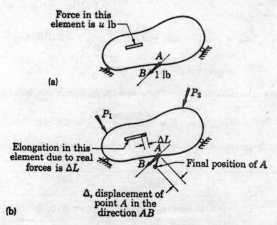

Fig. 15-16.   A body used in the derivation of the deflection formula by virtual work.

caused by the application of the unit virtual force will be designated by u, Fig. 15-16a, and can be found in statically determinate structures.

NEXT, with the virtual force remaining on the body, apply the actual or *real forces,* Fig. 15-16b, or introduce specified deformations, such as those due to a change in temperature.   This causes *real* internal deformations ΔL, which may be computed.   Owing to these deformations, the virtual force moves.

THEN, since the internal work is equal to the external work during the

* The virtual-work method is related to the classical procedures developed by A. Castigliano of Italy in 1875 and currently is finding greater favor among practicing engineers.

initial application of the virtual force, and since the internal work is equal to the external work for the real forces causing real deformations, the external work done by the unit *virtual* force (which "goes for a ride" a *real* amount Δ in the direction of this force *as the real forces are applied*) is also equal to the internal work caused by the internal *virtual* forces u moved *real* amounts ΔL.   Hence*

$$\underbrace{1^{lb} \times \Delta}_{\substack{\text{external} \\ \text{work}}} = \underbrace{\Sigma\,(u \times \Delta L)}_{\text{internal work}} \tag{15-8}$$

This virtual-work equation can be used to find a *real* deflection of a selected point caused by **any type** of *real* deformations occurring within a body, since **numerically** the real deflection is equal to the external work. The summation sign is necessary on the right-hand side of the equation in order to include all internal work. *Tensile forces and elongation of members are taken positive.* A positive result indicates that the deflection occurs in the *same* direction as the applied virtual force.   To aid in the application of Eq. 15-8, the meanings of the terms are summarized below:

Δ = *real* deflection of a point in the direction of the applied unit *virtual* force.

u = internal force(s) caused by the *virtual* force.

ΔL = *real* internal deformation(s) of a body.

15-10. Special Forms of the Virtual-Work Equation.

Trusses. If the real deformations of a body are *elastic* and are due *only to axial deformations*, such as occur in trusses, $\Delta L = PL/(AE)$, and Eq. 15-8 becomes

* For an elastic body, the first discarded part of the work is shown by the shaded triangle in Fig. 15-A; the second part, by the cross-hatched triangle.   The unshaded

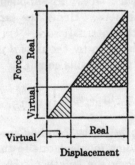

Fig. 15-A.

rectangle corresponds to the work considered.   Note that no factor of one-half appears in the formulated equation, since the external virtual force and the internal forces it sets up in a body are on the system when real deformations occur.

$$1^{lb} \times \Delta = \sum \frac{uPL}{AE} \tag{15-9}$$

where u is the force in a member due to the virtual force and P is the force in the same member due to the real loads. The terms L (length), A (area), and E have the usual meanings. The summation applies to all members of the truss.

Beams. If the deflection of a point on an *elastic* beam is desired by the virtual-work method, a unit virtual force must be *first* applied in the direction in which the deflection is sought. This virtual force will set up internal bending moments at various sections of the beam. These bending moments will be designated by m, as is shown in Fig. 15-17a. *Next,* as the real forces are applied to the beam, additional bending moments M develop which rotate the "plane sections" of the beam $M\,dx/(EI)$ radians (Eq. 11-12). Hence the internal work for an element of a beam done by the virtual moments m is $mM\,dx/(EI)$ (couple times angle). Integrating this over the length of the beam gives the internal work. Hence the special form of Eq. 15-8 for beams becomes

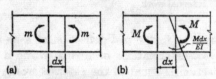

Fig. 15-17. Elements of a beam. (a) Virtual bending moments m, (b) real bending moment M, and the rotation of sections they cause.

$$1^{lb} \times \Delta = \int_0^L \frac{mM\,dx}{EI} \tag{15-10}$$

An analogous expression may be used to find the angular rotation of a particular section in a beam. For this case, instead of applying a virtual unit force, a *virtual unit couple* is applied to the beam at the section being investigated. This virtual couple sets up internal moments m along the beam. Then, as the real forces are applied, they cause rotations $M\,dx/(EI)$ of the cross-sections. Hence the same integral expression as in Eq. 15-10 applies for the internal work. On the other hand, the external work for this case is given by the *virtual* unit couple multiplied by the *real* rotation θ of the beam at this couple.

Hence

$$1 \text{ in.-lb} \times \theta = \int_0^L \frac{mM\,dx}{EI} \tag{15-11}$$

In Eqs. 15-10 and 15-11, m is the bending moment due to the *virtual* loading, and M is the bending moment due to the real loads. Since both m and M usually vary along the length of the beam, both must be expressed by appropriate functions.

Example 15-9. Find the vertical deflection of point B in the pin-jointed steel truss shown in Fig. 15-18a due to the following causes: (a) the elastic deformation of the members, (b) a shortening by 0.125 in. of the member AB by means of a turnbuckle, and (c) a drop in temperature of 120°F occurring in the member BC. The coefficient of thermal expansion of steel is 0.0000065 in. per inch per degree Fahrenheit. Neglect the effect of lateral buckling of the compression member.

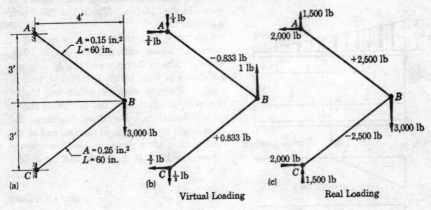

Virtual Loading   Real Loading

Fig. 15-18.

SOLUTION: *Case* (a). A virtual unit force is applied in the vertical direction, as shown in Fig. 15-18b, and the resulting forces u are determined and recorded on the same diagram (check these). Then the forces in each member due to the real force are also determined and recorded, Fig. 15-18c. The solution follows by means of Eq. 15-9. The work is carried out in tabular form.

Member	u, lb	P, lb	L, in.	A, in.²	uPL/A
AB	−0.833	+2,500	60	0.15	−833,000
BC	+0.833	−2,500	60	0.25	−500,000

From this table $\Sigma uPL/A = -1,333,000$. Hence,

$$1^{lb} \times \Delta = \sum \frac{uPL}{AE} = \frac{-1,333,000}{(30)10^6} = -0.0444 \text{ lb-in.}$$

and $\Delta = -0.0444$ in.

The negative sign means that point B deflects *down*. In this case, "negative work" is done by the virtual force acting upward when it is displaced in a downward direction. Note particularly the units and the signs of all quantities. Tensile forces in members are taken positive, and vice versa.

Case (b). Equation 15-8 is used to find the vertical deflection of point B due to the shortening of the member AB by 0.125 in. The forces set up in the bars by the virtual force acting in the direction of the deflection sought are shown in Fig. 15-18b. Then, since ΔL is −0.125 in. (shortening) for the member AB and is zero for the member BC,

$$1^{lb} \times \Delta = (-0.833)(-0.125) + (+0.833)(0) = +0.1042 \text{ lb-in.}$$

and $\Delta = +0.1042$ in. *up*.

Case (c). Again using Eq. 15-8, and noting that due to the *drop* in temperature, $\Delta L = -0.0000065(120)60 = -0.0468$ in. in the member BC,

$$1^{lb} \times \Delta = (+0.833)(-0.0468) = -0.0390 \text{ lb-in.}$$

and $\Delta = -0.0390$ in. *down*.

By superposition, the net deflection of point B due to all three causes is $-0.0444 + 0.1042 - 0.0390 = +0.0208$ in. *up*. To find this quantity, all three effects could have been considered simultaneously in the virtual-work equation.

Example 15-10. Find the deflection at the mid-span of a cantilever beam loaded as shown in Fig. 15-19a. The EI of the beam is constant.

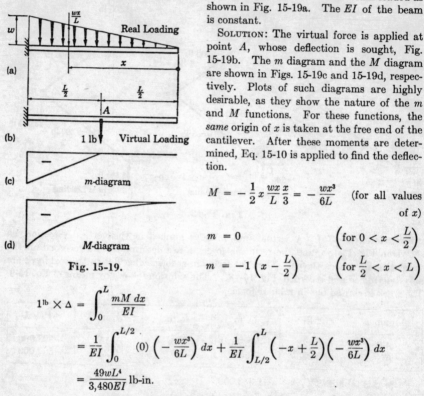

SOLUTION: The virtual force is applied at point A, whose deflection is sought, Fig. 15-19b. The m diagram and the M diagram are shown in Figs. 15-19c and 15-19d, respectively. Plots of such diagrams are highly desirable, as they show the nature of the m and M functions. For these functions, the *same* origin of x is taken at the free end of the cantilever. After these moments are determined, Eq. 15-10 is applied to find the deflection.

Fig. 15-19.

$$M = -\frac{1}{2} x \frac{wx}{L} \frac{x}{3} = -\frac{wx^3}{6L} \quad \text{(for all values of } x\text{)}$$

$$m = 0 \quad \left(\text{for } 0 < x < \frac{L}{2}\right)$$

$$m = -1\left(x - \frac{L}{2}\right) \quad \left(\text{for } \frac{L}{2} < x < L\right)$$

$$1^{lb} \times \Delta = \int_0^L \frac{mM\,dx}{EI}$$

$$= \frac{1}{EI}\int_0^{L/2}(0)\left(-\frac{wx^3}{6L}\right)dx + \frac{1}{EI}\int_{L/2}^L\left(-x+\frac{L}{2}\right)\left(-\frac{wx^3}{6L}\right)dx$$

$$= \frac{49wL^4}{3{,}480EI} \text{ lb-in.}$$

The deflection of point A is numerically equal to this quantity. The deflection due to shear has been neglected.

Example 15-11. Find the downward deflection of the end C caused by the applied force of 2 kips in the structure shown in Fig. 15-20a. Neglect deflection caused by shear. Let $E = 10^7$ psi.

SOLUTION: A unit virtual force of one kip is applied vertically at C. This force causes an axial force in member DB and in the part AB of the beam, Fig. 15-20b. Owing to this force, bending moments are also caused in the beam AC, Fig. 15-20c. Similar computations are made and are shown in Figs. 15-20d and e for the applied *real* force. The deflection of point C depends on the deformations caused by the axial forces, as well as flexure, hence the virtual-work equation is

$$1^{kip} \times \Delta = \sum \frac{uPL}{AE} + \int_0^L \frac{mM\,dx}{EI}$$

The first term on the right-hand side of this equation is computed from the table below. Then the integral for the internal virtual work due to bending is found. For the dif-

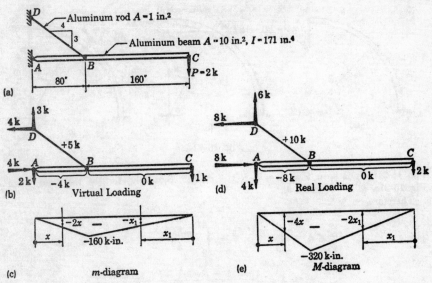

Fig. 15-20.

ferent parts of the beam, two origins of x's are used in writing the expressions for m and M, Figs. 15-20c and e.

Member	u, kips	P, kips	L, in.	A, in.²	uPL/A
DB	+5	+10	100	1.0	+5,000
AB	−4	−8	80	10.0	+256

From the table, $\Sigma uPL/A = +5,256$, or $\Sigma uPL/(AE) = +0.5256$ kip-in.

$$\int_0^L \frac{mM\,dx}{EI} = \int_0^{80} \frac{(-2x)(-4x)\,dx}{EI} + \int_0^{160} \frac{(-x_1)(-2x_1)\,dx_1}{EI}$$

$$= +2.39 \text{ kip-in.}$$

Therefore
$$1^{\text{kip}} \times \Delta = +0.5256 + 2.39 = 2.92 \text{ kip-in.}$$

and point C deflects 2.92 in. down.

Note particularly that two types of internal strain energy were superposed. Also note that the origins for the co-ordinate system for moments may be chosen as convenient; however, *the same origin must be used for the corresponding m and M.*

Example 15-12. Find the horizontal deflection, caused by the concentrated force P, of the end of the curved bar shown in Fig. 15-21a. The flexural rigidity EI of the bar is constant. Neglect the effect of shear on the deflection.

SOLUTION: If the radius of curvature of a bar is large in comparison with the cross-sectional dimensions (Art. 5-11), ordinary beam deflection formulas may be used replacing dx by ds. In this case, $ds = R\,d\theta$.

Applying a horizontal virtual force at the end in the direction of the deflection wanted

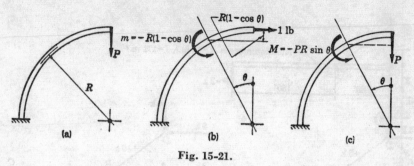

Fig. 15-21.

Fig. 15-21b, it is seen that $m = -R(1 - \cos \theta)$. Similarly, for the real load, from Fig. 15-21c, $M = -PR \sin \theta$.

Therefore,

$$1^{lb} \times \Delta = \int_0^L \frac{mM\,dx}{EI} \doteq \int_0^L \frac{mM\,ds}{EI}$$

$$= \int_0^{\pi/2} \frac{[-R(1 - \cos \theta)](-PR \sin \theta)\,R\,d\theta}{EI}$$

$$= + \frac{PR^3}{2EI} \text{ in.-lb}$$

The deflection of the end to the right is numerically equal to this expression.

15-11. Statically Indeterminate Problems. Statically indeterminate problems may be solved with the aid of the virtual-work method. However, the solution of such problems has little to do directly with virtual work. Geometrical (deformation) conditions must be used in the same manner as discussed in Chapter 12 to furnish auxiliary equations for supplementing the equations of statics. *The virtual-work method merely provides the means of determining deflections of structures artificially reduced to statical determinacy.* Much confusion is avoided if the above statement is clearly kept in mind.

Example 15-13. Find the forces in the pin-jointed bars of the steel structure shown in Fig. 15-22a if a force of 3,000 lb is applied at B.

Solution: The structure may be made statically determinate by cutting the bar DB at D. Then the forces in the members are as shown in Fig. 15-22b. In this determinate structure, the movement of point D must be determined. This can be done by applying a vertical virtual force at D, Fig. 15-22c, and using the virtual-work method. However, since the $uPL/(AE)$ term for the member BD is zero, the vertical movement of point D is the same as that of B. In Example 15-9 the latter quantity was found to be 0.0444 in. down and is so shown in Fig. 15-22b.

The movement of point D, shown in Fig. 15-22b, violates the conditions of the problem, and a force must be applied to bring it back where it belongs. This is done by finding the amount of upward movement caused by a one-pound *real* force applied at D. Then, X times this one-pound force (thus X is the force in BD) should close the gap and fulfill the conditions of the problem. The virtual-work method is used to find the deflection of D caused by the one-pound real force. The forces set up in the

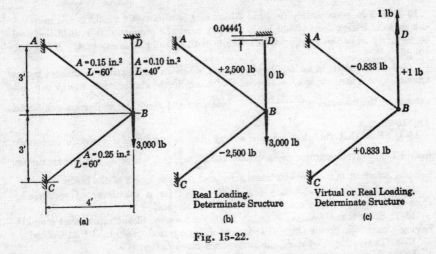

Fig. 15-22.

determinate structure by the virtual and the real forces are numerically the same, Fig. 15-22c. To differentiate between the two, forces in members caused by the real force are designated by u', by the virtual force by u. The solution is carried out in tabular form.

Member	u, lb	u', lb	L, in.	A, in.²	$uu'L/A$
AB	-0.833	-0.833	60	0.15	$+278$
BC	$+0.833$	$+0.833$	60	0.25	$+167$
BD	$+1,000$	$+1.000$	40	0.10	$+400$

From the table, $\Sigma uu'L/A = +845$. Therefore, since

$$1^{lb} \times \Delta = \sum \frac{uu'L}{AE} = \frac{+845}{30(10)^6} = 0.0000281 \text{ lb-in.}$$

the deflection of point D in the determinate structure due to a *one-pound real force at D is 0.0000281 in.*

To close the gap of 0.0444 in., the one-pound real force at D must be increased $X = 0.0444/0.0000281 = 1,580$ times. Therefore the actual force in the member DB must be 1,580 lb. The forces in the other two members may now be determined from statics, or by superposition of the forces shown in Fig. 15-22b with X times the u' forces shown in Fig. 15-22c. By either method, the force in AB is found to be $+1,180$ lb (tension) and in BC, $-1,180$ lb (compression).

Problems for Solution

15-1. What is the modulus of resilience for an aluminum alloy if its proportional limit at 70° F is 28,000 psi and $E = 10.3 \times 10^6$ psi?

15-2. A 40 in. long steel rod of 2 in. diameter is subjected to an axial energy load of 36 in.-lb that causes a tensile stress in the rod. (a) Determine the maximum tensile stress. $E = 30 \times 10^6$ psi. (b) If the same rod is machined down to a 1 in. diameter in the middle half of the bar, i.e., for a distance of 20 in., will the maximum stress increase or decrease and by how much?

15-3. A 2 in. square alloy-steel bar 30 in. long is a part of a machine and must resist an axial energy load of 900 in.-lb. What must the proportional limit of the steel be to safely resist the energy load elastically with a factor of safety of 4? $E = 30 \times 10^6$ psi.

15-4. Show that, in an axially loaded rod, when an initial stress σ_i changes by an amount σ_c to a final stress $\sigma_f = \sigma_i + \sigma_c$, the change in the elastic strain energy per unit volume of the material is $\dfrac{\sigma_c^2 + 2\,\sigma_i\,\sigma_c}{2E}$. Interpret the result on a diagram similar to Fig. 15-1b.

15-5. Show that the elastic strain energy due to bending for a simple uniformly loaded beam of rectangular cross-section is $\dfrac{\sigma_{\text{lmax}}^2}{2E}\dfrac{8}{45}\,AL$ where σ_{max} is the maximum bending stress, A is the cross-sectional area, and L is the length of the beam.

15-6. Show that $(U_i)_{\text{bending}} = (\sigma_{\text{max}}^2/2E)\,\tfrac{1}{9}$ Vol for a cantilever of rectangular cross-section supporting a concentrated load P at the end.

15-7. Show that $(U_i)_{\text{bending}} = (\sigma_{\text{max}}^2/2E)\,\tfrac{1}{3}$ Vol for a cantilever of constant strength having a parabolic profile (Fig. 10-18d) supporting a concentrated load P at the end.

15-8. Derive Eq. 15-4 using the generalized Hooke's law.

15-9. Determine the maximum amount of strain energy which a helical spring can absorb under a tensile load if it is $8\tfrac{3}{4}$ in. in outside diameter and is made of $\tfrac{3}{4}$ in. diameter steel wire. There are 10 active coils and the allowable shearing stress is 80,000 psi. Neglect correction for stress concentration and the effect of direct shear. $G = 12 \times 10^6$ psi.

15-10. Using the results of Example 15-6 and the data given there for a 2 in. by 6 in. beam, determine the length of a steel cantilever for which the deflection due to bending is equal to that caused by shear.

15-11. A simple beam of rectangular cross-section and span L is loaded with a concentrated load P at the middle of the span. Neglecting the weight of the beam and equating internal to external energy, (a) determine the maximum deflection caused by bending; (b) determine the maximum deflection caused by the shearing deformations. *Ans.* (a) $PL^3/48EI$.

15-12. (a) In terms of P, L, and EI, calculate the amount of elastic strain energy stored in the beam shown in the figure, caused by the applied loads. (b) By equating the internal to the external energy, determine the deflection at the loads. (*Hint:* due to symmetry, deflections at both loads are equal.) *Ans.* (b) $PL^3/48EI$.

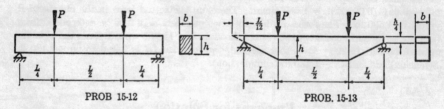

PROB 15-12   PROB. 15-13

15-13.* (a) Same as (a) in Prob. 15-12 for the beam shown in the figure with the exception that since I varies, the answer is to be in terms of P, L, and EI_0, where I_0 is the moment of inertia of the cross-section in the middle half of the beam. (b) Same as (b) in Prob. 15-12. *Ans.* (b) $0.029\,PL^3/EI_0$.

15-14. If the free fall of the 6 lb weight in Example 15-7 is 20 inches when the spring is removed, what maximum stress will occur in the rod? *Ans.* 35 ksi.

15-15. Determine the maximum instantaneous deflection of a helical spring caused by dropping a weight of 100 lb through a free distance of 8 in. The spring is 16 in. in outside diameter and is made of $1\frac{7}{8}$ in. diameter steel wire. There are 12 active coils. Neglect the deflection due to direct shear and the inertia of the spring. $G = 12 \times 10^6$ psi.

15-16. An 8 in. round wooden cantilever 12 ft long is placed in a horizontal position. If its end is struck by a 200 lb weight dropped from a height of 6 in., what will the maximum instantaneous deflection be? Neglect the inertia of the beam. $E = 1.2 \times 10^6$ psi.

15-17. A 3 in. wide by 2 in. deep (full size) wooden beam rests on a rigid support at one end and on a spring at the other as shown in the figure. Determine the maximum stress in the beam caused by a 10 lb weight falling through 4 in. Neglect the inertia of the beam and local dissipation of energy. $E = 1.333 \times 10^6$ psi. *Ans.* 655 psi.

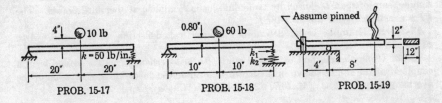

PROB. 15-17   PROB. 15-18   PROB. 15-19

15-18. An aluminum beam having a flexural rigidity $EI = 10^7$ lb-in.^{2} rests on a rigid support at one end and on two springs in series at the other as shown in the figure. The spring constants are: $k_1 = 1{,}667$ lb/in., and $k_2 = 1{,}500$ lb/in. Determine the largest instantaneous deflection of the beam at the middle caused by the falling weight. Neglect the inertia of the beam and local dissipation of energy. *Ans.* 0.20 in.

15-19. A man weighing 180 lb jumps onto a diving board from a height of 2 feet. If the board is of the dimensions shown in the figure, what is the maximum bending stress? $E = 1.6 \times 10^6$ psi. Use the moment-area method in establishing the deflection characteristics of the board. *Ans.* 8,560 psi.

15-20. The end of a 10 in. cantilever rests on the mid-span of a 20 in. simply supported beam. For either beam, $EI = 33{,}333$ lb-in.^{2} Determine the maximum instantaneous deflection of the cantilever if its end is struck by a 30 lb weight falling freely through a distance of $\frac{1}{2}$ in. *Ans.* 0.432 in.

15-21. In Example 15-9 determine the horizontal movement of point B for the three cases enumerated.

15-22. For the mast and boom arrangement shown in the figure, (a) determine the vertical movement of the load W caused by lengthening the rod AB a distance of $\frac{1}{2}$ in. (b) By how much must the rod BC be shortened to bring the weight W to its original position? *Ans.* (a) 0.167 in., (b) 0.347 in.

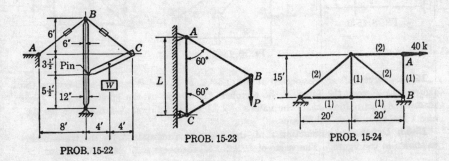

PROB. 15-22   PROB. 15-23   PROB. 15-24

15-23. A pin-joined system of three bars, each having a cross-sectional area A, is loaded as shown in the figure. (a) Determine the vertical and horizontal displacements of the joint B caused by the load P. (b) If by means of a turn-buckle the length of the member AC is shortened by $\frac{1}{2}$ in., what is the movement of the joint B? *Ans.* (a) $9PL/4AE\downarrow$, $PL/4\sqrt{3}\,AE\leftarrow$; (b) $\frac{1}{4}$ in.$\uparrow$, $1/4\sqrt{3}$ in.$\rightarrow$.

15-24. Determine the horizontal movement of joints A and B for the truss loaded as shown in the figure. Cross-sectional areas of members in square inches are shown in parentheses by the members. $E = 30 \times 10^6$ psi.

15-25. Using the method of virtual work, determine the maximum deflection for a uniformly loaded simple beam having a constant EI in terms of w, L, and EI. *Ans.* $5\ wL^4/384EI$.

15-26. Using the method of virtual work, determine the maximum deflection of a simple beam of span L caused by two equal loads P applied at the third points. The EI is constant. *Ans.* $23PL^3/648EI$.

15-27. In Example 15-12 determine the vertical deflection of the end. *Ans.* $\pi PR^3/4EI$.

15-28. Using the method of virtual work, for an overhanging beam loaded with a couple M at the end as shown in the figure, determine the deflection and rotation of the overhanging end. *Ans.* $(Ma/6EI)(2L + 3a)$, $M(\frac{1}{3}L + a)/EI$.

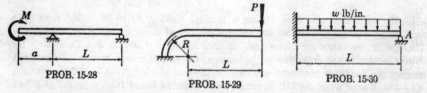

PROB. 15-28   PROB. 15-29   PROB. 15-30

15-29. Determine the vertical deflection of the end for the member loaded as shown in the figure. The EI is constant.

15-30. For the beam shown in the figure, using the method of virtual work, determine the reaction at A, treating this reaction as the redundant. *Ans.* $\frac{3}{8}\ wL$.

15-31. For the beam shown in the figure, using the method of virtual work, (a) determine the reaction at A, treating it as the redundant. (b) Determine the moment at B, treating it as a redundant. *Ans.* (a) $\frac{2}{3}P$, (b) $-\frac{1}{3}\ PL$.

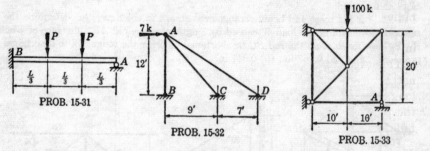

PROB. 15-31   PROB. 15-32   PROB. 15-33

15-32. Three bars are connected at the ends A, B, C, and D by pins as shown in the figure. Determine the force in the member AB caused by the applied load. Treat member AB as redundant. The values of L/A are as follows: $\frac{7}{15}$ for AD, $\frac{7}{20}$ for AC, and 1 for AB. *Ans.* $+5.83$ kips.

15-33. Determine the reaction at A, treating it as a redundant, for the truss loaded as shown in the figure. The value of L/A for all members is 1. *Ans.* 18.75 kips.

Chapter Sixteen

THICK-WALLED CYLINDERS

16-1. Introduction. The characteristic method of Mechanics of Materials for deriving stress analysis formulas depends on assumptions regarding deformations. In the torsion of circular rods, an assumption that shearing strains vary linearly from the axis is made; in bending, it is assumed that plane sections through the beam remain plane. In more complicated problems, it is usually impossible to make analogous assumptions. Therefore the analysis begins with considerations of a general infinitesimal element; Hooke's law is postulated, and the solution is said to be found after stresses acting on any element and its deformations are known. At the boundaries of a body, the equilibrium of known forces or prescribed displacements must be satisfied by the corresponding infinitesimal elements. This is the technique of the Mathematical Theory of Elasticity. Therefore it seems fitting in this last chapter of the book to solve a technically significant problem by these methods. This will be the problem of a thick-walled cylinder under pressure. Mathematically, it is a simple problem, yet the solution will display the characteristic method used in Elasticity.

16-2. Solution of the General Problem. * Consider a long cylinder whose cross-section has the dimensions shown in Fig. 16-1a. The inside radius of this cylinder is r_i, the outside radius is r_o. Let the internal pressure in the cylinder be p_i, the outside or external pressure be p_o. Stresses in the wall of the cylinder caused by these pressures are sought.

This problem can be conveniently solved by using cylindrical co-ordinates. A typical element is shown in Fig. 16-1b. Since the cylinder is long, every ring one inch thick measured perpendicular to the plane of the paper is stressed alike. The infinitesimal element is defined by two radii, r and $r + dr$, and an angle $d\varphi$, and it is considered one inch thick.

If the normal *radial* stress acting on the infinitesimal element at a distance r from the center of the cylinder is σ_r, this variable stress at a distance $r + dr$ will be $\sigma_r + \dfrac{d\sigma_r}{dr} dr$. (Recall an analogous situation in beams, where,

---

* This problem was originally solved by Lamé, a French engineer, in 1833 and is sometimes called the Lamé problem.

in a distance dx along the beam, M changes by $\dfrac{dM}{dx} dx$.)   Both normal *tangential* stresses acting on the other two faces of the element are σ_t. These stresses, analogous to the hoop stresses in a thin cylinder, are equal. Moreover, since from the condition of symmetry every element at the same radial distance from the center must be stressed alike, no shearing stresses act on the element shown.

The nature of the stresses acting on an infinitesimal element having been formulated, a characteristic elasticity solution for their magnitude proceeds along the following pattern of reasoning.

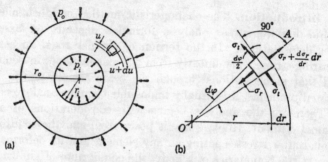

Fig. 16-1.   Thick-walled cylinder.

(a) *Statics.* The element chosen must be in static equilibrium   To express this mathematically requires the evaluation of *forces* acting on the element.   These forces are obtained by multiplying stresses by their respective areas.   The area on which σ_r acts is $(1)(r\,d\varphi)$; that on which $\sigma_r + d\sigma_r$ acts is $(1)(r + dr)\,d\varphi$; and each area on which σ_t acts is $(1)\,dr$. The weight of the element itself is neglected.   Since the angle included between the sides of the element is $d\varphi$, both tangential stresses are inclined $\frac{1}{2}\,d\varphi$ to the line perpendicular to OA.   Then, summing the forces along a radial line, $\Sigma F_r = 0$,

$$\sigma_r r\,d\varphi + 2\sigma_t\,dr\left(\frac{d\varphi}{2}\right) - \left(\sigma_r + \frac{d\sigma_r}{dr}\,dr\right)(r + dr)\,d\varphi = 0$$

Simplifying and neglecting the infinitesimals of higher order,

$$\sigma_t - \sigma_r - r\frac{d\sigma_r}{dr} = 0 \tag{16-1}$$

This one equation has two unknown stresses, σ_t and σ_r.   Intermediate steps are required to express this equation in terms of one unknown so that it can be solved.   This is done by introducing into the problem geometry of deformations and properties of materials.

(b) *Geometry.* The deformation of an element is described by its strains in the radial and tangential directions.   If u represents the *radial displacement* or *movement* of a cylindrical surface of radius r, Fig. 16-1a, $u + \dfrac{du}{dr}\, dr$ is the radial displacement or movement of the adjacent surface of radius $r + dr$. Hence, the strain ϵ_r of an element in the radial direction is

$$\epsilon_r = \frac{\left(u + \dfrac{du}{dr}\, dr\right) - u}{dr} = \frac{du}{dr} \tag{16-2}$$

The strain ϵ_t in the tangential direction follows by subtracting from the length of the circumference of the deformed cylindrical surface of radius $r + u$ the circumference of the unstrained cylinder of radius r and dividing the difference by the latter length. Hence

$$\epsilon_t = \frac{2\pi(r + u) - 2\pi r}{2\pi r} = \frac{u}{r} \tag{16-3}$$

Since the stresses acting on the element are principal stresses,* Eqs. 16-2 and 16-3 give the principal strains, expressed in terms of *one* unknown variable u.

(c) *Properties of Materials.* Stresses may be expressed in terms of strains with the aid of Hooke's law. This step introduces properties of materials into the problem. In terms of the present notation, according to Eq. 8-17, the radial and tangential stresses in terms of the principal strains are

$$\sigma_r = \frac{E}{1 - \mu^2} (\epsilon_r + \mu\epsilon_t) \tag{16-4}$$

$$\sigma_t = \frac{E}{1 - \mu^2} (\epsilon_t + \mu\epsilon_r) \tag{16-5}$$

(d) *Formulation of the Differential Equation.* Now the equilibrium equation, Eq. 16-1, may be expressed in terms of one variable u. Thus, one eliminates the strains ϵ_r and ϵ_t from Eqs. 16-4 and 16-5 by expressing them in terms of the displacement u, as given by Eqs. 16-2 and 16-3; then the radial and tangential stresses are

$$\sigma_r = \frac{E}{1 - \mu^2}\left(\frac{du}{dr} + \mu\, \frac{u}{r}\right) \quad \text{and} \quad \sigma_t = \frac{E}{1 - \mu^2}\left(\frac{u}{r} + \mu\, \frac{du}{dr}\right) \tag{16-6}$$

whence, by substituting these values into Eq. 16-1 and simplifying, the desired differential equation is obtained,

$$\frac{d^2u}{dr^2} + \frac{1}{r}\frac{du}{dr} - \frac{u}{r^2} = 0 \tag{16-7}$$

---

* Since an infinitesimal cylindrical element includes an *infinitesimal* angle between two of its sides, it may be treated as if it were an element in a cartesian co-ordinate system.

(e) Solution of the Differential Equation. As may be verified by substitution, the general solution of Eq. 16-7, which gives the radial displacement u of any point on the cylinder, is

$$u = Ar + \frac{B}{r} \tag{16-8}$$

where the constants A and B must be determined from the conditions of the problem. This is done by considering the conditions at the *boundaries* of the body.

Unfortunately, for the determination of the constants A and B, the displacement u is not known at either the inner or the outer boundary of the cylinder's wall. However, the known pressures are equal to the radial stresses acting on the elements at the respective radii. Hence

$$(\sigma_r)_{r=r_i} = -p_i \qquad \text{and} \qquad (\sigma_r)_{r=r_o} = -p_o \tag{16-9}$$

where the minus signs are used to indicate compressive stresses. Moreover, since u is given by Eq. 16-8 and $du/dr = A - B/r^2$, from Eq. 16-6 for σ_r and Eqs. 16-9,

$$\left.\begin{aligned}
(\sigma_r)_{r=r_i} = E\left(\frac{A}{1-\mu} - \frac{B}{1+\mu}\frac{1}{r_i^2}\right) = -p_i \\[2mm]
(\sigma_r)_{r=r_o} = E\left(\frac{A}{1-\mu} - \frac{B}{1+\mu}\frac{1}{r_o^2}\right) = -p_o
\end{aligned}\right\} \tag{16-10}$$

Solving these equations simultaneously for A and B yields

$$A = \frac{1-\mu}{E}\frac{p_i r_i^2 - p_o r_o^2}{r_o^2 - r_i^2} \qquad \text{and} \qquad B = \frac{1+\mu}{E}\frac{(p_i - p_o)r_i^2 r_o^2}{r_o^2 - r_i^2} \tag{16-11}$$

These constants, when used in Eq. 16-8, permit the determination of the radial displacements of any point on the elastic cylinder subjected to the specified pressures. Thus displacements of the inner and outer boundaries of the cylinder may be computed.

If Eq. 16-8 and its derivative, together with the constants given by Eqs. 16-11, are substituted into Eqs. 16-6, and the results are simplified, general equations for the radial and tangential stresses at any point of an elastic cylinder are obtained. These are

$$\left.\begin{aligned}
\sigma_r = C - \frac{D}{r^2} \qquad \text{and} \qquad \sigma_t = C + \frac{D}{r^2} \\[2mm]
\text{where} \qquad C = \frac{p_i r_i^2 - p_o r_o^2}{r_o^2 - r_i^2} \qquad \text{and} \qquad D = \frac{(p_i - p_o)r_i^2 r_o^2}{r_o^2 - r_i^2}
\end{aligned}\right\} \tag{16-12}$$

Note that $(\sigma_r + \sigma_t)$ is constant over the whole cross-sectional area of the cylinder. This means that the strain $\epsilon_z = -(\mu/E)(\sigma_r + \sigma_t)$ along the cylinder in the longitudinal direction is also constant. Therefore sections normal to the axis of the cylinder remain plane during deformation.

16-3. Special Cases: *Internal pressure only,* i.e., $p_i \neq 0$ and $p_o = 0$. For this case, Eqs. 16-12 simplify to

$$\left. \begin{aligned} \sigma_r &= \frac{p_i r_i^2}{r_o^2 - r_i^2}\left(1 - \frac{r_o^2}{r^2}\right) \\[2mm] \sigma_t &= \frac{p_i r_i^2}{r_o^2 - r_i^2}\left(1 + \frac{r_o^2}{r^2}\right) \end{aligned} \right\} \tag{16-12a}$$

Since $r_o^2/r^2 \geq 1$, σ_r is always a compressive stress and is maximum at $r = r_i$. Similarly, σ_t is always a tensile stress, and its maximum also occurs at $r = r_i$.

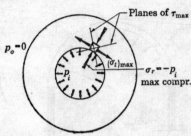

For materials such as mild steel, which fail in shear rather than in direct tension, the maximum shear theory of failure (Art. 9-7) should be used in design. For internal pressure only, the maximum shearing stress occurs on the inner surface of the cylinder, Fig. 16-2. At this surface, the tensile stress σ_t and the compressive stress σ_r

Fig. 16-2. An element in which τ_{max} occurs.

reach their respective maximum values. Substituting these principal stresses into Eq. 8-8 gives

$$\tau_{\text{max}} = \frac{\sigma_1 - \sigma_2}{2} = \frac{(\sigma_t)_{\text{max}} - (\sigma_r)_{\text{max}}}{2} = \frac{p_i r_o^2}{r_o^2 - r_i^2} \tag{16-12b}$$

External pressure only, i.e., $p_i = 0$ and $p_o \neq 0$. For this case, Eqs. 16-12 simplify to

$$\left. \begin{aligned} \sigma_r &= -\frac{p_o r_o^2}{r_o^2 - r_i^2}\left(1 - \frac{r_i^2}{r^2}\right) \\[2mm] \sigma_t &= -\frac{p_o r_o^2}{r_o^2 - r_i^2}\left(1 + \frac{r_i^2}{r^2}\right) \end{aligned} \right\} \tag{16-12c}$$

Since $r_i^2/r^2 \leq 1$, both stresses are always compressive. The maximum compressive stress is σ_t and occurs at $r = r_i$.

Equations 16-12c must not be used for very thin-walled cylinders. Buckling of the walls may occur and strength formulas give misleading results.

Example 16-1. Make a comparison of the tangential stress distribution caused by the internal pressure p_i as given by the exact formula of this chapter with the distribution given by the approximate formula for thin-walled cylinders of Chapter 9 if (a) $r_o = 1.1r_i$, and if (b) $r_o = 4r_i$, Fig. 16-3.

SOLUTION: *Case (a).* Using Eq. 16-12a for σ_t,

$$(\sigma_t)_{r=r_i} = (\sigma_t)_{\text{max}} = \frac{p_i r_i^2}{(1.1 r_i)^2 - r_i^2}\left[1 + \frac{(1.1 r_i)^2}{r_i^2}\right] = 10.5 p_i$$

$$(\sigma_t)_{r=r_o} = (\sigma_t)_{\min} = \frac{p_i r_i^2}{(1.1r_i)^2 - r_i^2}\left[1 + \left(\frac{1.1r_i}{1.1r_i}\right)^2\right] = 9.5p_i$$

while, since the wall thickness $t = 0.1r_i$, the *average* "hoop" stress given by Eq. 9-2 is

$$(\sigma_t)_{\text{av}} = \frac{p_i r_i}{t} = \frac{p_i r_i}{0.1r_i} = 10p_i$$

These results are shown in Fig. 16-3a. Note particularly that in using Eq. 9-2 **no** appreciable error is involved.

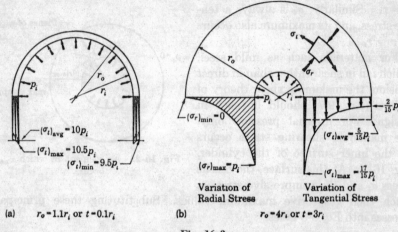

(a) $r_o = 1.1r_i$ or $t = 0.1r_i$ (b) $r_o = 4r_i$ or $t = 3r_i$

Fig. 16-3.

Case (*b*). By using Eq. 16-12a for σ_t, the exact tangential stresses are obtained as above. These are

$$(\sigma_t)_{r=r_i} = (\sigma_t)_{\max} = \frac{p_i r_i^2}{(4r_i)^2 - r_i^2}\left[1 + \frac{(4r_i)^2}{r_i^2}\right] = \frac{17}{15}\,p_i$$

$$(\sigma_t)_{r=r_o} = (\sigma_t)_{\min} = \frac{p_i r_i^2}{(4r_i)^2 - r_i^2}\left[1 + \left(\frac{4r_i}{4r_i}\right)^2\right] = \frac{2}{15}\,p_i$$

The values of the tangential stress computed for a few intermediate points are plotted in Fig. 16-3b. A striking variation of the tangential stress may be observed from this figure. The average tangential stress given by Eq. 9-2, using $t = 3r_i$, is

$$(\sigma_t)_{\text{av}} = \frac{p_i r_i}{t} = \frac{5}{15}\,p_i = \frac{1}{3}\,p_i$$

This stress is nowhere near the true maximum stress.

The radial stresses were also computed by using Eq. 16-12a for σ_r, and the results are shown by the shaded area in Fig. 16-3b.

It is interesting to note that no matter how thick a cylinder resisting internal pressure is made, the maximum tangential stress* will not be smaller than p_i. In practice, this necessitates special techniques to reduce the maximum stress. For example, in gun manufacture, instead of using a single cylinder, another cylinder is shrunk onto the smaller one,

---

* See Prob. 16-3.

which sets up initial *compressive stresses* in the inner cylinder and tensile stresses in the outer one. In operation, the compressive stress in the inner cylinder is released first, and only then does this cylinder begin to act in tension. A greater range of operating pressures is thereby obtained.

Problems for Solution

16-1. Verify the solution of Eq. 16-7.

16-2. Show that the ratio of the maximum tangential stress to the average tangential stress for a thick-walled cylinder subjected only to internal pressure is $(1 + \beta^2)/(1 + \beta)$, where $\beta = r_0/r_i$.

16-3. Show that no matter how large the outside diameter of a cylinder, subjected only to internal pressure, is made, the maximum tangential stress is not less than p_i. (*Hint:* let $r_o \to \infty$.)

16-4. An alloy-steel cylinder is 6 in. I.D. (inside diameter) and 18 in. O.D. If it is subjected to an internal pressure of $p_i = 24,000$ psi ($p_0 = 0$), (a) determine the radial and tangential stress distribution and show the results on a plot. (b) Determine the maximum (principal) shearing stress. (c) Determine the change in external and internal diameters. $E = 30 \times 10^6$ psi, $\mu = 0.3$.

16-5. Rework Prob. 16-4 with $p_i = 0$ and $p_0 = 12,000$ psi.

16-6. Rework Prob. 16-4 with $p_i = 24$ ksi and $p_0 = 12$ ksi.

16-7. Isolate one-half of the cylinder of Prob. 16-6 by passing a plane through the axis of the cylinder. Then, by integrating the tangential stresses over the respective areas, show that the isolated free-body is in equilibrium.

16-8. Design a thick-walled steel cylinder of 4 in. internal diameter for an internal pressure of 8,000 psi with a factor of safety of 2 against failure in shear. The yield point of steel in tension is 36,000 psi. *Ans.* 12 in.

16-9. A 16 in. O.D. steel cylinder with approximately a 10 in. bore (I.D.) is shrunk onto another steel cylinder of 10 in. O.D. with a 6 in. I.D. Initially the internal diameter of the outer cylinder was 0.01 in. smaller than the external diameter of the inner cylinder. The assembly was accomplished by heating the larger cylinder in oil. For both cylinders $E = 30 \times 10^6$ psi and $\mu = 0.3$. (a) Determine the pressure at the boundaries between the two cylinders. (*Hint:* the elastic increase in the diameter of the outer cylinder with the elastic decrease in the diameter of the inner cylinder accommodates the initial interference between the two cylinders.) (b) Determine the tangential and radial stresses caused by the pressure found in (a). Show the results on a plot. (c) Determine the internal pressure to which the composite cylinder may be subjected without exceeding a tangential stress of 20,000 psi in the inner cylinder. (*Hint:* after assembly, the cylinders act as one unit. The initial compressive stress in the inner cylinder is released first.) (d) Superpose the tangential stresses found in (b) with the tangential stresses resulting from the internal pressure found in (c). Show the results on a plot.

16-10. Set up the differential equation for a thin disk rotating with an angular velocity of ω rad per sec. The unit weight of the material is γ. (*Hint:* consider an element as in Fig. 16-1b and add an inertia term.) *Ans.* add a term $(1 - \mu^2) \gamma\omega^2 r/gE$ to Eq. 16-7.

APPENDIX TABLES

1. Typical Physical Properties of and Allowable Stresses for some Common Materials.
2. Useful Properties of Areas.
3. American Standard Steel I-Beams, Properties for Designing.
4. Steel Wide-Flange Beams, Properties for Designing.
5. American Standard Steel Channels, Properties for Designing.
6. Steel Angles with Equal Legs, Properties for Designing.
7. Steel Angles with Unequal Legs, Properties for Designing.
8. Standard Steel Pipe.
9. Screw Threads, American Standard.
10. American Standard Timber Sizes, Properties for Designing.
11. Deflections and Slopes of Elastic Curves for Variously Loaded Beams.

Acknowledgement: Data for Tables 3 through 11 are taken from *AISC Manual of Steel Construction* and are reproduced by permission of the American Institute of Steel Construction.

TABLE 1

Typical Physical Properties of and Allowable Stresses for Some Common Materials[a]

Material	Unit Weight lb/ft³	Ultimate Strength ksi			Yield Strength[g] ksi		Allow. Stresses[i] psi		Elastic Moduli ×10⁶ psi		Coef. of Thermal Expans. ×10⁻⁶ per °F
		Tens.	Comp.[c]	Shear	Tens.[h]	Shear	Tens. or Comp.	Shear	Tens. or Comp.	Shear	
Aluminum alloy { 17S-T	174	60	...	36	37	22			10.4	3.9	12.5
Aluminum alloy { 24S-T		68	...	41	46	28			10.6	4.0	
Cast iron { Grey	480	30	120	...[e]	...	...			13 –	6	5.8
Cast iron { Malleable		54	...	48	36	24			25	12	6.7
Concrete[b] { 7½ gal/sack	150	...	2	...[e]			−900[j]	60	2	...	6.0
Concrete[b] { 6 gal/sack		...	3	...			−1,350[j]	90	3	...	
Magnesium alloy, AM57S	112	44	...	20	31				6.5	...	14.4
Steel { 0.2% Carbon (hot-rolled)	490	65	...	48	35	24	±20,000	13,000	30[k]	12	6.5
Steel { 0.6% Carbon (hot-rolled)		100	...	80	60	36					
Steel { 0.6% Carbon (quenched)		120	...	100	75	45					
Steel { 3½% Ni, 0.4% C		200	...	150	150	90					
Wood { Douglas fir (coast)	30	...	7.4[d]	1.1[f]			±1,600[j]	100[j]	1.6	...	...
Wood { Southern pine (longleaf)	36	...	8.4[d]	1.5[f]			±2,000[j]	125[j]	1.6	...	

[a] Mechanical properties of metals depend not only on composition but also on heat treatment, previous cold working, etc. Data for wood are for clear 2 in. by 2 in. specimens at 12% moisture content. True values vary.
[b] 7½ gal/sack means 7½ gallons of water per 94 lb sack of Portland cement. Values given for 28 day old concrete.
[c] For short blocks only. For ductile materials the ultimate strength in compression is indefinite; may be assumed same as in tension.
[d] Compression parallel to grain on short blocks. Compression perpendicular to grain at proportional limit 950 psi, 1,190 psi, respectively. Values from Wood Handbook, U. S. Dept. of Agriculture.
[e] Fails in diagonal tension.
[f] Parallel to grain.
[g] For ductile materials compressive yield strength may be assumed the same.
[h] For most materials at 0.2% set.
[i] Much lower stresses required in machine design because of fatigue properties and dynamic loadings.
[j] For static loads only. In bending only. No tensile stress is allowed in concrete. Timber stresses are for select structural grade.
[k] AISC recommends the value of 29 × 10⁶ psi.

TABLE 2

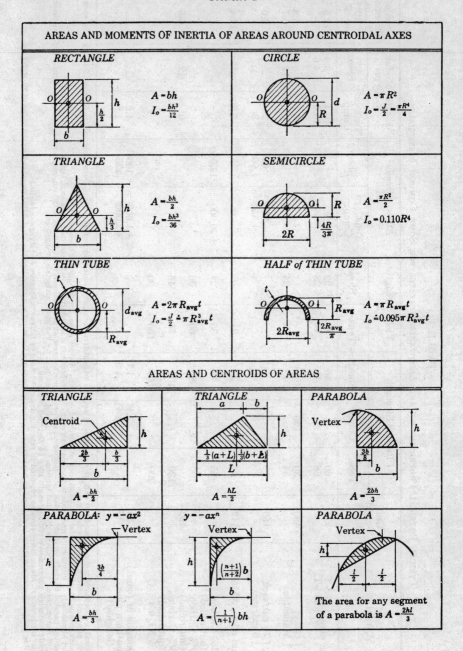

AREAS AND MOMENTS OF INERTIA OF AREAS AROUND CENTROIDAL AXES

RECTANGLE

$$A = bh$$
$$I_o = \frac{bh^3}{12}$$

CIRCLE

$$A = \pi R^2$$
$$I_o = \frac{J}{2} = \frac{\pi R^4}{4}$$

TRIANGLE

$$A = \frac{bh}{2}$$
$$I_o = \frac{bh^3}{36}$$

SEMICIRCLE

$$A = \frac{\pi R^2}{2}$$
$$I_o = 0.110 R^4$$

THIN TUBE

$$A = 2\pi R_{avg} t$$
$$I_o = \frac{J}{2} \doteq \pi R_{avg}^3 t$$

HALF of THIN TUBE

$$A = \pi R_{avg} t$$
$$I_o \doteq 0.095 \pi R_{avg}^3 t$$

AREAS AND CENTROIDS OF AREAS

TRIANGLE

Centroid

$$A = \frac{bh}{2}$$

TRIANGLE

$$\frac{1}{3}(a+L) \quad \frac{1}{3}(b+L)$$

$$A = \frac{hL}{2}$$

PARABOLA

Vertex

$$A = \frac{2bh}{3}$$

PARABOLA: $y = -ax^2$

Vertex

$$A = \frac{bh}{3}$$

$y = -ax^n$

Vertex

$$\left(\frac{n+1}{n+2}\right) b$$

$$A = \left(\frac{1}{n+1}\right) bh$$

PARABOLA

Vertex

The area for any segment of a parabola is $A = \frac{2hl}{3}$

TABLE 3

AMERICAN STANDARD
STEEL I BEAMS
PROPERTIES FOR DESIGNING

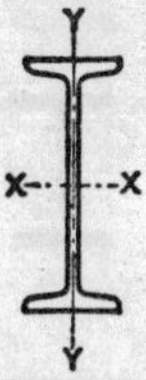

*Nominal Size	Weight per Foot	Area	Depth	Flange Width	Flange Thickness	Web Thickness	AXIS X-X I	AXIS X-X $\frac{I}{c}$	AXIS X-X r	AXIS Y-Y I	AXIS Y-Y $\frac{I}{c}$	AXIS Y-Y r
In.	Lb.	In.²	In.	In.	In.	In.	In.⁴	In.³	In.	In.⁴	In.³	In.
24 x 7⅞	120.0	35.13	24.00	8.048	1.102	.798	3010.8	250.9	9.26	84.9	21.1	1.56
	105.9	30.98	24.00	7.875	1.102	.625	2811.5	234.3	9.53	78.9	20.0	1.60
24 x 7	100.0	29.25	24.00	7.247	.871	.747	2371.8	197.6	9.05	48.4	13.4	1.29
	90.0	26.30	24.00	7.124	.871	.624	2230.1	185.8	9.21	45.5	12.8	1.32
	79.9	23.33	24.00	7.000	.871	.500	2087.2	173.9	9.46	42.9	12.2	1.36
20 x 7	95.0	27.74	20.00	7.200	.916	.800	1599.7	160.0	7.59	50.5	14.0	1.35
	85.0	24.80	20.00	7.053	.916	.653	1501.7	150.2	7.78	47.0	13.3	1.38
20 x 6¼	75.0	21.90	20.00	6.391	.789	.641	1263.5	126.3	7.60	30.1	9.4	1.17
	65.4	19.08	20.00	6.250	.789	.500	1169.5	116.9	7.83	27.9	8.9	1.21
18 x 6	70.0	20.46	18.00	6.251	.691	.711	917.5	101.9	6.70	24.5	7.8	1.09
	54.7	15.94	18.00	6.000	.691	.460	795.5	88.4	7.07	21.2	7.1	1.15
15 x 5½	50.0	14.59	15.00	5.640	.622	.550	481.1	64.2	5.74	16.0	5.7	1.05
	42.9	12.49	15.00	5.500	.622	.410	441.8	58.9	5.95	14.6	5.3	1.08
12 x 5¼	50.0	14.57	12.00	5.477	.659	.687	301.6	50.3	4.55	16.0	5.8	1.05
	40.8	11.84	12.00	5.250	.659	.460	268.9	44.8	4.77	13.8	5.3	1.08
12 x 5	35.0	10.20	12.00	5.078	.544	.428	227.0	37.8	4.72	10.0	3.9	.99
	31.8	9.26	12.00	5.000	.544	.350	215.8	36.0	4.83	9.5	3.8	1.01
10 x 4⅝	35.0	10.22	10.00	4.944	.491	.594	145.8	29.2	3.78	8.5	3.4	.91
	25.4	7.38	10.00	4.660	.491	.310	122.1	24.4	4.07	6.9	3.0	.97
8 x 4	23.0	6.71	8.00	4.171	.425	.441	64.2	16.0	3.09	4.4	2.1	.81
	18.4	5.34	8.00	4.000	.425	.270	56.9	14.2	3.26	3.8	1.9	.84
7 x 3⅝	20.0	5.83	7.00	3.860	.392	.450	41.9	12.0	2.68	3.1	1.6	.74
	15.3	4.43	7.00	3.660	.392	.250	36.2	10.4	2.86	2.7	1.5	.78
6 x 3⅜	17.25	5.02	6.00	3.565	.359	.465	26.0	8.7	2.28	2.3	1.3	.68
	12.5	3.61	6.00	3.330	.359	.230	21.8	7.3	2.46	1.8	1.1	.72
5 x 3	14.75	4.29	5.00	3.284	.326	.494	15.0	6.0	1.87	1.7	1.0	.63
	10.0	2.87	5.00	3.000	.326	.210	12.1	4.8	2.05	1.2	.82	.65
4 x 2⅝	9.5	2.76	4.00	2.796	.293	.326	6.7	3.3	1.56	.91	.65	.58
	7.7	2.21	4.00	2.660	.293	.190	6.0	3.0	1.64	.77	.58	.59
3 x 2⅜	7.5	2.17	3.00	2.509	.260	.349	2.9	1.9	1.15	.59	.47	.52
	5.7	1.64	3.00	2.330	.260	.170	2.5	1.7	1.23	.46	.40	.53

* Steel I-beams are designated by giving their depth in inches first; then the letter I to designate an I-beam; then the weight in pounds per linear foot. For example, 24 I 120.0.

TABLE 4

STEEL WIDE FLANGE BEAMS

PROPERTIES FOR DESIGNING

(ABRIDGED LIST)

Nominal Size*	Weight per Foot	Area	Depth	Flange Width	Flange Thickness	Web Thickness	AXIS X-X I	AXIS X-X $\frac{I}{c}$	AXIS X-X r	AXIS Y-Y I	AXIS Y-Y $\frac{I}{c}$	AXIS Y-Y r
In.	Lb.	In.²	In.	In.	In.	In.	In.⁴	In.³	In.	In.⁴	In.³	In.
36 x 16½	230	67.73	35.88	16.475	1.260	.765	14988.4	835.5	14.88	870.9	105.7	3.59
36 x 12	150	44.16	35.84	11.972	.940	.625	9012.1	502.9	14.29	250.4	41.8	2.38
33 x 15¾	200	58.79	33.00	15.750	1.150	.715	11048.2	669.6	13.71	691.7	87.8	3.43
33 x 11½	130	38.26	33.10	11.510	.855	.580	6699.0	404.8	13.23	201.4	35.0	2.29
30 x 15	172	50.65	29.88	14.985	1.065	.655	7891.5	528.2	12.48	550.1	73.4	3.30
30 x 10½	108	31.77	29.82	10.484	.760	.548	4461.0	299.2	11.85	135.1	25.8	2.06
27 x 14	145	42.68	26.88	13.965	.975	.600	5414.3	402.9	11.26	406.9	58.3	3.09
27 x 10	94	27.65	26.91	9.990	.747	.490	3266.7	242.8	10.87	115.1	23.0	2.04
24 x 14	130	38.21	24.25	14.000	.900	.565	4009.5	330.7	10.24	375.2	53.6	3.13
24 x 12	100	29.43	24.00	12.000	.775	.468	2987.3	248.9	10.08	203.5	33.9	2.63
24 x 9	76	22.37	23.91	8.985	.682	.440	2096.4	175.4	9.68	76.5	17.0	1.85
21 x 13	112	32.93	21.00	13.000	.865	.527	2620.6	249.6	8.92	289.7	44.6	2.96
21 x 9	82	24.10	20.86	8.962	.795	.499	1752.4	168.0	8.53	89.6	20.0	1.93
21 x 8¼	62	18.23	20.99	8.240	.615	.400	1326.8	126.4	8.53	53.1	12.9	1.71
18 x 11¾	96	28.22	18.16	11.750	.831	.512	1674.7	184.4	7.70	206.8	35.2	2.71
18 x 8¾	64	18.80	17.87	8.715	.686	.403	1045.8	117.0	7.46	70.3	16.1	1.93
18 x 7½	50	14.71	18.00	7.500	.570	.358	800.6	89.0	7.38	37.2	9.9	1.59
16 x 11½	88	25.87	16.16	11.502	.795	.504	1222.6	151.3	6.87	185.2	32.2	2.67
16 x 8½	58	17.04	15.86	8.464	.645	.407	746.4	94.1	6.62	60.5	14.3	1.88
16 x 7	50	14.70	16.25	7.073	.628	.380	655.4	80.7	6.68	34.8	9.8	1.54
	36	10.59	15.85	6.992	.428	.299	446.3	56.3	6.49	22.1	6.3	1.45
14 x 16	142	41.85	14.75	15.500	1.063	.680	1672.2	226.7	6.32	660.1	85.2	3.97
	†320	94.12	16.81	16.710	2.093	1.890	4141.7	492.8	6.63	1635.1	195.7	4.17
14 x 14½	87	25.56	14.00	14.500	.688	.420	966.9	138.1	6.15	349.7	48.2	3.70
14 x 12	84	24.71	14.18	12.023	.778	.451	928.4	130.9	6.13	225.5	37.5	3.02
	78	22.94	14.06	12.000	.718	.428	851.2	121.1	6.09	206.9	34.5	3.00

*Steel WF beams are designated by giving their nominal depth in inches first; then the letters WF to designate a wide-flange beam; then the weight in pounds per linear foot. For example, 36 WF 230.

† Column core section.

TABLE 4 (*Continued*)

Nominal Size	Weight per Foot	Area	Depth	Flange Width	Flange Thickness	Web Thickness	AXIS X-X I	AXIS X-X $\frac{I}{c}$	AXIS X-X r	AXIS Y-Y I	AXIS Y-Y $\frac{I}{c}$	AXIS Y-Y r
In.	Lb.	In.²	In.	In.	In.	In.	In.⁴	In.³	In.	In.⁴	In.³	In.
14 x 10	74	21.76	14.19	10.072	.783	.450	796.8	112.3	6.05	133.5	26.5	2.48
	68	20.00	14.06	10.040	.718	.418	724.1	103.0	6.02	121.2	24.1	2.46
	61	17.94	13.91	10.000	.643	.378	641.5	92.2	5.98	107.3	21.5	2.45
14 x 8	53	15.59	13.94	8.062	.658	.370	542.1	77.8	5.90	57.5	14.3	1.92
	43	12.65	13.68	8.000	.528	.308	429.0	62.7	5.82	45.1	11.3	1.89
14 x 6¾	38	11.17	14.12	6.776	.513	.313	385.3	54.6	5.87	24.6	7.3	1.49
	34	10.00	14.00	6.750	.453	.287	339.2	48.5	5.83	21.3	6.3	1.46
	30	8.81	13.86	6.733	.383	.270	289.6	41.8	5.73	17.5	5.2	1.41
12 x 12	85	24.98	12.50	12.105	.796	.495	723.3	115.7	5.38	235.5	38.9	3.07
	65	19.11	12.12	12.000	.606	.390	533.4	88.0	5.28	174.6	29.1	3.02
12 x 10	53	15.59	12.06	10.000	.576	.345	426.2	70.7	5.23	96.1	19.2	2.48
12 x 8	40	11.77	11.94	8.000	.516	.294	310.1	51.9	5.13	44.1	11.0	1.94
12 x 6½	36	10.59	12.24	6.565	.540	.305	280.8	45.9	5.15	23.7	7.2	1.50
	31	9.12	12.09	6.525	.465	.265	238.4	39.4	5.11	19.8	6.1	1.47
	27	7.97	11.95	6.500	.400	.240	204.1	34.1	5.06	16.6	5.1	1.44
10 x 10	112	32.92	11.38	10.415	1.248	.755	718.7	126.3	4.67	235.4	45.2	2.67
	100	29.43	11.12	10.345	1.118	.685	625.0	112.4	4.61	206.6	39.9	2.65
	89	26.19	10.88	10.275	.998	.615	542.4	99.7	4.55	180.6	35.2	2.63
	77	22.67	10.62	10.195	.868	.535	457.2	86.1	4.49	153.4	30.1	2.60
	49	14.40	10.00	10.000	.558	.340	272.9	54.6	4.35	93.0	18.6	2.54
10 x 8	45	13.24	10.12	8.022	.618	.350	248.6	49.1	4.33	53.2	13.3	2.00
	39	11.48	9.94	7.990	.528	.318	209.7	42.2	4.27	44.9	11.2	1.98
	33	9.71	9.75	7.964	.433	.292	170.9	35.0	4.20	36.5	9.2	1.94
10 x 5¾	29	8.53	10.22	5.799	.500	.289	157.3	30.8	4.29	15.2	5.2	1.34
	21	6.19	9.90	5.750	.340	.240	106.3	21.5	4.14	9.7	3.4	1.25
8 x 8	67	19.70	9.00	8.287	.933	.575	271.8	60.4	3.71	88.6	21.4	2.12
	58	17.06	8.75	8.222	.808	.510	227.3	52.0	3.65	74.9	18.2	2.10
	48	14.11	8.50	8.117	.683	.405	183.7	43.2	3.61	60.9	15.0	2.08
	40	11.76	8.25	8.077	.558	.365	146.3	35.5	3.53	49.0	12.1	2.04
	35	10.30	8.12	8.027	.493	.315	126.5	31.1	3.50	42.5	10.6	2.03
	31	9.12	8.00	8.000	.433	.288	109.7	27.4	3.47	37.0	9.2	2.01
8 x 6½	28	8.23	8.06	6.540	.463	.285	97.8	24.3	3.45	21.6	6.6	1.62
	24	7.06	7.93	6.500	.398	.245	82.5	20.8	3.42	18.2	5.6	1.61
8 x 5¼	20	5.88	8.14	5.268	.378	.248	69.2	17.0	3.43	8.5	3.2	1.20
	17	5.00	8.00	5.250	.308	.230	56.4	14.1	3.36	6.7	2.6	1.16

TABLE 5

AMERICAN STANDARD
STEEL CHANNELS
PROPERTIES FOR DESIGNING

Nominal Size *	Weight per Foot	Area	Depth	Flange Width	Flange Average Thickness	Web Thickness	AXIS X-X I	AXIS X-X $\frac{I}{c}$	AXIS X-X r	AXIS Y-Y I	AXIS Y-Y $\frac{I}{c}$	AXIS Y-Y r	x
In.	Lb.	In.²	In.	In.	In.	In.	In.⁴	In.³	In.	In.⁴	In.³	In.	In.
†18 x 4	58.0	16.98	18.00	4.200	.625	.700	670.7	74.5	6.29	18.5	5.6	1.04	.88
	51.9	15.18	18.00	4.100	.625	.600	622.1	69.1	6.40	17.1	5.3	1.06	.87
	45.8	13.38	18.00	4.000	.625	.500	573.5	63.7	6.55	15.8	5.1	1.09	.89
	42.7	12.48	18.00	3.950	.625	.450	549.2	61.0	6.64	15.0	4.9	1.10	.90
15 x 3⅜	50.0	14.64	15.00	3.716	.650	.716	401.4	53.6	5.24	11.2	3.8	.87	.80
	40.0	11.70	15.00	3.520	.650	.520	346.3	46.2	5.44	9.3	3.4	.80	.78
	33.9	9.90	15.00	3.400	.650	.400	312.6	41.7	5.62	8.2	3.2	.91	.79
12 x 3	30.0	8.79	12.00	3.170	.501	.510	161.2	26.9	4.28	5.2	2.1	.77	.68
	25.0	7.32	12.00	3.047	.501	.387	143.5	23.9	4.43	4.5	1.9	.79	.68
	20.7	6.03	12.00	2.940	.501	.280	128.1	21.4	4.61	3.9	1.7	.81	.70
10 x 2⅝	30.0	8.80	10.00	3.033	.436	.673	103.0	20.6	3.42	4.0	1.7	.67	.65
	25.0	7.33	10.00	2.886	.436	.526	90.7	18.1	3.52	3.4	1.5	.68	.62
	20.0	5.86	10.00	2.739	.436	.379	78.5	15.7	3.66	2.8	1.3	.70	.61
	15.3	4.47	10.00	2.600	.436	.240	66.9	13.4	3.87	2.3	1.2	.72	.64
9 x 2½	20.0	5.86	9.00	2.648	.413	.448	60.6	13.5	3.22	2.4	1.2	.65	.59
	15.0	4.39	9.00	2.485	.413	.285	50.7	11.3	3.40	1.9	1.0	.67	.59
	13.4	3.89	9.00	2.430	.413	.230	47.3	10.5	3.49	1.8	.97	.67	.61
8 x 2¼	18.75	5.49	8.00	2.527	.390	.487	43.7	10.9	2.82	2.0	1.0	.60	.57
	13.75	4.02	8.00	2.343	.390	.303	35.8	9.0	2.99	1.5	.86	.62	.56
	11.5	3.36	8.00	2.260	.390	.220	32.3	8.1	3.10	1.3	.79	.63	.58
7 x 2⅛	14.75	4.32	7.00	2.299	.366	.419	27.1	7.7	2.51	1.4	.79	.57	.53
	12.25	3.58	7.00	2.194	.366	.314	24.1	6.9	2.59	1.2	.71	.58	.53
	9.8	2.85	7.00	2.090	.366	.210	21.1	6.0	2.72	.98	.63	.59	.55
6 x 2	13.0	3.81	6.00	2.157	.343	.437	17.3	5.8	2.13	1.1	.65	.53	.52
	10.5	3.07	6.00	2.034	.343	.314	15.1	5.0	2.22	.87	.57	.53	.50
	8.2	2.39	6.00	1.920	.343	.200	13.0	4.3	2.34	.70	.50	.54	.52
5 x 1¾	9.0	2.63	5.00	1.885	.320	.325	8.8	3.5	1.83	.64	.45	.49	.48
	6.7	1.95	5.00	1.750	.320	.190	7.4	3.0	1.95	.48	.38	.50	.49
4 x 1⅝	7.25	2.12	4.00	1.720	.296	.320	4.5	2.3	1.47	.44	.35	.46	.46
	5.4	1.56	4.00	1.580	.296	.180	3.8	1.9	1.56	.32	.29	.45	.46
3 x 1½	6.0	1.75	3.00	1.596	.273	.356	2.1	1.4	1.08	.31	.27	.42	.46
	5.0	1.46	3.00	1.498	.273	.258	1.8	1.2	1.12	.25	.24	.41	.44
	4.1	1.19	3.00	1.410	.273	.170	1.6	1.1	1.17	.20	.21	.41	.44

* Steel channels are designated by giving their depth in inches first; then the symbol ⊔ to designate a channel; then the weight in pounds per linear foot. For example, 15 ⊔ 50.0.

† Car and shipbuilding channel; not an American Standard.

TABLE 6

STEEL ANGLES
EQUAL LEGS
PROPERTIES FOR DESIGNING

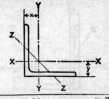

Size	Thickness	Weight per Foot	Area	AXIS X-X AND AXIS Y-Y				AXIS Z-Z
				I	$\frac{I}{c}$	r	x or y	r
In.	In.	Lb.	In.²	In.⁴	In.³	In.	In.	In.
8 x 8	1⅛	56.9	16.73	98.0	17.5	2.42	2.41	1.56
	1	51.0	15.00	89.0	15.8	2.44	2.37	1.56
	⅞	45.0	13.23	79.6	14.0	2.45	2.32	1.57
	¾	38.9	11.44	69.7	12.2	2.47	2.28	1.57
	⅝	32.7	9.61	59.4	10.3	2.49	2.23	1.58
	⁹⁄₁₆	29.6	8.68	54.1	9.3	2.50	2.21	1.58
	½	26.4	7.75	48.6	8.4	2.50	2.19	1.59
6 x 6	1	37.4	11.00	35.5	8.6	1.80	1.86	1.17
	⅞	33.1	9.73	31.9	7.6	1.81	1.82	1.17
	¾	28.7	8.44	28.2	6.7	1.83	1.78	1.17
	⅝	24.2	7.11	24.2	5.7	1.84	1.73	1.18
	⁹⁄₁₆	21.9	6.43	22.1	5.1	1.85	1.71	1.18
	½	19.6	5.75	19.9	4.6	1.86	1.68	1.18
	⁷⁄₁₆	17.2	5.06	17.7	4.1	1.87	1.66	1.19
	⅜	14.9	4.36	15.4	3.5	1.88	1.64	1.19
	⁵⁄₁₆	12.5	3.66	13.0	3.0	1.89	1.61	1.19
5 x 5	⅞	27.2	7.98	17.8	5.2	1.49	1.57	.97
	¾	23.6	6.94	15.7	4.5	1.51	1.52	.97
	⅝	20.0	5.86	13.6	3.9	1.52	1.48	.98
	½	16.2	4.75	11.3	3.2	1.54	1.43	.98
	⁷⁄₁₆	14.3	4.18	10.0	2.8	1.55	1.41	.98
	⅜	12.3	3.61	8.7	2.4	1.56	1.39	.99
	⁵⁄₁₆	10.3	3.03	7.4	2.0	1.57	1.37	.99
4 x 4	¾	18.5	5.44	7.7	2.8	1.19	1.27	.78
	⅝	15.7	4.61	6.7	2.4	1.20	1.23	.78
	½	12.8	3.75	5.6	2.0	1.22	1.18	.78
	⁷⁄₁₆	11.3	3.31	5.0	1.8	1.23	1.16	.78
	⅜	9.8	2.86	4.4	1.5	1.23	1.14	.79
	⁵⁄₁₆	8.2	2.40	3.7	1.3	1.24	1.12	.79
	¼	6.6	1.94	3.0	1.1	1.25	1.09	.80
3½ x 3½	½	11.1	3.25	3.6	1.5	1.06	1.06	.68
	⁷⁄₁₆	9.8	2.87	3.3	1.3	1.07	1.04	.68
	⅜	8.5	2.48	2.9	1.2	1.07	1.01	.69
	⁵⁄₁₆	7.2	2.09	2.5	.98	1.08	.99	.69
	¼	5.8	1.69	2.0	.79	1.09	.97	.69
3 x 3	½	9.4	2.75	2.2	1.1	.90	.93	.58
	⁷⁄₁₆	8.3	2.43	2.0	.95	.91	.91	.58
	⅜	7.2	2.11	1.8	.83	.91	.89	.58
	⁵⁄₁₆	6.1	1.78	1.5	.71	.92	.87	.59
	¼	4.9	1.44	1.2	.58	.93	.84	.59
	³⁄₁₆	3.71	1.09	.96	.44	.94	.82	.59
2½ x 2½	½	7.7	2.25	1.2	.72	.74	.81	.49
	⅜	5.9	1.73	.98	.57	.75	.76	.49
	⁵⁄₁₆	5.0	1.47	.85	.48	.76	.74	.49
	¼	4.1	1.19	.70	.39	.77	.72	.49
	³⁄₁₆	3.07	.90	.55	.30	.78	.69	.49

TABLE 7

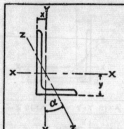

STEEL ANGLES
UNEQUAL LEGS

PROPERTIES FOR DESIGNING

Size	Thickness	Weight per Foot	Area	AXIS X-X				AXIS Y-Y				AXIS Z-Z	
				I	$\frac{I}{c}$	r	y	I	$\frac{I}{c}$	r	x	r	Tan α
In.	In.	Lb.	In.²	In.⁴	In.³	In.	In.	In.⁴	In.³	In.	In.	In.	
8 x 6	1	44.2	13.00	80.8	15.1	2.49	2.65	38.8	8.9	1.73	1.65	1.28	.543
	⅞	39.1	11.48	72.3	13.4	2.51	2.61	34.9	7.9	1.74	1.61	1.28	.547
	¾	33.8	9.94	63.4	11.7	2.53	2.56	30.7	6.9	1.76	1.56	1.29	.551
	⅝	28.5	8.36	54.1	9.9	2.54	2.52	26.3	5.9	1.77	1.52	1.29	.554
	⁹⁄₁₆	25.7	7.56	49.3	9.0	2.55	2.50	24.0	5.3	1.78	1.50	1.30	.556
	½	23.0	6.75	44.3	8.0	2.56	2.47	21.7	4.8	1.79	1.47	1.30	.558
	⁷⁄₁₆	20.2	5.93	39.2	7.1	2.57	2.45	19.3	4.2	1.80	1.45	1.31	.560
8 x 4	1	37.4	11.00	69.6	14.1	2.52	3.05	11.6	3.9	1.03	1.05	.85	.247
	⅞	33.1	9.73	62.5	12.5	2.53	3.00	10.5	3.5	1.04	1.00	.85	.253
	¾	28.7	8.44	54.9	10.9	2.55	2.95	9.4	3.1	1.05	.95	.85	.258
	⅝	24.2	7.11	46.9	9.2	2.57	2.91	8.1	2.6	1.07	.91	.86	.262
	⁹⁄₁₆	21.9	6.43	42.8	8.4	2.58	2.88	7.4	2.4	1.07	.88	.86	.265
	½	19.6	5.75	38.5	7.5	2.59	2.86	6.7	2.2	1.08	.86	.86	.267
	⁷⁄₁₆	17.2	5.06	34.1	6.6	2.60	2.83	6.0	1.9	1.09	.83	.87	.269
7 x 4	⅞	30.2	8.86	42.9	9.7	2.20	2.55	10.2	3.5	1.07	1.05	.86	.318
	¾	26.2	7.69	37.8	8.4	2.22	2.51	9.1	3.0	1.09	1.01	.86	.324
	⅝	22.1	6.48	32.4	7.1	2.24	2.46	7.8	2.6	1.10	.96	.86	.329
	⁹⁄₁₆	20.0	5.87	29.6	6.5	2.24	2.44	7.2	2.4	1.11	.94	.87	.332
	½	17.9	5.25	26.7	5.8	2.25	2.42	6.5	2.1	1.11	.92	.87	.335
	⁷⁄₁₆	15.8	4.62	23.7	5.1	2.26	2.39	5.8	1.9	1.12	.89	.88	.337
	⅜	13.6	3.98	20.6	4.4	2.27	2.37	5.1	1.6	1.13	.87	.88	.339
6 x 4	⅞	27.2	7.98	27.7	7.2	1.86	2.12	9.8	3.4	1.11	1.12	.86	.421
	¾	23.6	6.94	24.5	6.3	1.88	2.08	8.7	3.0	1.12	1.08	.86	.428
	⅝	20.0	5.86	21.1	5.3	1.90	2.03	7.5	2.5	1.13	1.03	.86	.435
	⁹⁄₁₆	18.1	5.31	19.3	4.8	1.90	2.01	6.9	2.3	1.14	1.01	.87	.438
	½	16.2	4.75	17.4	4.3	1.91	1.99	6.3	2.1	1.15	.99	.87	.440
	⁷⁄₁₆	14.3	4.18	15.5	3.8	1.92	1.96	5.6	1.9	1.16	.96	.87	.443
	⅜	12.3	3.61	13.5	3.3	1.93	1.94	4.9	1.6	1.17	.94	.88	.446
	⁵⁄₁₆	10.3	3.03	11.4	2.8	1.94	1.92	4.2	1.4	1.17	.92	.88	.449
6 x 3½	½	15.3	4.50	16.6	4.2	1.92	2.08	4.3	1.6	.97	.83	.76	.344
	⅜	11.7	3.42	12.9	3.2	1.94	2.04	3.3	1.2	.99	.79	.77	.350
	⁵⁄₁₆	9.8	2.87	10.9	2.7	1.95	2.01	2.9	1.0	1.00	.76	.77	.352
	¼	7.9	2.31	8.9	2.2	1.96	1.99	2.3	0.85	1.01	.74	.78	.355
5 x 3½	¾	19.8	5.81	13.9	4.3	1.55	1.75	5.6	2.2	.98	1.00	.75	.464
	⅝	16.8	4.92	12.0	3.7	1.56	1.70	4.8	1.9	.99	.95	.75	.472
	½	13.6	4.00	10.0	3.0	1.58	1.66	4.1	1.6	1.01	.91	.75	.479
	⁷⁄₁₆	12.0	3.53	8.9	2.6	1.59	1.63	3.6	1.4	1.01	.88	.76	.482
	⅜	10.4	3.05	7.8	2.3	1.60	1.61	3.2	1.2	1.02	.86	.76	.486
	⁵⁄₁₆	8.7	2.56	6.6	1.9	1.61	1.59	2.7	1.0	1.03	.84	.76	.489
	¼	7.0	2.06	5.4	1.6	1.61	1.56	2.2	.83	1.04	.81	.76	.492

TABLE 7 (*Continued*)

Size	Thickness	Weight per Foot	Area	AXIS X-X				AXIS Y-Y				AXIS Z-Z	
				I	$\frac{I}{c}$	r	y	I	$\frac{I}{c}$	r	x	r	Tan α
In.	In.	Lb.	In.²	In.⁴	In.³	In.	In.	In.⁴	In.³	In.	In.	In.	
5 x 3	½	12.8	3.75	9.5	2.9	1.59	1.75	2.6	1.1	.83	.75	.65	.357
	⁷⁄₁₆	11.3	3.31	8.4	2.6	1.60	1.73	2.3	1.0	.84	.73	.65	.361
	⅜	9.8	2.86	7.4	2.2	1.61	1.70	2.0	.89	.84	.70	.65	.364
	⁵⁄₁₆	8.2	2.40	6.3	1.9	1.61	1.68	1.8	.75	.85	.68	.66	.368
	¼	6.6	1.94	5.1	1.5	1.62	1.66	1.4	.61	.86	.66	.66	.371
4 x 3½	⅝	14.7	4.30	6.4	2.4	1.22	1.29	4.5	1.8	1.03	1.04	.72	.745
	½	11.9	3.50	5.3	1.9	1.23	1.25	3.8	1.5	1.04	1.00	.72	.750
	⁷⁄₁₆	10.6	3.09	4.8	1.7	1.24	1.23	3.4	1.4	1.05	.98	.72	.753
	⅜	9.1	2.67	4.2	1.5	1.25	1.21	3.0	1.2	1.06	.96	.73	.755
	⁵⁄₁₆	7.7	2.25	3.6	1.3	1.26	1.18	2.6	1.0	1.07	.93	.73	.757
	¼	6.2	1.81	2.9	1.0	1.27	1.16	2.1	.81	1.07	.91	.73	.759
4 x 3	⅝	13.6	3.98	6.0	2.3	1.23	1.37	2.9	1.4	.85	.87	.64	.534
	½	11.1	3.25	5.1	1.9	1.25	1.33	2.4	1.1	.86	.83	.64	.543
	⁷⁄₁₆	9.8	2.87	4.5	1.7	1.25	1.30	2.2	1.0	.87	.80	.64	.547
	⅜	8.5	2.48	4.0	1.5	1.26	1.28	1.9	.87	.88	.78	.64	.551
	⁵⁄₁₆	7.2	2.09	3.4	1.2	1.27	1.26	1.7	.73	.89	.76	.65	.554
	¼	5.8	1.69	2.8	1.0	1.28	1.24	1.4	.60	.90	.74	.65	.558
3½ x 3	½	10.2	3.00	3.5	1.5	1.07	1.13	2.3	1.1	.88	.88	.62	.714
	⁷⁄₁₆	9.1	2.65	3.1	1.3	1.08	1.10	2.1	.98	.89	.85	.62	.718
	⅜	7.9	2.30	2.7	1.1	1.09	1.08	1.9	.85	.90	.83	.62	.721
	⁵⁄₁₆	6.6	1.93	2.3	.95	1.10	1.06	1.6	.72	.90	.81	.63	.724
	¼	5.4	1.56	1.9	.78	1.11	1.04	1.3	.59	.91	.79	.63	.727
3½x2½	½	9.4	2.75	3.2	1.4	1.09	1.20	1.4	.76	.70	.70	.53	.486
	⁷⁄₁₆	8.3	2.43	2.9	1.3	1.09	1.18	1.2	.68	.71	.68	.54	.491
	⅜	7.2	2.11	2.6	1.1	1.10	1.16	1.1	.59	.72	.66	.54	.496
	⁵⁄₁₆	6.1	1.78	2.2	.93	1.11	1.14	.94	.50	.73	.64	.54	.501
	¼	4.9	1.44	1.8	.75	1.12	1.11	.78	.41	.74	.61	.54	.506
3 x 2½	½	8.5	2.50	2.1	1.0	.91	1.00	1.3	.74	.72	.75	.52	.667
	⁷⁄₁₆	7.6	2.21	1.9	.93	.92	.98	1.2	.66	.73	.73	.52	.672
	⅜	6.6	1.92	1.7	.81	.93	.96	1.0	.58	.74	.71	.52	.676
	⁵⁄₁₆	5.6	1.62	1.4	.69	.94	.93	.90	.49	.74	.68	.53	.680
	¼	4.5	1.31	1.2	.56	.95	.91	.74	.40	.75	.66	.53	.684
3 x 2	½	7.7	2.25	1.9	1.0	.92	1.08	.67	.47	.55	.58	.43	.414
	⁷⁄₁₆	6.8	2.00	1.7	.89	.93	1.06	.61	.42	.55	.56	.43	.421
	⅜	5.9	1.73	1.5	.78	.94	1.04	.54	.37	.56	.54	.43	.428
	⁵⁄₁₆	5.0	1.47	1.3	.66	.95	1.02	.47	.32	.57	.52	.43	.435
	¼	4.1	1.19	1.1	.54	.95	.99	.39	.26	.57	.49	.43	.440
	³⁄₁₆	3.07	.90	.84	.41	.97	.97	.31	.20	.58	.47	.44	.446
2½ x 2	⅜	5.3	1.55	.91	.55	.77	.83	.51	.36	.58	.58	.42	.614
	⁵⁄₁₆	4.5	1.31	.79	.47	.78	.81	.45	.31	.58	.56	.42	.620
	¼	3.62	1.06	.65	.38	.78	.79	.37	.25	.59	.54	.42	.626
	³⁄₁₆	2.75	.81	.51	.29	.79	.76	.29	.20	.60	.51	.43	.631

TABLE 8

STANDARD STEEL PIPE

Nom. Dia. In.	Outside Dia. In.	Inside Dia. In.	Thick-ness In.	Weight per Foot Lb.		I In.⁴	A In.²	r In.
				Plain Ends	Thread & Cplg.			
1/8	.405	.269	.068	.24	.25	.001	.072	.12
1/4	.540	.364	.088	.42	.43	.003	.125	.16
3/8	.675	.493	.091	.57	.57	.007	.167	.21
1/2	.840	.622	.109	.85	.85	.017	.250	.26
3/4	1.050	.824	.113	1.13	1.13	.037	.333	.33
1	1.315	1.049	.133	1.68	1.68	.087	.494	.42
1 1/4	1.660	1.380	.140	2.27	2.28	.195	.669	.54
1 1/2	1.900	1.610	.145	2.72	2.73	.310	.799	.62
2	2.375	2.067	.154	3.65	3.68	.666	1.075	.79
2 1/2	2.875	2.469	.203	5.79	5.82	1.530	1.704	.95
3	3.500	3.068	.216	7.58	7.62	3.017	2.228	1.16
3 1/2	4.000	3.548	.226	9.11	9.20	4.788	2.680	1.34
4	4.500	4.026	.237	10.79	10.89	7.233	3.174	1.51
5	5.563	5.047	.258	14.62	14.81	15.16	4.300	1.88
6	6.625	6.065	.280	18.97	19.19	28.14	5.581	2.25
8	8.625	8.071	.277	24.70	25.00	63.35	7.265	2.95
8	8.625	7.981	.322	28.55	28.81	72.49	8.399	2.94
10	10.750	10.192	.279	31.20	32.00	125.9	9.178	3.70
10	10.750	10.136	.307	34.24	35.00	137.4	10.07	3.69
10	10.750	10.020	.365	40.48	41.13	160.7	11.91	3.67
12	12.750	12.090	.330	43.77	45.00	248.5	12.88	4.39
12	12.750	12.000	.375	49.56	50.71	279.3	14.58	4.38

TABLE 9

SCREW THREADS, AMERICAN STANDARD

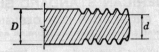

DIAMETER		AREA		Number of Threads per Inch	DIAMETER		AREA		Number of Threads per Inch
Total D In.	Net d In.	Total Dia., D Sq. In.	Net Dia., d Sq. In.		Total D In.	Net d In.	Total Dia., D Sq. In.	Net Dia., d Sq. In.	
¼	.185	.049	.027	20	3	2.675	7.069	5.621	4
⅜	.294	.110	.068	16	3¼	2.925	8.296	6.720	4
½	.400	.196	.126	13	3½	3.175	9.621	7.918	4
⅝	.507	.307	.202	11	3¾	3.425	11.045	9.214	4
¾	.620	.442	.302	10	4	3.675	12.566	10.608	4
⅞	.731	.601	.419	9					
					4¼	3.798	14.186	11.330	2⅞
1	.838	.785	.551	8	4½	4.028	15.904	12.741	2¾
1⅛	.939	.994	.693	7	4¾	4.255	17.721	14.221	2⅝
1¼	1.064	1.227	.890	7					
1⅜	1.158	1.485	1.054	6	5	4.480	19.635	15.766	2½
1½	1.283	1.767	1.294	6	5¼	4.730	21.648	17.574	2½
1¾	1.490	2.405	1.744	5	5½	4.953	23.758	19.268	2⅜
					5¾	5.203	25.967	21.262	2⅜
2	1.711	3.142	2.300	4½					
2¼	1.961	3.976	3.021	4½	6	5.423	28.274	23.095	2¼
2½	2.175	4.909	3.716	4					
2¾	2.425	5.940	4.619	4					

TABLE 10

TIMBER
AMERICAN STANDARD SIZES
PROPERTIES FOR DESIGNING
NATIONAL LUMBER MANUFACTURERS ASSOCIATION

Nominal Size	American Standard Dressed Size	Area of Section	Weight per Foot	Moment of Inertia	Section Modulus	Nominal Size	American Standard Dressed Size	Area of Section	Weight per Foot	Moment of Inertia	Section Modulus
In.	In.	In.²	Lb.	In.⁴	In.³	In.	In.	In.²	Lb.	In.⁴	In.³
2 x 4	1⅝x3⅝	5.89	1.64	6.45	3.56	10x10	9½x9½	90.3	25.0	679	143
6	5⅝	9.14	2.54	24.1	8.57	12	11½	109	30.3	1204	209
8	7½	12.2	3.39	57.1	15.3	14	13½	128	35.6	1948	289
10	9½	15.4	4.29	116	24.4	16	15½	147	40.9	2948	380
12	11½	18.7	5.19	206	35.8	18	17½	166	46.1	4243	485
14	13½	21.9	6.09	333	49.4	20	19½	185	51.4	5870	602
16	15½	25.2	6.99	504	65.1	22	21½	204	56.7	7868	732
18	17½	28.4	7.90	726	82.9	24	23½	223	62.0	10274	874
3 x 4	2⅝x3⅝	9.52	2.64	10.4	5.75	12x12	11½x11½	132	36.7	1458	253
6	5⅝	14.8	4.10	38.9	13.8	14	13½	155	43.1	2358	349
8	7½	19.7	5.47	92.3	24.6	16	15½	178	49.5	3569	460
10	9½	24.9	6.93	188	39.5.	18	17½	201	55.9	5136	587
12	11½	30.2	8.39	333	57.9	20	19½	224	62.3	7106	729
14	13½	35.4	9.84	538	79.7	22	21½	247	68.7	9524	886
16	15½	40.7	11.3	815	105	24	23½	270	75.0	12437	1058
18	17½	45.9	12.8	1172	134						
						14x14	13½x13½	182	50.6	2768	410
4 x 4	3⅝x3⅝	13.1	3.65	14.4	7.94	16	15½	209	58.1	4189	541
6	5⅝	20.4	5.66	53.8	19.1	18	17½	236	65.6	6029	689
8	7½	27.2	7.55	127	34.0	20	19½	263	73.1	8342	856
10	9½	34.4	9.57	259	54.5	22	21½	290	80.6	11181	1040
12	11½	41.7	11.6	459	79.9	24	23½	317	88.1	14600	1243
14	13½	48.9	13.6	743	110						
16	15½	56.2	15.6	1125	145	16x16	15½x15½	240	66.7	4810	621
18	17½	63.4	17.6	1619	185	18	17½	271	75.3	6923	791
						20	19½	302	83.9	9578	982
6 x 6	5½x5½	30.3	8.40	76.3	27.7	22	21½	333	92.5	12837	1194
8	7½	41.3	11.4	193	51.6	24	23½	364	101	16763	1427
10	9½	52.3	14.5	393	82.7						
12	11½	63.3	17.5	697	121	18x18	17½x17½	306	85.0	7816	893
14	13½	74.3	20.6	1128	167	20	19½	341	94.8	10813	1109
16	15½	85.3	23.6	1707	220	22	21½	376	105	14493	1348
18	17½	96.3	26.7	2456	281	24	23½	411	114	18926	1611
20	19½	107.3	29.8	3398	349	26	25½	446	124	24181	1897
8 x 8	7½x7½	56.3	15.6	264	70.3	20x20	19½x19½	380	106	12049	1236
10	9½	71.3	19.8	536	113	22	21½	419	116	16150	1502
12	11½	86.3	23.9	951	165	24	23½	458	127	21089	1795
14	13½	101.3	28.0	1538	228	26	25½	497	138	26945	2113
16	15½	116.3	32.0	2327	300	28	27½	536	149	33795	2458
18	17½	131.3	36.4	3350	383	24x24	23½x23½	552	153	25415	2163
20	19½	146.3	40.6	4634	475	26	25½	599	166	32472	2547
22	21½	161.3	44.8	6211	578	28	27½	646	180	40727	2962
						30	29½	693	193	50275	3408

All properties and weights given are for dressed size only.
The weights given above are based on assumed average weight of 40 pounds per cubic foot.

TABLE 11

DEFLECTIONS AND SLOPES OF ELASTIC CURVES FOR VARIOUSLY LOADED BEAMS

LOADING	EQUATION OF ELASTIC CURVE (UPWARD DEFLECTION POSITIVE)	SLOPE AT END	MAX DEFL.
	$y = -\dfrac{P}{6EI}(2L^3 - 3L^2x + x^3)$	$\theta = +\dfrac{PL^2}{2EI}$	$y_{max} = -\dfrac{PL^3}{3EI}$ at $x = 0$
	$y = -\dfrac{w}{24EI}(x^4 - 4L^3x + 3L^4)$	$\theta = +\dfrac{wL^3}{6EI}$	$y_{max} = -\dfrac{wL^4}{8EI}$ at $x = 0$
	$y = -\dfrac{W}{60EIL^2}(x^5 - 5L^4x + 4L^5)$	$\theta = +\dfrac{WL^2}{12EI}$	$y_{max} = -\dfrac{WL^3}{15EI}$ at $x = 0$
	$y = -\dfrac{wx}{24EI}(L^3 - 2Lx^2 + x^3)$	$\theta = \mp\dfrac{wL^3}{24EI}$	$y_{max} = -\dfrac{5wL^4}{384EI}$ at $x = \dfrac{L}{2}$
	When $O < x < a$ $y = -\dfrac{Pbx}{6EIL}(L^2 - b^2 - x^2)$ When $a = b = \dfrac{L}{2}$ ONLY $y = -\dfrac{Px}{48EI}(3L^2 - 4x^2)$ For $O < x < \dfrac{L}{2}$	For details see Example 11-5 $\theta = +\dfrac{PL^2}{16EI}$	 $y_{max} = -\dfrac{PL^3}{48EI}$ at $x = \dfrac{L}{2}$ --
	$y = +\dfrac{M_0x}{6EIL}(x^2 - L^2)$	$\theta_A = -\dfrac{M_0L}{6EI}$ $\theta_B = +\dfrac{M_0L}{3EI}$	$y_{max} = -\dfrac{ML^2}{9\sqrt{3}\,EI}$ at $x = \dfrac{L}{\sqrt{3}}$
	$y_a = -\dfrac{Pa^2}{6EI}(3L - 4a)$ at $x = a$ $y_{max} = -\dfrac{Pa}{24EI}(3L^2 - 4a^2)$ at $x = \dfrac{L}{2}$ $\theta_{ends} = \mp\dfrac{Pa}{2EI}(L - a)$		

INDEX

A

Abbreviations and symbols, xiii
Allowable stress:
  definition of, 17
  in bending, 253, 254, 423
  in riveted joints, 372, 376
  in torsion, 54, 57
  table of, 423
Angle of twist:
  circular shaft, 60
  rectangular shaft, 63
Angle sections, properties for designing, 429, 430
Area-moment method (see *Moment-area method*)
Areas, useful properties of, 424
Axes:
  principal, 101, 166
  neutral, 96
Axial force diagrams, 84
Axial loads (also see *Columns*):
  definition of, 6
  deformation due to, 31
  stresses due to, 6

B

Beam-columns, 360
Beams:
  bending moments in, 83
  bending stresses in, 99, 100, 253
  built-in (see *Beams, fixed*)
  cantilever, 76
  cover plated, 135, 257
  connections for, 373
  constant strength, 257
  continuous, 76
  crippling of, 255
  curved, 117
  definitions of, 72
  deflection of (see *Deflection*)
  design of, 104, 237–260
  elastic curve for, 250, 270
  elastic strain energy in, 394
  fixed, 76, 320, 323, 325
  flexure formula for, 100
  inelastic bending of, 109
  lateral instability of, 94, 363
  maximum bending stresses in, 100, 238

Beams (*Cont'd*)
  neutral axis in, 96
  of two materials, 113
  of variable cross-section, 109, 256
  overhanging, 76
  prismatic, 108, 237
  reactions of, 77, 318
  radius of curvature of, 270
  reinforced concrete, 116
  restrained, 76, 322
  section modulus of, 104
  shear in, 81, 238
  shearing stresses in, 127, 137
  stresses in, 98, 137, 238
  simple, 76
  simply supported, 76
  statically indeterminate, 10, 310–334
  uniform strength (see *Constant strength*)
  unsymmetrical bending of, 166
Bearing stress, 9
Bending:
  combined with axial loads, 156–166
  of beams (see *Beams*)
  pure, 86, 94, 237
  inelastic, 109
  deflections due to, 269–302
  strain energy in, 394
  stresses due to, 98, 237
  unsymmetrical, 166
Bending moment:
  and elastic curve, relation between, 250, 271
  and shear, relation between, 128, 242
  definition of, 83
  diagrams, 84, 242–251, 299
  diagrams by summation method, 242
  diagrams by cantilever parts, 299
  sign convention for, 84
Bending moment diagrams (see *Bending moment*)
Biaxial stress, 186, 212
Boilers:
  design of, 222–227
  joints for, 226, 375–379
Bredt's formula for tubes in torsion, 65
Buckling:
  of beams, 363
  of columns, 342–363
  of pressure vessels, 227
Butt joints, 226, 368, 374, 377